THE

STONEHAM CATALOGUE

OF

BRITISH STAMPS

1840 - 2007

Fourteenth Edition

Published by

MACHIN COLLECTORS CLUB
8 JANNYS CLOSE
AYLSHAM, NORFOLK, NR11 6DL
ENGLAND

£17.95

First edition: February 1978
Second edition: November 1978
Third edition: September 1978
Fourth edition: September 1980
Fifth edition: September 1981
Sixth edition: August 1982
Seventh edition: September 1984
Eight edition: November 1985
Ninth edition: October 1989
Tenth edition: October 1991
Eleventh edition: August 1995
Twelfth edition: September 1998
Thirteenth edition: April 2006
Fourteenth edition February 2008

Printed and Bound by J. H. Haynes & Co. Ltd., Sparkford
Published by The Machin Collectors Club
8 Jannys Close, Aylsham, Norfolk, NR11 6DL U.K.
Telephone/Fax: 01263 733586
email: machins@supanet.com
Web Site: www.machins.org
MCC Shop: www.mccshop.co.uk
Internet Auction Site: www.stampmart.org.uk

Index to Advertisers

Contents

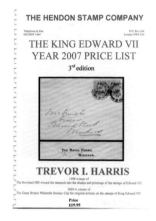

Contents

Foreword

Welcome to the fourteenth edition of the Stoneham Great Britain stamp catalogue. In this latest edition we have continued to improve and extend the scope of the work in response to readers comments and suggestions.

May I take this opportunity to thank all of you that contacted me after the publication of the 13th edition. Your comments and ideas were really helpful - it cannot be stressed too highly how valuable readers comments and suggestions are to publishers and editors. Now that the Stoneham has re-established itself as an important reference for collectors and dealers alike, your feedback will ensure that we are providing what YOU want - and not what we THINK you want.

When the MCC were granted permission to re-publish the Stoneham catalogue, after a break of over seven years, we were not sure whether it would have maintained its appeal. We need not have worried - the thirteenth edition received excellent reviews from collectors and the philatelic trade alike, and we hope this edition will continue to expand the Stoneham 'family' even further. There have been several changes and improvements incorporated in this edition and they can be summarised as follows:

Firstly, this catalogue will now be published every two years i.e. 2010, 2012, 2014 etc. usually to coincide with the opening day of Spring Philatex, which the Machin Collectors Club attends as a stand holder. Even with the bullish market at present, especially on earlier scarce material, we find it very difficult to justify asking collectors to pay for a new catalogue every year.

Improvements to the contents of this edition include:-

* Sequential page numbering instead of sectional numbering.

* QV Imperfs and 'Printed on gum side' errors now listed

* KGVI Imperfs and tête-bêche errors now included

* QEII Wildings Cylinder Blocks listed and priced

* New Basic Machin listings

Naturally all issues since the previous edition have been added, up to December 2007.

Other presentational changes have been made to make the catalogue easier to read and use. We hope you enjoy this latest edition of the Stoneham, and if you have any comments please write/phone/email/fax - we will be very pleased to hear from you.

Melvyn Philpott

Aylsham, February 2008

Acknowledgements

The introduction of colour to this catalogue meant that every illustration had to re-scanned. Many of the contributors below very kindly provided material for this, but I must thank MCC member Ronnie Briggs especially, who spent many hours scanning, cropping, straightening etc. the images contained within.

Further thanks go to all of the following dealers, MCC members and individuals without whose contribution this publication would never have reached the bookshelf - Many thanks to you all.

M W Arnold	Ian Beckett	Tony Bellew
John Bennie	Jim Bond	John Brain
Gerry Brown	Ian De La Rue Brown	Ross Candlish
Tony Child	Andrew Claridge	Paul Dauwalder
Alan Grant	Frank Goldberg	Chris Harman
Tony Hender	Richard Highton	Mike and Sue Holt
Mike Jackson	Andrew G.Lajer	Grahame W. Mann
Peter Mollett	Brian Morris	Alan Musry
Jim Nicholson	Tom Pierron	Norman Sharpe
James Skinner	Alec Withell	

For the technically minded this catalogue was compiled using Adobe Creative Suite CS2®:

Adobe Indesign®   Adobe Photoshop®   Adobe Illustrator®

on a custom built computer supplied by Aylsham Computer Centre, Aylsham, NORFOLK

Explanation and Abbreviations

Prices. All prices quoted are in English Pounds. Prices over £10 are shown with the £ sign. Less than ten pounds, the amount is shown in decimal form, without the £ sign. e.g. 9.50- nine pounds 50 pence. 50 - 50 pence.
The market prices shown are strictly related to the condition of the stamps, and these are specified at the beginning of most sections. Older issues of stamps in exceptional condition will always command a large premium.

Price Column Symbols

U/M - Unmounted mint, never hinged	F/U - Fine used
M/M - Mounted mint, light hinge mark	A/U - Average used ✉ - Stamp on cover

First Day Covers. Commemorative issues are priced as being illustrated covers with circular 'First Day of Issue' handstamps or special illustrated postmarks. Plain covers are worth up to 60% less. The only exceptions are the commemorative issues of King George V where illustrated covers are very rare. From the 1964 Shakespeare issue, plain covers have no greater value than the equivalent value of the used stamps.

Paper and Gums. Whilst certain variations in paper did apply to earlier issues, and these are listed when significant, the Machin decimal issues have provided a whole new area of study for collectors. The various paper and gum combinations are shown separately in this section under the conventional abbreviations.
These are:
GA - Gum Arabic. The original type of gum, with a more or less shiny surface.
PVA - Polyvinyl Alcohol gum, colourless with a matt surface.
PVAD or **Dex.** - Polyvinyl Alcohol gum with dextrin added, matt surface but with a greenish blue tinge.
OCP - Original Coated Paper, slightly creamy to white, but does not fluoresce under ultra violet light.
FCP - Fluorescent Coated Paper, generally whiter than OCP, and fluorescent under ultra violet light.
FBO - Fluorescent Brightening agent Omitted from paper.
ACP - Advanced Coated Paper, appears very bright under ultra violet light
Low OBA - Low Optical Brightening Agent - appears dull like PCP.
OFNP - OBA Free Non Phosphor paper.
OFPP - OBA Free Phosphorised paper.

Phosphor Bands. The position of the bands are abbreviated throughout in the following form:
CB - centre band. LB - side band at left. RB - side band at right. 2B - two bands, one at each side. AOP - 'All over' phosphor, either PPP or PCP.
PPP - Pre-printed phosphor (all over). PCP - Phosphor coated paper (all over). PCPI - Matt surface. PCP2 - Shiny surface.

CBar or 2Bar indicates that band(s) are short at the top *and* bottom

There are different coloured phosphor bands, which react in different manners under an ultra-violet light. These were applied to the Wilding issues, and are now included in this catalogue. Furthermore, the Machin series saw the introduction of Yellow and Blue fluors. These are described in the introductory notes for this series starting on Page G1.

Colours and Shades. The colour and shade descriptions for the older (classic) issues may not be considered very accurate by modem colour/shade standards, but they are traditional and have become recognised and accepted over many years.

Throughout this catalogue, colour/shade descriptions have been abbreviated when necessary, and in the following manner:

bis. - bistre	**bl.** - blue	**blk.** - black	**brn.** - brown	**brz.** - bronze
car. - carmine	**chest.** - chestnut	**choc.** - chocolate	**cin.** - cinnamon	**emer.** - emerald
grn. - green	**ind.** - indigo	**mag.** - magenta	**mar.** - maroon	**myr.** - myrtle
och. - ochre	**ol.** - olive	**or.** - orange	**pur.** - purple	**pr.** - Prussian
redd. - reddish	**sep.** - sepia	**scar.** - scarlet	**sl.** - slate	**tur.** - turquoise
ult. - ultramarine	**ver.** - vermilion	**vio.** - violet	**yel.** - yellow	**multi.** - multicoloured
bt. - bright	**dk.** - dark	**dl.** - dull	**dp.** - deep	**lt.** - light
pl. - pale				

Other Abbreviations

Horiz. - horizontal	**inv.** - inverted	**litho.** - lithography	**M.C.** - Maltese Cross	**perf.** - perforation
photo. - photogravure	**(TL)** - traffic light (gutter pair)	**typo.** - typography	**vert.** - vertical	**wmk.** - watermark.

Illustrations   Definitive issues are full size and commemorative issues are generally three-quarters size. Booklet panes are half size.

Issue Dates   These are expressed in the British style, i.e. day/month/year

Fine Used Stamps and Their Scarcity

Queen Victoria - Line Engraved and Surface Printed

It is important for collectors to realise that from 1840 and certainly in the succeeding 50 years cancellations were designed to completely deface the stamps and in fact were called "obliterators". The Maltese Cross and later the Barred Oval of 1844 were the first to be used and it is only when one of these has not been centrally applied to the stamp. i.e. Queen Victoria's profile left clear that the term fine used is applied. In reality the even greater use of superlatives is applied to stamps that exist in these conditions, and it is why of course on imperforate issues this condition with four clear margins can command a considerable premium.

On Surface Printed issues the Duplex cancellation, which came into use in 1853. appears most prevalent, but it was still intended to be an obliterator, and was supposed to be applied so that the number in bars defaced the stamp whilst the adjoining CDS (circular date stamp) was left clear on the left hand side to be read by postal clerks. It is therefore an exception to find these stamps with a CDS cancel and is due either to misapplication of the handstamp, or they were used telegraphically or for other Post Office purposes.

Most higher values (2d to £5) were used on overseas mail, parcels, registered packages and international telegraphs, as well as internal Post Office accounting. In the latter case once the stamp has been removed from the "form" it is impossible to be sure how it was used and these are now accepted by collectors. The stamps suffered very heavy and often smudgy cancellations and the incidence of a fine CDS postmark is small, is highly collectable and of course worth a premium.

King Edward VII

The majority of low values, i.e. ½d and 1d are found with CDS, having been used by both rural and larger post offices to cancel the colossal volume of mail in the form of postcards, which was at its peak in the Edwardian period. The Duplex cancellation was still in use and with it a squared circle, and in 1902 a machine cancel with the wavy lines also came into use.

Higher denomination stamps from 1d were mainly used on parcels and overseas mail, but also very often, either on their own or in combination, on Inland Parcel Post slips, which meant they received a cancellation in the form of a CDS. The Channel Island CDS was also used on Edward VII high values 2s 6d - £1 as a receipt for payment of tobacco duty.

Kings George V, Edward VIII and George VI

As machine cancellations were now well established, this, coupled with the introduction of slogan postmarks. had the result that almost all mail passing through Head Post Offices was cancelled with anything but a CDS.

The wide use of the Double Circle and Single Circle CDS at almost all other Post Offices meant that the majority of low value stamps, i.e. ½d to 2d, are readily found in fine used condition, but above that value it is much more difficult. As with previous reigns a clear CDS on a high value stamp commands a premium.

It is possible to find George V stamps with Duplex cancellations and squared circles. These postmarks were not supposed to be used but were not withdrawn, and when discovered do add an element of interest to a collection.

Queen Elizabeth II

An enormous number of different postmarks are now in use. CDS, double CDS, machine cancels, slogans, meter marks, registered and parcel cancels to name but a few.

Really fine single circle date stamps are just as difficult to find and equally as elusive on the high values. Stamps with parts of 'First Day of Issue' postmarks are totally acceptable. as postally used.

Furthermore, genuine postally used examples of the modern Machin issues are often sought, and found, in kiloware. But how do you put a value on the many hours spent finding them?

Introduction

A Guide to Fakes and Repairs - Be on Your Guard!

Regretfully the incidence of stamps that are being repaired continues to grow particularly for scarcer items where demand continues to motivate prices. The following points should help you in sorting out the wheat from the chaff.

Q.V. Line Engraved Issues

Beware of re-backed imperforate stamps, especially the 1840 1d black and 2d blue, and the 3 embossed issues. Tests to check whether the stamp has been re-backed are as follows:

1. Immerse stamp in Ronosol - This will show any thickening of the paper as a line and, as a re-backed stamp has in effect an extra thickness, it will show up as a clear line in the liquid.
2. Ultra violet light - If a modern glue has been used this will give a slight fluorescence which of course will end where the new paper meets the old.
3. A good quality magnifying glass - To see where the design has been painted in, especially in the margins and on the corners, as it is quite normal for re-backed copies to start life as slightly cut down 3 margin examples!

A further warning on the line engraved issues

Take extra care when purchasing copies on cover as this is a very neat way of getting rid of a stamp which has a 'thin' or tear. Unused copies should also be treated with great care as frequently they are found to be chemically cleaned and re-gummed. In the late 19th century many people used to thread stamps on cotton to make decorations, and holes were made by the needle piercing the stamp.
Finally, beware of faked coloured postmarks (e.g. Maltese Crosses), and also faked postmarks on cover, especially the rarer ones.

Q.V. Surface Printed Issues

The following are points to watch when purchasing Surface Printed.
1. Cleaned off postmarks - These can easily be spotted with an ultra violet lamp.
2. High values with fiscal cancellations cleaned off - Use an ultra violet lamp.
3. Repairs to used stamps utilising portions of other stamps - Usually found on small piece or part of an envelope.
4. Re-gumming - To check use all the following methods:
   (a) High powered glass to check between perfs for gum on face.
   (b) Place stamp face down in palm of hand and the top and bottom edges should curl up; if they stay flat or curl the other way it is 90% certain that the stamp has been re-gummed.
   (c) Lightly draw fingers across edge of perfs; if the perfs appear sharp and hard to the touch, this is again an indication of re-gumming.
5. Re-perfing - Normally found on cut down wing margin copies. but this is also a method of making a slightly spoilt stamp appear acceptable by re-perfing it and making it smaller to cover up any tears. etc.
6. Repaired Perforations - When a stamp has missing perforations an expert repairer can add perfs. to make the stamp appear sound. Immersing the stamp in Ronosol, with special attention to the perfs. should show up any repairs or added perforations.
7. Colours changed by water immersion - Many surface printed stamps are printed in fugitive inks and any moisture will affect the colour. A good example is the 1883 Lilac and Green issue.
8. Fiscal cancellations covered by faked postmarks - again usually found on small piece or part cover.
9. Facsimiles of the High Values cut out and used with faked postmarks.
10. Altered plate numbers. These are manufactured by scratching out and/or bleaching.
11. Blued paper. This can be artificially created by soaking a stamp in a very mild solution of ink.

Kings George V, George VI and Queen Elizabeth II

Some of the foregoing problems also exist with these reigns and the special points to watch are painted in or scratched out varieties, i.c. the "Pencf" flaw, "Q" for "0" and "no cross on crown" on George V issues.
First Day Covers from the 1924 Wembley Exhibition up to the 1966 World Cup Winners issue are known with forged postmarks. Rare shades can be created by chemical means, the 1935 Silver Jubilee Prussian Blue is an example and should be purchased only with a recognised certificate. Toned paper varieties can be chemically created. Cleaned and re-gummed High Values. Missing colour varieties artificially produced by chemical or other means. e.g. Christmas 1966 issues - Queen's head removed with surgical spirit. These can be easily detected under UV light.

Graphite line varieties created with Indian ink or Letraset, and phosphor bands applied with nail varnish. Both of the latter are easily detected by the fact that the genuine graphite lines never get on the face of the stamp or between the perfs., and phosphor bands react under an ultra violet lamp.

The foregoing warnings cover the most obvious areas, and the collector should always take great care to examine valuable stamps before acquisition.

Watermark Detection

As many collectors are aware the second biggest problem after colour (shades) in collecting GB. stamps, is the detection of the watermark. After a quick look through this catalogue you will notice how the watermark can radically affect the scarcity and value of stamps. Various products have come on to the market purporting to be the answer to watermark detection, but only one has had real success. This works on the principle that a watermark is a thinning of the paper, and therefore, can he made to show up by using a specially designed ink sachet and a roller which theoretically "fills in" the thinner portions created by the watermark and shows the outline as a darker colour. It is also effective on stamps on postcards and covers provided that the card or cover itself has no watermark and has no embossed or relief pattern. "Ronosol" lighter fuel works reasonably well when used against a black plastic background and there are various proprietary brands of watermark fluid which do the same basic task. However, fluids are not successful on certain types of paper especially that used on QEII postage dues, and of course, are completely incapable of showing the watermark of a stamp on cover.

There are also watermark detectors of the light emitting variety which use filters to show up the watermark the devices using a combination of light and pressure are probably the most successful types for detecting watermarks.

With experience one can detect watermarks by looking for the differences where the watermarks are limited e.g. the shape of the Crown. Watermarks can also be seen on occasions by holding the stamp in a horizontal position near a good source of light, like a window.

All illustrations of watermarks are as viewed from the *back* of the stamp.

Controls

Control letters were introduced in 1884 on the 1d lilac Die II, to aid in the financial control of stocks. The control was not part of the plate and was changed or replaced when necessary. In the Victorian period, only the 1d Lilac and ½d 'Jubilee' issues had control letters. For both these issues, the control was located in the bottom margin under the eleventh stamp. The letters were changed irregularly, about twice a year.

The system was continued for the ½d and 1d Edwardian stamps, and the control letter was at first changed annually in October. In 1903, the Inland Revenue suggested adding a number to represent the year. The letter was then changed about April and each year the number appeared with two different letters. For the Edwardian ½d value, the control was located under the second stamp, except for controls 'A' and 'B' which were under the eleventh. All the 1d controls are located under the eleventh stamp.

George V controls were used for all values from ½d to 1s. The control was located under the second stamp, except the 1d value where it is found under the eleventh. Controls printed at Somerset House each had a full stop after the letter. In 1912, 1914 and from 1918 to 1924 inclusive, there appeared three letters with each year number, otherwise there were two controls for each year.

The system continued for the photogravure issues, but the control was then etched into the cylinder. When this had to be changed, the old one was filled in and a new one etched. The use of controls continued through the brief reign of King Edward VIII into that of King George VI, and was discontinued in 1947.

Many different types of perforating machine were used, giving rise to different combinations of marginal perforation. As far as controls are concerned, the perforation types can be simplified to the basic two type; the margin being either imperforate (I) or perforated through (P).

Notes applicable to all Controls listed in this catalogue

Detailed listings of controls of all definitive issues from 1887- 1947 together with Postage Due controls can be found at the back of the catalogue.

The pricing policy is based on the value of single mounted mint stamps with control attached, all in fine condition and with upright watermark, up to and including the King George V Block Cypher definitives. In the ease of all issues from 1934 where cylinder numbers were printed in the margins besides the control, prices are for corner pairs, corner blocks of four or six as appropriate.

Introduction

All pre-QE2 commemorative issues are priced as cylinder control blocks of six with the exception of the 1929 Postal Union Congress which is priced for single stamps.

Later issues had the fractional type of control. and in a number of cases the control is found with a surrounding box of lines or part box, thus -

$$\frac{X}{35} \quad \text{or} \quad \boxed{\begin{array}{c} X \\ \hline 35 \end{array}} \quad \text{or} \quad \frac{X}{35} \quad \text{or} \quad \boxed{\begin{array}{c} X \\ 35 \end{array}} \quad \text{or} \quad \boxed{\begin{array}{c} X \\ \hline 35 \end{array}}$$

Where these exist, the price is followed by a symbol (*). With one or two rare exceptions the price is broadly the same for all degrees of boxing.

Watermark varieties and rare shades with control are not separately priced, but would he approximately 10% more than the price of the equivalent stamp without control.

Stamps with 'Official' overprints exist with control in the same issues as the appropriate plain stamps. These are generally scarce and are shown in the listings.

Where no prices are shown, i.e. blank areas in the tabulations, the controls either do not exist, or if marked with a star are very rare and therefore not priced.

Collecting and Pricing Stamps on Cover

Once again, the prices of stamps on cover are included and the following notes set out the principles which have guided the editors in assessing prices. It will be appreciated that every cover is different in some detail, and that consequently prices are not mandatory and should be taken as a guide only, when an individual cover is being valued. The term 'on cover' refers to the various types of Envelopes. Wrappers, Folders, Entires or Postcards used to carry correspondence. Stamps "on piece" do not qualify, and should generally be priced at the same value as the stamp or stamps alone. "On piece" refers to stamps cut out from the paper but with the postmark intact.

    The Envelope was the same as we know it today with a gummed flap at the back, but frequently having a wax seal.
    The Wrapper was quite simply a piece of paper wrapped around a folded letter sheet and fastened with a wax seal.
    A Folded Entire was a letter sheet, usually a double page folded, interlocked and again fastened with a wax seal.
    Postcards can be plain or illustrated.
    Printed Postal Stationery to which extra stamps have been applied.

These were all used during the reign of Queen Victoria, but later only the Envelopes, Postcards and Postal Stationery survived.

Prices of Covers

Queen Victoria - Line Engraved and Surface Printed issues

All the prices in this catalogue relate to covers with average Used or stamps Grade Ill. Please refer to the illustrations and descriptions given on the relevant pages. For other grades the price should be adjusted upwards or downwards by the same percentages quoted.

Kings Edward VII, George V, Edward VIII and George VI issues

All the prices relate to covers with Fine Used stamps, having light neat cancellations and leaving the entire stamp design clearly and easily seen. Heavy cancellations and other defects can reduce the values to as little as 30% or less of the quoted catalogue prices. A stamp neatly tied to the cover by a circular date stamp applied to the corner and leaving two thirds or more of the design completely clear may be classified as Superb Used, and would carry a premium of 50 - 100% above the catalogue price.

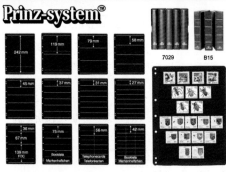

images, **quantities** and **values** of every **missing colour error** from 1952 to date. An unparalleled reference featuring **800** information-filled pages in **full colour.** Over 80 countries covered, **1,250-plus errors** detailed, more than **2,500 images.** The definitive resource for **Great Britain** and **Commonwealth**

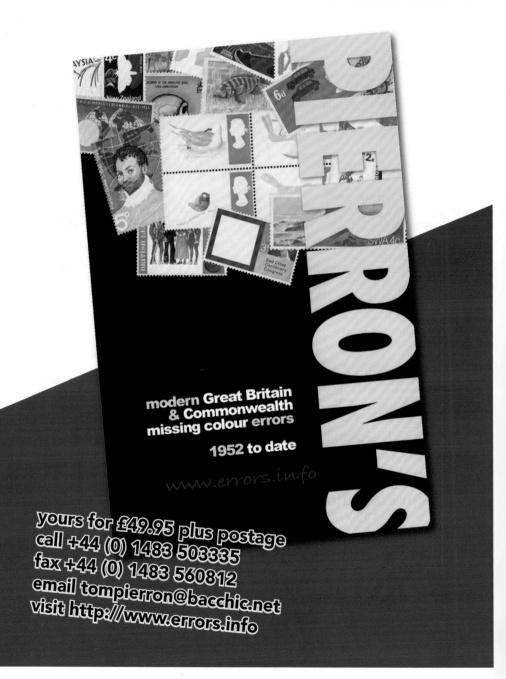

Mulreadys

Designed by William Mulready, engraved by John Thompson and printed by William Clowes.

'Mulreadys' were introduced at the same time as adhesive labels on 6th May 1840. They were designed by William Mulready and printed in sheets of 12. Each impression on the sheet had its own unique number that could be substituted, if worn or damaged. Mulreadys were used as a convenient mode of advertising and many collectors have found it to be a rewarding study. Generally they were of a commercial nature and used by insurance companies, Banks, Tax Offices and many other organisations.

No.	Colour	Unused	F/U	No.	Colour	Unused	F/U
1840 (6 May)				Envelope			
Envelope				MU3	**2d Blue**	£140	£600
MU1	**1d Black**	£80	£160	MU3a	Red Maltese Cross	-	£600
MU1a	Red Maltese Cross	-	£175	MU3b	Black Maltese Cross	-	£600
MU1b	Black Maltese Cross	-	£160	MU3c	1844 cancel	-	£900
MU1c	1844 cancel	-	£300	MU3d	First Day Use	-	
MU1d	Advertisement	£180	£250				
MU1e	First Day Use	-	£7000				

     Printed from six forms with 80 unique numbers known.   Printed from one forme with 13 unique numbers known.

No.	Colour	Unused	F/U	No.	Colour	Unused	F/U
Wrapper				Wrapper			
MU2	**1d Black**	£75	£160	MU4	**2d Blue**	£140	£600
MU2a	Red Maltese Cross	-	£160	MU4a	Red Maltese Cross	-	£650
MU2b	Black Maltese Cross	-	£160	MU4b	Black Maltese Cross	-	£600
MU2c	1844 cancel	-	£300	MU4c	1844 cancel	-	£650
MU2d	Advertisement	-	£250	MU4d	Advertisement	-	£900
MU2e	First Day Use	-	£7000	MU4e	First Day Use	-	

     Printed from six formes with 78 unique numbers known.   Printed from one forme with 12 unique numbers known.

Beginning with the Penny Black issued on 6 May 1840 and Twopence Blue, issued 2 days later; the four values ½d, 1d, 1½d and 2d spanned a period of usage of just forty years. They have presented a complex study for collectors of British stamps. In the following pages the main varieties are listed according to shade, watermarks, plate numbers, dies, alphabets and papers. The different plates, except where they are shown on the stamp design, can only be identified by minute detail differences.

Inverted watermark varieties for almost all of these stamps are recorded and we now list them.

The prices stated relate to stamps that comply with the following conditions:

Imperforate Issues

Mounted Mint (M/M)   Stamps should have four clear margins, at least 75% original gum and be reasonably lightly hinged. Stamps without gum must be purchased with caution as many line engraved issues have been chemically cleaned to remove postmarks and pen cancels. Stamps with large margins and/or margins with inscriptions are worth a considerable premium.

Used   This is probably the most difficult area to describe as so much depends on the eye of the beholder. For example, under Grade I category the cancel on the Grade II illustration would be quite acceptable to the majority of collectors. The descriptions of the margins are also problematical: most text books state that the top quality stamps should have large even margins. However, many stamps have one side or even two that may show some of the adjoining stamp(s) which of course makes it anything but even. The cancellation should be obvious. A clear profile or full crisp cancel is a personal choice. The four categories listed overleaf are suggested as a guide to quality. All the following points should be taken into account.

(a)	Margins
(h)	The clarity and neatness of cancellation
(c)	The back of the stamp
(d)	The condition of the surface
(e)	Whether it has any creasing
(I)	Any tears or pin holes
(g)	Any thinning
(h)	Has the stamp been chemically cleaned?

Perforated Issues

Mounted Mint (M/M)   Stamps should have at least 75% original gum and be reasonably centred.

Average Used (A/U)   Please refer to the relevant page for used categories of the Perforated Issues.

Used Categories of the Imperforate Issues

Grade	*Price Guide*

Grade 1- Superb
Four extra large margins, light sharp and clear obliteration leaving profile reasonably clear. The Back should be clean and perfect with no discolouration. The surface and colour should also be clean and the printing clear.

Fine used price + up to 100%

Grade II - Fine Used
Four good margins, clear obliteration, surface and colour clean, with the back showing no discolouration.

As catalogue

Grade III - Average Used
Four margins, one or two cut close, but not into the design. Slight discolouration on the back acceptable, the obliteration may he heavier and less distinctive. The surface, however, should have no defects.

As catalogue

Grade IV - Sound Used
Margins very close, one or two sides almost cutting into the design. The obliteration may be heavier and the back slightly discoloured but no other defects should be apparent.
A stamp that has creases, thins, margins that cut into the design, tears, or rubbing on the face, does not fit any of the categories described. Examples of these would normally cost less than 20% of the Grade Ill price.

Average used price less 50%

Please note that although the above refers primarily to the Maltese Cross cancellation, the same remarks are applicable, in the main, to the 1844 obliterators

Line Engraved Issues 1840 - 1881

Incidence of Inverted Watermarks

by Tony Child

In the eleventh edition we published, for the first time anywhere, a priced list which reflects the relative scarcity of different plates of 1d line engraved stamps. That listing was updated and amended in the twelfth edition and has been further updated and amended for this edition.

The information that follows is based on over 15 years of research and the examination of thousands of 1d line engraved stamps having an inverted watermark. Only stamps which have been examined by the author and the plating checked are taken into account (save where a copy of a certificate from a recognised expertisation committee has been provided). In every case, that plating has been verified by another expert in the plating of 1d line engraved stamps.

While further research will result in revisions to the published information, it can be said with some confidence that the tables below reflect the relative scarcity of different plates. However, perhaps perversely, market prices do not necessarily reflect scarcity. For example:

(a) Plate 1a is the second most common plate of the 1d black issue with inverted watermark but 1d blacks from plate 1a with inverted watermark are often priced higher than stamps from other plates which are less common with that variety.

(b) Plate 107 is generally regarded as the scarcest of the imperforate series of Die I, Alphabet I plates from plates 12-131. Yet plate 107 with inverted watermark is far from being the scarcest plate with inverted watermark. However, plate 107 stamps with that variety continue to attract a substantial premium.

(c) Stamps from the 1d Die II, Alphabet III perforation 14 with watermark Large Crown on white paper with inverted watermark are plentiful. Some of the more common plates with upright watermark are as scarce or, in some cases, scarcer with inverted watermark than plate 64 which is scarce with upright watermark. Yet stamps from plate 64 with inverted watermark continue to fetch high prices. In the recent 'Statham' sale at Grosvenor Auctions, a damaged copy of plate 64 with inverted watermark with a missing corner realised over £1200 (inclusive of buyers premium), a price not consistent with the relative scarcity of that plate.

(d) Stamps from the 1d Die II, Alphabet III, perforation 16, with Watermark Large Crown on white paper with inverted watermark are scarce. But the second most common plate with inverted watermark is plate 45, one of the scarcest plates in that issue with upright watermark. A copy of plate 45 with inverted watermark with a few trimmed perforations realised over £800 (inclusive of buyers premium) in the 'Statham' sale.

(e) The 1864 1d plates issue (letters in all four corners) is very common with inverted watermark although a number of plates are rare in that condition. The key plate (other than 77!) with upright watermark is the scarce plate 225.

This is far from being the scarcest plate with inverted watermark yet continues to command a four figure sum when available.

Notes on Pricing

This is a controversial area. Please read the following notes before considering the price listings. The pricing is for good sound used copies. Fine or very fine copies attract a significant premium. Damaged copies are worth less but copies with relatively minor faults from scarcer plates may retain the 'good used' value.

Multiples with inverted watermarks are scarce and blocks of four (or larger) are rare. Multiples attract a significant premium as do stamps with inverted watermarks on covers or entires. Inverted watermark stamps with distinctive cancellations may be expected to cost more than those with a common or garden numeral cancel.

Imperforate 1d red stamps with inverted watermark are far more common than most of the perforate issues. That is true of both Alphabet I (plates 12 to 131) and Alphabet II (plates 132 to 177) issues. The price listed below is for 4 margin copies. Three margin copies are worth less.

The demand for inverted watermark stamps has increased especially for the 1864 1d plates issue. The demand for earlier issues continues to be constrained by the difficulty for collectors in being sure that a stamp offered as plate 5, for example, is in fact from that plate. There continues to be misplated material on the market. Prices from dealers' lists and auction realisations have been taken into account in the pricing tables, as has the relative scarcity and demand for individual plates. The editor welcomes any information, critical or otherwise, which will add to or improve this listing.

Price Listings

A dash in a column indicates that a particular plate is not known to exist with inverted watermark. A hash (#) indicates that a particular plate is believed not to exist with inverted watermark. Prices may go up as demand increases but may also go down as the incidence of accurately plated copies increases.

1d Blacks

All plates (except plate 10) are known with inverted watermark. Plate 1b is relatively common. Plate 1a is the next most common but is scarce. Plates 2, 4, 5, 8 and 9 are next in order of rarity. Plate 6 is rare. Plate 7 is even rarer. Only one copy has been identified from plates 3 and 11 respectively. The latter was in the Seymour sale but its present whereabouts is unknown. A copy of 'plate 10' was offered on eBay in the last few years but was readily identifiable as being from plate 1b. 85% of all 1d Blacks with inverted watermarks come from plate 1b.

1d Black

Plate		Plate		Plate	
1a	£1000	1b	£1000	2	£1750
3	£1200	4	£2200	5	£2250
6	£3000	7	£3000	8	£2000
9	£2500	10	-	11	

1d Reds from black plates

Plate		Plate		Plate	
1b	£2500	2	-	5	-
8	£2500	9	£2500	10	£2250
11	-				

1d Red, Imperforate, Watermark Small Crown, Plates 12-131, Die I, Alphabet I

Most plates exist with inverted watermark. Imperforate 1d Reds with inverted watermark are relatively common far more so than many of the early perforated issues. Plate 24 is by far the most common of the "Maltese Cross" plates, followed by plates 45, 31, 25, 32 and 29. Plate 98 is the Alphabet I plate most commonly found with inverted watermark, closely followed by plate 100. Other relatively common plates are 69, 129, 122, 105, 109, 110, 114, 113, 97, 46, 61, 74, 76, 96, 97, 121 and 124. Prices are for four margin stamps.

Plate		Plate		Plate	
12	£400	13	-	14	£400
15	£200	16	-	17	£100
18	£300	19	£100	20	£200
21	£200	22	£250	23	£400
24	£40	25	£80	26	£200
27	£300	28	£80	29	£80
30	-	31	£60	32	£80
33	£300	34	£100	35	-
36	-	37	£200	38	£200
39	£100	40	£400	41	£80
42	£200	43	£200	44	£200
45	£60	46	£60	47	£250
49	£300	49	-	50	£80
51	£200	52	£200	53	£200
54	£250	55	-	56	£80
57	£200	58	£100	59	£300
60	£80	61	£60	62	£60
63	£100	64	£80	65	£300
66	£80	67	£300	68	£200
69	£40	70	£100	71	£100
72	£80	73	£300	74	£60
75	£300	76	£60	77	-
78	£400	79	£200	80	£100
81	-	82	£200	83	£250
84	£200	85	£200	86	£80
87	£100	88	£100	89	£80
90	£250	91	£80	92	£80
93	£80	94	£100	95	£100
96	£60	97	£60	98	£30
99	£100	100	£30	101	£60
102	£200	103	£100	104	£100
105	£40	106	£100	107	* £250
108	£60	109	£40	110	£40
111	£80	112	£60	113	£60
114	£60	115	£60	116	£80
117	£60	118	£80	119	£100
120	£100	121	£60	122	£40
123	£80	124	£60	125	£100
126	£100	127	£100	128	£80
129	£40	130	£80	131	£100

* A copy of plate 107 with inverted watermark realised over £450 (inclusive of premium) in the "Statham" sale.

1d Red, Imperforate, Watermark Small Crown, Plates 132-177, Die I, Alphabet II

All plates except 176 have been recorded with inverted watermark. Like their Alphabet I counterparts, stamps from this issue with inverted watermark are relatively common. Prices are for four margin stamps.

Plate		Plate		Plate	
132	£100	133	£80	134	£100
135	£80	136	£60	137	£60
138	£100	139	£100	140	£100
141	£60	142	£100	143	£60
144	£400	145	£80	146	£100
147	£100	148	£200	149	£100
150	£100	151	£100	152	£100
153	£60	154	£60	155	£60
156	£60	157	£100	158	£80
159	£100	160	£60	161	£80
162	£100	163	£60	164	£40
165	£80	166	£60	167	£40
168	£40	169	£60	170	£60
171	£80	172	£80	173	£60
174	£200	175	£1500	176	-
177	£1500				

A copy of plate 173 (a common plate with inverted watermark) realised £300 (inclusive of premium) in the "Statham" sale; a copy of plate 177 with inverted watermark (one of three recorded copies) realised over £2500 (inclusive of premium) in the same sale!

1d Die I, Alphabet I, Perf 16 (Archer), Watermark Small Crown, Plates 92 to 101, 107 and 111*

Only plates 99 and 100 have been recorded with inverted watermark. There is only one recorded copy of plate 99 (price £1500) but a number of copies are known from plate 100 (price £500). However, a fine used copy of plate 100 with inverted watermark realised over £1380 (inlusive of prmium) in the "Statham" sale.

* An RPS certificated copy of plate 111 with upright watermark exists.

1d Die I, Alphabet II, Perf 16, Watermark Small Crown, Plates 155, 157, 162 - 204, R1 - R6

All plates have been recorded with inverted watermark except the rare plate 168 and plate R4. Stamps from this issue with inverted watermark are relatively common. Plate 176 is the most common plate with inverted watermark, followed by plates 180, 167, 191, 195, 203, R5, 164, 183, 172 and R5 all of which exist in numbers

Plate		Plate		Plate	
155	£300	157	£250	162	£100
163	£80	164	£40	165	£400
166	£80	167	£40	168	#
169	£100	170	-	171	£150
172	£40	173	£60	174	£100
175	£250	176	£30	178	£100
179	£250	180	£30	181	£150
182	£100	183	£60	184	£100
185	£100	186	£100	187	£150
188	£200	189	£100	190	£40
191	£40	192	£80	193	£100
194	£100	195	£40	196	£200
197	£60	198	£80	199	£100
200	£80	201	£300	202	£80
203	£40	204	£400	R1	£100
R2	£250	R3	£100	R4	-
R5	£40	R6	£80		

1d Die I, Alphabet II, Perf 14, Watermark Small Crown, Plates 194-198, 200-204, R1-R6

All plates are recorded with inverted watermark except the rare plate 195. Stamps from this issue with watermark inverted are scarce although plates 198, 203 and R5 are less scarce than other plates

Plate		Plate		Plate	
194	£400	195	#	196	£200
197	£200	198	£100	200	£300
202	£150	203	£100	204	£400
R1	£250	R2	£200	R3	£150
R4	£250	R5	£100	R6	£150

1d Die II, Alphabet II, Perf 14, Watermark Small Crown, Plates 1-21

All plates are recorded with inverted watermark except plate 13. Stamps from this issue with watermark inverted are generally scarce except plate 5 and, to a lesser extent, plates 1 and 11

Plate		Plate		Plate	
1	£100	2	£150	3	£200
4	£250	5	£80	6	£250
7	£200	8	£150	9	£150
10	£300	11	£100	12	£300
13	-	14	£250	15	£200
16	£400	17	£400	18	£300
19	£200	20	£300	21	£200

1d Die II, Alphabet II, Perf 16, Watermark Small Crown, Plates 1-15

All plates are recorded with inverted watermark except plate 12. Stamps from this issue with inverted watermark are generally scarce except plates 1 and 5 which are relatively common.

Plate		Plate		Plate	
1	£50	2	£100	3	£250
4	£400	5	£60	6	£200
7	£200	8	£200	9	£400
10	£300	11	£300	12	-
13	£350	14	£300	15	£200

1d Die II, Alphabet II, Perf 16, Watermark Large Crown, Plates 1-15, blued paper

Stamps from this issue with inverted watermark are very scarce. Plate 5 is scarce but is the most common (or rather least scarce). To date, only 6 plates have been recorded with watermark inverted. Prices are £200 (plate 5), £300 (plate 8), £350 (plates 1 and 2) and £400 (plates 6 and 14).

1d Die II, Alphabet II, Perf 14, Watermark Large Crown, Plates 1-21, blued paper

All plates are recorded with inverted watermark except the rare plate 3 and plate 13. The 'Plate 13' in the "Statham" sale turned out on close examinatuion to be plate 14. This is still a difficult issue to find with watermark inverted but plate 19 is relatively common thus, as are plates 5 and 15.

Plate		Plate		Plate	
1	£150	2	£100	3	#
4	£400	5	£70	6	£250
7	£300	8	£100	9	£250
10	£250	11	£150	12	£150
13	-	14	£100	15	£70
16	£100	17	£400	18	£100
19	£50	20	£150	21	£100

1d Die II, Alphabet III, Perf 14, Watermark Small Crown, Plates 22-27 and 31*

Only plates 24 and 26 have been recorded with inverted watermark. There is only one recorded copy of plate 26 (price £1500) but a number of copies are known from plate 24 (price £400)

* An RPS certificated copy of plate 31 with upright watermark exists.

1d Die II, Alphabet III, Perf 14, Watermark Large Crown, Blued paper, Plates 22-38, 40, 42-49, 53*

Plates 27 and 33 are commonly found with inverted watermark. The next most common plates are 35, 26 and 37. Apart from these, stamps from this issue with watermark inverted are scarce but all plates from 23 to 46 exist thus.

Plate		Plate		Plate	
22	#	23	£400	24	£400
25	£300	26	£60	27	£30
28	£100	29	£300	30	£250
31	£300	32	£100	33	£40
34	£100	35	£60	36	£100
37	£100	38	£100	40	£100
42	£300	43	£200	44	£200
45	£200	46	£200	47	-
48	#	49	#	53	#

* An RPS certificated copy of plate 53 with upright watermark exists.

1d Die II, Alphabet III, Perf 14, Watermark Large Crown, (transitional issues), Plates 27, 31-38, 40, 42-49, 52, 53*, 55

This stamp is not often seen with inverted watermark but plates 27, 33, 34, 36, 37, 38, 44, 46, 47 and 49 have been recorded thus. Plates 44 and 37 are the most common (price £80); other prices are: Plates 27, 33, 34, 36 and 47 - £120; Plates 38, 46 and 49 - £200.

* Most copies of plate 53 are correctly classified as transitional issues although copies do exist in a rose red shade on white paper (but not with watermark inverted!).

1d Die II, Alphabet III, Perf 14, Watermark Large Crown, White paper, Plates 27, 33, 34, 36-39, 41-49, 52, 53, 55-68 and R17

All plates exist with watermark inverted except the rare plate 53. Plates 44, 39 and 42 are very common. Watermark type II is common on plates 39, 68, 66, 57 and R17 but is otherwise quite scarce.

Plate		Plate		Plate	
27	£60	33	£300	34	£40
36	£70	37	£80	38	£100
39	£20	41	£100	42	£25
43	£40	44	£20	45	£300
46	£70	47	£40	48	£50
49	£30	52	£80	53	#
55	£60	56	£80	57	£50
58	£40	59	£200	60	£200
61	£200	62	£100	63	£80
64	* £200	65	£2000	66	£70
67	£250	68	£40	R17	£200

* A copy of plate 64 (with missing corner) realised over £1200 (inclusive of premium) in the "Statham" sale. A copy of plate 65 realised over £2750 (inclusive of premium) in that sale.

1d Die II, Alphabet III, Perf 16, Watermark Large Crown, White paper, Plates 27, 34, 36-38, 42-49, 52, 55-60

This stamp is very scarce with watermark inverted. Only plate 44 is seen with any frequency (price £100). Other plates recorded with watermark inverted are plate 45 (price £300), plate 42 (price £350), and plates 57, 58 and 60 (price £400).

A copy of plate 45 with a few clipped perfs realised over £800 in the "Statham' sale.

1d Die II, Alphabet III, Perf 14, Watermark Large Crown, White paper, Plates 50 and 51.

Both plates exist with watermark inverted and both are found with watermarks type 1 and type 2. Neither plate is scarce with watermark inverted (price £50 each plate)

1d Die II, Alphabet II, Perf 14, Watermark Large Crown, White paper, Plates R15 and R16

Both plates exist with watermark inverted but plate 16 is rare thus. Plate R15 exists with watermarks type 1 and type 2 (price £50). Only two copies have been recorded of plate R16 (watermark type 1) price £300.

1864 1d "plates", Watermark Large Crown, letters in all four corners

This issue with inverted watermark is very much in demand by collectors, partly as a result of the publication of a priced list in previous editions of the Stoneham catalogue and partly because the plate number appears on the face of the stamp. However, buyers should beware that plating is not always straightforward.

All plates exist with inverted watermark except the exceedingly rare plate 77 and possibly plate 93. No authenticated copy of plate 93 with watermark inverted has been seen although many imposters have been, even copies of "plate 93" from important collections. The reason is that poor engraving and/or the effect of a postmark makes plate 83 (the most common plate with inverted watermark) appear as plate 93. Do not accept a plated stamp as being from plate 93 unless it has been compared with an authenticated copy of plate 93 (or the imprimatur sheet) and the position in the corner square of all four letterings match. The editor welcomes receipt of copies of "plate 93" with watermark inverted for verification.

The same is true of plate 191, an exceedingly rare plate with inverted watermark. Copies of plate 101 (a very common plate with inverted watermark) or 181, a scarce plate thus, are often passed off as plate 191. The comments above with regard to plate 93 apply.

As noted, the most common plate with inverted watermark is plate 83, followed by plates 101, 141, 136, 71, 154 and 208. Other plates commonly found with inverted watermark are 74, 84, 86, 133, 158, 167, 176, 201 and 216. Among the scarcest plates with inverted watermark are plates 89, 102, 103, 107, 110, 116, 124, 125, 132, 134, 143, 145, 147, 148, 152, 163, 168, 172, 175, 181, 182, 183, 184, 191, 193, 194, 206, 211, 212, 213, 215, 217, and plates 219 to 225. There is no correlation between the scarcity of stamps with upright watermark from difficult plates and those difficult plates with inverted watermarks.

Plate	F/U	G/U	Plate	F/U	G/U
71	£25	£15	72	£80	£50
73	£50	£35	74	£40	£25
76	£80	£50	77	#	#
78	£80	£50	79	£50	£35
80	£80	£50	81	£80	£50
82	£100	£75	83	£20	£10
84	£40	£25	85	£50	£35
86	£30	£20	87	£100	£75
88	£40	£25	89	£100	£75
90	£50	£35	91	£50	£35
92	£50	£35	93	-	-
94	£50	£35	95	£80	£50
96	£50	£35	97	£40	£25
98	£40	£25	99	£40	£25
100	£100	£75	101	£20	£10
102	£250	£200	103	£250	£200
104	£80	£50	105	£40	£25
106	£80	£50	107	£100	£75
108	£50	£35	109	£100	£75
110	£150	£110	111	£40	£25
112	£80	£50	113	£50	£35
114	£80	£50	115	£50	£35
116	£150	£110	117	£20	£10
118	£30	£20	119	£50	£35
120	£80	£50	121	£80	£50
122	£80	£50	123	£100	£75

Plate	F/U	G/U	Plate	F/U	G/U
124	£150	£110	125	£120	£90
127	£50	£35	129	£80	£50
130	£80	£50	131	£80	£50
132	£150	£110	133	£40	£25
134	£100	£75	135	£50	£35
136	£25	£15	137	£50	£35
138	£100	£75	139	£80	£50
140	£50	£35	141	£20	£10
142	£80	£50	143	£200	£160
144	£80	£50	145	£300	£250
146	£50	£35	147	£120	£90
148	£100	£75	149	£80	£50
150	£80	£50	151	£80	£50
152	£100	£75	153	£50	£35
154	£25	£15	155	£50	£35
156	£50	£35	157	£30	£20
158	£30	£20	159	£100	£75
160	£40	£25	161	£50	£35
162	£100	£75	163	£100	£75
164	£50	£35	165	£50	£35
166	£80	£50	167	£40	£25
168	£100	£75	169	£40	£25
170	£80	£50	171	£100	£75
172	£100	£75	173	£50	£35
174	£50	£35	175	£200	£160
176	£30	£20	177	£50	£35
178	£100	£75	179	£50	£35
180	£80	£50	181	£200	£160
182	£120	£90	183	£200	£160
184	£120	£90	185	£50	£35
186	£50	£35	187	£80	£50
188	£40	£25	189	£100	£75
190	£40	£25	191	£500	£400
192	£50	£35	193	£120	£90
194	£200	£160	195	£50	£35
196	£100	£75	197	£100	£75
198	£40	£25	199	£80	£50
200	£30	£20	201	£30	£20
202	£50	£35	203	£40	£25
204	£80	£50	205	£100	£75
206	£250	£200	207	£40	£25
208	£25	£15	209	£50	£35
210	£50	£35	211	£120	£90
212	£100	£75	213	£300	£250
214	£80	£50	215	£150	£110
216	£25	£15	217	£300	£250
218	£50	£35	219	£120	£90
220	£150	£110	221	£100	£75
222	£200	£160	223	£300	£250
224	£500	£400	225	£1500	£1000

Engraved by Charles and Frederick Heath
Printer: Perkins, Bacon & Petch.

Small Crown
Watermark

1840 (6 May) Wmk. Small Crown. White paper. Imperforate

No.			M/M	F/U	G/U	✉
V1	**1d**	**Greyish black**. Plate 1a	£7000	£200	£120	£275
V1a		Wmk. inverted		£400	£300	
V1b		Grey black (worn plate)	£4200	£200	£120	£275
V1c		Intense black	£10000	£200	£120	£275
V2	**1d**	**Black**. Plate 1b	£6000	£140	£85	£200
V2a		Wmk. inverted		£250	£180	
V2b		Intense black	£6000	£160	£95	£200
V3	**1d**	**Black**. Plate 2	£6000	£160	£95	£210
V3a		Wmk. inverted	£4000	£500	£400	
V3b		Intense black	£7000	£160	£95	£210
V3c		Grey black (worn plate)	£7000	£170	£100	£220
V4	**1d**	**Black**. Plate 3	£7000	£160	£110	£230
V4a		Wmk. inverted		£1800	£1200	
V4b		Grey black	£7000	£180	£110	£220
V5	**1d**	**Black**. Plate 4	£6000	£160	£100	£210
V5a		Wmk. inverted		£500	£400	
V5b		Intense black	£6500	£160	£100	£210
V6	**1d**	**Black.** Plate 5	£6500	£150	£100	£210
V6a		Wmk inverted		£500	£400	
V6b		Intense black	£6500	£160	£110	£220
V7	**1d**	**Black.** Plate 6	£6000	£160	£100	£220
V7a		Wmk. inverted	£20000	£850	£700	
V7b		Intense black	£6500	£160	£100	£220
V8	**1d**	**Black.** Plate 7	£6500	£160	£100	£220
V8a		Wmk. inverted	£20000	£1200	£1000	
V8b		Greyish black	£6500	£170	£100	£220
V9	**1d**	**Black.** Plate 8	£7000	£180	£110	£240
V9a		Wmk. inverted	£20000	£500	£400	
V10	**1d**	**Black.** Plate 9	£8500	£180	£110	£240
V10a		Wmk. inverted		£500	£400	
V11	**1d**	**Black.** Plate 10	£16000	£275	£175	£400
V11a		Grey black	£16000	£275	£175	£400
V12	**1d**	**Black.** Plate 11	£14000	£2200	£1500	£4000
V12a		Wmk. inverted		£3000		
V12b		Grey black	£13000	£1800	£1300	£3500
V13	**2d**	**Blue**. Plate 1 (8.5.40)	£18000	£400	£250	£600
V13a		Wmk. inverted	£50000	£700	£450	
V13b		Deep blue	£20000	£400	£260	£600
V13c		Steel blue	£30000	£420	£270	£650
V13d		Pale blue	£24000	£400	£270	£675
V13e		Milky blue	£30000	£500	£300	£750
V13f		Violet blue		£800	£475	£1200
V14	**2d**	**Blue.** Plate 2	£24000	£500	£275	£700
V14a		Wmk. inverted		£2000	£1500	
V14b		Deep blue	£26000	£500	£275	£720
V14c		Pale blue	£24000	£550	£300	£750

1841 (10 Feb.) Wmk. Small Crown. Blued paper. Imperforate.

Die I. Alphabet I

No.			M/M	F/U	G/U	✉
V15	**1d**	**Red brown.** Plate 1b	£12000	£150	£90	£225
V15a		Wmk. inverted		£1200	£800	
V16	**1d**	**Red brown.** Plate 2	£5000	£120	£75	£175
V17	**1d**	**Red brown.** Plate 5	£2000	£70	£40	£110

No.			M/M	F/U	G/U	✉
V18	**1d**	**Red brown.** Plate 8	£3000	£60	£35	£90
V18a		Wmk. inverted		£1500		
V19	**1d**	**Red brown.** Plate 9	£2000	£60	£35	£95
V19a		Wmk. inverted		£1200		
V20	**1d**	**Red brown.** Plate 10	£1500	£55	£35	£100
V20a		Wmk. inverted		£1800		
V21	**1d**	**Red brown.** Plate 11	£1500	£45	£30	£90

The above stamps were printed from 'black' plates and there are several shades

No.			M/M	F/U	G/U	✉
V22	**1d**	**Red brown.** Plates 12 - 131	£110	6.00	2.50	£10
V22a		Wmk. inverted	£195	£40	£25	
V22b		Deep red brown	£100	£12	5.00	£14
V22c		Pale red brown	£120	£12	6.00	£17
V22d		Lake red	£1200	£300	£180	£500
V22e		Orange brown	£300	£70	£30	£70
V22f		Red brown on lavender	£400	£85	£40	£80
		tinted paper. Plates 118 - 131				

1841 (3 March) White lines added to design. Wmk Small Crown. Bluish paper. Imperforate.

No.			M/M	F/U	G/U	✉
V23	**2d**	**Blue.** Plate 3	£1400	£35	£20	£100
V23a		Wmk. inverted	£3000	£300	£190	
V23b		Deep blue	£1500	£40	£22	£110
V23c		Pale blue	£1600	£40	£22	£110
V24	**2d**	**Blue.** Plate 4	£1200	£40	£20	£100
V24a		Wmk. inverted		£130	£80	
V24b		Deep blue	£1200	£40	£20	£100
V24c		Pale blue	£1200	£40	£20	£100
V24d		Violet blue on thick lavender				
		tinted paper	£2000	£300	£100	£375

1852 (6 Feb.) Change to Alphabet II. Wmk. Small Crown. Bluish paper. Imperforate.

Die I. Alphabet II

No.			M/M	F/U	G/U	✉
V25	**1d**	**Red brown.** Plates 132 - 175	£125	9.50	4.00	£15
V25a		Wmk. inverted	£600	£40	£30	
V25b		Lake red	£1000	£300	£150	£350
V25c		Orange brown	£300	£50	£18	£55
V25d		Red brown on lavender				
		tinted paper. Plates 132 - 136	£500	£95	£50	£100

1850 Wmk Small Crown. Bluish paper. Archer experimental perf. 16

Die I. Alphabet I

No.			M/M	F/U	G/U	✉
V26	**1d**	**Red brown.** Plates 92 -101	£800	£400	£250	£1250
V26a		Wmk. inverted		£1000	£700	

1854 (Feb.) - 55 Wmk. Small Crown. Bluish paper. Perf 16

Die I. Alphabet I

No.			M/M	F/U	G/U	✉
V27	**2d**	**Deep blue.** Plate 4 (13.5.54)	£1400	£40	£25	£75
V27a		Wmk. inverted		£120	£60	
V27b		Pale blue	£1700	£65	£40	£80

No.		M/M	F/U	G/U	✉

Die I. Alphabet II

V28	**1d Red brown.** Plates 155, 157, 162 - 204, R1 - R6	£125	8.00	3.00	£10
V28a	Wmk. inverted	£400	£50	£30	
V28b	Yellow brown	£140	£15	6.00	£20
V28c	Brick red	£160	£12	6.00	£20
V28d	Orange brown	£385	£60	£25	£60
V28e	Plum	£700	£120	£50	£120
V29	**2d Blue.** Plate 5 (28.8.55)	£2000	£150	£70	£200
V29a	Wmk. inverted	£2500	£300	£200	

Die II. Alphabet II

V30	**1d Red brown.** Plates 1 - 15 (1.3.55)	£170	£15	8.00	£15
V30a	Wmk. inverted	£400	£90	£60	
V30b	Yellow brown	£180	£19	£12	£18
V30c	Brick red	£190	£22	£10	£20
V30d	Plum	£450	£85	£40	£50

1855 (Jan.) Wmk. Small Crown. Bluish paper. Perf 14

Die I. Alphabet I

| V31 | **2d Blue.** Plate 4 (22.2.55) | £2000 | £180 | £75 | £120 |
| V31a | Wmk. inverted | | £300 | £250 | |

Die I. Alphabet II

V32	**1d Red brown.** Plates 194 - 204 R1 - R6	£225	£25	£12	£27
V32a	Wmk. inverted		£175	£110	
V32b	Yellow brown	£400	£25	£15	£25
V32c	Brick red	£250	£50	£30	£40
V32d	Orange brown	£320	£60	£40	£50
V32e	Plum	£500	£120	£60	£85
V33	**2d Blue.** Plate 5 (5.7.55)	£1700	£120	£60	£120
V33a	Wmk. inverted		£275	£175	

Die II. Alphabet II

V34	**1d Red brown.** Plates 1 - 21 (28.2.55)	£180	£20	£12	£20
V34a	Wmk. inverted	£450	£120	£80	
V34b	Deep red brown	£225	£20	£10	£20
V34c	Orange brown	£500	£95	£60	£65
V34d	Plum	£750	£150	£70	£100

Die II. Alphabet III

| V35 | **1d Red brown.** Plates 22 - 27 (18.8.55) | £1000 | £250 | £130 | £500 |
| V35a | Wmk. inverted | | £600 | £400 | |

Large Crown Watermark	Large Crown Watermark *(modified and introduced in March 1861)*

1855 (15 May) Wmk. Large Crown. Bluish paper. Perf 16

Die I. Alphabet II

| V36 | **2d Blue.** Plate 5 (20.7.55) | £1800 | £120 | £75 | £190 |
| V36a | Wmk. inverted | | £350 | £250 | |

Die II. Alphabet II

V37	**1d Red brown.** Plates 1 - 15 (15.5.55)	£300	£45	£30	£55
V37a	Wmk. inverted		£200	£150	
V37b	Deep red brown	£300	£50	£30	£60

1855 (June) Wmk. Large Crown. Bluish paper. Perf 14

Die I. Alphabet II

V38	**2d Blue.** Plate 5 (20.7.55)	£850	£16	9.00	£50
V38a	Greenish blue	£950	£18	£10	£60
V38b	Wmk. inverted		£150	£90	

Die I. Alphabet III

| V39 | **2d Blue.** Plate 6 (2.7.57) | £1000 | £16 | 9.00 | £50 |
| V39a | Wmk. inverted | | £150 | £90 | |

Die II. Alphabet II

V40	**1d Red brown.** Plates 1 - 21	£110	7.00	5.00	£10
V40a	Wmk. inverted		£70	£50	
V40b	Yellow brown	£130	£15	8.00	£12
V40c	Plum	£350	£90	£50	£80

Die II. Alphabet III

V41	**1d Red brown.** Plates 22 - 38, 40, 42 - 49 (8.55)	£90	6.00	3.50	5.00
V41a	Wmk. inverted	£400	£60	£40	
V41b	Brick red	£130	7.00	5.00	6.00
V41c	Brown rose	£130	£12	8.00	9.00
V41d	Orange brown	£200	£20	£12	£14
V41e	Orange red	£200	£20	£12	£20
V41f	Plum	£1250	£225	£125	£200
V41g	Deep claret on deep blue paper	£500	£80	£45	£60

1857 Wmk. Large Crown. Cream toned paper. Perf 14

Die II. Alphabet III

V42	**1d Red orange.** Plates 27 - 55	£175	£30	£17	£22
V42a	Wmk. inverted	£450	£120	£80	
V42b	Orange brown	£190	£30	£15	£20
V42c	Pale red	£190	£30	£15	£20
V42d	Pale rose	£190	£30	£15	£20

1857 (26 Dec.) - 58 New colours on 1d and thin white lines on 2d. Wmk. Large Crown. White paper. Perf 16

Die I Alphabet III

| V43 | **2d Blue.** Plate 6 (1.12.58) | £4000 | £160 | £100 | £220 |
| V43a | Wmk. inverted | | £700 | £500 | |

Die II. Alphabet III

| V44 | **1d Rose red.** Plates various 27 - 60 | £550 | £30 | £12 | £25 |
| V44a | Wmk. inverted | | £130 | £80 | |

1856 (Nov) - 63 Wmk. Large Crown. White paper. Perf 14

Die II. Alphabet II

V45	**1d Rose red.** Plates R15, R16 (1862)	£95	6.00	3.50	£10
V45a	Wmk. inverted		£85	£60	
V45b	Pale rose red	£95	6.00	3.50	£10
V45c	Pale red. Plate R15	£125	£50	£20	£35

Die II. Alphabet III

V46	**1d Rose red.** Plates various 27 - 68, R17 (1856)	£25	3.50	2.00	3.50
V46a	Wmk. inverted	£30	£30	£20	
V46b	Deep rose red (7.56)	£25	4.00	2.50	3.50
V46c	Pale red (4.56)	£60	5.00	2.50	5.50
V46d	Pale rose (3.56)	£60	5.50	2.50	6.00
V46e	Pale rose pink (1863)	£70	6.00	2.50	7.00
V46f	Red brown (1856)	£350	£100	£80	£120
V46g	Bright rose red (3.56)	£175	£35	£15	£25

Die II. Alphabet IV

V47	**1d Rose red.** Plates 50, 51 (1861)	£110	7.50	4.50	£12
V47a	Wmk. inverted	£170	£70	£50	
V47b	Pale rose red	£110	7.50	4.50	£12

			M/M	F/U	G/U	✉

Letters in all four corners and plate numbers shown in the design.
Printer: Perkins, Bacon & Co.

Halfpenny Watermark

Plate Number (20) at right

No.			M/M	F/U	G/U	✉
V62	½d	**Rose red.** Plate 19	£80	£15	8.00	£40
V62a		Wmk. inverted		£80	£55	
V62b		Wmk. reversed		£70	£50	
V62c		Wmk. inv. and rev.		£80	£55	
V63	½d	**Rose red.** Plate 20	£75	£20	£10	£60
V63a		Wmk. inverted		£80	£55	
V63b		Wmk. reversed		£80	£55	
V63c		Wmk. inv. and rev.	£120	£40	£25	

** Beware of stamps from Plate 19 with the figure '1' obscured or removed

Plate Number (219) at right

1870 (1 Oct.) Wmk. Halfpenny. Perf 14

No.			M/M	F/U	G/U	✉
V49	½d	**Rose red.** Plate 1	£80	£40	£20	£75
V49a		Wmk. inverted	£100	£75		
V49b		Wmk. inverted and rev.	£75	£50		
V50	½d	**Rose red.** Plate 3	£60	7.00	3.00	£25
V50a		Wmk. inverted	£120	£75	£50	
V50b		Wmk. reversed	£100	£60	£40	
V50c		Wmk. inv. and rev.	£75	£20	£10	
V51	½d	**Rose red.** Plate 4	£60	7.00	3.00	£20
V51a		Wmk. inverted	£85	£40	£25	
V51b		Wmk. reversed	£110	£80	£50	
V51c		Wmk. inv. and rev.		£50	£40	
V52	½d	**Rose red.** Plate 5	£35	5.00	3.00	£20
V52a		Wmk. inverted		£35	£20	
V52b		Wmk. reversed		£25	£12	
V52c		Wmk. inv. and rev.		£50	£30	
V53	½d	**Rose red.** Plate 6	£50	5.00	3.00	£20
V53a		Wmk. inverted		£40	£30	
V35b		Wmk. reversed		£75	£50	
V53c		Wmk. inv. and rev.		£60	£40	
V54	½d	**Rose red.** Plate 8	£95	£30	£15	£65
V54a		Wmk. inverted	£100	£70		
V54b		Wmk. reversed	£75	£50		
V54c		Wmk. inv. and rev.	£60	£40		
V55	½d	**Rose red.** Plate 9 **	£1500	£270	£170	£850
V55a		Wmk. inverted		£500	£400	
V56	½d	**Rose red.** Plate 10	£50	5.00	3.00	£20
V56a		Wmk. inverted		£75	£50	
V56b		Wmk. inv. and rev.		£50	£35	
V57	½d	**Rose red.** Plate 11	£50	5.00	3.00	£20
V57a		Wmk. inverted	£120	£60	£40	
V57b		Wmk. reversed		£75	£50	
V57c		Wmk. inv. and rev.		£12	8.00	
V58	½d	**Rose red.** Plate 12	£50	5.00	3.00	£20
V58a		Wmk. reversed		£100	£75	
V58b		Wmk. inv. and rev.	£75	£15	£10	
V59	½d	**Rose red.** Plate 13	£50	5.00	3.00	£20
V59a		Wmk. inverted		£75	£50	
V59b		Wmk. reversed		£30	£20	
V59c		Wmk. inv. and rev.		£60	£40	
V60	½d	**Rose red.** Plate 14	£50	5.00	3.00	£20
V60a		Wmk. reversed		£60	£40	
V60b		Wmk. inv. and rev.		£60	£40	
V61	½d	**Rose red.** Plate 15	£60	9.00	5.00	£20
V61a		Wmk. inverted	£100	£75		
V61b		Wmk. reversed	£70	£50		
V61c		Wmk. inv. and rev.	£70	£50		

1864 (1 April) Wmk. Large Crown. Perf 14

No.			M/M	F/U	G/U	✉
V64	1d	**Rose red.** Plate 71	£24	2.00	1.00	4.00
V64a		Wmk. inverted		£25	£15	
V65	1d	**Rose red.** Plate 72	£24	2.00	1.00	4.00
V65a		Wmk. inverted		£80	£50	
V66	1d	**Rose red.** Plate 73	£24	2.00	1.00	4.00
V66a		Wmk. inverted		£50	£35	
V67	1d	**Rose red.** Plate 74	£20	2.00	1.00	4.00
V67a		Wmk. inverted		£40	£25	
V68	1d	**Rose red.** Plate 76	£20	1.00	60	4.00
V68a		Wmk. inverted		£80	£50	
V69	1d	**Rose red.** Plate 77	£120000	#	#	
V70	1d	**Rose red.** Plate 78	£30	1.00	60	4.00
V70a		Wmk. inverted		£80	£50	
V71	1d	**Rose red.** Plate 79	£20	1.50	60	4.00
V71a		Wmk. inverted		£50	£35	
V72	1d	**Rose red.** Plate 80	£20	1.50	1.00	3.00
V72a		Wmk. inverted		£80	£50	
V73	1d	**Rose red.** Plate 81	£27	1.00	60	4.00
V73a		Wmk. inverted		£80	£50	
V74	1d	**Rose red.** Plate 82	£100	3.00	1.10	£10
V74a		Wmk. inverted		£100	£75	
V75	1d	**Rose red.** Plate 83	£120	3.50	2.50	£15
V75a		Wmk. inverted		£20	£10	
V76	1d	**Rose red.** Plate 84	£30	1.50	1.00	5.00
V76a		Wmk. inverted		£40	£25	
V77	1d	**Rose red.** Plate 85	£18	1.50	1.00	3.00
V77a		Wmk. inverted		£50	£35	
V78	1d	**Rose red.** Plate 86	£20	2.00	1.00	3.00
V78a		Wmk. inverted		£30	£20	
V79	1d	**Rose red.** Plate 87	£14	1.50	80	3.00
V79a		Wmk. inverted		£100	£75	
V80	1d	**Rose red.** Plate 88	£130	5.00	2.75	£20
V80a		Wmk. inverted		£40	£25	
V81	1d	**Rose red.** Plate 89	£16	1.50	60	1.00
V81a		Wmk. inverted		£100	£75	
V82	1d	**Rose red.** Plate 90	£15	1.50	60	5.00
V82a		Wmk. inverted		£50	£35	
V83	1d	**Rose red.** Plate 91	£22	3.00	1.50	3.00
V83a		Wmk. inverted		£50	£35	
V84	1d	**Rose red.** Plate 92	£16	1.50	60	3.00
V84a		Wmk. inverted		£50	£35	
V85	1d	**Rose red.** Plate 93	£22	1.50	70	4.00
V85a		Wmk. inverted	-	-		
V86	1d	**Rose red.** Plate 94	£22	2.75	1.25	3.00
V86a		Wmk. inverted		£50	£35	

No.		M/M	F/U	G/U	◉
V87	**1d Rose red.** Plate 95	£18	1.50	60	3.00
V87a	Wmk. inverted		£80	£50	
V88	**1d Rose red.** Plate 96	£18	1.50	60	3.00
V88a	Wmk. inverted		£50	£35	
V89	**1d Rose red.** Plate 97	£18	1.50	70	3.00
V89a	Wmk. inverted		£40	£25	
V90	**1d Rose red.** Plate 98	£18	3.00	1.75	6.00
V90a	Wmk. inverted		£40	£25	
V91	**1d Rose red.** Plate 99	£22	2.50	1.10	6.00
V91a	Wmk. inverted		£40	£25	
V92	**1d Rose red.** Plate 100	£22	1.50	70	£15
V92a	Wmk. inverted		£100	£75	
V93	**1d Rose red.** Plate 101	£24	4.00	2.25	5.00
V93a	Wmk. inverted		£20	£10	
V94	**1d Rose red.** Plate 102	£17	1.50	70	3.00
V94a	Wmk. inverted		£250	£200	
V95	**1d Rose red.** Plate 103	£22	1.50	70	5.00
V95a	Wmk. inverted		£250	£200	
V96	**1d Rose red.** Plate 104	£27	2.75	1.10	£15
V96a	Wmk. inverted		£80	£50	
V97	**1d Rose red.** Plate 105	£37	4.00	2.50	£12
V97a	Wmk. inverted		£40	£25	
V98	**1d Rose red.** Plate 106	£20	1.50	65	4.00
V98a	Wmk. inverted		£80	£50	
V99	**1d Rose red.** Plate 107	£22	3.00	1.75	6.00
V99a	Wmk. inverted		£100	£75	
V100	**1d Rose red.** Plate 108	£26	1.50	70	£12
V100a	Wmk. inverted		£50	£35	
V101	**1d Rose red.** Plate 109	£38	1.50	80	£10
V101a	Wmk. inverted		£100	£75	
V102	**1d Rose red.** Plate 110	£22	5.00	2.25	8.00
V102a	Wmk. inverted		£150	£110	
V103	**1d Rose red.** Plate 111	£26	1.50	80	3.00
V103a	Wmk. inverted		£40	£25	
V104	**1d Rose red.** Plate 112	£29	1.50	80	8.00
V104a	Wmk. inverted		£80	£50	
V105	**1d Rose red.** Plate 113	£20	6.00	3.00	5.00
V105a	Wmk. inverted		£50	£35	
V106	**1d Rose red.** Plate 114	£130	7.00	3.25	£10
V106a	Wmk. inverted		£80	£50	
V107	**1d Rose red.** Plate 115	£45	1.50	80	£10
V107a	Wmk. inverted		£50	£35	
V108	**1d Rose red.** Plate 116	£36	6.00	3.25	6.00
V108a	Wmk. inverted		£150	£110	
V109	**1d Rose red.** Plate 117	£20	1.50	60	3.00
V109a	Wmk. inverted		£20	£10	
V110	**1d Rose red.** Plate 118	£20	1.50	70	3.00
V110a	Wmk. inverted		£30	£20	
V111	**1d Rose red.** Plate 119	£20	1.50	70	3.00
V111a	Wmk. inverted		£50	£35	
V112	**1d Rose red.** Plate 120	£12	1.20	60	3.00
V112a	Wmk. inverted		£80	£50	
V113	**1d Rose red.** Plate 121	£18	5.50	2.50	4.00
V113a	Wmk. inverted		£80	£50	
V114	**1d Rose red.** Plate 122	£12	1.20	60	3.00
V114a	Wmk. inverted		£80	£50	
V115	**1d Rose red.** Plate 123	£16	1.50	70	3.00
V115a	Wmk. inverted		£100	£75	
V116	**1d Rose red.** Plate 124	£12	1.50	50	3.00
V116a	Wmk. inverted		£150	£110	
V117	**1d Rose red.** Plate 125	£17	1.50	1.00	3.00
V117a	Wmk. inverted		£120	£90	
V118	**1d Rose red.** Plate 127	£20	2.00	1.00	4.00
V118a	Wmk. inverted		£50	£35	
V119	**1d Rose red.** Plate 129	£19	2.00	1.00	3.00
V119a	Wmk. inverted		£80	£50	
V120	**1d Rose red.** Plate 130	£20	1.50	80	3.00
V120a	Wmk. inverted		£80	£50	
V121	**1d Rose red.** Plate 131	£30	9.00	4.50	6.00
V121a	Wmk. inverted		£80	£50	
V122	**1d Rose red.** Plate 132	£80	£20	£10	£30
V122a	Wmk. inverted		£150	£110	
V123	**1d Rose red.** Plate 133	£55	7.50	4.25	£20
V123a	Wmk. inverted		£40	£25	
V124	**1d Rose red.** Plate 134	£12	1.50	60	3.00
V124a	Wmk. inverted		£100	£75	
V125	**1d Rose red.** Plate 135	£42	£15	8.00	£15
V125a	Wmk. inverted		£50	£35	
V126	**1d Rose red.** Plate 136	£78	8.00	5.50	8.00
V126a	Wmk. inverted		£25	£15	
V127	**1d Rose red.** Plate 137	£13	1.50	70	3.00
V127a	Wmk. inverted		£50	£35	
V128	**1d Rose red.** Plate 138	£15	1.50	70	3.00
V128a	Wmk. inverted		£100	£75	
V129	**1d Rose red.** Plate 139	£26	9.00	4.50	£15
V129a	Wmk. inverted		£80	£50	
V130	**1d Rose red.** Plate 140	£15	1.50	60	3.00
V130a	Wmk. inverted		£50	£35	
V131	**1d Rose red.** Plate 141	£50	3.00	1.50	£15
V131a	Wmk. inverted		£20	£10	
V132	**1d Rose red.** Plate 142	£27	9.00	5.00	£12
V132a	Wmk. inverted		£80	£50	
V133	**1d Rose red.** Plate 143	£20	7.00	3.00	8.00
V133a	Wmk. inverted		£200	£160	
V134	**1d Rose red.** Plate 144	£50	£10	5.00	£14
V134a	Wmk. inverted		£80	£50	
V135	**1d Rose red.** Plate 145	£13	1.50	70	3.00
V135a	Wmk. inverted		£300	£250	
V136	**1d Rose red.** Plate 146	£13	3.00	1.50	3.00
V136a	Wmk. inverted		£50	£35	
V137	**1d Rose red.** Plate 147	£20	2.00	80	4.50
V137a	Wmk. inverted		£120	£90	
V138	**1d Rose red.** Plate 148	£20	3.00	1.50	3.00
V138a	Wmk. inverted		£100	£75	
V139	**1d Rose red.** Plate 149	£20	3.00	1.50	3.00
V139a	Wmk. inverted		£80	£50	
V140	**1d Rose red.** Plate 150	£12	1.50	60	3.00
V140a	Wmk. inverted		£80	£50	
V141	**1d Rose red.** Plate 151	£20	6.00	3.50	8.00
V141a	Wmk. inverted		£80	£50	
V142	**1d Rose red.** Plate 152	£16	3.00	1.25	6.00
V142a	Wmk. inverted		£100	£75	
V143	**1d Rose red.** Plate 153	£50	6.00	2.50	£25
V143a	Wmk. inverted		£50	£35	
V144	**1d Rose red.** Plate 154	£14	1.50	60	4.00
V144a	Wmk. inverted		£25	£15	
V145	**1d Rose red.** Plate 155	£14	1.50	70	4.00
V145a	Wmk. inverted		£50	£35	
V146	**1d Rose red.** Plate 156	£14	1.50	60	4.00
V146a	Wmk. inverted		£50	£35	
V147	**1d Rose red.** Plate 157	£14	1.50	60	4.00
V147a	Wmk. inverted		£30	£20	
V148	**1d Rose red.** Plate 158	£18	1.50	60	3.00
V148a	Wmk. inverted		£30	£20	
V149	**1d Rose red.** Plate 159	£18	1.50	60	3.00
V149a	Wmk. inverted		£100	£75	
V150	**1d Rose red.** Plate 160	£18	1.50	60	3.00
V150a	Wmk. inverted		£40	£25	
V151	**1d Rose red.** Plate 161	£18	5.00	1.50	£12
V151a	Wmk. inverted		£50	£35	
V152	**1d Rose red.** Plate 162	£16	4.00	1.75	5.00
V152a	Wmk. inverted		£100	£75	
V153	**1d Rose red.** Plate 163	£16	2.00	70	5.00
V153a	Wmk. inverted		£100	£75	
V154	**1d Rose red.** Plate 164	£14	2.00	85	6.00
V154a	Wmk. inverted		£80	£50	
V155	**1d Rose red.** Plate 165	£13	1.50	60	3.00
V155a	Wmk. inverted		£50	£35	
V156	**1d Rose red.** Plate 166	£13	3.00	1.50	4.00
V156a	Wmk. inverted		£80	£50	
V157	**1d Rose red.** Plate 167	£13	1.50	60	3.00
V157a	Wmk. inverted		£40	£25	
V158	**1d Rose red.** Plate 168	£13	5.00	2.00	6.00
V158a	Wmk. inverted		£100	£75	
V159	**1d Rose red.** Plate 169	£16	5.00	1.10	£10
V159a	Wmk. inverted		£40	£25	
V160	**1d Rose red.** Plate 170	£12	1.50	60	3.00
V160a	Wmk. inverted		£80	£50	

No.			M/M	F/U	G/U	✉
V161	1d Rose red. Plate 171		£12	1.50	60	3.00
V161a	Wmk. inverted			£100	£75	
V162	1d Rose red. Plate 172		£12	1.50	60	3.00
V162a	Wmk. inverted			£100	£75	
V163	1d Rose red. Plate 173		£20	5.00	3.00	8.00
V163a	Wmk. inverted			£50	£35	
V164	1d Rose red. Plate 174		£12	1.50	60	3.00
V164a	Wmk. inverted			£50	£35	
V165	1d Rose red. Plate 175		£20	3.00	1.20	6.00
V165a	Wmk. inverted			£200	£160	
V166	1d Rose red. Plate 176		£20	3.00	1.20	6.00
V166a	Wmk. inverted			£30	£20	
V167	1d Rose red. Plate 177		£16	1.50	60	3.00
V167a	Wmk. inverted			£50	£35	
V168	1d Rose red. Plate 178		£12	2.00	1.00	£10
V168a	Wmk. inverted			£100	£75	
V169	1d Rose red. Plate 179		£16	2.00	1.00	4.00
V169a	Wmk. inverted			£50	£35	
V170	1d Rose red. Plate 180		£16	3.00	1.00	£15
V170a	Wmk. inverted			£80	£50	
V171	1d Rose red. Plate 181		£13	1.50	60	2.00
V171a	Wmk. inverted			£200	£150	
V172	1d Rose red. Plate 182		£35	2.00	1.25	£14
V172a	Wmk. inverted			£120	£90	
V173	1d Rose red. Plate 183		£16	2.00	1.00	4.00
V173a	Wmk. inverted			£200	£160	
V174	1d Rose red. Plate 184		£12	1.50	60	8.00
V174a	Wmk. inverted			£120	£90	
V175	1d Rose red. Plate 185		£16	2.00	75	£10
V175a	Wmk. inverted			£50	£35	
V176	1d Rose red. Plate 186		£16	2.00	75	8.00
V176a	Wmk. inverted			£50	£35	
V177	1d Rose red. Plate 187		£13	1.50	70	4.00
V177a	Wmk. inverted			£80	£50	
V178	1d Rose red. Plate 188		£19	5.00	2.50	£10
V178a	Wmk. inverted			£40	£25	
V179	1d Rose red. Plate 189		£20	4.00	2.00	£14
V179a	Wmk. inverted			£100	£75	
V180	1d Rose red. Plate 190		£13	3.00	1.75	£14
V180a	Wmk. inverted			£40	£25	
V181	1d Rose red. Plate 191		£12	4.00	2.00	8.00
V181a	Wmk. inverted			£500	£400	
V182	1d Rose red. Plate 192		£14	1.50	60	3.00
V182a	Wmk. inverted			£50	£35	
V183	1d Rose red. Plate 193		£14	1.50	60	6.00
V183a	Wmk. inverted			£120	£90	
V184	1d Rose red. Plate 194		£14	4.00	2.00	8.00
V184a	Wmk. inverted			£200	£160	
V185	1d Rose red. Plate 195		£14	4.00	2.00	4.00
V185a	Wmk. inverted			£50	£35	
V186	1d Rose red. Plate 196		£14	2.00	1.00	6.00
V186a	Wmk. inverted			£100	£75	
V187	1d Rose red. Plate 197		£20	6.00	3.00	£10
V187a	Wmk. inverted			£100	£75	
V188	1d Rose red. Plate 198		£14	3.00	1.50	6.00
V188a	Wmk. inverted			£40	£25	
V189	1d Rose red. Plate 199		£17	3.00	1.50	6.00
V189a	Wmk. inverted			£80	£50	
V190	1d Rose red. Plate 200		£17	1.50	60	8.00
V190a	Wmk. inverted			£30	£20	
V191	1d Rose red. Plate 201		£14	3.00	1.50	4.00
V191a	Wmk. inverted			£30	£20	
V192	1d Rose red. Plate 202		£16	5.00	2.00	£10
V192a	Wmk. inverted			£50	£35	
V193	1d Rose red. Plate 203		£14	7.00	4.00	£10
V193a	Wmk. inverted			£40	£25	
V194	1d Rose red. Plate 204		£15	1.50	60	£10
V194a	Wmk. inverted			£80	£50	
V195	1d Rose red. Plate 205		£15	2.00	70	£14
V195a	Wmk. inverted			£100	£75	
V196	1d Rose red. Plate 206		£15	7.00	4.00	£14
V196a	Wmk. inverted			£250	£200	
V197	1d Rose red. Plate 207		£15	7.00	4.00	£14
V197a	Wmk. inverted			£40	£25	

No.			M/M	F/U	G/U	✉
V198	1d Rose red. Plate 208		£16	8.00	4.50	£16
V198a	Wmk. inverted			£25	£15	
V199	1d Rose red. Plate 209		£15	8.00	4.50	£16
V199a	Wmk. inverted			£50	£35	
V200	1d Rose red. Plate 210		£18	9.00	5.00	£14
V200a	Wmk. inverted			£50	£35	
V201	1d Rose red. Plate 211		£22	£14	8.00	£50
V201a	Wmk. inverted			£120	£90	
V202	1d Rose red. Plate 212		£17	£11	4.00	£30
V202a	Wmk. inverted			£100	£75	
V203	1d Rose red. Plate 213		£17	£10	4.00	£30
V203a	Wmk. inverted			£300	£250	
V204	1d Rose red. Plate 214		£20	£15	6.00	£30
V204a	Wmk. inverted			£80	£50	
V205	1d Rose red. Plate 215		£20	£15	6.00	£30
V205a	Wmk. inverted			£150	£110	
V206	1d Rose red. Plate 216		£20	£15	6.00	£30
V206a	Wmk. inverted			£25	£15	
V207	1d Rose red. Plate 217		£20	4.00	1.75	£30
V207a	Wmk. inverted			£300	£250	
V208	1d Rose red. Plate 218		£18	5.00	2.75	£50
V208a	Wmk. inverted			£50	£35	
V209	1d Rose red. Plate 219		£45	£40	£30	£55
V209a	Wmk. inverted			£120	£90	
V210	1d Rose red. Plate 220		£16	4.00	2.50	£30
V210a	Wmk. inverted			£150	£110	
V211	1d Rose red. Plate 221		£18	£13	7.00	£45
V211a	Wmk. inverted			£100	£75	
V212	1d Rose red. Plate 222		£25	£22	£12	£50
V212a	Wmk. inverted			£200	£160	
V213	1d Rose red. Plate 223		£36	£50	£30	£50
V213a	Wmk. inverted			£300	£250	
V214	1d Rose red. Plate 224		£38	£50	£30	£55
V214a	Wmk. inverted			£500	£400	
V215	1d Rose red. Plate 225		£850	£380	£250	£1000
V215a	Wmk. inverted			£1500	£1000	

Notes - Beware of stamps from Plate 177 with the figure 1 obscured
Prices for 1d red inverted watermarks are for used only, as there is insufficient information at present to provide accurate prices for mint.

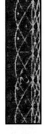

1870 (1 Oct) Wmk. Large Crown. Perf 14

No.		M/M	F/U	G/U	⊡
V216	**1½d Rose red.** Plate 1	£140	£20	7.00	£90
V216a	Wmk. inverted		£175	£105	
V217	**1½d Rose red.** Plate 3	£100	£13	7.00	£75
V217a	Wmk. inverted		£110	£70	
Varieties					
V216b	1½d error. Lettered OP-PC	£12,000	£900	£550	
V216c	Imperf	£1800			
V217b	Imperf Error of colour	£1800			

Plate 12

1858 (July) Thick white lines. Wmk. Large Crown. Perf. 14

No.		M/M	F/U	G/U	⊡
V218	**2d Blue.** Plate 7	£475	£14	7.00	£45
V218a	Wmk. inverted		£400	£300	
V219	**2d Blue.** Plate 8	£370	£12	9.00	£40
V219a	Wmk. inverted		£30	£20	
V220	**2d Blue.** Plate 9	£80	4.00	3.00	£20
V220a	Wmk. inverted	£200	£25	£14	
V221	**2d Blue.** Plate 12	£650	£35	£20	£65
V221a	Wmk. inverted		£120	£90	

1869 (July) Thin white lines. Wmk. Large Crown. Perf. 14

No.		M/M	F/U	G/U	⊡
V222	**2d Blue.** Plate 13	£75	5.50	3.50	£20
V222a	Wmk. inverted		£35	£30	
V223	**2d Blue.** Plate 14	£85	7.00	4.00	£25
V223a	Wmk. inverted		£40	£35	
V224	**2d Blue.** Plate 15	£75	7.00	5.00	£25
V224a	Wmk. inverted		£90	£50	

The Embossed issues. introduced in 1847 were unique in British stamp production. Produced at Somerset House on manual presses, each stamp was separately embossed, and consequently the spacing of the impressions was extremely variable from wide margins to overlapping in many instances. It is consequently difficult to find examples with four good margins. The quality of embossing varied from clear sharp impressions to blunted and blurred examples.

The die numbers were inserted in the form of metal plugs in the base of the bust together with the letters "W.W." (the initials of the master engraver William Wyon). The numbers can be read under magnification. but are often illegible due to the embossing having been flattened. These are of slightly less value (approximately 20% less).

Collectors are warned against cut-outs from Postal Stationery using the same design and 'four margin' examples which have been rebacked. The two silk threads go right through the paper, 5mm apart, on the l0d and 1s values and as a consequence it is usually reasonably easy to spot re-backed items. Also, the 6d value is watermarked, whereas the Postal Stationery 6d is without watermark and gum, and does not have a pendant curl. Later examples of the 6d had green tinted gum.

Prices shown in columns one and two are for stamps with margins all round.
Columns 3 & 4 indicate used prices for stamps with 3 clear margins.

Printer: Somerset House

VR Watermark

1847 (1 March) Wmk. VR Imperforate

V225	**6d Mauve**. Die 1WW	£3500	£400	£100	£250
V225a	Wmk. upright	£3000	£400	£100	£250
V225b	Wmk. inverted	£3000	£400	£100	£250
V225c	Wmk. reversed	£3000	£400	£100	£250
V225d	Wmk. inv. and rev.	£3400	£400	£100	£250
V225e	Lilac	£3000	£400	£85	£250
V225f	Purple	£3000	£400	£90	£250
V225g	Violet	£5000	£1500	£900	£450

10d on Dickinson silk thread paper

1848 (6 Nov.) No Wmk. Dickinson silk thread paper. Imperforate

V226	**10d Brown.** Die W.W.1	£2700	£650	£250	£600
V226a	Deep brown	£2700	£700	£250	
V227	**10d Brown.** Die 2. W.W. (1850)	£2700	£650	£250	£600
V227a	Deep brown	£2700	£750	£250	
V228	**10d Brown.** Die 3. W.W. (1853)	£2700	£600	£250	£600
V228a	Deep brown	£2700	£700	£250	
V229	**10d Brown.** Die 4 W.W. (1854)	£2700	£600	£300	£900
V229a	Deep brown	£2700	£650	£250	
V230	**10d Brown.** Die 5. W.W.*				

* Only two copies are recorded of V230

1s on Dickinson silk thread paper

1847 (11 Sept.) No Wmk. Dickinson silk thread paper. Imperforate

V231	**1s Green.** Die W.W. 1	£2800	£400	£100	£150
V231a	Deep green	£3000	£450	£120	£200
V231b	Pale green	£2800	£450	£100	£150
V232	**1s Green.** Die W.W. 2	£2800	£450	£100	£150
V232a	Deep green	£3000	£450	£120	£200
V232b	Pale green	£2750	£450	£120	£150

SURFACE PRINTED

The Surface Printed issues form a very interesting part of British stamp production, with a wide variety of shades, watermarks and plate numbers to be collected. All these differences can be readily distinguished, contrasting with the difficulties of the Line Engraved period.

To clarify the listing of stamps for this period they are divided into logical groups as follows:

1. No corner letters
2. Small white corner letters
3. Large white corner letters
4. Large coloured corner letters
5. New design - low values
6. Lilac and Green issue
7. Jubilee issue

All the varieties for each value are listed in sequence within each grouping.

The pricing basis for Surface Printed issues is as follows:

Unmounted mint (U/M) (Jubilee issue only)	Full original gum, well centred, full perforations and good colour.
Mounted Mint (M/M)	At least 75% original gum, full perforations and clean fresh colours.

Fine used and Average Used (F/U, A/U)

Grade I	Grade II	Grade III	Grade IV
Superb Used	Fine Used	Average Used	Sound Used
Well centred with all perforations, true colour and circular date stamp.	Reasonably centred with all perforations, true colour and light cancel of the period or clear profile.	Reasonably centred with all perforations and reasonable colour with heavy, but no unsightly cancel.	Could be off centre, possibly one or two short but not missing perforations, reasonable colour and heavy cancel.

WARNING

Re-gumming of stamps is becoming more prevalent, and this abuse can be detected in two possible ways.

1. Place the stamps face down in the palm of the hand and the heat of the hand should cause the edges of the stamp to curl upwards. If it remains flat or curls towards the palm then it is almost certainly re-gummed.

2. Examination with a magnifying glass should reveal any gum that has crept onto the face of the stamp or particularly around the fibres of the perforations.

Stamps that have no gum or have been cleanly regummed are worth approximately 20% of the mounted mint prices, provided they have retained their original colours.

Wing Margins on Surface Printed Issues

All the issues on paper watermarked Emblems, Spray and the three varieties of Garter were printed in sheets consisting of panes. These were broken up on distribution. The panes consisted of normal sized stamps apart from the left and right respectively. They are known as wing margins. It has not always been fashionable to collect wing margins and often the margins have been removed and reperforated. Reperforated examples can be detected easily with a knowledge of the letter combinations that make up wing margin stamps.

EMBLEMS AND SPRAY - D, E, H or I in S.E. corner of stamp.

GARTER - F or G in S.E. corner of stamp.

The issues of 1855 - 62 did not have corner letters but did have wing margins.

The 4d and 8d on Large Garter exist correctly with and without wing margins. Official action was taken to remove some of their wing margins with the result that the 'F' and 'G' stamps here can be found with and without, and in the case of the 8d. with a guillotined edge.

SURFACE PRINTED "ABNORMALS"

The Printers, De La Rue, were obliged to submit samples of each new plate to Somerset House for approval before starting production. Up to six sheets were sent, one of which was retained as the Imprimatur Sheet.

Occasionally some of the remaining sheets were perforated and used. If approval for production was given, then there would be no way of differentiating these stamps apart from a pre-issue dated postmark. However, sometimes due to a change of policy on colour or paper, etc., the issue did not proceed. These stamps are classified as Abnormals. These are by their nature very rare, sought after and valuable. The condition is generally poor but as always with such rare items it detracts little from their value.

There are amongst the Imprimaturs eight potential Abnormals of which no copies have yet been found - we list these with a price for the Imprimatur copies outside the Official Archives.

No corner letters

Printer De La Rue & Co.

Small Garter Watermark

1855 (31 July) Wmk. Small Garter. Blue glazed paper. Perf 14

No.			M/M	F/U	G/U	✉️
V234	4d	Carmine	£2400	£150	£75	£150
V234a		Wmk. inverted		£370	£220	
V234b		Bright carmine	£2400	£150	£75	£150
V234c		Deep carmine	£2500	£170	£80	£160
V234d		Pale carmine	£2400	£150	£80	£160
V235	4d	Carmine on white paper	£3500	£350	£220	£600

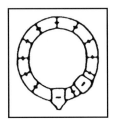
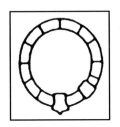

Medium Garter Watermark   Large Garter Watermark

1856 (25 Feb.) Wmk. Medium Garter. Blue glazed paper. Perf 14

No.			M/M	F/U	G/U	✉️
V236	4d	Carmine	£2800	£180	£85	£160
V236a		Wmk. inverted		£380	£200	
V236b		Pale carmine	£3200	£180	£85	£180
V236c		Deep carmine	£3400	£190	£85	£190

1856 (Sept.) Wmk. Medium Garter. White paper. Perf 14

No.			M/M	F/U	G/U	✉️
V237	4d	Pale carmine	£2700	£190	£90	£280
V237a		Wmk. inverted		£275	£170	

1856 (1 Nov.) New colour. Wmk. Medium Garter. White paper. Perf 14

No.			M/M	F/U	G/U	✉️
V238	4d	Rose	£2700	£180	£100	£220
V238a		Deep rose	£2700	£190	£100	£250

1857 (Jan.) Wmk. Large Garter. White paper. Perf 14

No.			M/M	F/U	G/U	✉️
V239	4d	Rose	£520	£22	£14	£35
V239a		Wmk. inverted		£55	£34	
V239b		Rose carmine	£550	£22	£14	£45
V240	4d	Rose carmine on thick glazed paper	£1500	£70	£35	£110

Emblems watermark

1856 (21 Oct.) Wmk. Emblems. Perf 14

No.			M/M	F/U	G/U	✉️
V241	6d	Lilac. Plate (1)	£450	£45	£15	£80
V241a		Wmk. inverted		£100	£30	
V241b		Wmk. inv. and rev		£95	£50	
V241c		Wmk. reversed		£250	£150	
V241d		Pale lilac	£450	£45	£15	£50
V241e		Deep lilac	£550	£50	£20	£60

1856 (1 Nov.) Wmk. Emblems. Perf 14

No.			M/M	F/U	G/U	✉️
V242	1s	Green	£650	£75	£30	£85
V242a		Wmk. inverted		£175	£95	
V242b		Wmk. reversed		£400	£225	
V242c		Pale green	£650	£75	£30	£85
V242d		Deep green	£1400	£175	£75	£180
V242e		Imperf				

Small white corner letters

Printer: De La Rue & Co.

Plate numbers shown in brackets do not appear on the design.

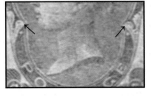

Without dots   Abnormal
Unshaded spandrels   Plate (3) with dots added (arrowed)

1862 (2 May) Wmk. Emblems. Perf 14

No.			M/M	F/U	G/U	✉️
V243	3d	Carmine rose. Plate (2)	£550	£120	£55	£110
V243a		Wmk. inverted		£200	£120	
V243b		Pale carmine rose	£550	£120	£55	£110
V243c		Wmk. inverted		£200	£120	
V243d		Deep carmine rose	£850	£150	£75	£180
Varieties						
VAB1	3d	Plate (2) with shaded spandrels. Abnormal	£6000	£6000		
VAB1a		Imprimatur	£1800			
VAB2	3d	Plate (3) with dots added Line perf 14. Abnormal	£8000	£4500		
VAB2a		Imprimatur	£2200			
VAB2b		Imperf	£3500			

1862 (15 Jan.) Wmk. Large Garter. Perf 14

No.			M/M	F/U	G/U	✉️
V244	4d	Pale red. Plate (3)	£450	£35	£15	£55
V244a		Wmk. inverted		£85	£35	
V244b		Bright red	£450	£40	£20	£65

1863 (16 Oct.) Hairlines added to corners. Wmk. Large Garter. Perf 14

No.			M/M	F/U	G/U	▣
V245	**4d**	**Pale red.** Plate (4)	£380	£30	£15	£50
V245a		Wmk. inverted		£75	£30	
V245a		Imperf	£3000			
V245b		Bright red	£420	£35	£20	£55

1862 (1 Dec.) Wmk. Emblems. Perf 14

V246	**6d**	**Lilac.** Plate (3)	£550	£35	£15	£60
V246a		Wmk. inverted		£95	£65	
V246b		Deep lilac	£850	£40	£20	£75

1864 (20 April) Hairlines added to corners. Wmk. Emblems. Perf 14

V247	**6d**	**Lilac.** Plate (4)	£850	£60	£25	£85
V247a		Imperf	£3000			
V247b		Wmk. inverted	£2500	£115	£70	
V247c		Imperf. Wmk. inverted				

1862 (15 Jan) Wmk. Emblems. Perf 14

V248	**9d**	**Bistre.** Plate (2)	£1500	£200	£95	£250
V248a		Wmk. inverted		£300	£175	
V248b		Wmk. reversed		£300	£175	
V248c		Straw	£1500	£200	£90	£250
Varieties						
VAB3	9d	Plate (3) with hairlines				
		Abnormal	£8500	£5500		
VAB3a		Imprimatur	£5500			

1862 (1 Dec.) Wmk. Emblems. Perf 14

V249	**1s**	**Green.** Plate *	£800	£75	£35	£95
V249a		Wmk. inverted		£120	£70	
V249b		Wmk. inv. and rev.		£120	£70	
V249c		Wmk. reversed				
V249d		Deep green	£1000	£110	£50	£125
V249e		Deep green Imperf				

　　　　　　* Plate 2 was used, although shown as a '1'

Varieties				
VAB4	1s	Plate 2 with hairlines		
		Abnormal	£15000	
VAB4a		Imprimatur	£6000	

Large white corner letters

Printer: De La Rue & Co.

 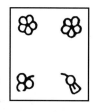

Emblems Watermark　　　Spray Watermark

1865 (1 March) Wmk. Emblems. Perf 14

V250	**3d**	**Rose.** Plate 4	£550	£60	£30	£85
V250a		Wmk. inverted		£150	£100	

Varieties				
VAB5	3d	Rose Plate 5. Abnormal		
		Imprimatur	£1200	

1867 (July) Wmk. Spray. Perf 14

No.			M/M	F/U	G/U	▣
V251	**3d**	**Rose.** Plate 4	£230	£75	£40	£100
V251		Wmk. inverted	£900	£200	£120	
V252	**3d**	**Rose.** Plate 5	£220	£25	£10	£40
V252a		Wmk. inverted	£475	£75	£45	
V252b		Imperf	£2500			
V252c		Deep rose	£220	£25	£10	£40
V253	**3d**	**Rose.** Plate 6	£220	£25	£10	£40
V253a		Wmk. inverted	£450	£90	£45	
V253b		Imperf	£2500			
V254	**3d**	**Rose.** Plate 7	£260	£25	£10	£45
V254a		Wmk. inverted	£450	£85	£45	
V255	**3d**	**Rose.** Plate 8	£200	£20	7.00	£40
V255a		Wmk. inverted	£475	£95	£60	
V255b		Imperf	£2500			
V256	**3d**	**Rose.** Plate 9	£230	£25	7.00	£40
V256a		Wmk. inverted	£500	£120	£80	
V257	**3d**	**Rose.** Plate 10	£300	£45	£10	£70
V257a		Wmk. inverted	£900	£175	£100	

 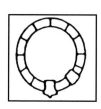

Large Garter Watermark

1865 (4 July) Wmk. Large Garter. Perf 14

V258	**4d**	**Vermilion.** Plate 7	£250	£40	£12	£40
V259	**4d**	**Vermilion.** Plate 8	£250	£40	£12	£40
V259a		Wmk. inverted	£250	£40	£20	
V260	**4d**	**Vermilion.** Plate 9	£250	£30	£12	£40
V260a		Wmk. inverted	£250	£30	£12	
V261	**4d**	**Vermilion.** Plate 10				
V261a		Wmk. inverted	£250	£30	£15	£40
V262	**4d**	**Vermilion.** Plate 11				
V262a		Wmk. inverted	£250	£25	£12	£40
V262b		Imperf				
V263	**4d**	**Vermilion.** Plate 12	£250	£22	£10	£40
V263a		Wmk. inverted	£250	£22	£10	
V263b		Imperf				
V264	**4d**	**Vermilion.** Plate 13	£250	£25	£12	£40
V265	**4d**	**Vermilion.** Plate 14	£300	£25	£10	£50

With hyphen　　　Without hyphen　　　Hexagonal

1865 (1 April) SIX-PENCE hyphenated. Wmk. Emblems. Perf 14

V266	**6d**	**Lilac.** Plate 5	£400	£40	£15	£40
V266a		Wmk. inverted		£85	£50	
V266b		Wmk. reversed		£140	£80	
V266c		Deep lilac	£450	£40	£17	£50

No.			M/M	F/U	G/U	☒
V267	**6d**	**Lilac.** Plate 6	£950	£90	£25	£70
V267a		Wmk. inverted		£120	£50	
V267b		Deep lilac	£1000	£70	£30	£95

1867 (21 June) SIX-PENCE hyphenated. Wmk. Spray. Perf 14

No.			M/M	F/U	G/U	☒
V268	**6d**	**Lilac.** Plate 6	£5500	£50	£18	£50
V268a		Wmk. inverted		£150	£70	
V268b		Deep lilac	£550	£50	£20	£50
V268c		Violet	£550	£50	£20	£50
V268d		Purple	£550	£55	£20	£60

1869 (8 March) SIX PENCE without hyphen. Wmk. Spray. Perf 14

No.			M/M	F/U	G/U	☒
V269	**6d.**	**Mauve** Plate 8	£300	£25	£10	£30
V269a		Wmk. inverted		£90	£50	
V269b		Imperf	£4000			
V269c		Violet	£300	£25	£10	£30
V270	**6d.**	**Mauve** Plate 9	£300	£25	£10	`£30
V270a		Wmk. inverted		£95	£60	
V270b		Imperf	£4000			
Varieties						
VAB6	6d	Mauve. Plate 10 Abnormal			£17000	
VAB6a		Imprimatur			£7500	

1872 (12 April) New colour and hexagonal design. Wmk. Spray. Perf 14

No.			M/M	F/U	G/U	☒
V271	**6d**	**Chestnut**	£300	£30	£10	£50
V271a		Wmk. inverted	£100	£70		
V271b		Chestnut	£300	£30	£12	£50
V271c		Pale buff	£350	£25	£15	£50
V272	**6d**	**Pale buff.** Plate 12	£1000	£120	£40	£175
		(30.10.72)				
V272a		Wmk. inverted		£350	£130	
Varieties						
VAB7	**6d**	**Chestnut.** Plate 12. Abnormal	£2500			
VAB7a		Imprimatur	£2750			

1865 (1 Dec.) Wmk. Emblems. Per 14

No.			M/M	F/U	G/U	☒
V273	**9d**	**Straw.** Plate 4	£1100	£220	£110	£400
V273a		Wmk. inverted		£400	£250	
Varieties						
VAB8	9d	Straw. Plate 5 . Abnormal	£10000			
VAB8a		Imprimatur	£5000			

1867 (3 Oct.) Wmk. Spray. Perf 14

No.			M/M	F/U	G/U	☒
V274	**9d**	**Straw.** Plate 4	£750	£100	£40	£200
V274a		Wmk. inverted		£225	£140	
V274b		Pale straw	£750	£100	£40	£200
V247c		Imperf Pale straw	£4500			
V274d		Deep straw	£850	£110	£45	£200

1867 (1 July) Wmk. Spray. Perf 14

No.			M/M	F/U	G/U	☒
V275	**10d**	**Red brown.** Plate 1	£1200	£150	£45	£300
V275a		Wmk. inverted		£350	£180	
V275b		Pale red brown	£1200	£150	£45	£300
V275c		Deep red brown	£1400	£190	£90	£350
V275d		Imperf	£4000			
Varieties						
VAB9	10d	Red brown. Plate 1. Wmk.				
		Emblems. Abnormal	£24000			
VAB10	10d	Red brown. Plate 2. Wmk.				
		Spray. Abnormal	£17500	£6000		
VAB10a		Imprimatur	£5500			

1865 (Feb.) Wmk. Emblems. Perf 14

No.			M/M	F/U	G/U	☒
V276	**1s.**	**Green.** Plate 4	£750	£60	£20	£85
V276a		Imperf between	£8000			
V276b		Wmk. inverted		£190	£110	
V276c		Imperf Wmk. inverted				
Varieties						
VAB11		1s. Green. Plate 5. Abnormal				
VAB11a		Imprimatur	£2500			

1867 (13 July) Wmk. Spray. Perf 14

No.			M/M	F/U	G/U	☒
V277	**1s.**	**Pale green.** Plate 4	£350	£25	£10	£35
V277a		Wmk. inverted	£1000	£75	£45	
V277b		Imperf	£3000	£1500		
V277c		Deep geen	£400	£25	£10	£35
V278	**1s.**	**Pale green.** Plate 5	£340	£12	7.00	£35
V278a		Wmk. inverted		£120	£80	
V279	**1s.**	**Pale green.** Plate 6	£450	£12	7.00	£30
V279a		Wmk. inverted		£120	£70	
V280	**1s.**	**Pale green.** Plate 7	£450	£50	£30	£65
V280a		Wmk. inverted		£150	£100	
V280b		Imperf between				

1867 (1 July) Wmk. Spray. Perf 14

No.			M/M	F/U	G/U	☒
V281	**2s**	**Deep blue.** Plate 1	£1700	£110	£60	£275
V281a		Wmk. inverted		£255	£180	
V281b		Imperf Deep blue	£5500			
V281c		Dull blue	£1300	£100	£45	£275
V281d		Pale blue	£1500	£100	£45	£275
V281e		Imperf Pale blue				
V281f		Milky blue	£6000	£500	£220	£1000
V281g		Cobalt	£7500	£1400	£900	£3500
Varieties						
VAB12		2s Blue. Plate 3. Abnormal		£5000		
VAB12a		Imprimatur	£6000			

1880 (27 Feb) New colour. Wmk. Spray. Perf 14

No.			M/M	F/U	G/U	☒
V282	**2s**	**Pale brown.** Plate 1	£8500	£1600	£950	£12000
V282a		Wmk. inverted		£2400	£1400	
V282b		Imperf Pale brown				
V282c		Brown	£8500	£1600	£950	£10000

Large white corner letters

Printer: De La Rue & Co.

Maltese Cross   Large Anchor
Watermark   Watermark

1887 (1 July) Wmk. Maltese Cross. Perf 15½ x 15

No.			M/M	F/U	G/U
V284	**5s**	**Rose.** Plate 1	£2300	£250	£100
V284a		Pale rose	£2300	£250	£100
V284b		Imperf	£8000		
V285	**5s**	**Rose.** Plate 2	£2900	£300	£120

Varieties

VAB13		5s Rose. Plate 4. Abnormal			
VAB13a		Imprimatur	£10000		

1882 (25 Nov.) Wmk. Large Anchor. Perf 14

V286	**5s**	**Rose.** Plate 4	£8500	£1100	£500
V287	**5s**	**Rose.** Plate 4 on blued paper	£8500	£1200	£550

1868 (26 Sept.) Wmk. Maltese Cross. Perf 15½ x 15

V288	**10s**	**Grey green.** Plate 1	£22000	£1300	£500

1883 (Feb.) Wmk. Large Anchor. Perf 14

V289	**10s**	**Grey green.** Plate 1	£36000	£2250	£950
V290	**10s**	**Grey green.** Plate 1 on blued paper	£36000	£2250	£950

1883 (Feb.) Wmk. Maltese Cross. Perf 15½ x 15

V291	**£1**	**Brown lilac.** Plate 1	£30000	£2400	£1200

1883 (Feb.) Wmk. Large Anchor. Perf 14

V292	**£1**	**Brown lilac.** Plate 1	£37000	£4000	£1500
V293	**£1**	**Brown lilac.** Plate 1 on blued paper	£38000	£4000	£1500

1882 (21 March) Wmk. Large Anchor. Perf 14

V294	**£5**	**Orange.** Plate 1	£6500	£3500	£2000
V295	**£5**	**Orange.** Plate 1 on blued paper	£22500	£5500	£2500

Large coloured corner letters

Printer: De La Rue & Co.

Small Anchor
Watermark

1875 (1 July) Wmk. Small Anchor. Perf 14

A. Blued paper

No.			M/M	F/U	G/U	✉
V296	**2½d**	**Rosy mauve.** Plate 1	£300	£70	£35	£75
V296a		Imperf				
V296b		Wmk. inverted	£900	£150	£85	
V297	**2½d**	**Rosy mauve.** Plate 2	£5000	£800	£500	£1000
V297a		Wmk. inverted				
V298	**2½d**	**Rosy mauve.** Plate 3			£2500	£5000

B. White paper.

V299	**2½d**	**Rosy mauve.** Plate 1	£220	£30	£10	£30
V299a		Wmk. inverted	£650	£100	£65	
V300	**2½d**	**Rosy mauve.** Plate 2	£220	£30	£10	£30
V300a		Wmk. inverted	£550	£100	£70	
V301	**2½d**	**Rosy mauve.** Plate 3	£290	£60	£20	£75
V301a		Wmk. inverted	£850	£120	£75	

Varieties

V300b	**2½d**	error of lettering LH-FL	£8500	£900	£600	£2500
VAB14	**2½d**	Rosy mauve. Plate 4 Abnormal				
VAB14a		Imprimatur	£1200			
VAB15	**2½d**	Rosy mauve. Plate 5. Abnormal				
VAB15a		Imprimatur	£1200			

Orb
Watermark

Imperial Crown
Watermark

1876 (16 May) Wmk. Orb. Perf 14

V302	**2½d**	**Rosy mauve.** Plate 3	£300	£65	£20	£65
V302a		Wmk. inverted	£900	£150	£80	
V303	**2½d**	**Rosy mauve.** Plate 4	£220	£25	£10	£25
V303a		Wmk. inverted	£300	£70	£40	
V304	**2½d**	**Rosy mauve.** Plate 5	£220	£25	£10	£25
V304a		Wmk. inverted	£400	£70	£40	
V305	**2½d**	**Rosy mauve.** Plate 6	£220	£25	£10	£25
V305a		Wmk. inverted	£400	£50	£45	
V306	**2½d**	**Rosy mauve.** Plate 7	£220	£25	£10	£25
V306a		Wmk. inverted	£400	£60	£40	
V307	**2½d**	**Rosy mauve.** Plate 8	£220	£25	£10	£25
V307a		Wmk inverted	£450	£80	£45	
V308	**2½d**	**Rosy mauve.** Plate 9	£220	£25	£10	£25
V308a		Wmk inverted	£500	£80	£50	
V309	**2½d**	**Rosy mauve.** Plate 10	£300	£30	£10	£30
V309a		Wmk. inverted	£500	£180	£500	
V310	**2½d**	**Rosy mauve.** Plate 11	£220	£25	£10	£25
V310a		Wmk inverted	£450	£80	£40	
V311	**2½d**	**Rosy mauve.** Plate 12	£220	£25	£10	£25
V311a		Wmk inverted	£450	£70	£40	

No.			M/M	F/U	G/U	▣
V312	2½d	**Rosy mauve.** Plate 13	£220	£20	£10	£25
V312a		Wmk. inverted	£500	£70	£40	
V313	2½d	**Rosy mauve.** Plate 14	£220	£20	£10	£25
V313a		Wmk. inverted	£500	£70	£40	
V314	2½d	**Rosy mauve.** Plate 15	£220	£20	£10	£25
V314a		Wmk. inverted	£500	£70	£40	
V315	2½d	**Rosy mauve.** Plate 16	£220	£20	£10	£25
V315a		Wmk. inverted	£600	£75	£40	
V316	2½d	**Rosy mauve.** Plate 17	£800	£150	£80	£250
V316a		Wmk. inverted	£1800	£300	£200	

1880 (5 Feb.) New colour. Wmk. Orb. Perf.14

V317	2½d	**Blue.** Plate 17	£180	£25	£10	£35
V317a		Wmk. inverted	£300	£100	£65	
V318	2½d	**Blue.** Plate 18	£180	£20	£10	£35
V318a		Wmk. inverted	£300	£90	£60	
V319	2½d	**Blue.** Plate 19	£180	£20	£10	£35
V319a		Wmk. inverted	£300	£75	£50	
V320	2½d	**Blue.** Plate 20	£180	£20	£10	£35
V320a		Wmk. inverted	£300	£75	£50	

1881 (23 March) Wmk. Imperial Crown. Perf.14

V321	2½d	**Blue.** Plate 21	£175	£14	5.00	£25
V322	2½d	**Blue.** Plate 22	£120	£10	5.00	£20
V323	2½d	**Blue.** Plate 23	£120	£10	5.00	£20
V323a		Wmk. inverted		£220	£140	

Surcharged '3d'

1873 (5 July) Wmk. Spray. Perf.14

V324	3d	**Rose.** Plate 11	£200	£20	7.00	£30
V324a		Wmk. inverted	£375	£120	£75	
V325	3d	**Rose.** Plate 12	£200	£20	7.00	£30
V325a		Wmk. inverted	£400	£120	£75	
V326	3d	**Rose.** Plate 14	£200	£20	7.00	£30
V326a		Wmk. inverted	£400	£80	£50	
V327	3d	**Rose.** Plate 15	£200	£20	7.00	£30
V327a		Wmk. inverted	£450	£80	£50	
V328	3d	**Rose.** Plate 16	£200	£20	7.00	£30
V328a		Wmk. inverted	£450	£80	£50	
V329	3d	**Rose.** Plate 17	£200	£20	7.00	£30
V330	3d	**Rose.** Plate 18	£200	£20	7.00	£30
V330a		Wmk. inverted	£450	£90	£60	
V331	3d	**Rose.** Plate 19	£220	£75	£14	£40
V331a		Wmk. inverted	£450	£120	£80	
V332	3d	**Rose.** Plate 20	£220	£35	£20	£60
V332a		Wmk. inverted	£450	£100	£70	
Varieties						
VAB16	3d	Rose. Plate 21. Abnormal				
VAB16a		Imprimatur	£900			

1881 (Feb.) Wmk. Imperial Crown. Perf. 14

V333	3d	**Rose.** Plate 20	£280	£50	£25	£120
V333a		Wmk. inverted		£220	£120	
V334	3d	**Rose.** Plate 21	£240	£45	£22	£100
V334a		Wmk. Inverted		£220	£120	

1883 (1 Jan.) Surcharged '3d' in carmine. Wmk. Imperial Crown. Perf. 14

V335	3d	**Surcharge on 3d lilac.**				
		Plate 21	£200	£80	£40	£200
V335a		Wmk. inverted	-			

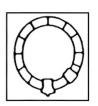

Large Garter Watermark

1876 (1 March) Wmk. Large Garter. Perf. 14

V336	4d	**Vermilion.** Plate 15	£950	£180	£70	£275
V336a		Wmk. inverted	-	£450	£225	
Varieties						
VAB17	4d	Vermilion. Plate 16. Abnormal	-		£13500	
VAB17a		Imprimatur	£3000			

1877 (12 March) New colour. Wmk. Large Garter. Perf. 14

V337	4d	**Sage green.** Plate 15	£400	£110	£40	£175
V337a		Wmk. inverted	-	£220	£130	
V338	4d	**Sage green.** Plate 16	£300	£110	£35	£175
V338a		Wmk. inverted	-	£200	£120	
Varieties						
VAB18	4d	Sage green. Plate 17. Abnormal	- £12000			
VAB18a		Imprimatur	£6000			

1880 (15 Aug.) New colour. Wmk. Large Garter. Perf. 14

V339	4d	**Grey brown.** Plate 17	£1000	£220	£110	£350
V339a		Imperf	£6000			
V339b		Wmk. inverted	-	£550	£350	

1880 (9 Dec.) Wmk. Imperial Crown. Perf. 14

V340	4d	**Grey brown.** Plate 17	£180	£30	£10	£40
V340a		Wmk. inverted	-	£275	£175	
V340b		Pale grey brown	£180	£30	£10	£40
V341	4d	**Grey brown.** Plate 18	£180	£30	£10	£40
V341a		Wmk. inverted	-	£275	£175	

Surcharged '6d'

1874 (31 March) Wmk. Spray. Perf. 14

V342	6d	**Grey.** Plate 13	£220	£25	£10	£5(
V342a		Wmk. inverted	£650	£110	£80	
V343	6d	**Grey.** Plate 14	£220	£25	£10	£5(
V343a		Wmk. inverted	£650	£110	£80	
V344	6d	**Grey.** Plate 15	£220	£25	£10	£50
V344a		Wmk. inverted	£650	£110	£80	
V345	6d	**Grey.** Plate 16	£220	£25	£10	£5(
V345a		Wmk. inverted	£650	£110	£80	

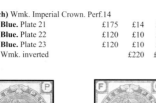

No.			M/M	F/U	G/U	✉
V346	**6d Grey.** Plate 17		£300	£60	£30	£120
V346a	Wmk. inverted		£850	£200	£140	
Varieties						
VAB19	6d Buff. Plate 13. Abnormal		-£10000			
VAB19a	Imprimatur		£6000			
VAB20	6d Grey. Plate 18. Abnormal		-	-		
VAB20a	Imprimatur		£1000			

1881 (1 Jan.) Wmk. Imperial Crown. Perf. 14

V347	**6d Grey.** Plate 17		£200	£40	£17	£70
V347a	Wmk. inverted		-	£300	£200	
V348	**6d Grey.** Plate 18		£200	£40	£17	£70

1883 (1 Jan.) Surcharged '6d' in carmine. Wmk. Imperial Crown. Perf. 14

V349	**6d Surcharge on 6d lilac.**					
	Plate 18		£250	£80	£40	£220
V349a	Wmk. inverted		£1000	£500	£300	

V350		V350B

1876 (11 Sept.) Wmk. Large Garter. Perf. 14

V350	**8d Orange.** Plate 1		£475	£140	£50	£200
V350a	Wmk. inverted		-	£350	£200	
V350B	**8d Purple-brown** (unissued)		£5500			
Varieties						
VAB21	8d Orange. Plate 2. Abnormal		-	-		
VAB21a	Imprimatur		£2200			

1873 (1 Sept.) Wmk. Spray. Perf. 14

V351	**1s Green.** Plate 8		£300	£50	£30	£70
V351a	Wmk. inverted		£750	£100	£70	
V352	**1s Green.** Plate 9		£300	£60	£30	£70
V353	**1s Green.** Plate 10		£300	£75	£35	£70
V354	**1s Green.** Plate 11		£300	£50	£25	£70
V355	**1s Green.** Plate 12		£300	£30	£15	£80
V356	**1s Green.** Plate 13		£300	£30	£15	£80
V356a	Wmk. inverted		£750	£120	£80	
Varieties						
VAB22	1s Green. Plate 14. Abnormal		-£16000			
VAB22a	Imprimatur		£5500			

1880 (14 Oct.) New colour. Wmk. Spray. Perf. 14

V357	**1s Orange brown.** Plate 13		£1400	£250	£110	£500
V357a	Wmk. inverted		£4500	£600	£350	

1880 (29 May) Wmk. Imperial Crown. Perf. 14

V358	**1s Orange brown.** Plate 13		£260	£65	£30	£90
V358a	Wmk. inverted		£950	£350	£250	
V359	**1s Orange brown.** Plate 14		£260	£65	£30	£90
V359a	Wmk. inverted		£950	£350	£250	
Varieties						
VAB23	1s Purple. Plate 13. Abnormal		-	-		
VAB23a	Imprimatur		£2500			
VAB24	1s Purple. Plate 14 and line perf. 14. Abnormal *		£4500			
VAB24a	Imprimatur Plate 14		£3000			

* This stamp originates from the 'Stamp Committee of 1890' Souvenir Stamp Collection.

New designs. Low values 1880 - 83.
Printer: De La Rue & Co.

Imperial Crown
Watermark

1880 (1 Jan.) - 84 Wmk. Imperial Crown. Perf. 14

V360	**½d Deep green** (14.10.80)	£20	5.00	3.00	9.00
V360a	Imperf				
V360b	Wmk. inverted	-	£250	£180	
V360bb	No watermark	£4000			
V360c	Pale green	£20	5.00	3.00	9.00
V361	**1d Venetian red**	6.00	3.00	2.00	6.00
V361a	Imperf				
V361b	Wmk. inverted	-	£275	£175	
V362	**1½d Venetian red** (14.10.80)	£50	£20	8.00	£55
V363	**2d Rose** (8.12.80)	£80	£25	£10	£90
V363a	Wmk. inverted	£850	£375	£300	
V363b	Deep rose	£85	£30	£15	£90
V363c	Pale rose	£85	£30	£15	£90
V364	**5d Indigo** (15.3.81)	£275	£50	£25	£100
V364a	Imperf				
V364b	Wmk. inverted	-	£2750	£2000	
	Set of 5	£400	£95	£40	

Penny lilacs 1881 - 1901.
Printer: De La Rue & Co.

Die I	Die II
14 dots in each corner	16 dots in each corner

1881 (12 July) Wmk. Imperial Crown. Perf. 14. A. Die I.

V365	**1d Lilac**	£60	£10	4.00	£10
V365a	Pale lilac	£60	£10	4.00	£10
V365b	Wmk. inverted	-	-	£350	
V365c	Bluish lilac	£250	£50	£25	£60
B. Die II					
V366	**1d Lilac** (12.12.81)	1.50	20	10	2.00
V366a	Wmk. inverted	£40	£30	£20	
V366b	No watermark	£400	-	-	
V366c	Deep purple	2.50	40	20	2.00
V366d	Printed both sides	£650			
V366e	Printed on gum side	£600			
V366f	Imperf three sides	£4500			
V366g	Mauve	2.50	40	20	2.00
V366h	Imperf (pair) Mauve	£3000			
V366i	Bluish lilac	£300	£80	£40	£85

For controls on this issue, please refer to the section on controls.

Large coloured corner letters
Printer: De La Rue & Co.

Large
Anchor Watermark

1883 (2 July) - 84 Wmk. Anchor. Perf. 14
A. Blued paper

No.			M/M	F/U	G/U
V367	**2s6d**	**Lilac**	£2000	£500	£250
V368	**5s**	**Rose**	£6500	£1400	£600
V369	**10s**	**Ultramarine**	£25000	£4000	£2000
V369a		Cobalt	£30000	£5500	£2500
B. White paper					
V370	**2s6d**	**Lilac** (1884)	£200	£60	£25
V370a		Wmk. inverted		£3500	£2700
V370b		Deep lilac	£200	£50	£20
V371	**5s**	**Rose**	£350	£90	£40
V371a		Wmk. inverted		£4150	
V371b		Crimson	£300	£90	£40
V372	**10s**	**Ultramarine**	£850	£275	£100
V372a		Pale ultramarine	£850	£275	£100
V372b		Cobalt	£16000	£4000	£1200

Large white corner letters

Imperial Crown
Watermark

Orb
Watermark

1884 (1 April) Wmk. Three Imperial Crowns. Perf. 14

No.			M/M	F/U	G/U
V373	**£1**	**Brown lilac**	£16000	£1300	£500
V373a		Wmk. inverted	-	£5500	
Varieties					
V373b	£1	Broken frame, lettered JC	£15000	£1750	£800
V373c	£1	Broken frame, lettered TA	£15000	£1750	£800

1888 (1 Feb.) Wmk. Three Orbs. Perf. 14

No.			M/M	F/U	G/U
V374	**£1**	**Brown lilac**	£32000	£2400	£1100
Varieties					
V374a	£1	Broken frame, lettered JC	£40000	£2800	£1400
V374b	£1	Broken frame, lettered TA	£40000	£2800	£1400

1891 (27 Jan.) Wmk. Three Imperial Crowns. Perf. 14

No.			M/M	F/U	G/U
V375	**£1**	**Green**	£1900	£475	£275
V375a		Wmk. inverted	£37000	-	£3750
Varieties					
V375b	£1	Broken frame, lettered JC	£5500	£1000	£625
V375c	£1	Broken frame, lettered TA	£5500	£1000	£625

Lilac and Green issue

Printer: De La Rue & Co.

Coloured letters in all four corners except for the ½d.

Imperial Crown
Watermark

Watermark sideways
(from the back)

1883 (1 Aug.) 9d only, **1884 (1 April)** all other values. Wmk. Imperial
Crown (sideways to right on 2d, 2½d, 6d and 9d). Perf. 14

No.			M/M	F/U	G/U	▣
V376	½d	**Slate blue**	5.00	1.50	50	4.00
V376a		Imperf	£1300			
V376b		Wmk. inverted	-	£150	£100	
V377	1½d	**Lilac**	£35	£12	5.50	£25
V377a		Imperf	£1300			
V377b		Wmk. inverted	£350	£150	£100	
V378	2d	**Lilac**	£60	£20	8.00	£30
V378a		Imperf				
V378b		Wmk. sideways-inverted	-	-	£250	
V379	2½d	**Lilac**	£25	4.00	2.00	£10
V379a		Imperf	£1700			
V379b		Wmk. sideways-inverted	-	-	£150	
V380	3d	**Lilac**	£60	£25	9.00	£35
V380a		Imperf	£1800			
V380b		Wmk. inverted	-	-	£450	
V381	4d	**Dull green**	£140	£50	£25	£125
V381a		Imperf	£1000			
V382	5d	**Dull green**	£140	£60	£30	£130
V382a		Imperf	£2200			
V382b		Line under 'd', unissued	£6500			
V383	6d	**Dull green**	£180	£60	£25	£130
V383a		Imperf	£600			
V383b		Wmk. sideways-inverted	-	-	£850	
V384	9d	**Dull green**	£400	£200	£80	£350
V384a		Wmk. sideways-inverted	£650	£225	£90	
V385	1s	**Dull green**	£320	£110	£50	£200
V385a		Imperf				
V385b		Wmk. inverted	-	-	£750	
		Set of 10	£1300	£400	£155	

All prices quoted are for stamps in the correct colour. Washed examples or
colour changelings have little value.
Unless stated otherwise, prices from this point forwards are for U/M (never
hinged), M/M and F/U. On cover prices remain where appropriate.

The 'Jubilee' issue
Printer: De La Rue & Co.

Duty plate Die I
square dots right of 'd'

Duty plate Die II
vert. lines right of 'd'

Imperial Crown
Watermark

1887 (1 Jan.) - 1900 Wmk. Imperial Crown. Perf. 14 (comb)

No.			U/M	M/M	F/U	▣
V386	½d	**Vermilion**	1.20	60	15	3.00
V386a		Printed on gum side	£2000			
V386b		Imperf				
V386c		Wmk. Inverted	£35	£25	£40	
V386d		Pale vermilion	1.50	50	15	3.00
V386e		Orange vermilion	1.50	50	15	4.00
V386f		Deep vermilion	£12	6.00	2.00	4.00
V387	½d	**Dull blue green** (17.4.1900)	1.25	50	20	3.00
V387a		Printed on gum side	£4000			
V387b		Imperf		£4000		
V387c		Wmk. inverted	£30	£20	£45	
V387d		Bright blue green	2.00	1.00	30	3.00
V388	1½d	**Pale purple and pale green**	£13	6.00	1.50	£20
V388a		Wmk. inverted	£500	£375	£250	
V388b		Purple and pale green	£15	8.00	1.50	£20
V388c		Deep purple and pale green	£20	£14	2.00	£20
V389	2d	**Grey green and carmine**	£18	£9	3.50	£15
V389a		Wmk. inverted	£550	£350	£250	
V389b		Yellow green and carmine	£20	£9	3.50	£20
V389c		Deep green and carmine	£40	£16	7.50	£30
V389d		Green and vermilion	£300	£200	£100	£400
V390	2½d	**Purple** on blue paper	£12	7.00	70	7.00
V390a		Printed on gum side	£5000	£4000		
V390b		Imperf		£5000		
V390c		Wmk. inverted	£1000	£750	£500	
V390d		Pale purple on blue paper	£15	5.00	70	7.00
V390e		Deep purple on blue paper	£20	9.00	80	8.00
V391	3d	**Purple** on yellow paper	£70	9.00	£12	£15
V391a		Wmk. inverted	-	£1500	£500	
V391b		Imperf Wmk. inverted		£5000		
V391c		Deep purple on yellow paper	£50	8.00	95	£15
V391d		Purple on orange paper (1890)	£900	£250	£125	£400
V392	4d	**Green and deep brown**	£30	£12	6.00	£30
V392a		Wmk. inverted	£850	£400	£300	
V392b		Green and purple brown	£30	£13	6.00	£30
V392c		Imperf Green & purple brown		£5000		
V392d		Green and deep chocolate brown	£55	£25	8.00	£30
V393	4½d	**Green and carmine** (15.9.92)	5.00	3.50	£14	£70
V393a		Wmk. inverted	-	-	£600	
V393b		Deep green and carmine	8.50	4.50	£15	£70
V393c		Green and dull scarlet	£12	7.00	£18	£100
V393d		Green and deep bright carmine	£950	£350	£200	£750
V394	5d	**Dull purple & blue** (Die I)	£600	£170	£30	£150
V395	5d	**Dull purple & blue** (Die II)	£40	£16	6.00	£35
V395a		Wmk. inverted	-	£7500	£500	
V395b		Dull purple & bright blue	£40	£15	6.00	£35
V396	6d	**Purple** on rose red paper	£30	£12	6.00	£55
V396a		Wmk. inverted	£1500	£1200	£700	
V396b		Deep purple on rose red	£30	£12	5.00	£55
V396c		Slate purple on rose red	£35	£15	5.00	£55
V397	9d	**Dull purple and blue**	£60	£30	£25	£140
V397a		Wmk. inverted	£1400	£1000	£450	
V397b		Slate purple and blue	£60	£30	£25	£140
V397c		Dull purple and bright blue	£60	£30	£25	£140

No.			U/M	M/M	F/U	No.
V398	10d	**Dull purple and carmine**				
		(24.2.90)	£42	£30	£25	£200
V398a		Imperf				
V398b		Wmk. inverted	£3000	£1750	£500	
V398c		Dull purple and dull scarlet	£100	£70	£45	£250
V398d		Dull purple and deep bright				
		carmine	£420	£200	£100	£350
V399	1s	**Dull green**	£340	£95	£30	£125
V399a		Wmk. inverted	£900	£550	£550	
V399b		Grey green	£270	£100	£30	£140
V400	1s	**Green and carmine** (11.7.1900)	£48	£32	£55	£600
V400a		Wmk. inverted	£1000	£650	£800	
		Set of 14	£500	£175	£125	

Warning

Many of the colours are highly fugitive, especially the 1½d, 2d, 4d, 4½d, 9d
and both 1s values. Any contact with water seriously affects these colours.

Overprinted by De La Rue & Co.

Collectors are warned that examples of all the 'official' overprints are known to have been forged, and great care should be taken in purchasing the scarcer and higher priced stamps. Some guidance in checking the authenticity of overprints is given below:
(a)   Exact comparison with a known genuine overprint.
(b)   The impression should be easily read from the back of the stamp as the overprint usually has a heavy impression.
(c)   The postmark should obviously be on top of the overprint, and many forged examples can be detected by the overprint being on top of the postmark.
(d)   If in doubt, obtain an expert opinion and a certificate.

1882 - 1901 Inland Revenue. Surface printed issues overprinted 'I.R. OFFICIAL' in two lines in black. Wmk. Imperial Crown. Perf. 14

1881 Large coloured corner letters

No.			M/M	F/U	G/U
V401	**6d**	**Grey** (30.10.82)	£170	£20	£15

1880 - 84 Low values

V402	**½d**	**Deep green** (28.10.82)	£40	£14	7.00
V402a		Pale green	£50	£15	8.00
V403	**½d**	**Slate blue** (8.5.85)	£40	£12	5.00

1881 1d Lilac

V404	**1d**	**Lilac** (Die II) (27.9.82)	3.00	70	35
V404a		Wmk. inverted	-	-	£750
V404b		Blue-black overprint	£200	£40	£25

1883 - 84 'Lilac and Green' issue

V405	**2½d**	**Lilac** (12.3.85)	£200	£40	£25
V406	**1s**	**Dull green** (12.3.85)	£3000	£650	£350

1887 - 1900 'Jubilee' issue

V407	**½d**	**Vermilion** (21.8.88)	3.50	1.00	60
V408	**½d**	**Blue green** (4.01)	4.50	7.00	4.50
V409	**2½d**	**Purple** on blue paper (20.10.89)	£45	6.00	3.50
V410	**6d**	**Purple** on rose paper (14.6.01)	£200	£20	£15
V411	**1s**	**Green** (15.3.89)	£400	£50	£30
V412	**1s**	**Green and carmine** (12.01)	£1600	£400	£300

1885 - 1902 High values overprinted 'I.R. OFFICIAL' in two lines in black. Wmk. Large Anchor. Perf. 14

1885 (12 March) A. Blued paper

V413	**5s**	**Rose**	£5500	£700	£450
V414	**10s**	**Ultramarine**	£9000	£2700	£2000

1890 (March) B. White paper

V415	**5s**	**Rose**	£2500	£700	£500
V415a		Blue-black overprint	£3000	£1000	£600
V416	**10s**	**Ultramarine**	£4200	£900	£600
V416a		Blue-black overprint	£4500	£1200	£750
V416b		Cobalt	£11500	£1800	£800

1885 (12 March) Wmk. Three Imperial Crowns. Perf. 14

V417	**£1**	**Brown lilac**	£25000	£13000	

1890 (March) Wmk. Three Orbs. Perf. 14

V418	**£1**	**Brown lilac**	£37000	£17000	

1892 (13 April) Wmk. Three Imperial Crowns. Perf. 14

V419	**£1**	**Green**	£4000	£800	£550

1883 - 1900 Government Parcels. Surface printed issues overprinted 'GOVᵀ. PARCELS' in two lines in black. Wmk. Imperial Crown. Perf. 14

1881 Large coloured corner letters

V420	**1s**	**Orange brown.** Plate 13 (1.7.83)	£650	£70	£35
V421	**1s**	**Orange brown.** Plate 14 (1.7.83)	£1100	£120	£60

1881 1d Lilac

V422	**1d**	**Lilac** (Die II) (6.97)	£50	£10	5.00
V422a		Wmk. inverted	£2700	£1700	£850

1883 - 84 'Lilac and Green' issue

V423	**1½d**	**Lilac** (30.4.86)	£180	£30	£12
V424	**6d**	**Dull green** (30.4.86)	£1100	£250	£100
V425	**9d**	**Dull green** (1.8.83)	£950	£150	£80

1887 - 1900 'Jubilee' issue

V426	**1½d**	**Dull purple & green** (20.10.87)	£25	3.50	2.00
V427	**2d**	**Green and carmine** (24.10.91)	£45	8.00	4.00
V428	**4½d**	**Green and carmine** (9.92)	£95	£60	£25
V428a		Wmk. inverted	-	£2000	£1000
V429	**6d**	**Purple** on rose paper (19.12.87)	£45	£10	7.00
V430	**9d**	**Dull purple and blue** (21.8.88)	£75	£20	8.00
V431	**1s**	**Green** (25.3.90)	£140	£60	£30
V432	**1s**	**Green and carmine** (11.1.1900)	£170	£90	£30

1896 - 1902 Office of Works. Surface printed issues overprinted 'O.W. OFFICIAL' in two lines in black. Wmk. Imperial Crown. Perf. 14

1881 1d Lilac

V433	**1d**	**Lilac** (Die II) (24.3.96)	£90	£20	£10

1887 - 1900 'Jubilee' issue

V434	**½d**	**Vermilion**	£150	£50	£30
V435	**½d**	**Blue green**	£150	£75	£50
V436	**5d**	**Purple and blue** (Die II)	£1500	£375	£200
V437	**10d**	**Dull purple and carmine**	£2200	£700	£350

M/M   F/U   G/U   No.

M/M   F/U   G/U

½d, 1d   2½d, 6d

1896 - 1901 War Office. Surface printed issues overprinted 'ARMY OFFICIAL' in two lines in black. Wmk. Imperial Crown. Perf. 14

1881 1d Lilac

		M/M	F/U	G/U
V438	**1d Lilac** (Die II) (1.9.96)	2.00	50	25

1887 - 1900 'Jubilee' issue

		M/M	F/U	G/U
V439	**½d Vermilion** (1.9.96)	3.00	50	25
V439a	Wmk. inverted	£400	£250	-
V440	**½d Blue green** (4.1.1900)	3.00	4.00	2.00
V440a	Wmk. inverted	£400	£250	-
V441	**2½d Purple** on blue paper (1.9.96)	£20	£15	9.50
V442	**6d Purple** on rose paper (7.11.1901)	£50	£25	£15

1902 (19 Feb.) Board of Education. Surface printed issues overprinted 'BOARD OF EDUCATION' in three lines in black. Wmk. Imperial Crown. Perf. 14

1887 - 1900 'Jubilee' issue

		M/M	F/U	G/U
V443	**5d Purple and blue** (Die II)	£1400	£350	£185
V444	**1s Green and carmine**	£3750	£2200	£1300

Introductory Notes

It is recommended that identification is best carried out by a series of eliminations and the following chart provides a degree of guidance.

Certain printings can be positively distinguished by perforation size (e.g. Harrison Perf. 15 x 14) or the chalky paper test - lightly rub the surface of the margin of the stamp with a small piece of silver and the chalk surfaced paper will react with a black mark that looks like a pencil stroke. This can be removed with a light rubber. All chalky papers, with the exception of the 6d, are De La Rue printings.

The exercise then continues with the clues listed. Quality of printing, gum, centring, perforations, date of cancel (when available), plus the differences illustrated below, and finally a comparison of the various shades of colour.

USED STAMPS - beware colour changes being produced by water immersion on the following values - ½d, 1½d, 2d, 3d, 4d green and brown, 5d, 6d, 9d, 10d and 1s, as many of the colours were highly fugitive, especially the greens and purples. Those stamps with affected colours (washed out and pale) are worth very much less.

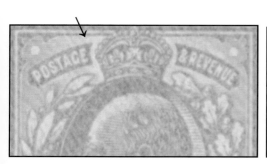

A   B

X   Y

A	**DE LA RUE**	Shading lines around the crown are light and gradually darken towards the frame sides.
B	**HARRISON** (Somerset House 6d)	Shading lines are virtually the same depth from frame to edge of crown giving a 'halo' effect.
X	**DE LA RUE**	Top 'frame' line to right of value tablet extending upwards (appears to be a single line) is always very thin and/or indistinct.
Y	**SOMERSET HOUSE**	The same 'frame' line is distinct and thick.

PRINTERS	DE LA RUE		HARRISON		SOMERSET HOUSE	
Perf. size	14	14	14	15 x 14	14	14
Paper type	Ordinary, smooth and coated	Chalky	Ordinary, less smooth		Ordinary, less smooth, Plate glazed, appears chalky, but does not react to silver test	
Quality of printing	Fine		Coarser		Coarser	
Gum	Yellowish		Colourless (See Note II)		Colourless	
Centring	Good		Poor		Less poor	
Perforations	Generally clean		Often ragged		Often ragged	
Date of cancel	From 1902, seldom after 1910		From 1911		From 1911	
½d	See Illustration A		See Illustration B	*		
1d	See Illustration A		See Illustration B some shades also fluoresce gold	*		
1½ d	See Illustration X Dull purple Slate purple	C			See Illustration Y Reddish purple Slate purple	
2d	Green is yellowish or bluish	C			Green is dull to deep greyish	
2½d	Straight blues See Illustration A		Duller blues See Illustration B	*		
3d	Paper appears chalky when not so	C	Purple appears as shades of brown on lemon paper	*		
4d Bi-colour	Only De La Rue	C				
4d Orange	Finer impression, brownish, pale to deep orange		White specks in solid background. Coarser impression. Bright orange shades	*		
5d	Purple and slate purple	C			Reddish tinge to purple	
6d	See Illustration A dull and slate purple (does not fluoresce)	C			See Illustration B Reddish purples, some fluoresce (see Note I)	C
7d	No olive tinge to grey black				Grey is tinged with olive	
9d	Purple is dull or slate	C			Purple is reddish	
10d	Purple is dull or slate	C			Purple is reddish	
1s	Pale bluish green shades	C			Pale to dark green	
2s 6d	Lilac and dull purple (does not fluoresce)	C			Reddish to deep black purple. Dull greyish purple (fluoresces gold)	
5s	Carmine (shows on reverse)				Carmine-reds	
10s	Pale to deep ultramarine				Coarse printing: dull pale to deep ultramarine	
£1	Bluish green				Less bluish but deeper green	

Notes:

(I)   6d Dickinson Paper. Somerset House experimental printing
A coated paper that does not react to the silver test. Shades are dull to deep rose purple with white gum

(II)   There is an exception to the colourless gum on the printing of the Harrison Penny value. A small printing was made with a double gum - very yellowish, as a result of complaints from the public that the stamps did not appear to be gummed at all. The last of the 6d Somerset House also had yellow gum, but the shades of deep purple were quite different from De La Rue.

6d   Somerset House also had yellow gum, but the shades of deep purple were quite different from De La Rue

C   Denotes chalky paper variety exists

*   Variety exists (Perf. 15 x 14)

Printer: De La Rue & Co. in Typography

½d, 1d, 6d

Imperial Crown
Watermark

1902 (1 Jan) - 11 Wmk. Imperial Crown. Perf. 14

A. Ordinary paper

No.			U/M	M/M	F/U	✉
E1	½d	**Blue green**	1.50	50	20	25
E1a		Wmk. inverted	£2500	£1750	£1000	
E1b		Dull blue green	2.00	50	20	25
E1c		Deep blue green	9.50	5.50	60	70
E2	½d	**Yellow green** (26.11.04)	2.00	50	15	25
E2a		Wmk. inverted	£20	£10	3.00	5.00
E2b		Pale yellow green	1.50	50	15	25
E2c		Wmk. inverted	£20	£10	3.00	5.00
E3	1d	**Scarlet**	1.50	50	10	25
E3a		Wmk. inverted	6.00	3.75	95	3.00
E3b		Bright scarlet	1.50	50	10	25
E3c		Wmk. inverted	6.00	3.75	1.50	4.00
E3d		Deep bright scarlet	5.00	2.75	50	75
E3e		Rose carmine	£16	9.00	3.50	6.50
E3f		Deep rose carmine	£35	£28	£10	£15
E3g		Blood-red A	£450	£275	£55	£85
E3h		Deep blood-red A	£850	£550	£95	£125
E4	1½d	**Dull purple and green** (21.3.02)	£50	£20	6.00	£15
E4a		Slate purple & green	£55	£22	8.00	£15
E4b		Wmk. Inverted			£500	
E4c		Deep slate purple & green	£70	£45	8.00	£15

No.			U/M	M/M	F/U	✉
E5	2d	**Yellowish green & carmine** (25.3.02)	£55	£25	8.00	£20
E5a		Grey green & carmine	£55	£25	8.00	£20
E5b		Yellowish green & carmine*	£100	£70	£40	£60
E5c		Yellowish green & vermilion (1903)	£240	£160	£40	£60
E6	2½d	**Ultramarine**	£20	£10	2.00	7.00
E6a		Pale ultramarine	£20	£10	2.00	7.00
E6b		Deep ultramarine	£30	£15	6.00	7.00
E6c		Wmk. inverted	-	£2000		
E7	3d	**Dull purple** on yellow paper (orange yellow back) (20.3.02)	£50	£20	3.00	£15
E7a		Deep purple on yellow paper (orange yellow back)	£55	£25	3.00	£15
E7b		Wmk. inverted	-	£2000		
E8	4d	**Green and brown** (27.3.02)	£70	£30	£10	£20
E8a		Green and grey brown	£70	£30	£10	£20
E8b		Wmk. inverted	-	-	£1600	
E8c		Green and chocolate brown	£80	£35	£10	£20
E9	4d	**Pale orange** (1.11.09)	£25	6.00	8.00	£20
E9a		Red orange	£25	6.00	6.00	£20
E9b		Brown orange	£175	£115	£85	£135
E10	5d	**Dull purple and ultramarine** (14.5.02)	£80	£25	7.00	£25
E10a		Slate purple and ultramarine	£80	£25	7.00	£25
E11	6d	**Slate purple**	£50	£22	6.00	£25
E11a		Pale dull purple	£50	£22	6.00	£25
E12	7d	**Grey black** (4.5.10)	8.00	4.00	£10	£100
E12a		Pale grey black	£25	£15	£20	£100
E12b		Deep grey black	£100	£60	£95	£220
E12c		Very deep grey black Ä	£180	£120	£150	£250
E13	9d	**Dull purple & ultramarine** (7.4.02)	£130	£40	£35	£120
E13a		Slate purple and ultramarine	£150	£40	£35	£120
E13b		Slate purple and deep ultramarine	£125	£75	£35	£120
E14	10d	**Dull purple and carmine** (3.7.02)	£140	£45	£30	£145
E14b		Slate purple and carmine	£140	£45	£30	£145
E14c		Slate purple and bright carmine *	£220	£140	£75	£200
E14d		Slate purple & carmine pink	£750	£450	£85	£220
E15	1s	**Dull green and carmine** (24.3.02)	£130	£45	£10	£85
E15a		Dull green & bright carmine	£130	£45	£10	£85
E15b		Dull green and bright carmine *	£200	£130	£75	£175
		Set of 15	£650	£200	£85	

Varieties

No.			U/M	M/M	F/U	✉
E16	2d	Tyrian plum (1910). Unissued		£80000		
E17	2½d	Purple on blue paper. Unissued		£50000	£35000	
E14a	10d	No cross on crown	£420	£275	£150	£300

B. Chalk surfaced paper

No.			U/M	M/M	F/U	✉
E18	1½d	**Pale dull purple and green** (6.9.05)	£50	£25	8.00	£15
E18a		Slate purple & bluish green	£50	£25	8.00	£15
E18b		Deep slate purple and bluish green	£70	£35	9.00	£15
E19	2d	**Grey green & carmine** (6.9.05)	£50	£22	9.00	£25
E19a		Deep grey green and scarlet	£55	£25	9.00	£25
E19b		Grey green and scarlet	£55	£25	9.00	£25
E19c		Pale blue green & carmine	£100	£55	£15	£40
E19d		Wmk. inverted	£20000		-	

No.		U/M	M/M	F/U	✉
E20	**3d Purple** on lemon paper (lemon back) (31.3.06)	£60	£20	8.00	£20
E20a	Pale purple on lemon paper (lemon back)	£60	£20	8.00	£20
E20b	Dull reddish purple on yellow paper (lemon back)	£275	£100	£27	£40
E20c	Pale reddish purple on orange yellow paper (orange yellow back)	£220	£100	£25	£60
E20d	Dull purple on orange yellow paper (orange yellow back)	£220	£100	£30	£100
E21	**4d Green and chocolate brown** (19.1.06)	£40	£20	£10	£25
E21a	Deep green and chocolate brown	£40	£20	£10	£25
E21b	Wmk. inverted	-	-	£2000	
E22	**5d Dull purple and ultramarine** (19.5.06)	£85	£30	£10	£25
E22a	Slate purple and ultramarine	£75	£25	£10	£25
E22b	Wmk. inverted	£4000	£2750	£1250	
E22c	Deep slate purple and ultramarine	£90	£35	£10	£25
E23	**6d Dull purple** (1.10.05)	£50	£20	9.00	£30
E23a	Slate purple	£50	£20	9.00	£30
E23b	Pale dull purple	£50	£20	9.00	£30
E23c	Wmk. inverted	-	-	£2000	
E24	**9d Dull purple & ultramarine** (29.6.05)	£125	£50	£30	£120
E24a	Slate purple and ultramarine	£130	£50	£30	£120
E24b	Slate purple and pale ultramarine	£130	£50	£35	£180
E24c	Wmk. inverted	-	-	£1500	
E24d	Slate purple and deep ultramarine	£180	£120	£50	£150
E25	**10d Dull purple and carmine** (6.9.05)	£130	£45	£35	£150
E25a	Slate purple and carmine	£130	£45	£35	£150
E25c	Dull purple and scarlet (9.10)	£130	£50	£40	£150
E25e	Slate purple and scarlet	£130	£60	£40	£150
E25f	Slate purple & deep carmine	£300	£200	£90	£300
E25g	Slate purple & deep carmine (shiny)	£1500	£1000	£300	£1000
E26	**1s Dull green and carmine** (6.9.05)	£130	£50	£20	£120
E26a	Dull green & scarlet	£130	£50	£20	£120
E26b	Deep dull green & scarlet	£130	£50	£20	£120
E26c	Dull green & pale carmine	£130	£50	£20	£120
	Set of 9 (cheapest)	£600	£250	£90	

Varieties

No.		U/M	M/M	F/U	✉
E25b	10d No cross on crown	£400	£220	£125	£300
E25d	10d No cross on crown	£400	£220	£125	£300

1911 (3 May - Nov.) Wmk. Imperial Crown.
Printer: Harrison and Sons in Typography
A. Perf. 14

No.		U/M	M/M	F/U	✉
E27	**½d Dull yellow green** (3.5.11)	2.50	1.50	70	2.00
E27a	Wmk. inverted	£27	£14	£15	£35
E27b	Dull green	2.50	1.25	40	1.00
E27c	Deep dull green	9.00	6.00	2.00	6.00
E27d	Pale bluish green	£45	£26	£20	£30
E27e	Wmk. sideways	-	-	£18000	
E27f	Deep dull yellow green (blotchy)	£50	£35	£25	£50
E27g	Olive green	£55	£45	£20	£50
E27h	Bright green (6.11)	£300	£185	£100	£200
E27i	Deep bright green	£250	£175	£100	£200

No.		U/M	M/M	F/U	✉
E28	**1d Rose red** (3.5.11)	5.00	2.75	5.50	7.50
E28a	No watermark	£40	£27	£85	
E28b	Wmk. inverted	£20	£15	£17	£30
E28c	Deep rose red	8.00	4.50	5.50	7.00
E28d	Pale rose carmine	£50	£35	7.00	£20
E28e	Wmk. inverted	£50	£32	9.00	£20
E28f	Rose carmine	£50	£30	9.00	£20
E28g	Wmk. inverted	£60	£35	£15	£35
E28h	Aniline rose *	£150	£100	£95	£180
E28i	Wmk. inverted	£150	£100	£95	£200
E28j	Intense rose red Ã	£275	£200	£85	£300
E28k	Deep rose carmine	£295	£225	£75	£150
E28m	Aniline pink *	£800	£500	£180	£600
E29	**2½d Bright blue** (10.7.11)	£90	£30	£15	£30
E29a	Dull blue	£90	£30	£15	£30
E29b	Deep bright blue	£110	£50	£30	£35
E29c	Wmk. inverted	£700	£495		
E29d	Deep dull blue	£130	£90	£45	£60
E30	**3d Purple** on lemon (12.9.11)	£100	£70	£130	£400
E30a	Grey purple on lemon	£100	£70	£130	£400
E30b	Grey on lemon	£3500	£2800	-	
E31	**4d Bright orange** (13.7.11)	£105	£45	£80	£100
E31a	Deep bright orange	£110	£55	£80	£100
	Set of 5	£280	£140	£170	

B. Perf. 15 x 14

No.		U/M	M/M	F/U	✉
E32	**½d Dull green** (30.10.11)	£45	£27	£25	£45
E32a	Pale bluish green	£50	£30	£25	£45
E32b	Deep dull green	£65	£40	£30	£45
E32c	Deep dull green (blotchy)	£800	£550	£250	£450
E33	**1d Rose carmine** (5.10.11)	£25	£15	7.50	£20
E33a	Pale rose carmine	£25	£15	7.50	£20
E33b	Deep rose carmine	£35	£20	12.50	£20
E33c	Rose red	£45	£25	£16	£30
E33d	Deep rose red	£70	£50	£30	£50
E33e	Intense rose red	£450	£300	£95	£200
E34	**2½d Bright blue** (14.10.11)	£35	£20	7.00	£20
E34a	Dull blue	£35	£20	7.00	£20
E34b	Wmk. inverted	-	-	£400	
E34c	Deep dull blue	£65	£45	£16	£25
E34d	Deep bright blue	£65	£45	£10	£25
E35	**3d Purple** on lemon (22.9.11)	£45	£25	5.00	£20
E35a	Grey purple on lemon	£60	£27	5.00	£20
E35b	Grey on lemon	£2700	£2200		
E36	**4d Bright orange** (22.11.11)	£40	£20	7.00	£40
E36a	Deep bright orange	£45	£25	7.00	£40
E36b	Very deep orange	£85	£65	£20	
	Set of 5	£120	£75	£40	

1911 (13 July) - 13 Wmk. Imperial Crown. Perf. 14
Printer: Somerset House in Typography
A. Ordinary paper

No.		U/M	M/M	F/U	✉
E37	**1½d Dull purple and green** (13.7.11)	£40	£20	£10	£40
E37a	Dull reddish purple & green	£60	£25	£10	£40
E37b	Dull reddish purple and bright green	£40	£20	£10	£40
E37c	Slate purple and green	£37	£20	£12	£40
E37d	Deep plum and deep green	£200	£130	£55	£75
E37e	Deep plum and pale green	£250	£140	£65	£75
E37f	Reddish purple and bright green	£75	£35	£12	£50
E37g	Reddish purple and yellow green	£75	£35	£12	£50
E38	**2d Deep dull green and red** (8.8.11)	£35	£15	£10	£30
E38a	Grey green & bright carmine	£35	£15	£10	£30
E38b	Deep dull green and carmine	£40	£17	£10	£30
E38c	Deep dull green and bright carmine	£40	£17	£12	£35

No.			U/M	M/M	F/U	✉
E39	5d	**Deep dull reddish purple**				
		and bright blue (7.8.11)	£35	£17	£10	£40
E39a		Deep reddish purple and				
		bright blue	£35	£17	£10	£40
E39b		Deep plum and cobalt blue	£35	£17	£12	£40
E39c		Pale plum and cobalt blue *	£75	£50	£18	£40
E40	6d	**Dull purple** * (31.10.11)	£30	£20	£10	£50
E40a		Pale dull purple	£50	£27	£12	£50
E40b		Reddish purple *	£35	£20	£12	£60
E40d		Pale reddish purple	£45	£22	£14	£65
E40e		Dark purple	£40	£25	£15	£65
E40f		Royal purple *	£75	£40	£65	£250
E40g		Deep reddish purple *	£75	£40	£20	£65
E40h		Dull lilac *	£200	£150	£75	£140
E41	7d	**Slate grey** (1.8.12)	£15	£10	£12	£130
E41a		Pale grey	£17	£12	£14	£130
E41b		Deep slate grey (5.13)	£125	£80	£40	£150
E42	9d	**Dull reddish purple and**				
		blue (24.7.11)	£95	£40	£40	£140
E42a		Deep dull reddish purple and				
		blue	£140	£65	£45	£140
E42b		Reddish purple and light blue	£140	£65	£50	£150
E42c		Slate purple & cobalt blue *	£150	£70	£50	£160
E42d		Deep dull reddish purple and				
		deep bright blue	£160	£70	£55	£175
E42e		Deep plum and cobalt blue	£150	£70	£55	£175
E43	10d	**Dull reddish purple and**				
		carmine (9.10.11)	£100	£45	£40	£175
E43a		Dull purple and scarlet	£120	£60	£45	£195
E43b		Deep dull purple and				
		carmine	£120	£60	£45	£200
E43d		Deep plum and carmine	£120	£60	£45	£220
E43e		Deep dull purple and scarlet	£150	£70	£50	£230
E43f		Dull reddish purple and				
		scarlet	£165	£110	£70	£250
E43g		Dull reddish purple and				
		aniline scarlet *	£320	£200	£80	£270
E43h		Dull purple and deep scarlet	£275	£190	£100	£300
E43i		Dull reddish purple and				
		aniline pink *	£375	£250	£190	£450

No.			U/M	M/M	F/U	✉
E44	1s	**Green & carmine** (17.7.11)	£100	£40	£15	£100
E44a		Green and scarlet	£135	£45	£18	£120
E44b		No watermark	£1800	£1200	-	
E44c		Wmk. inverted	£130	£90	-	
E44d		Deep green and scarlet	£105	£40	£15	£120
E44e		Green and bright scarlet	£120	£50	£17	£130
E44f		Dark green and scarlet	£150	£70	£30	£150
		Set of 8 (cheapest)	£440	£240	£120	
Varieties						
E40c	6d	No cross on crown	£600	£400	£250	£650
E43c	10d	No cross on crown	£1000	£750	£250	£500
B. Chalk surfaced paper						
E45	6d	**Deep plum** (7.13)	£40	£20	£70	£150
E45b		Bright magenta (31.10.11)	£7500	£4500	!	
E45c		Pale plum	£95	£65	£75	£120
Variety						
E45a	6d	No cross on crown	£600	£400	£250	£450
C. "Dickinson" coated paper						
E46	6d	**Dull purple** (3.13)	£300	£180	£120	£300
E46a		Dull reddish purple	£300	£180	£130	£300
E46b		Deep dull reddish purple	£300	£190	£150	£400

* Fluorescent reaction when viewed under an ultra violet lamp.
! Used examples do not exist.
Ä Only purchase with a certificate of authenticity.

B. Chalk surfaced paper

No.			U/M	M/M	F/U
E50	**2s6d**	**Dull purple** (7.10.1905)	£420	£160	£85
E50a		Pale dull purple	£450	£160	£90
E50b		Slate purple	£450	£175	£100
E50c		Wmk. inverted	£3500	£2500	£1600

1902 (16 July) Wmk. Three Imperial Crowns. Perf. 14

E51	**£1**	**Dull blue green**	£1500	£900	£450
E51a		Wmk. inverted		£20000	
		Set of 4	£3100	£1300	£850

1911 (27 Sept.) - 12 Wmk. Large Anchor. Perf. 14
Printer: Somerset House in Typography

E52	**2s6d**	**Dark purple**	£360	£140	£90
E52a		Wmk. inverted			-
E52b		Dull reddish purple	£360	£140	£90
E52c		Pale dull reddish purple	£380	£150	£90
E52d		Dull greyish purple *	£850	£350	£200
E53	**5s**	**Carmine** (29.2.12)	£550	£180	£100
E53a		Carmine red	£550	£180	£100
E54	**10s**	**Blue** (14.1.12)	£1100	£400	£270
E54a		Bright blue	£1100	£390	£280
E54b		Deep blue	£1200	£400	£300

1911 (3 Sept.) Wmk. Three Imperial Crowns. Perf. 14

E51	**£1**	**Deep green**	£1400	£950	£450
		Set of 4	£3200	£1550	£800

*   Fluorescent (gold) reaction under an ultra violet lamp.

Large Anchor
Watermark

Imperial Crown
Watermark

1902 (5 April) - 1905 Wmk. Large Anchor. Perf. 14
Printer: De La Rue & Co. in Typography.
A. Ordinary paper.

E47	**2s6d**	**Lilac**	£420	£130	£75
E47a		Wmk. inverted	£2800	£1700	£950
E47b		Slate purple	£450	£140	£75
E48	**5s**	**Bright carmine**	£550	£190	£85
E48a		Deep bright carmine	£570	£190	£85
E48b		Wmk. inverted	-	-	£2250
E49	**10s**	**Ultramarine**	£1100	£400	£250
E49a		Deep ultramarine	£1200	£420	£275

No.			U/M	M/M	F/U

No.			U/M	M/M	F/U

Overprinted by De La Rue & Co.

1902 (4 Feb.) - 1904 Inland Revenue. De La Rue printings overprinted "I.R. OFFICIAL" in two lines in black. Wmk. Imperial Crown. Perf. 14

			U/M	M/M	F/U
E56	½d	**Blue green**	£25	£12	2.00
E57	1d	**Scarlet**	£20	£8	1.00
E58	2½d	**Ultramarine** (19.2.02)	£950	£550	£80
E59	6d	**Dull purple** (14.3.04)	£140000		
				£100000	
					£70000
E60	1s	**Green and carmine** (29.4.02)	£1300	£800	£250

1902 (29 April) Wmk. Large Anchor. Perf. 14

			U/M	M/M	F/U
E61	5s	**Carmine**	£12000	£7000	£3500
E62	10s	**Ultramarine**	£50000	£30000	£17000

1902 (29 April) Wmk. Three Imperial Crowns. Perf. 14

			U/M	M/M	F/U
E63	£1	**Dull blue green**	£35000	£25000	£12000

Controls   Prices for a M/M single stamp

½d	Letter A		£120
	Letter B		£120
1d	Letter A		£120
	Letter B		£120

1902 (19 Feb. - Dec.) Government Parcels. De La Rue printings overprinted 'GOV^T. PARCELS' in two lines in black. Wmk. Imperial Crown. Perf. 14

			U/M	M/M	F/U
E64	1d	**Scarlet** (30.10.02)	£40	£20	6.00
E65	2d	**Green and carmine** (29.4.02)	£110	£80	£20
E66	6d	**Dull purple**	£220	£140	£20
E67	9d	**Purple & ultramarine** (28.8.02)	£400	£275	£60
E68	1s	**Green and carmine** (17.12.02)	£800	£500	£90

Controls   Prices for a M/M single stamp

1d	Letter A		£190

1902 (11 Feb.) - 1903 Office of Works. De La Rue printings overprinted 'O.W. OFFICIAL' in two lines in black. Wmk. Imperial Crown. Perf. 14

			U/M	M/M	F/U
E69	½d	**Blue green**	£400	£300	£80
E70	1d	**Scarlet**	£400	£300	£80
E71	2d	**Green and carmine** (29.3.02)	£1400	£950	£200
E72	2½d	**Ultramarine** (20.3.02)	£1700	£1200	£300
E73	10d	**Purple and carmine** (28.5.03)	£17000	£11000	£3500

Controls   Prices for a M/M single stamp

½d	Letter A		£1200
	Letter B		£1200
1d	Letter A		£1200
	Letter B		£1200

½d, 1d, 6d   6d (1903)

1902 (11 Feb.) - 1903 War Office. De La Rue printings overprinted 'ARMY OFFICIAL' in two lines in black. Wmk. Imperial Crown. Perf. 14

			U/M	M/M	F/U
E74	½d	**Blue green**	4.00	2.50	1.00
E75	1d	**Scarlet**	3.00	2.00	1.00
E76	6d	**Dull purple** (23.8.02)	£120	£50	£30
E77	6d	**Dull purple** (9.03)	£1800	£1200	£550

Controls   Prices for a M/M single stamp

½d	Letter A		£60
	Letter B		£60
1d	Letter A		£60
	Letter B		£60

1902 (19 Feb.) - 1904 Board of Education. De La Rue printings overprinted 'BOARD OF EDUCATION in three lines in black. Wmk. Imperial Crown. Perf. 14

			U/M	M/M	F/U
E78	½d	**Blue green**	£120	£80	£20
E79	1d	**Scarlet**	£120	£80	£20
E80	2½d	**Ultramarine**	£2200	£1400	£130
E81	5d	**Purple and blue** (6.2.04)	£10000	£2500	£2500
E82	1s	**Green and carmine** (23.12.02)	£65000	£40000	£20000

Controls   Prices for a M/M single stamp

½d	Letter A		£300
1d	Letter A		£350

1902 (19 Feb. - April) Royal Household. De La Rue printings overprinted 'R.H. OFFICIAL' in two lines in black. Wmk. Imperial Crown. Perf. 14

			U/M	M/M	F/U
E83	½d	**Blue green** (29.4.02)	£280	£180	£120
E84	1d	**Scarlet**	£280	£140	£95

Controls   Prices for a M/M single stamp

½d	Letter A		£900
1d	Letter A		£900

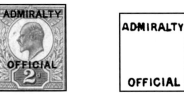

Setting I	Setting II
(thin)	(Letter 'M' varies)

1902 (3 March) - 04 The Admiralty. De La Rue printings overprinted 'ADMIRALTY OFFICIAL' in two lines in black. Wmk. Imperial Crown. Perf. 14

A. Setting I

No.			U/M	M/M	F/U
E85	½d	Blue green	£30	£17	8.00
E86	1d	Scarlet	£20	£12	4.00
E87	1½d	Purple and green	£300	£140	£70
E88	2d	Green and carmine	£350	£170	£75
E89	2½d	Ultramarine	£500	£290	£75
E90	3d	Purple on yellow	£400	£225	£80

B. Setting II

No.			U/M	M/M	F/U
E91	½d	Blue green	£65	£30	£10
E92	1d	Scarlet	£65	£30	£10
E93	1½d	Purple and green	£800	£550	£350
E94	2d	Green and carmine	£1300	£900	£350
E95	2½d	Ultramarine	£1700	£1200	£550
E96	3d	Purple on yellow	£1200	£850	£160

J. A. C. Harrison' sketch based on
Bertram Mackennal's 'coinage' head.

The early issues of King George V were generally considered unsuccessful due to the inexperience of the recently appointed printers - Harrison & Sons - and the use of Downey's three quarter face portrait. Some adaptations were made to the two values in use (½d and 1d) which lead to Dies 1B and 2. Despite many paper and ink trials it was decided to adopt a profile head for all the low values to 1s. Several types were considered and the final work was based on Bertram Mackennal's coinage head (½d, 1½d, 2d, 3d and 4d values) and medal head (1d, 2½d - large size, the rest 5d to 1s smaller size). Mackennal also designed the frames for the ½d to 4d, whilst G.W. Eve designed the rest.

Some of the 1912-13 printings were done at Somerset House but apart from these and the 6d values, Harrison were the printers until 1924, when Waterlow took over the contract. The 6d value, which also had a wide fiscal use, was printed by Somerset House until 1934. There were also very small printings by Somerset House of the 2½d in 1917 and the 1½d in 1926, to help in emergencies. Harrison regained the contract in 1934, commencing with the final 'block cypher' issues.

Probably the most interesting area from this period are the shades. It started with a period of experimentation, then the First World War interrupted supplies of some dyes used in the inks which led to improvisation. A vast range of shades are available for collectors and some wonderful studies can be produced. In addition, all the shades can be collected with a variety of watermarks - inverted, reversed, inverted and reversed - as well as upright and indeed, none at all. The varieties may be also combined with the controls issued.

The High Values were produced by three printers - Waterlow, De La Rue and Bradbury, Wilkinson - and were again based on the work of Bertram Mackennal. The stamps were recess printed and the master die engraved by J.A.C. Harrison. Harrison was also responsible for the 1924/25 Wembley, 1929 P.U.C. £1 engravings and much other work of this period.

The conditions that led to the wide range of shades in the low values applied even more so to the High Values, because the printing process was more reflective and a wide quality of papers and gums had to be used.

Pricing

The basis for pricing of stamps of this reign is as follows:

Unmounted Mint (U/M)	Full original gum, full perforations and good colour.
Mounted Mint (M/M)	Lightly hinged, full perforations and clear colour without toning.
Fine Used (F/U)	Clear and light postmark on a reasonably well centred stamp, with full perforations.

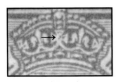 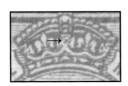  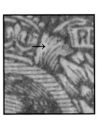

     ½d Die 1A   *½d Die 1B*   *1d Die 1A*   *1d Die 1B*

     Type 1   *Type 2*   *Type 3*   *Type 4*
  Die 1A or 1B   *Die 2*   *Die 1A or 1B*   *Die 2*

Downey Head Issues 1911 - 12

½d   **DIE 1A** Centre jewel of cross in middle of crown is suggested by a comma (arrowed). Top scale on right hand dolphin ends with a triangle.

          DIE 1B Centre jewel in crown is suggested by a crescent (arrowed). Top scale on right hand dolphin has only two sides.

          DIE 2   One thick line in ornament above 'FP' of 'Halfpenny' compared with two thinner lines on Dies 1A and 1B (arrowed). The beard has also been lightened and is better defined.

1d   **DIE 1A** The second line of shading is complete on the ribbon at the right of the crown (arrowed). On the large leaf that overlaps the right hand side ribbons, there is a line of shading to the left of the central line.

          DIE 1B The second line of shading on the ribbon is broken (arrowed); on the leaf the line of shading is much smaller.

          DIE 2   The lion is shaded and the beard is more defined (arrowed); the ends of the ribbons above the figures '1' are removed.

Imperial Crown   Royal Cypher
Watermark   Watermark

1911 (22 June) Wmk. Imperial Crown. Types 1 and 3. Die 1A. Perf. 15 x 14
Printers: Harrison & Sons and Somerset House

No.			U/M	M/M	F/U	⊡
G1	½d	**Green**	6.00	3.00	50	2.00
G1a		Pale green	7.25	3.00	50	2.00
G1b		Deep green	£15	6.00	1.00	3.00
G1c		Bluish green	£260	£200	£90	
G2	1d	**Carmine red**	5.00	2.50	40	2.00
G2a		Wmk. inverted	£1100	£700	£1650	
G2b		No watermark	£400	£200	£450	
G2c		Wmk. sideways	-	-	£12000	
G2d		Carmine red. Chalky paper	£200	£150	-	
G2e		Pale carmine red	8.00	3.00	1.00	2.00
G2g		Carmine	£16	8.00	2.50	2.00
G2h		Pale carmine	£18	£10	1.00	2.00
G2i		Deep carmine red	£25	£15	4.00	4.50
G2j		Rose pink	£85	£45	£15	£30
G2k		Deep carmine, varnish ink	£1800	£1400	*	
Varieties						
G1d	½d	Green. Perf. 14		£10000	£200	£650
G2f	1d	No cross on crown	£500	£185	£100	£300

No. G2l, Perf 14, is probably a colour trial and has been deleted.

1911 - 12 Wmk. Imperial Crown. Types 1 and 3. Die 1B. Perf. 15 x 14

No.			U/M	M/M	F/U	⊡
G3	½d	**Bright green**	8.00	4.00	1.00	2.00
G3a		Wmk. inverted	£12	7.00	2.50	£10
G3b		Green	£10	7.00	1.00	2.00
G3c		Wmk. sideways	-	-	£2500	
G3d		Yellow green	£12	8.00	1.00	2.00
G3e		Pale bright green	£10	6.00	1.00	2.00
G3f		Deep green	£25	£15	6.50	8.50
G3g		Bright yellow green	£35	£17	7.00	£12
G3h		Bluish green	£180	£110	£40	£90
G3i		Very deep green	£275	£210	£45	£100
G3j		Deep green, varnish ink	£2700	£2200	*	
G4	1d	**Carmine**	7.50	4.00	30	1.00
G4a		Wmk. inverted	9.00	5.00	2.50	4.00
G4b		Pale carmine	8.00	4.00	30	1.00
G4d		Bright carmine	£13	8.00	1.00	1.25
G4e		Carmine red	£10	6.50	50	1.00
G4f		Pale carmine red	£11	7.50	75	1.25
G4g		Deep carmine	£25	£13	1.00	1.25
G4h		Deep bright carmine	£50	£30	4.00	7.00
G4i		Rose pink	£70	£40	£10	£20
G4j		Carmine, varnish ink	£1800	£1400	*	

No.			U/M	M/M	F/U	⊡
G5	1d	**Scarlet** (6.12)	£21	£14	6.50	8.00
G5a		Wmk. inverted	£20	£14	5.00	7.50
G5b		No watermark	£750	£500	£500	
G5c		Bright scarlet	£21	£14	6.00	7.00
G5d		Pale scarlet	£35	£25	6.00	£12
G5e		Aniline scarlet	£135	£85	£60	£90
Varieties						
G4c	1d	No cross on crown	£350	£250	£170	£250

1912 (Aug.) Wmk. Royal Cypher. Types 1 and 3. Die 1B. Perf. 15 x 14

No.			U/M	M/M	F/U	⊡
G6	½d	**Green**	£50	£30	£11	£16
G6a		Wmk. inverted	£50	£30	£11	£16
G6b		Wmk. inv. and rev.	£400	£300	£250	
G6c		Wmk. reversed	£400	£300	£175	
G6d		No watermark	£950	£500	£500	
G6e		Pale green	£50	£30	£11	£16
G6f		Deep green	£75	£45	£15	£25
G6g		Deep green, varnish ink	£1900	£1400	*	
G7	1d	**Scarlet** (6.12)	£30	£15	6.00	£10
G7a		Wmk. inverted	£30	£15	5.00	5.00
G7b		Wmk. inv. and rev.	£450	£350	£100	
G7c		Wmk. reversed	£400	£250	£200	
G7d		Bright scarlet	£30	£15	6.00	£10
G7e		Pale scarlet	£30	£15	8.00	£12
G7f		Deep bright scarlet	£55	£40	9.00	£14
G7g		Bright scarlet, varnish ink	£1500	£1200		

Cross on crown   No cross on crown

1912 (1 Jan) Wmk. Imperial Crown. Types 2 and 4. Die 2. Perf. 15 x 14

No.			U/M	M/M	F/U	⊡
G8	½d	**Green**	5.00	2.00	25	1.00
G8b		Wmk. inverted	£300	£200	£140	
G8c		Yellow green	5.50	2.50	25	1.00
G8d		Pale green	9.00	5.00	50	1.00
G8e		Deep green	£11	7.00	1.00	1.50
G8f		Bright yellow-green	£18	£12	1.50	2.00
G8g		Myrtle green	£85	£55	9.00	£15
G8h		Bluish green	£75	£55	£16	£25
G9	1d	**Scarlet**	3.25	1.25	20	1.00
G9b		Wmk. inverted	£175	£125	£90	
G9c		Bright scarlet	3.50	1.25	15	1.00
G9d		Wmk. inverted	£175	£125	£100	
G9e		Deep bright scarlet	4.00	2.00	50	1.00
G9f		Very deep bright scarlet	£65	£50	£20	£30
G9g		Aniline scarlet	£150	£95	£40	£60
Varieties						
G8a	½d	No cross on crown	£70	£50	£25	£50
G9a	1d	No cross on crown	£70	£40	£15	£40
G9da	1d	No cross on crown	£200	£125	£100	
G9ga	1d	No cross on crown	£600	£425	£350	£500

1912 (Aug.) Wmk. Royal Cypher. Types 2 and 4. Die 2. Perf. 15 x 14

No.			U/M	M/M	F/U	⊡
G10	½d	**Green**	5.00	2.50	30	1.00
G10b		Wmk. inverted	£95	£50	£45	
G10c		Wmk. inv. and rev.	8.00	5.00	3.00	
G10d		Wmk. reversed	£75	£50	£40	
G10e		No watermark	£400	£300	£250	
G10f		Pale green	5.50	2.75	35	1.00
G10g		Deep green	6.00	3.50	1.25	1.50
G10h		Yellow green	6.00	3.50	1.25	2.00

No.			U/M	M/M	F/U	✉
G11	**1d**	**Scarlet**	3.50	2.00	30	1.00
G11b		Wmk. inverted	£16	£10	6.00	
G11c		Wmk. inv. and rev.	£16	£10	6.00	
G11d		Wmk. reversed	£20	£15	£12	
G11e		No watermark	£250	£175	£150	
G11f		Bright scarlet	4.00	2.25	35	1.00
G11g		Deep bright scarlet	£25	£18	1.50	1.75
Varieties						
G10a	½d	No cross on crown	£90	£60	£40	£60
G11a	1d	No cross on crown	£60	£40	£30	£45

Multiple Royal
Cypher Watermark

1912 (Oct.) Wmk. Multiple Royal Cypher. Types 2 and 4. Die 2.
Perf. 15 x 14

No.			U/M	M/M	F/U	✉
G12	**½d**	**Green**	£10	4.50	2.00	2.50
G12c		Wmk. inverted	£13	9.00	7.50	4.50
G12d		Wmk. inv. and rev.	£22	£15	£18	
G12e		Wmk. reversed	£14	8.00	6.00	
G12f		Wmk. sideways	-	-	£2250	
G12g		Yellow green	12.50	7.00	4.50	7.00
G12h		Pale green	£13	7.00	4.50	7.00
G12i		Deep green	£20	£12	5.50	8.00
G13	**1d**	**Scarlet**	£15	7.00	3.50	8.00
G13c		Wmk. inverted	£20	£13	£12	
G13d		Wmk. inv. and rev.	£1000	£700	£400	
G13e		Wmk. reversed	£20	£12	£12	
G13f		Wmk. sideways	£170	£110	£120	
G13g		Bright scarlet	£17	12.50	4.25	£10
G13h		Deep bright scarlet	£85	£55	£12	£15
Varieties						
G12a	½d	No cross on crown	£220	£140	£85	£110
G12b		Imperforate	£120	£80	-	
G13a	1d	No cross on crown	£140	£100	£80	£125
G13b		Imperforate	£110	£80	-	

* These stamps should only be purchased with a certificate

Have you read the notes at the
beginning of the catalogue?

Royal Cypher
Watermark

1912 (Aug.) - 22 Wmk. Royal Cypher. Perf. 15 x 14. 6d on chalky paper
Printers: Harrison & Sons and Somerset House

No			U/M	M/M	F/U	✉
G14	**½d**	**Green** (1913)	40	20	10	15
G14a		Wmk. inverted	3.00	2.00	2.00	4.00
G14b		Wmk. inv. and rev.	3.50	2.00	1.50	
G14c		Wmk. reversed	£15	9.00	8.00	
G14d		No watermark	£50	£35	£25	
G14e		Bright green	2.00	1.00	10	15
G14f		Deep green	7.50	4.00	2.00	2.00
G14g		Pale green	7.50	4.00	2.00	2.00
G14h		Deep bright green	7.00	5.00	2.00	2.00
G14i		Yellow green	7.00	3.00	1.00	1.50
G14j		Cobalt green	£25	£15	3.00	5.50
G14k		Apple green	£17	£10	4.00	6.00
G14l		Blue green	£35	£22	9.00	£12
G14m		Pale olive green	£75	£50	£15	£20
G14n		Olive green	£75	£55	£15	£20
G14o		Bright yellow green	£40	£20	*	
G14p		Very pale green	£170	£140	*	
G14q		Deep cobalt green	£275	£200	*	
G14r		Very deep green	£225	£170	*	
G14s		Myrtle green	£250	£200	*	
G14t		Deep myrtle green	£750	£600	*	

No.		U/M	M/M	F/U	✉
G14u	Very yellow (cyprus) green	£7500	£5500	*	
G15	**1d Scarlet** (10.12)	50	20	10	1.00
G15a	Wmk. inverted	3.00	2.00	2.00	4.00
G15b	Wmk. inv. and rev.	4.00	2.25	2.50	
G15c	Wmk. reversed	£22	£12	8.00	
G15d	No watermark	£65	£40	£45	
G15e	Bright scarlet	1.00	60	10	1.00
G15f	Bright scarlet. 'Q' for 'O'	£175	£110	£120	£200
G15g	Vermilion	5.00	3.00	1.50	2.50
G15h	Brick red	4.00	3.00	1.00	2.50
G15i	Deep scarlet	£10	6.50	2.00	60
G15j	Carmine red	7.00	4.50	1.50	1.25
G15k	Deep bright scarlet	£20	£15	2.00	3.25
G15l	Pale rose red	£12	8.00	2.50	3.00
G15m	Pale red	£14	8.00	1.00	2.25
G15n	Bright carmine red	£22	£14	2.75	4.00
G15o	Deep brick red	£70	£50	3.50	6.00
G15p	Scarlet vermilion	£110	£80	8.00	9.00
G15q	Orange vermilion	£160	£120	£50	£70
G15r	Deep carmine red	£320	£270	7.00	£10
G15s	Pink	£320	£270	*	
G15t	Deep orange vermilion	£320	£275	£100	£140
G16	**1½d Red brown** (10.12)	3.00	2.00	20	1.25
G16a	Wmk. inverted	7.50	4.50	1.50	4.00
G16b	Wmk. inv. and rev.	£12	8.00	4.50	
G16c	Wmk. reversed	£40	£30	£30	
G16d	Red brown. 'PENCF'	£225	£170	£200	£300
G16e	Deep red brown	5.00	3.00	1.00	2.00
G16f	Chestnut	3.00	2.00	50	1.00
G16g	Chestnut. 'PENCF'	£100	£80	£75	£15
G16h	Chocolate brown	£10	7.00	1.00	2.00
G16ha	No watermark	£180	£120	£120	
G16j	Orange brown	7.00	4.00	1.00	1.00
G16k	Pale red-brown	£13	8.00	1.00	2.00
G16l	Yellow brown	£14	8.00	4.00	6.00
G16m	Bright yellow brown	£17	£12	4.50	6.00
G16n	Deep chocolate brown	£75	£50	7.00	£10
G16o	Bright chestnut	£70	£50	8.50	£12
G16p	Deep yellow brown	£70	£50	£15	£20
G16q	Bright orange brown	£70	£50	£20	£20
G16r	Chocolate	£240	£190	£50	£70
G16s	Very deep red brown	£270	£190	£60	£70
G16t	Brown	£360	£300	*	
G16u	Pale brown	£460	£380	*	
G17	**2d Orange** (Die I)	2.20	1.50	25	2.00
G17a	Wmk. inverted	£14	8.00	5.00	£14
G17b	Wmk. inv. and rev.	£13	7.00	£10	
G17c	Wmk. reversed	£15	£10	£12	
G17d	No watermark	£220	£170	£150	£150
G17e	Bright orange	5.00	2.75	50	2.00
G17f	Reddish orange	4.50	3.00	50	2.00
G17g	Pale orange	8.50	6.00	1.00	2.00
G17h	Deep bright orange	£20	£14	2.50	3.00
G17i	Orange yellow	£10	5.00	2.00	3.00
G17j	Brown orange	£40	£25	3.00	5.50
G17k	Deep reddish orange	£110	£80	£20	£40
G17l	Intense bright orange	£1750	£1250	*	
G18	**2d Orange** (Die II) (9.21)	6.50	4.00	1.00	3.00
G18a	Wmk. inverted	£25	£15	£17	£30
G18b	Wmk. inv. and rev.	£75	£50	£50	
G18c	Wmk. reversed	£20	£12	£10	
G18d	No watermark	£1100	£850	£800	
G18e	Pale orange	6.00	4.00	2.00	3.50
G18f	Bright orange	8.00	6.00	2.00	3.50
G18g	Deep orange	£17	£12	2.50	4.00
G19	**2½d Bright blue** (10.12)	£13	£10	2.00	3.00
G19a	Wmk. inverted	£90	£60	£75	
G19b	Wmk. inv. and rev.	£30	£20	£12	
G19c	Wmk. reversed	£35	£25	£35	
G19d	No watermark	£1250	£1000	£1000	£1000
G19e	Blue	£14	9.00	2.00	4.00
G19f	Cobalt blue	£18	£12	2.50	4.00
G19g	Pale blue	£20	£15	2.25	4.50
G19h	Dull blue	£20	£12	2.25	4.50
G19i	Ultramarine	£25	£14	2.75	4.50
G19j	Deep blue	£20	£15	2.25	3.50
G19k	Powder blue	£40	£20	2.50	4.00
G19l	French blue	£90	£60	4.00	4.00
G19m	Milky blue	£35	£20	9.00	£20
G19n	Violet blue	£30	£20	9.00	£20
G19o	Cobalt violet blue	£30	£20	9.00	£20
G19p	Deep bright blue	£300	£250	*	
G19q	Royal blue	£475	£350	*	
G19r	Dull Prussian blue	£950	£750	*	
G19s	Indigo blue	£2500	£1650	*	
G19t	Pale milky blue	£1350	£1050	*	
G20	**3d Violet** (10.12)	5.50	3.25	70	4.00
G20a	Wmk. inverted	£120	£75	£120	
G20b	Wmk. inv. and rev.	£35	£25	£40	
G20c	Wmk. reversed	£200	£120	£150	
G20d	No watermark	£350	£250	£275	
G20e	Bluish violet	10.50	7.00	1.20	4.50
G20f	Pale violet	10.50	7.00	2.00	4.25
G20g	Bright violet	9.00	7.50	2.00	4.25
G20h	Dull violet	9.00	7.00	2.25	4.75
G20i	Lavender violet	£20	£12	2.25	4.75
G20j	Dull reddish violet	£15	£10	2.00	4.25
G20k	Reddish violet	£20	9.00	3.00	7.00
G20l	Heliotrope	£50	£30	3.00	7.00
G20m	Brownish violet	£70	£40	4.00	£10
G20n	Very deep violet	£150	£85	£12	£40
G20o	Very pale violet	£225	£165	*	
G21	**4d Grey green** (1.13)	£15	3.50	60	5.00
G21a	Wmk. inverted	£40	£25	£40	
G21b	Wmk. inv. and rev.	£60	£40	£50	
G21c	Wmk. reversed	£65	£45	£50	
G21d	No watermark	£275	£200	£200	
G21e	Slate green	£20	13.50	£26	6.00
G21f	Pale grey green	£18	£10	1.00	6.25
G21g	Pale slate green	£25	£15	1.00	6.25
G21h	Bluish green grey	£25	£15	3.00	7.00
G21i	Deep grey green	£30	£20	8.00	£10
G21j	Deep slate green	£195	£140	7.50	£10
G22	**5d Brown** (6.13)	8.00	4.00	1.00	5.50
G22a	Wmk. inverted	£575	£375	£550	
G22b	Wmk. inv. and rev.	£220	£150	£150	
G22c	Reddish brown	£18	£10	1.00	5.50
G22d	Yellow brown	£11	5.00	1.00	5.50
G22e	Yellow brown. No wmk	£375	£300	£300	
G22f	Ginger brown	£23	£17	8.00	£10
G22g	Ochre brown	£100	£75	£20	£15
G22h	Bistre brown	£150	£100	£35	£50
G23	**6d Reddish purple.** Chalky (8.13)	£13	7.00	1.00	7.50
G23a	Wmk. inverted	£50	£35	£50	
G23b	Wmk. inv. and rev.	£40	£25	£35	
G23c	Wmk. reversed	£850	£650	£750	
G23d	No watermark	£750	£500	£500	
G23e	Pale reddish purple	£15	8.50	1.75	7.50
G23f	Rosy mauve	£14	7.00	1.75	7.50
G23g	Purple	£17	8.00	1.75	7.50
G23h	Plum	£17	9.00	1.75	7.50
G23i	Deep reddish purple	£25	£13	4.00	7.50
G23j	Dull purple	£22	£12	7.50	9.50
G23k	Slate purple	£120	£80	£30	£45
G24	**6d Reddish purple.** Chalky. Perf. 14 (1921)	£85	£50	£45	£100
G25	**7d Olive** (8.13)	£17	£10	6.00	£15
G25a	Wmk. inverted	£15	£27	£35	
G25b	Wmk. inv. and rev.	£1850	£1400	-	
G25c	No watermark	£450	£350	£250	
G25d	Olive grey	£16	£10	2.50	£15
G25e	Sage green	£70	£35	5.50	£20
G25f	Bronze green	£50	£35	£15	£20
G26	**8d Black on yellow**	£30	£15	8.00	£25
G26a	Wmk. inverted	£110	£75	£150	
G26b	Wmk. inv. and rev.	£2000	£1600	£1600	
G26c	Wmk. reversed	£175	£140	£250	
G26d	No watermark	£1750	£1300	£1350	
G26e	Black on yellow buff (granite paper)	£30	£15	8.00	£25

No.			U/M	M/M	F/U	✉
G27	**9d**	**Agate** (6.13)	£12	7.00	3.00	£10
G27a		Wmk. inverted	£110	£65	£100	
G27b		Wmk. inv. and rev.	£70	£50	£70	
G27c		No watermark	£650	£450	£450	
G27d		Pale agate	£18	£10	3.50	10.50
G27e		Deep agate	£18	£10	3.75	£10
G27f		Very deep agate	£450	£350	*	
G28	**9d**	**Olive green** (9.22)	£160	£70	£16	£50
G28a		Wmk. inverted	£750	£475	£600	
G28b		Wmk. inv. and rev.	£650	£400	£550	
G28c		Pale olive green	£160	£75	£16	£50
G28d		Deep olive green	£200	£95	£18	£60
G29	**10d**	**Turquoise blue** (8.13)	£20	£10	8.00	£17
G29a		Wmk. inverted	£2500	£1750	£1750	
G29b		Wmk. inv. and rev.	£225	£160	£175	
G29c		Greenish blue	£22	£15	8.00	£17
G29d		Pale turquoise blue	£22	£15	8.00	£17
G29e		Bright turquoise blue	£30	£18	8.00	£17
G29f		Deep turquoise blue	£80	£50	£15	£25
G30	**1s**	**Bistre brown** (8.13)	£18	£10	1.50	3.00
G30a		Wmk. inverted	£220	£140	£170	
G30b		Wmk. inv. and rev.	£75	£50	£75	
G30c		No watermark	£1100	£850	£850	
G30d		Deep bistre brown	£25	£15	2.00	3.00
G30e		Olive bistre	£25	£15	2.25	3.50
G30f		Pale buff brown	£25	£15	2.25	3.50
G30g		Buff brown	£25	£15	2.25	3.50
G30h		Pale olive bistre	£25	£15	2.25	3.50
G30i		Olive brown	£60	£40	2.75	3.50
G30j		Fawn brown	£110	£75	15.50	£20
G30k		Deep bronze brown	£525	£435	*	
		Set of 14	£120	£65	£25	

Multiple Royal
Cypher Watermark

1913 (Aug.) Wmk. Multiple Royal Cypher. Perf. 15 x 14

No.			U/M	M/M	F/U	✉
G31	**½d**	**Green**	£100	£65	£60	£250
G31a		Wmk. inverted	£425	£325	£425	
G31b		Bright green	£100	£65	£60	£150
G31c		Wmk sideways			£15000	
G32	**1d**	**Scarlet**	£400	£115	£100	£600
G32a		Wmk. inverted	£700	£500	£500	
G32b		Dull scarlet	£300	£115	£125	£450
		Set of 2	£330	£165	£170	

Multiple Block   Experimental
Cypher Watermark   Watermark

1924 (April) Wmk. Multiple Block Cypher. Perf. 15 x 14 Printers: Harrison & Sons, Waterlow & Sons and Somerset House.

No			U/M	M/M	F/U	✉
G33	**½d**	**Green**	50	25	10	1.00
G33a		Wmk. inverted	5.00	2.50	40	2.50
G33b		Wmk. sideways	£11	7.00	5.50	12.50
G33c		Pale green	60	40	25	1.00
G33d		Bright green	30	15	25	1.00
G33e		Deep green	2.50	1.50	75	1.00
G33f		Deep bright green	5.50	3.50	1.00	1.50
G33g		Yellow green	£15	£10	2.00	3.50
G34	**1d**	**Scarlet**	50	25	5	1.00
G34a		Wmk. inverted	4.50	2.50	50	2.00
G34b		Wmk. sideways	£20	£10	8.00	£18
G34c		Scarlet. Inverted 'Q' for 'O'	£375	£275	£150	£500
G34d		Pale scarlet	70	30	10	1.00
G34e		Scarlet vermilion	70	30	15	1.00
G34f		Deep scarlet vermilion	£30	£17	2.50	1.75
G35	**1½d**	**Red brown**	90	30	5	1.50
G35c		Wmk. inverted	2.50	1.25	50	3.00
G35d		Wmk. sideways	£15	8.00	2.50	9.50
G35e		Yellow brown	90	35	30	1.50
G35f		Deep red brown	3.00	2.00	35	1.50
G35g		Orange brown	3.00	2.00	45	1.50
G35h		Chestnut	2.50	1.50	60	1.50
G35i		Bright chestnut	3.00	2.00	65	1.50
G35j		Chocolate brown	5.25	3.75	80	2.00
G35k		Deep yellow brown	6.00	4.00	80	2.00
G35l		Bright yellow brown	7.50	4.50	1.50	2.00
G35m		Pale red brown	£18	£13	4.50	5.50
G36	**2d**	**Orange** (Die II)	1.25	80	1.25	3.00
G36a		Wmk. inverted	£35	£25	£35	
G36b		Wmk. sideways	£150	£55	£50	£180
G36c		No watermark	£1800	£1250	£1250	
G36d		Yellow orange	3.00	2.00	1.00	3.00
G36e		Deep orange	6.00	4.00	1.00	3.00
G36f		Pale yellow orange	£12	8.00	1.50	3.00
G36g		Deep yellow orange	£20	£13	2.00	4.00
G37	**2½d**	**Blue**	5.00	2.75	1.00	2.00
G37a		Wmk. inverted	£50	£35	£75	
G37b		No watermark	£2000	£1500	£1500	
G37c		Pale blue	8.00	5.00	1.50	2.00
G37d		Bright blue	6.00	4.00	1.00	2.00
G37e		Ultramarine	£10	6.00	1.25	2.00
G38	**3d**	**Violet**	9.00	3.50	1.25	4.00
G38a		Wmk. inverted	£55	£40	£75	
G38b		Deep violet	£12	8.00	1.25	4.00
G38c		Pale violet	£21	£12	1.50	4.00
G38d		Bright violet	£14	9.00	1.50	4.00
G38e		Pale reddish violet	£22	£15	4.00	5.50
G38f		Deep brownish violet	£30	£20	5.00	7.00
G39	**4d**	**Grey green**	£12	7.00	2.00	5.00
G39a		Wmk. inverted	£120	£75	£100	
G39b		Deep grey green	£18	£12	60	5.00
G39c		Very deep grey green	£32	£22	5.00	£10
G40	**5d**	**Brown**	£25	£15	1.50	5.00
G40a		Wmk. inverted	£80	£50	£75	
G40b		Deep brown	£30	£20	1 50	5.00
G40c		Reddish brown	£60	£40	2.50	5.00
G40d		Bright ochre brown	£22	£13	2.50	5.00
G40e		Deep ochre brown	£50	£35	3.00	5.50

No.			U/M	M/M	F/U	☜	No

No.			U/M	M/M	F/U	☜
G41	6d	**Reddish purple.** Chalky. (1936)	£10	7.00	1.25	4.00
G41a		Wmk. inverted	£60	£50	£60	
G41b		Wmk. inv. and rev.	£325	£200	£250	
G41c		Rosy-mauve. Chalky	£20	£14	1.50	4.00
G41d		Deep reddish purple. Chalky	£20	£13	1.75	4.00
G41e		Plum. Chalky	£22	£14	3.50	5.00
G42	6d	**Purple** (1934)	3.00	1.50	1.00	3.00
G42a		Wmk. inverted	£65	£45	£60	
G42b		Rosy-mauve (1926)	6.00	3.50	1.00	3.00
G42c		Reddish purple	5.00	3.00	1.00	3.00
G42d		Pale rosy mauve	8.00	5.00	1.00	3.00
G42e		Deep reddish purple	8.00	5.00	1.00	3.00
G42f		Deep purple	£12	8.00	2.00	3.00
G43	9d	**Olive green**	£13	8.00	2.00	7.00
G43a		Wmk. inverted	£95	£60	£75	
G43b		Deep olive green	£15	£10	2.00	7.00
G43c		Pale olive green	£15	£10	2.00	7.00
G43d		Olive yellow green	£45	£25	7.50	£15
G44	10d	**Turquoise blue**	£45	£20	£16	£35
G44a		Wmk. inverted	£2250	£1350	£1500	
G44b		Dull greenish blue	£50	£26	£17	£35
G44c		Deep greenish blue	£70	£40	£20	£35
G44d		Deep dull greenish blue	£70	£40	£24	£40
G45	1s	**Bistre brown**	£27	£14	1.50	5.00
G45a		Wmk. inverted	£400	£275	£300	
G45b		Buff brown	£35	£20	1.50	5.00
G45c		Fawn brown	£42	£26	1.50	5.00
G45d		Pale buff brown	£42	£20	1.50	5.00
G45e		Deep fawn brown	£140	£75	6.50	£10
		Set of 12	£110	£65	9.50	

Varieties

G35a	1½d	Red-brown. Tête-bêche pair	£550	£350	£500
G35b	1½d	Red-brown. Tête-bêche gutter pair	£575	£375	£550

Photogravure

Over a period of two years, stamps were printed with reduced design sizes to accommodate more accurate perforating of the stamps. The formats and sizes listed refer to the design and not the measurement of the whole stamp.

Multiple Block
Cypher Watermark

1934 (20 Aug.) Wmk. Multiple Block Cypher. Perf. 15 x 14
Large Format (18.6 x 22.5mm)

G46	1d	**Scarlet** (24.9)	1.50	80	1.00	3.00
G46a		Bright scarlet	1.50	80	1.00	3.00
G46b		Wmk. inverted	£100	£65	£95	
G47	1½d	**Red brown**	1.25	75	1.00	3.00
G47a		Bright red brown	1.25	75	70	3.00
G47b		Wmk. inverted	£160	£110	£140	
		Set of 2	2.75	1.50	1.50	

1934 Wmk. Multiple Block Cypher. Perf. 15 x 14
Intermediate Format (18.3 x 22.2mm)

G48	½d	**Green**	1.25	1.00	1.00	2.00
G48a		Bluish green	1.50	1.00	1.00	2.00
G48b		Wmk. inverted	£25	£17	£18	£55
G49	1d	**Scarlet**	8.00	5.00	2.00	2.50
G49a		Bright scarlet	9.00	5.00	2.00	2.50
G49b		Pale scarlet	£15	£10	3.00	2.50
G49c		Wmk. inverted	£25	£16	£18	£55
G50	1½d	**Red brown**	8.00	3.50	75	2.50
G50a		Wmk. inverted	£17	£12	£10	£25
G51	2d	**Orange**	4.00	2.25	1.50	3.50
G51a		Bright orange	4.00	2.25	1.50	3.50
		Set of 4	£20	£12	5.00	

1935 - 36 Wmk. Multiple Block Cypher. Perf. 15 x 14
Small Format (18.0 x 21.7mm)

No.		Description	U/M	M/M	F/U	
G52	½d	**Green**	25	10	5	1.00
G52a		Bluish green	25	10	5	1.00
G53	1d	**Scarlet**	35	20	5	1.00
G53a		Bright scarlet	50	30	5	1.00
G54	1½d	**Red brown**	25	10	5	1.00
G54a		Bright red brown	25	10	5	1.00
G55	2d	**Orange**	60	35	10	2.00
G55a		Bright orange	75	45	10	2.00
G56	2½d	**Bright blue** (18.3.35)	1.50	1.00	30	3.00
G56a		Ultramarine	1.75	1.25	30	3.00
G57	3d	**Violet** (18.3.35)	1.50	1.00	30	3.00
G57a		Reddish violet	1.50	1.00	30	4.00
G57b		Wmk. inverted			£2500	
G58	4d	**Deep grey green** (2.12.35)	2.00	1.25	30	1.25
G58a		Wmk. inverted			£2500	
G58b		Blackish green	£10	5.00	1.00	4.00
G59	5d	**Yellowish brown** (17.2.35)	6.00	3.50	50	2.00
G59a		Deep yellow brown	8.50	4.50	50	2.00
G60	9d	**Deep olive green** (2.12.35)	£11	7.00	60	2.50
G61	10d	**Turquoise blue** (24.2.36)	£17	8.50	5.50	£25
G62	1s	**Bistre brown** (24.2.36)	£19	9.00	50	2.00
		Set of 11 values	£50	£30	7.50	

1935 Wmk. Multiple Block Cypher inverted (ex booklets)

No.		Description	U/M	M/M	F/U	
G52a	½d	**Green**	£10	7.50	1.25	6.00
G53a	1d	**Scarlet**	£10	7.50	1.25	6.00
G54a	1½d	**Red brown**	2.00	1.75	50	2.00
		Set of 3 values	£20	£15	2.75	

1935 Wmk. Multiple Block Cypher sideways

No.		Description	U/M	M/M	F/U	
G52b	½d	**Green**	£10	7.00	2.00	£15
G53b	1d	**Scarlet**	£20	£12	4.50	£25
G54b	1½d	**Red brown**	9.00	6.00	2.50	£15
G55b	2d	**Orange**	£160	£65	£80	£250
		Set of 4	£180	£80	£85	

'SEAHORSES'

Guide Notes To Assist Identification

Four printings were made during this issue and major problems only arise when attempting to differentiate between the first Waterlow printing and the De La Rue issue.

The Bradbury Wilkinson printings were a different size to the others - the stamps being 22.5mm to 23mm in height against the 22mm of the other two printers. On many examples, they also printed a small coloured guide dot centred between the top frame line and the top of the stamp.

The second Waterlow printing was re-engraved, the most obvious difference being the crossed lines behind the King's head.

When sorting 'Seahorses' we suggest the following steps be taken:

> Step 1 Check for crossed lines behind the King's head, all stamps with this are Waterlow re-engraved.

> Step 2 Measure the height of the remaining stamps and all stamps measuring 22.5mm to 23mm are Bradbury Wilkinson.

All remaining stamps are either Waterlow or De La Rue. The following chart will help collectors to sort the first Waterlow and De La Rue printings.

	Waterlow	**De La Rue**
Gum	White, evenly applied.	Streaky and yellowish.
Perfs	Teeth, evenly spaced.	Upper teeth on both sides are wider than the rest. Holes are always smaller and undulating.
Colours		
2s6d	Sepia to deep sepia. Colours do not show through.	Yellow and brown shades. Colours often show through.
5s	Rose carmine shades. Colours do not show through.	Pale carmine * to deep carmine. Colour invariably shows through
10s	Indigo blue shades.	Pale blue * to deep blue.

* The pale shades on De La Rue were caused by plate wear and are quite distinct.

Waterlow
De La Rue
Bradbury Wilkinson

Waterlow
Re-engraved

Definitives
No.

Seahorses
U/M M/M F/U No

King George V
U/M M/M F/U

Royal Cypher Watermark

1913 (July) Wmk. Royal Cypher. Perf. 11 x 12
Printer: Waterlow Bros. & Layton

No.			U/M	M/M	F/U
G63	2s6d	Sepia brown	£350	£100	£80
G63a		Deep sepia brown	£350	£100	£80
G64	5s	Carmine red	£650	£230	£130
G64a		Rose carmine	£650	£230	£130
G64b		Pale rose carmine	£650	£230	£130
G65	10s	Indigo blue	£900	£400	£250
G65a		Indigo	£900	£400	£250
G66	£1	Dull blue green	£2750	£1800	£800
G66a		Green	£2750	£1800	£800
G66b		Deep green	£2750	£1800	£800
		Set of 4	£4500	£2400	£1250

1915 (Dec.) Wmk. Royal Cypher. Perf. 11 x 12
Printer: De La Rue & Co.

No.			U/M	M/M	F/U
G67	2s6d	Pale brown	£380	£170	£100
G67a		Pale brown (worn plate)	£380	£170	£100
G67b		Wmk. inverted	£1400	£850	£850
G67c		Wmk. reversed	£1400	£775	£850
G67d		Seal brown	£400	£250	£160
G67e		Wmk. inverted	£1400	£750	£650
G67f		Wmk. reversed	£1400	£675	£650
G67g		Grey brown	£400	£250	£100
G67h		Yellow brown	£400	£180	£100
G67i		Wmk. inverted	£1400	£750	£750
G67j		Wmk. reversed	£1400	£650	£650
G67k		Wmk. inverted and reversed	£3000	£2200	-
G67l		No watermark	£4000	-	-
G67m		Pale yellow brown	£380	£180	£100
G67n		Deep yellow brown	£380	£200	£100
G67o		Wmk. inverted	£1400	£650	£650
G67p		Wmk. reversed	£1400	£700	£750
G67q		Bright yellow brown	£400	£200	£110
G67r		Very deep brown	£1400	£900	£475
G67s		Wmk. inverted	£2400	£1300	£1300
G67t		Wmk. reversed	£1800	£1000	£750
G67u		Blackish brown	£1300	£800	£500
G67v		Cinnamon brown	£1400	£975	£500
G68	5s	Bright carmine	£700	£275	£180
G68a		Pale carmine (worn plate)	£700	£275	£180
G68b		Carmine	£700	£275	£180
G68c		Wmk. inverted	£2700	£1600	£1000
G68d		Wmk. reversed	£2700	£1600	£900
G68e		Wmk. inverted and reversed	£3200	£2000	£900
G68f		No watermark	£3200	£1600	£1400

No			U/M	M/M	F/U
G69	10s	Blue	£2200	£1200	£500
G69a		Wmk. inverted and reversed	-	-	-
G69b		Pale blue	£2200	£1200	£500
G69c		Deep blue	£2300	£1200	£600
G69d		Deep blue (worn plate)	£2300	£1200	£600
G69e		Deep bright blue	£3400	£2800	£1700
G69f		Bright Cambridge blue	£5500	£3000	£2500
		Set of 3	£3200	£1600	£750

1918 (Dec.) Wmk. Royal Cypher. Perf. 11 x 12
Printer: Bradbury Wilkinson & Co.

No			U/M	M/M	F/U
G70	2s6d	Olive brown	£250	£65	£30
G70a		Chocolate brown	£250	£65	£30
G70b		Pale brown	£250	£65	£35
G70c		Reddish brown	£280	£65	£35
G71	5s	Rose red	£350	£100	£35
G71a		Rose carmine	£300	£100	£35
G72	10s	Dull blue	£550	£200	£110
G72a		Dull grey blue	£550	£200	£110
		Set of 3	£950	£320	£160

1918 (Dec.) Re-engraved. Wmk. Royal Cypher. Perf. 11 x 12 Printer: Waterlow & Sons

No			U/M	M/M	F/U
G73	2s6d	Chocolate brown	£95	£45	£12
G73a		Reddish brown	£95	£55	£15
G74	5s	Bright rose red	£300	£100	£45
G75	10s	Indigo	£450	£180	£55
		Set of 3	£780	£300	£105

1924 (3 April) British Empire Exhibition 1924. Wmk. Multiple Block Cypher. Line perf. 14
Printer: Waterlow & Sons in Recess

No.			U/M	M/M	F/U	✉
G76	**1d**	**Scarlet**	5.00	3.00	3.50	7.00
G76a		Comb perf. 14	5.00	3.00	4.00	7.00
G77	**1½d**	**Brown**	£12	6.00	4.00	£12
G77a		Comb perf. 14	£12	7.00	6.50	£12
		Set of 2	£16	9.00	6.50	
		First Day Cover				£325

1925 (9 May) British Empire Exhibition 1925. Dated '1925'. Wmk. Multiple Block Cypher. Comb perf. 14
Printer: Waterlow & Sons in Recess

			U/M	M/M	F/U	✉
G78	**1d**	**Scarlet**	8.00	7.00	£10	£20
G79	**1½d**	**Brown**	£48	£20	£28	£65
		Set of 2	£46	£25	£35	
		First Day Cover				£1750

Large Royal Cypher
Watermark

1929 (10 May) Postal Union Congress, London 1929. Wmk. Multiple Block Cypher. Perf. 15 x 14
Printer: Waterlow & Sons in Typography

			U/M	M/M	F/U	✉
G80	**½d**	**Green**	1.00	50	25	30
G81	**1d**	**Scarlet**	1.80	1.00	65	1.50
G82	**1½d**	**Purple brown**	2.20	1.20	50	30
G83	**2½d**	**Blue**	£15	7.00	5.00	£15
G83b		Pale Blue	£20	£14	8.00	£18
		Set of 4	£18	8.50	6.00	
		First Day Cover				£380

Wmk. Large Royal Cypher. Perf. 12
Printer: Bradbury, Wilkinson & Co. in Recess

			U/M	M/M	F/U	✉
G84	**£1**	**Black**	£800	£500	£500	£1200
		First Day Cover				£8500

1929 Wmk. inverted

			U/M	M/M	F/U	✉
G80a	**½d**	**Green**	£17	8.00	6.00	£30
G81a	**1d**	**Scarlet**	£20	£10	£13	£30
G82a	**1½d**	**Purple brown**	£14	7.00	3.50	£15
G83a	**2½d**	**Blue**	£850	£550	£350	
G83c		Pale Blue	£2250	£1000	£600	
		Set of 3 (½d to 1½d)	£38	£22	£21	

1929 Wmk. sideways

			U/M	M/M	F/U	✉
G80b	**½d**	**Green**	£70	£35	£12	£100
G81b	**1d**	**Scarlet**	£70	£55	£50	£150
G82b	**1½d**	**Purple brown**	£50	£35	£20	£100
		Set of 3	£165	£95	£75	

1935 (7 May) Silver Jubilee. Wmk. Multiple Block Cypher. Perf. 15 x 14
Printer: Harrison & Sons in Photogravure

			U/M	M/M	F/U	✉
G85	**½d**	**Green.** Type I	40	5	15	10
G85b		Green. Type III	£6	5.00	5.00	8.00
G86	**1d**	**Scarlet.** Type I	80	30	50	40
G86b		Scarlet. Type III	£12	5.00	5.00	9.00
G87	**1½d**	**Red brown.** Type I	70	25	25	15
G87b		Red brown. Type III	1.20	1.00	50	5.00
G88	**2½d**	**Blue**	2.50	1.75	2.00	£10
G88		Prussian blue	£9000	£6500	£8000	
		Set of 4	4.00	2.00	£10	
		First Day Cover				£350

TYPE II. Wmk. Inverted

			U/M	M/M	F/U	✉
G85a	**½d**	**Green**	7.00	4.00	6.00	£12
G86a	**1d**	**Scarlet**	£13	6.00	6.00	£20
G87a	**1½d**	**Red brown**	1.25	50	50	7.00
		Set of 3	£20	£10	£12	

Silver Jubilee Types

There are three types of the ½d, 1d and 1½d values. The first type is from the sheet printing and the other two from booklets.

Type I	Ex sheets	Upright watermark
Type II	Ex booklet	All with watermark inverted
Type III	Ex booklet	Upright watermark

½d Type I

½d Type III

½d Type I - the 'FPE' of 'Halfpenny' is solid throughout whereas in Type III it is shaded at the bottom and solid at the top. The two lines underneath 'Halfpenny' are also noticeably thinner on the booklet printing.

1d Type I

1d Type III

1d Type I & Type III - are the most difficult to differentiate. Although the shading within the crown on the right is deeper in Type III, the easiest method of distinguishing Type III is to check the perforations to see if they have been cut straight on either the top or bottom, proving that they are from booklets.

½d Type I

1½d Type I

1½d Type I - the two lines above 'Silver Jubilee' are evenly printed whereas in Type III there is a definite thickening of the frame line above 'JU' of 'JUBILEE'.

King Edward VIII

Printer: Harrison and Sons

Multiple Crown E8R
Watermark

1936 (1 Sept) Wmk. Multiple Crown E8R. Perf. 15 x 14

No.	Value	Colour	U/M	M/M	F/U	✉
ED1	½d	Green	10	6	15	40
ED2	1d	Scarlet	14	7	15	40
ED3	1½d	Red brown	14	9	15	45
ED4	2½d	Bright blue	14	11	40	3.50
		Set of 4	40	27	50	

1936 Wmk. inverted

No.	Value	Colour	U/M	M/M	F/U	✉
ED1a	½d	Green	5.50	2.10	1.80	6.50
ED2a	1d	Scarlet	5.50	2.40	1.80	7.00
ED3a	1½d	Red brown	60	30	40	3.00
		Set of 3	9.50	4.40	4.00	

King George VI

Printer: Harrison & Sons in Photogravure

Multiple Crown GVIR
Watermark

1937 (10 May) Dark Colours. Wmk. Multiple Crown GVIR. Perf. 15 x 14

No.			U/M	M/M	F/U	▣
B1	½d	Green	10	5	20	15
B2	1d	Scarlet	10	5	20	15
B3	1½d	Red brown (30.7.37)	10	5	20	15
B3a		Imperf three sides (pair)				
B4	2d	Orange (31.1.38)	90	40	20	25
B5	2½d	Ultramarine	15	5	20	20
B5a		Tête-bêche (horiz pair)				

No			U/M	M/M	F/U	▣
B6	3d	Violet (31.1.38)	1.40	1.10	40	1.65
B7	4d	Grey green (21.11.38)	20	15	20	80
B7a		Imperf pair				
B7b		Imperf three sides (pair)				
B8	5d	Brown (21.11.38)	1.50	80	30	1.50
B8a		Imperf pair				
B8b		Imperf three sides (pair)				
B9	6d	Purple (30.1.39)	90	50	20	60
B10	7d	Emerald green (27.2.39)	2.50	1.40	60	1.25
B10a		Imperf three sides (pair)				
B11	8d	Carmine (27.2.39)	3.50	1.50	50	1.50
B12	9d	Olive green (1.5.39)	3.50	1.70	45	1.50
B13	10d	Turquoise blue (1.5.39)	3.00	1.70	45	1.50
B13a		Imperf (pair)				
B14	11d	Plum (29.12.47)	1.40	1.05	70	2.75
B15	1s	Bistre brown (1.5.39)	4.00	1.70	20	55
		Set of 15	£19	9.50	3.95	

1937 (Aug.) Wmk. inverted

			U/M	M/M	F/U	▣
B1a	½d	Green	5.00	2.00	30	2.50
B2a	1d	Scarlet	£24	6.00	1.40	£28
B3a	1½d	Red brown	9.00	2.20	30	3.50
B4a	2d	Orange (6.40)	£40	9.75	2.10	£35
B5a	2½d	Ultramarine (6.40)	£32	10.75	1.90	£28
		Set of 5	£115	£30	5.00	

1938 (Jan.) Wmk. sideways

			U/M	M/M	F/U	▣
B1b	½d	Green	40	15	25	3.00
B2b	1d	Scarlet (2.38)	13.50	5.50	3.85	£15
B3b	1½d	Red brown (2.38)	55	25	40	3.00
B4b	2d	Orange (2.38)	£27	£15	17.50	£55
B5b	2½d	Ultramarine (6.40)	£46	£15	£15	£65
		Set of 5	£82	£32	£30	

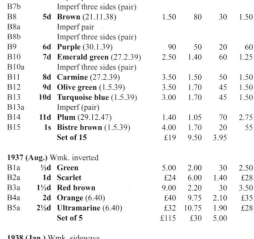

1941 (21 July) Pale colours Wmk. Multiple Crown GVIR. Perf. 15 x 14

			U/M	M/M	F/U	▣
B16	½d	Pale green (1.9.41)	10	5	10	15
B16a		Imperf (pair)				
B16b		Tête-bêche (horiz pair)				
B17	1d	Pale scarlet (11.8.41)	10	5	10	20
B17a		Imperf (pair)				
B17b		Imperf three sides (horiz. pair)				
B18	1½d	Pale red brown (28.9.42)	25	20	35	40
B19	2d	Pale orange (6.10.41)	20	15	20	40
B19a		Imperf (pair)				
B19b		Tête-bêche (horiz pair)				
B20	2½d	Light ultramarine (21.7.41)	10	5	10	30
B20a		Imperf (pair)	£2500			
B17b		Imperf three sides (horiz. pair)				
B17b		Tête-bêche (horiz pair)				
B21	3d	Pale violet (3.11.41)	70	45	20	75
		Set of 6	1.10	90	90	

No.   U/M   M/M   F/U   ✉   No   U/M   M/M   F/U   ✉

1942 (March) Wmk. inverted

No.			U/M	M/M	F/U	✉
B16a	½d	Pale green	2.00	1.00	30	3.00
B19a	2d	Pale orange	1.30	1.00	55	5.00
B20a	2½d	Light ultramarine	70	40	40	75
		Set of 3	3.30	2.00	1.00	

1942 (June) Wmk. sideways

B17a	1d	Pale scarlet (10.42)	1.90	1.15	1.40	8.50
B19a	2d	Pale orange (6.42)	9.00	6.25	6.75	£25
B20b	2½d	Light ultramarine ('42)	5.00	5.00	3.50	£28
		Set of 3	14.50	9.50	9.50	

1950 (2 Oct.) New colours. Wmk. Multiple Crown GVIR. Perf. 15 x 14

B22	½d	Pale orange (3.5.51)	15	10	10	15
B22a		Imperf (pair)				
B22b		Tête-bêche (horiz pair)				
B22b		Orange	20	10	10	15
B23	1d	Light ultramarine	15	10	10	15
B23a		Imperf (pair)				
B23b		Imperf three sides (horiz. pair)				
B24	1½d	Pale green	20	10	20	45
B25	2d	Pale red brown	30	15	20	45
B25a		Imperf three sides (horiz. pair)				
B25b		Tête-bêche (horiz pair)				
B25c		Bright red brown	60	25	25	60
B26	2½d	Scarlet	10	10	10	25
B26a		Tête-bêche (horiz pair)				
B27	4d	Light ultramarine	70	60	60	75
		Set of 6	1.10	75	1.00	

1951 (May). Wmk inverted

B22a	½d	Pale orange	10	8	18	75
B23a	1d	Light ultramarine (3.52)	1.75	90	50	4.00
B24a	1½d	Pale green (3.52)	2.00	80	1.50	4.50
B25a	2d	Pale red brown	3.20	2.50	2.50	5.50
B26a	2½d	Scarlet	65	30	35	3.00
		Set of 5	6.50	4.10	4.00	

1951 (3 May) Wmk. sideways

B23b	1d	Light ultramarine (5.51)	20	10	25	75
B24b	1½d	Pale green (14.9.51)	1.00	45	90	7.00
B25d	2d	Red brown (5.51)	25	15	65	5.00
B25d		Bright red brown	75	40	75	2.50
B26b	2½d	Scarlet	35	25	50	2.00
		Set of 4	1.40	95	2.00	

Large Crown GVIR Watermark

1939 (21 Aug.) - 48 Wmk. Large Crown GVIR. Perf.14
Printer: Waterlow & Sons in Recess

B28	2s6d	Brown (4.9.39)	£35	15.50	4.00	£18
B29	2s6d	Yellow green (9.3.42)	5.00	2.00	20	1.25
B30	5s	Red (21.8.39)	£12	5.50	75	3.00
B31	10s	Dark blue (30.10.39)	£190	£70	£14	£80
B31a		Steel blue	£200	£80	£20	£95
B32	10s	Ultramarine (30.11.42)	£20	9.50	3.50	£12
B33	£1	Brown (1.10.48)	7.50	8.50	9.50	£100
		Set of 6	£245	£82	£27	

1951 (3 May) 'Festival' issue. Wmk. Large Crown GVIR. Perf.11 x 12
Printer: Waterlow & Sons in Recess

B34	2s6d	Yellow green	5.00	2.50	40	90
B35	5s	Red	£11	5.50	1.00	4.00
B36	10s	Ultramarine	12.50	8.00	3.50	£25
B37	£1	Brown	£19	11.75	8.50	£75
		Set of 4	45	£24	9.50	

Printer: Harrison &Sons in Photogravure. Perf. 15 x 14 (except where shown)

Multiple Crown
GVIR Watermark

1937 (13 May) Coronation

			U/M	M/M	F/U	✉
B38	1½d	**Maroon**	18	10	15	40
		First Day Cover				£20

Cylinder control block of six - A37 2.50

1948 (26 April) Royal Silver Wedding (£1 Perf. 14 x 15)

			U/M	M/M	F/U	✉
B47	2½d	**Ultramarine**	10	5	10	10
B48	**£1**	**Blue**	£20	£14	£17	£35
		Set of 2	£20	£14	£17	£35
		First Day Cover				£275

1948 (10 May) Channel Islands Liberation

			U/M	M/M	F/U	✉
B49	1d	**Scarlet**	5	5	10	20
B50	2½d	**Ultramarine**	10	10	15	40
		Set of 2	11	12	25	
		First Day Cover (C. I. pmk)				£10

1940 (6 May) Centenary of First Adhesive Postage Stamps. Perf. 14½ x 14

			U/M	M/M	F/U	✉
B39	½d	**Green**	10	10	10	30
B40	1d	**Scarlet**	30	15	15	55
B41	1½d	**Red Brown**	25	15	35	1.00
B42	2d	**Orange**	35	25	40	60
B43	2½d	**Ultramarine**	1.10	45	35	40
B44	3d	**Violet**	1.60	1.00	1.30	£20
		Set of 6	2.60	2.00	2.30	
		First Day Cover				£25

1948 (29 July) Olympic Games

			U/M	M/M	F/U	✉
B51	2½d	**Ultramarine**	10	5	10	10
B52	3d	**Violet**	30	10	30	40
B53	6d	**Bright purple**	1.50	60	40	60
B54	1s	**Brown**	2.50	1.10	70	1.50
		Set of 4	4.00	1.60	1.00	
		First Day Cover				£40

Cylinder control block of six - G40

½d - 1.75	1d - 2.50	1½d - 3.50
2d - 2.00	2½d - 9.00	3d - £35

1946 (11 June) Victory

			U/M	M/M	F/U	✉
B45	2½d	**Ultramarine**	6	5	10	15
B46	3d	**Violet**	8	5	10	15
		Set of 2	15	10	15	
		First Day Cover				£40

Cylinder control block of six - S46

2½d - 90	3d - 1.00

1949 (10 Oct.) Universal Postal Union

No.			U/M	M/M	F/U	☒
B55	2½d	Ultramarine	5	5	10	30
B56	3d	Violet	15	8	22	40
B57	6d	Bright purple	25	15	40	60
B58	1s	Brown	70	30	70	1.50
		Set of 4	90	50	1.10	
		First Day Cover				£12

1951 (3 May) Festival of Britain

No.			U/M	M/M	F/U	☒
B59	2½d	Scarlet	10	5	10	20
B60	4d	Ultramarine	15	10	20	30
		Set of 2	20	13	30	
		First Day Cover				£8

Wilding Definitives

Queen Elizabeth II

Introductory Notes

Source

There can be a considerable difference in the scarcity of any single stamp just through its source. The source of each stamp can easily be identified by looking at the condition of the perforation on each side, which can be either cut or torn.

Guillotined perforations

Torn perforations with fibrous ends

On the illustrations below the arrows indicate guillotined <u>edges</u>

Sheet Stamps: These have torn perforations on all four sides

Horizontal and Sideways Coil Stamps: These have guillotined perforations on the top and bottom

Vertical Coil Stamps: These have guillotined perforations at the left and right

Stamps from coils made up from sheets (that is those coils which also include coil joins) have the sheet margins at the vertical sides of the sheets (in the case of vertical coils) or from the horizontal sides of the sheets (in the case of horizontal coils) removed by tearing. The result of this is that upright watermark coils stamps do exist with perforations on three edges torn and just one side guillotined.

Booklet Stamps from Panes of Two: These have top and bottom perforations guillotined are usually supplied with margin attached to distinguish them from Horizontal coil stamps.

Booklet Panes of Four: These have guillotined perforations on one side (left or right) or on two adjacent sides (bottom/left). Stamps with guillotined perforations on bottom/right adjacent two sides can be from booklet panes of four **or** six.

Booklet Stamps from Panes of Six: These have guillotined perforations on one side (top or bottom) or on two adjacent sides.

Pane of two   Pane of four   Pane of six

Identifying Photo/Typo/Flexo Phosphor Printing on
Queen Elizabeth II Wilding Definitives

'PHOTO'

Phosphor was applied by the photogravure printing process, for which the printing roller surface was 'photo-etched' with acid. The band printing area is composed of a multitude of diagonal screen lines (150 or 250 to the inch, set diagonally across the bands), and as they are photo-etched they are recessed into the cylinder surface, and are relatively shallow though deep enough to retain ink left from the inking roller; after inking excess ink is removed from the roller by the so-called 'doctor blade', leaving the ink in the screen lines, which is then applied to the stamps in the printing web.

As the 'photo.' screen is shallow there is no impression of 'tram-lines' left by the roller on the printed stamps. However, the portion of the plate which is not etched presses closely on the stamps and 'glazes' the portion of the stamp without phosphor, so this portion of the finished stamps appears slightly glossy when viewed at a very shallow angle to the light (in the manner adopted when looking at phosphor bands by the naked eye in daylight, but setting the stamp at the shallowest angle possible).

Careful examination of the 'photo.' phosphor band, by looking diagonally across the band at a very shallow angle to the light, will often make it possible to see the diagonal 'photo. screen' lines. However, these diagonal screen lines are not always obvious because they can become a little blurred or clogged with phosphor ink.

'Photo' phosphor bands are printed continuously, so the bands extend across the entire top & bottom margins. The bands at the side margins are the same width as in all other positions across the sheet.

As a rule Wilding Coil issues have 'photo.' printed phosphor, whereas other sources have phosphor printed by one of the other methods or by 'photo.' All Green Phosphor issues are printed with 'photo.' phosphor and can be examined as standards for the features mentioned above..

'TYPO'

Phosphor was applied by the typographic method, much like the familiar letterpress system, in which the (phosphor) ink is applied from the raised portions of the printing plate surface. The printing plate or roller is of metal, and so the edges of the bands are sharply defined.

The 'typo.' application of the phosphor normally leaves an impression of the roller on the stamp, presenting as 'tram-lines' down the stamp, visible on the reverse of the stamp coinciding with the edges of the phosphor band. The portion of the stamp between the phosphor displays a photonegative effect when viewed at a very shallow angle to the light (in the manner adopted when looking at phosphor bands by the naked eye in daylight, but setting the stamp at the shallowest angle possible).

Typically, sheet issues of the 'typo.' printed two band phosphor stamps show a narrow '6mm.' band down the marginal side of side marginal stamps. These are listed by Stanley Gibbons as 'narrow band at left' or 'narrow band at right' varieties on the Typo. issues. All Phosphor Graphite two band issues have 'typo.' printed phosphor bands, exhibiting the 'tram-lines' on reverse in many cases, showing the 'narrow band at left or right' on side marginal copies, and also exhibiting the photonegative effect to the ink printing between the phosphor bands as mentioned above. So the Phosphor-Graphite issues can be taken as the standard to examine the features of 'typo.' phosphor.

'Typo.' phosphor bands stop short in the top and bottom margins of the sheet, though sometimes this is not obvious because the margins are guillotined close to the stamps cutting within the ends of the phosphor bands. 'Typo.' phosphor printing was used on both sheet and on some booklet panes of four issues. Doubt has been cast on the use of Typo. printing for phosphor on se-tenant 1d./3d. panes

'FLEXO.'

Phosphor bands are applied using rubber rollers inked with metal cylinders on which the 'phosphor bands' are photo-etched. As a result there is no impression of the printing plate on the stamps (that is there are no tram-lines to be seen on the reverse). Also there are normally no 'screen lines', or at best just traces of them, to be found as described under 'Photo' (above), because the photo etching for the phosphor in the 'Flexo.' process is applied to the inking cylinder and not to printing cylinder. Differentiating between 'Photo.' and 'Flexo' printings cannot always be positive, but as a general rule 'Flexo.' Wilding issues are from booklets.

Controversy: there has been some debate over the incidence of Typo., Photo., or Flexo. printings of phosphor on some Wildings booklet issues in particular, resulting in an authoritative article and correspondence in the 'GB Journal' (published by the Great Britain Philatelic Society. In view of this the pages following do not include separate 'Typo.' or 'Flexo.' listings.

No.

U/M M/M F/U

All Wilding issues were printed by Harrison and Sons Ltd in Photogravure.

Watermark Tudor Crown Upright

No.			U/M	M/M	F/U
✓ **1952 (5 Dec.) Perf. 15 x 14**					
W1	½d	**Orange red** - Sheets (31.8.53)	10	5	20
W1a		Book pane BP75	25	15	20
W1b		Book pane BP76	75	45	
W1c		Book pane BP77	1.50	35	
W1d		Vertical coil	1.50	1.00	
W1e		Horizontal coil	1.50		
W2	1d	**Deep ultramarine** - Sheets (31.8.53)	18	8	20
W2a		Book pane BP78	2.50	1.50	
W2b		Book pane BP79	1.25	70	
W2c		Book pane BP80	1.50	85	
W2d		Book pane BP81	£75		
W2e		Book pane BP82	8.50	4.50	
W2f		Book pane BP83	8.50	4.50	
W2g		Vertical coil	4.00	2.40	
W2h		Horizontal coil	2.50	1.35	
W3	1½d	**Green** - sheets	10	5	20
W3a		Book pane BP84	25	15	
W3b		Book pane BP85	1.50	80	
W4	1½d	**Deep green** - sheets	25	12	
W4a		Book pane BP8	25	15	
W4b		Book pane BP85	1.00	60	
W4c		Book pane BP86	1.50	85	
W4d		Vertical coil	75	40	1.00
W5	2d	**Red brown** - Sheets (31.8.53)	12	8	20
W5a		Book pane BP87	4.50	2.40	
W5b		Vertical coil	3.00	1.50	
W6	2½d	**Carmine red** - Sheets. Type I	10	4	20
		Vertical coil	£15	7.00	
W7	2½d	**Carmine red.** Type II			
		Book pane BP88 (5.53)	50	30	60
W8	3d	**Deep violet** - Sheets (18.1.54)	0.90	50	25
W8a		Vertical coil			
W8b		Horizontal coil			
W9	4d	**Ultramarine** - Sheets (2.11.53)	2.00	1.00	50
W9a		Horizontal coil	5.50	2.90	
W10	5d	**Brown** - Sheets (6.7.53)	40	40	1.50
W11	6d	**Red purple** - Sheets (18.1.54)	2.50	1.10	40
W11a		Vertical coil	5.00	2.20	
W12	7d	**Pastel green** - Sheets (8.2.54)	5.00	2.20	2.00
W13	8d	**Cerise** - Sheets (6.7.53)	50	50	50
W14	9d	**Greyish green** - Sheets (8.2.54)	£13	4.00	2.00
W15	10d	**Deep blue** - Sheets (8.2.54)	8.50	3.50	2.00
W16	11d	**Plum** - Sheets (8.2.54)	£16	9.25	7.50
W17	1s	**Bistre brown** - Sheets (6.7.53)	50	42	45
W18	1s3d	**Deep green** - Sheets (2.11.53)	2.70	3.00	75
W19	1s6d	**Grey blue** - Sheets (2.11.53)	7.50	3.50	1.50

Watermark Tudor Crown Sideways

No.			U/M	M/M	F/U
1954 (8 Oct.) Wmk. Tudor Crown sideways					
W3s	1½d	**Green** - Sideways coil (15.10.54)	10	10	25
W5s	2d	**Red brown** - Sideways coil	40	20	50
W6s	2½d	**Carmine red** - Sideways coil 15.4.54)			
		Type 1	2.50	1.65	3.00

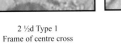

2 ½d Type 1
Frame of centre cross
is weak

2 ½d Type II
Frame of centre cross
strengthened

Watermark Tudor Crown Inverted

1954 (March). Wmk. Tudor Crown inverted

No.		U/M	M/M	F/U
W1i	½d **Orange red** - Book pane BP75a	45	25	35
W1ia	Book pane BP76a	75	40	
W2i	1d **Deep ultramarine** - Book pane BP78a	4.00	2.25	2.50
W2ia	Book pane BP79a	5.50	3.00	
W2ib	Book pane BP81a	£75	£50	
W2ic	Book pane BP82a	8.50	4.50	
W2id	Book pane BP83a	8.50	4.50	
W3i	1½d **Green** - Book pane BP84a	28	18	35
W3ia	Book pane BP85a	1.25	65	
W5i	2d **Red brown** - Book pane BP87a	£18	£11	9.00
W7i	2½d **Carmine red** - Book pane BP88a (Type II)	10	5	25

Coil join pairs

No.				
W1cj	½d **Orange red**	3.00		
W2cj	1d **Deep ultramarine**	6.00		
W8cj	3d **Deep violet**	12.50		
W8cja	3d **Deep violet** (vert.)	2.00		
W9cj	4d **Ultramarine**	£10		
W11cj	6d **Red purple** (vert.)	£10		

Watermark St. Edwards Crown Upright

1955 (Sept.) Wmk. St. Edward's Crown. Perf. 15 x 14

No.		U/M	M/M	F/U
W20	½d **Orange red** - Sheets	15	10	20
W20a	Book pane BP89	25	13	
W20b	Book pane BP90	75	40	
W20c	Book pane BP91	1.75	95	
W20d	Vertical coil	1.00	45	
W20e	Horizontal coil	1.00	45	
W21	1d **Deep ultramarine** - Sheets (19.9.55)	20	10	20
W21a	Book pane BP92	45	25	
W21b	Book pane BP93	1.00	55	
W21c	Book pane BP94	1.75	95	
W21d	Book pane BP95	4.50	2.50	
W21e	Vertical coil	3.50	1.80	
W21f	Horizontal coil	3.50	1.80	
W22	1½d **Green** - Sheets (9.55)	15	10	20
W22a	Book pane BP96	45	25	
W23	1½d **Deep green** -Sheets	35	20	10
W23a	Book pane BP96	35	20	
W23b	Book pane BP97	1.25	70	
W23c	Book pane BP98	1.75	90	
W23d	Vertical coil	2.50	1.30	

No.		U/M	M/M	F/U
W24	2d **Red brown** - Sheets (6.9.55)	20	10	20
W24a	Book pane BP99	5.00	2.60	
W24b	Vertical coil	3.00	1.30	
W25	2d **Light red brown** - Sheets (17.10.56)	20	10	20
W25a	Book pane BP100	2.50	1.30	
W25b	Vertical coil	3.50	1.80	
W26	2½d **Carmine red** (Type I) - Sheets (28.9.55)	20	10	20
W26a	Vertical coil	1.50	1.00	
W27	2½d **Carmine red** (Type II) - Sheets	30	15	35
W25a	Book pane BP101	20	15	
W28	3d **Deep violet** - Sheets (17.7.56)	20	15	20
W28a	Book pane BP102	65	35	
W28b	Book pane BP103	3.50	1.80	
W28c	Vertical coil			
W28d	Horizontal coil			
W29	4d **Ultramarine** - Sheets (14.11.55)	1.50	75	60
W29a	Vertical coil			
W29b	Horizontal coil	4.00	2.25	
W30	5d **Brown** - Sheets (21.9.55)	3.40	2.10	2.95
W31	6d **Red purple** - Sheets (20.12.55)	2.60	1.60	75
W31a	Vertical coil			
W32	6d **Deep claret** - Sheets (8.5.58)	3.00	2.00	1.00
W32a	Vertical coil			
W33	7d **Pastel green** - Sheets (23.4.56)	£27	£11	5.00
W34	8d **Cerise** - Sheets(21.12.55)	4.00	2.10	75
W35	9d **Greyish green** - Sheets (15.12.55)	£12	6.00	1.50
W36	10d **Deep blue** - Sheets (22.9.55)	£11	3.50	1.50
W37	11d **Plum** - Sheets (28.10.55)	20	15	60
W38	1s **Bistre brown** - Sheets (3.11.55)	£14	3.50	30
W39	1s3d **Deep green** - Sheets (27.3.56)	£13	6.00	75
W40	1s6d **Grey blue** - Sheets (27.3.56)	£12	6.00	65

Watermark St. Edwards Crown Inverted

1955 (Sept.) Wmk. St. Edward's Crown inverted

No.		U/M	M/M	F/U
W20i	½d **Orange red** - Book pane BP89a	10	5	15
W20ia	Book pane BP90a	45	30	
W21i	1d **Deep ultramarine** - Book pane BP92a	40	30	40
W21ia	Book pane BP93a	75	40	
W21ib	Book pane BP95a	4.50	2.50	
W22i	1½d **Green** - Book pane BP96a	15	10	20
W22ia	Book pane BP97a	75	40	
W24i	2d **Red brown** - Book pane BP99a	7.50	3.00	3.30
W25i	2d **Light red brown** - Book pane BP100a (1.57)	3.50	3.00	1.40
W27i	2½d **Carmine red** (Type II) - Book pane BP101a	20	15	30
W28i	3d **Deep violet** - Book pane BP102a (1.10.57)	1.50	30	50
W28ia	Book pane BP103a	3.50	1.80	

Watermark St. Edwards Crown Sideways

1956 (7 March) Wmk. St. Edward's Crown sideways

			U/M	M/M	F/U
W22s	1½d	**Green** - Sideways coil	15	10	25
W24s	2d	**Red brown** - Sideways coil (31.7.56)	20	10	35
W25s	2d	**Light red brown** - Sideways coil (5.3.57)	4.00	3.80	3.30
W27s	2½d	**Carmine red** (Type II) - Sideways coil (23.3.56)	60	40	75
W28s	3d	**Deep violet** - Sideways coil (9.12.57)	£11	4.80	6.50

Coil join pairs

W20cj	½d	**Orange red**	1.50	
W21cj	1d	**Deep ultramarine**	7.50	
W28cj	3d	**Deep violet**	£20	
W28cja		Deep violet (vert.)	£20	
W29cj	4d	**Ultramarine**	£10	
W29cja		Ultramarine (vert.)	£10	
W31cj	6d	**Red purple** (vert.)	£10	
W32cj	6d	**Deep claret** (vert.)	£10	

Graphite Lined Issue

This issue was introduced in the Southampton postal area, for the experimental use of an automatic letter facing machine.

1957 (19 Nov.) Graphite lined. Wmk. St. Edward's Crown. Perf. 15 x 14. Two vertical graphite lines on back under gum, except 2d value with one line only.

			U/M	M/M	F/U
W41	½d	**Orange red** - Sheets	25	10	25
W41a		Vertical coil	50	30	
W42	1d	**Deep ultramarine** - Sheets	30	15	30
W42a		Vertical coil	45	30	
W43	1½d	**Green** - Sheets	80	40	80
W43a		Horizontal coil	1.75	85	
W44	2d	**Light red brown** - Sheets	1.20	50	60
W44a		Vertical coil	4.75	2.55	
W44b		Horizontal coil	3.75	2.50	
W45	2½d	**Carmine red** (Type II) - Sheets	3.00	2.00	3.20
W45a		Horizontal coil	7.50	4.00	
W46	3d	**Deep violet** - Sheets	45	30	30
W46a		Horizontal coil	1.75	95	

Coil join pairs

W43cj	1½d	**Green**	7.50	
W44cj	2d	**Light red brown**	£10	
W44cja		Light red brown (vert.)	£10	
W45cj	2½d	**Carmine red.** Type II	£15	
W46cj	3d	**Deep violet**	8.00	

Multiple Crowns Watermark Upright
Cream Paper

1958 (28 Oct.) Wmk. Multiple Crowns. Cream paper. Perf. 15 x 14.

			U/M	M/M	F/U
W47	½d	**Orange red** - Sheets (25.11.58)	10	5	10
W47a		Book pane BP104	35	20	
W47b		Book pane BP105	1.00	65	
W47c		Vertical coil	35	20	
W47d		Horizontal coil	35	20	
W48	1d	**Deep ultramarine** - Sheets (11.58)	25	12	10
W48a		Book pane BP106	35	20	
W48b		Book pane BP107	1.00	65	
W48c		Vertical coil	2.00	1.20	
W488d		Horizontal coil			
W49	1½d	**Green** - Sheets (12.58)	20	14	15
W49a		Book pane BP108	75	40	
W49b		Book pane BP109	1.50	85	
W50	1½d	**Deep green** - Sheets	45	30	30
W50a		Book pane BP108	75	45	
W50b		Book pane BP109	1.00	65	
W50c		Vertical coil	1.50	85	
W51	2d	**Light red brown** - Sheets (4.12.58)	20	14	10
W51a		Book pane BP110	6.50	3.75	
W51b		Vertical coil	1.75	1.00	
W52	2½d	**Carmine red** (Type I) - Sheets (11.9.59)	2.50	1.65	1.00
W52a		Vertical coil			
W53	2½d	**Carmine red** (Type II) - Sheets (4.10.61)	30	20	15
W53a		Book pane BP111	1.75	85	65
W54	3d	**Deep violet** - Sheets (8.12.58)	15	10	15
W54a		Book pane BP112	40	25	
W54b		Book pane BP113	2.50	1.40	
W54c		Vertical coil	3.50	1.80	
W55	4d	**Ultramarine** - Sheets (29.10.58)	1.50	80	50
W55a		Vertical coil			
W55b		Horizontal coil	3.50	1.85	
W56	4½d	**Chestnut red** - Sheets (9.2.59)	50	30	30
W57	5d	**Brown** - Sheets (10.11.58)	2.50	1.45	45
W58	6d	**Claret** - Sheets (23.12.58)	90	50	20
W58a		Vertical coil	4.50	2.50	
W59	7d	**Pastel green** - Sheets (26.11.58)	1.65	85	50
W60	8d	**Cerise** - Sheets (24.2.59)	2.50	1.60	60
W61	9d	**Greyish green** - Sheets (24.3.59)	2.50	1.60	60
W62	10d	**Deep blue** - Sheets (17.6.59)	2.50	1.60	45
W63	1s	**Bistre brown** - Sheets (30.10.58)	1.85	1.00	35
W64	1s3d	**Deep green** - Sheets (17.6.59)	2.50	1.60	55
W65	1s6d	**Grey blue** - Sheets (16.12.58)	10.50	6.00	2.30
		Presentation pack 10s8d. (W35, W45/71) (1960)		£90	
		Presentation pack $1.80 (W35, W45/71) US Edition (1960)		£150	

No.   U/M   M/M   F/U   No.   U/M   M/M   F/U

Multiple Crowns Watermark Inverted
Cream Paper

1958 (Nov.) Wmk. Multiple Crowns inverted. Cream paper. Perf. 15 x 14

No.			U/M	M/M	F/U
W47i	½d	**Orange red** - Book pane BP104a	20	14	15
W47ia		Book pane BP105a	50	35	
W48i	1d	**Deep ultramarine** - Book pane BP106a	18	10	15
W48ia		Book pane BP107a	60	35	
W49i	1½d	**Green** - Book pane BP108a	60	40	30
W49ia		Book pane BP109a	1.50	1.00	
W51i	2d	**Light red brown** - Book pane BP110a (10.4.61)	£72	£40	£30
W53i	2½d	**Carmine red** (Type II) - Book pane BP112a	5.00	1.90	95
W54i	3d	**Deep violet** - Book pane BP112a	10	7	10
W51ia		Book pane BP113a	2.50	1.65	

Multiple Crowns Watermark Sideways Left
Cream Paper

1958 (24 Oct.) Wmk. Multiple Crowns. Cream paper. Watermark sideways - Crown to left

No.			U/M	M/M	F/U
W47sl	½d	**Orange red** - Book pane BP105b (26.5.61)	1.55	85	30
W48sl	1d	**Deep ultramarine** - Book pane BP107b (26.5.61)	1.55	85	35
W49sl	1½d	**Green** - Book pane BP109b (26.5.61)	4.50	2.50	1.70
W51sl	2d	**Light red brown** - Sideways coil (3.4.59)	1.00	65	50
W52sl	2½d	**Carmine red** (Type I) (10.11.60) Sideways coil	85	45	
W54sl	3d	**Deep violet** - Book pane BP113b	1.55	80	50
W54sla		Sideways coil	2.00	1.10	

Multiple Crowns Watermark Sideways Right
Cream Paper

1958 (24 Oct.) Wmk. Multiple Crowns. Cream paper. Watermark sideways - Crown to right

No.			U/M	M/M	F/U
W47sr	½d	**Orange red** - Book pane BP105c (26.5.61)	1.55	85	30
W48sr	1d	**Deep ultramarine** - Book pane BP107c (26.5.61)	1.55	85	35
W49sr	1½d	**Green** - Book pane BP109c (26.5.61)	4.50	2.50	1.70
W54sr	3d	**Deep violet** - Book pane BP113c	1.55	85	50

Coil join pairs

No.			U/M	M/M	F/U
W47cj	½d	**Orange red**		2.00	
W48cj	1d	**Deep ultramarine**		2.00	
W49cj	1½d	**Green**		2.00	
W49cja		Green (vert.)		2.00	
W55cj	4d	**Ultramarine**		£10	
W55cja		Ultramarine (vert.)		£10	
W58cj	6d	**Claret** (vert.)		£10	

Multiple Crowns Watermark Upright
Whiter Paper

Wmk. Multiple Crowns. Whiter paper. Perf. 15 x 14

No.			U/M	M/M	F/U
W66	½d	**Orange red** - Sheets	5	3	5
W66a		Book pane BP114	1.50	85	
W66b		Vertical coil	35	20	
W66c		Chalky paper - Book pane BP128	1.35	75	
W67	1d	**Deep ultramarine** - Sheets	6	4	5
W67a		Book pane BP117	55	30	
W67b		Vertical coil	40	25	
W67c		Horizontal coil	65	35	
W68	1½d	**Green** - Sheets	5	3	10
W68a		Book pane BP121	2.00	1.10	
W69	1½d	**Deep green** - Sheets	30	20	30
W69a		Book pane BP121	2.75	1.50	
W69b		Horizontal coil	75	45	
W70	2d	**Light red brown** - Sheets	5	3	5
W70a		Vertical coil	1.50	90	
W71	2½d	**Carmine red** (Type I) - Sheets	5.00	3.50	
W71a		Vertical coil	50	20	
W72	2½d	**Carmine red** (Type II) - Sheets	5	5	5
W72a		Book pane BP123	2.00	1.20	40
W72b		Chalky paper - Book pane BP129	12	7	
W73	3d	**Deep violet** - Sheets	5	3	10
W73a		Book pane BP124	35	20	
W73b		Vertical coil	1.50	85	
W74	4d	**Ultramarine** - Sheets	15	10	10
W74a		Vertical coil			
W74b		Horizontal coil			
W75	4d	**Deep ultramarine** - Sheets	12	7	5
W75a		Book pane BP126	60	35	
W75b		Vertical coil	95	55	
W76	4½d	**Chestnut red** - Sheets	10	5	15
W77	5d	**Brown** - Sheets	15	9	20
W78	6d	**Claret** - Sheets	15	9	10
W78a		Vertical coil	2.75	1.55	
W79	7d	**Pastel green** - Sheets	22	13	25
W80	8d	**Cerise** - Sheets	25	15	20
W81	9d	**Greyish green** - Sheets	25	15	30
W82	10d	**Deep blue** - Sheets	40	27	20
W83	1s	**Bistre brown** - Sheets	25	15	15
W84	1s3d	**Deep green** - Sheets	25	15	15
W85	1s6d	**Grey blue** - Sheets	2.75	1.50	25

Multiple Crowns Watermark Sideways Left
Whiter Paper

No.			U/M	M/M	F/U
W66sl	½d	**Orange red** - Book pane BP115	1.55	85	
W66sla		Book pane BP116	10	5	10
W67sl	1d	**Deep ultramarine** - Book pane BP118			
			1.55	85	1.25
W67sla		Book pane BP119-120	45	28	40
W68sl	1½d	**Green** - Book pane BP122	7.50	4.25	3.00
W70sl	2d	**Light red brown** - Sideways coil	30	17	25
W71sl	2½d	**Carmine red** (Type I) - Sideways coil	18	10	20
W72sl	2½d	**Carmine red** (Type II) - Book pane			
		BP116	35	20	45
W72sla		Sideways coil	2.90	1.60	
W73sl	3d	**Deep violet** - Book pane BP125	1.55	85	
W73sla		Book pane BP119-120	10	5	
W73slb		Sideways coil	45	25	40
W74sl	4d	**Ultramarine** - Book pane BP127	75	30	40
W74sla		Sideways coil	65	35	40

Multiple Crowns Watermark Sideways Right
Whiter Paper

No.			U/M	M/M	F/U
W66sr	½d	**Orange red** - Book pane BP115a	1.55	85	1.25
W66sra		Book pane BP116a	10	5	
W67sr	1d	**Deep ultramarine** - Book pane BP118a			
			1.55	85	1.25
W67sra		Book pane BP119a	45	25	
W68sr	1½d	**Green** - Book pane BP122a	7.50	4.00	3.00
W72sr	2½d	**Carmine red** (Type II) - Book pane			
		BP116a	35	20	45
W73sr	3d	**Deep violet** - Book pane BP125a	1.55	85	
W73sra		Book pane BP119a-BP120a	10	5	10
W74sr	4d	**Ultramarine** - Book pane BP127a	1.20	70	20

Multiple Crowns Watermark Inverted
Whiter Paper

No.			U/M	M/M	F/U
W66i	½d	**Orange red** - Book pane BP114a	55	30	20
W66ia		Chalky paper - Book pane BP128a	1.35	80	1.50
W67i	1d	**Deep ultramarine** - Book pane BP117a			
			45	25	40
W68i	1½d	**Green** - Book pane BP121a	1.95	1.00	40
W72i	2½d	**Carmine red** (Type II) - Book pane			
		BP123a	4.50	2.40	1.00
W72ia		Chalky paper BP129a	30	20	75
W73i	3d	**Deep violet** - Book pane BP124a	10	8	15
W74i	4d	**Ultramarine** - Book pane BP126a	1.20	70	35

Multiple Crowns Watermark
Graphite Lined

1958 (24 Nov.) Graphite lined. Wmk. Multiple Crowns. Perf. 15 x 14.
Two vertical graphite lines on back under gum, except 2d value with one line only.

No.			U/M	M/M	F/U
W86	½d	**Orange red** - Book pane BP130			
		(16.6.59)	7.50	4.50	8.00
W86a		Vertical coil	3.50	2.50	3.50
W87	1d	**Deep ultramarine** - Vertical coil			
		(18.12.58)	70	45	85
W87a		Bright ultramarine - Book pane			
		BP131	1.50	85	1.00
W87b		Two lines at left - Vertical coil	75	50	
W87c		Two lines at right - Vertical coil	75	50	
W87d		One line at left - Vertical coil	75	50	
W87e		One line at right - Vertical coil	75	50	
W87f		Three lines - Vertical coil	£15	8.50	
W88	1½d	**Green** - Book pane BP132 (4.8.59)	£56	£38	£48
W89	2d	**Light red brown** - Sheets	3.00	2.20	2.00
W89a		Vertical coil	10.50	6.00	
W90	2½d	**Carmine red** (Type II) - Sheets			
		(9.6.59)	5.00	2.80	4.50
W90a		Book pane BP133	7.50	5.00	
W91	3d	**Deep violet** - Sheets	25	10	25
W91a		Book pane BP134	40	25	
W91b		Vertical coil	7.50	5.00	
W91c		Horizontal coil			
W92	4d	**Ultramarine** - Sheets (29.4.59)	2.00	1.35	2.50
W93	4½d	**Chestnut** - Sheets (3.6.59)	3.50	1.90	2.70

Multiple Crowns Watermark Inverted
Graphite Lined

1959 (4 Aug.) Graphite Lined. Wmk. Multiple Crowns inverted

No.			U/M	M/M	F/U
W86i	½d	**Orange red** - Book pane BP130a	1.60	95	1.70
W86i	1d	**Deep ultramarine** - Book pane BP131a	80	40	40
W88i	1½d	**Green** * - Book pane BP132a	£18	£13	£14
W90i	2½d	**Carmine red** (Type II) - Book pane BP133a	£35	£20	£25
W91i	3d	**Deep violet** - Book pane BP134a	30	12	35

* These stamps are from booklets only and the prices quoted are for stamps with good perforations all round. Trimmed perf. examples can be purchased at a considerable discount.

Coil join pairs

W66cj	2d	**Light red brown** (vert.)	£12	
W68cj	3d	**Deep violet**	1.50	

Phosphor-Graphite
St. Edwards Crown Watermark

This further experimental issue was also introduced in the Southampton postal area, the phosphor bands serving the same purpose as the graphite lines to facilitate automatic letter facing.

1959 (18 Nov.) Phosphor and Graphite Lined. Wmk. St. Edward's Crown. Perf 15 x 14. Two phosphor bands on face and two graphite lines on back, except 2d value with 1 band and 1 graphite line.

			U/M	M/M	F/U
W94	½d	**Orange red** - Sheets	2.50	95	2.70
W94a		Narrow band left - Sheets	5.25		
W94b		Narrow band right	5.25		
W95	1d	**Deep ultramarine** - Sheets	7.00	3.50	7.50
W95a		Narrow band left - Sheets	£10		
W95b		Narrow band right - Sheets	£10		
W96	1½d	**Green** - Sheets	2.50	1.50	2.70
W96a		Narrow band left - Sheets	5.00		
W96b		Narrow band right - Sheets	5.00		

Phosphor-Graphite
Multiple Crowns Watermark

			U/M	M/M	F/U
W97	2d	**Light red brown** - Sheets	2.50	1.70	2.50
W98	2½d	**Carmine red** (Type II) - Sheets	£10	6.00	8.00
W98a		Narrow band left - Sheets	18.50		
W98b		Narrow band right - Sheets	18.50		
W99	3d	**Deep violet** - Sheets	4.75	3.25	4.50
W99a		Narrow band left - Sheets	£13		
W99b		Narrow band right - Sheets	£13		
W100	4d	**Ultramarine** - Sheets	£10	5.00	£9
W100a		Narrow band left - Sheets	17.50		
W100b		Narrow band right - Sheets	17.50		
W101	4½d	**Chestnut** - Sheets	£14	£9	8.00
W101a		Narrow band left - Sheets	£40		
W101b		Narrow band right - Sheets	£40		
		Presentation pack 3s8d (W71/78 each x 2) (1960)	£150		
		Presentation pack 50c (W71/78 each x 2) US Edition (1960)	£300		
Variety					
W97a	2d	**Light red brown**. Error. Wmk. St. Edward's Crown.	£90	£50	£60
W98a	2½d	**Carmine red**. Error. Wmk. St. Edward's Crown.*	£2000	-	-

* This was not officially issued

Multiple Crowns Watermark
Green Phosphor

1960 (22 June) Phosphor issue. Wmk. Multiple Crowns. Perf. 15 x 14. Two phosphor bands on face, except where otherwise stated.

			U/M	M/M	F/U
W102	½d	**Orange red** - Sheets	1.00	60	75
W102a		Book pane BP135	1.25	70	
W102b		Vertical coil	2.50	1.40	
W103	1d	**Deep ultramarine** - Sheets	1.00	60	75
W103a		Book pane BP136	1.50	1.00	
W103b		Vertical coil	2.50	1.50	
W104	1½d	**Green** - Sheets	1.25	75	80
W104a		Book pane BP137	2.75	1.50	
W105	2d	**Light red brown** - Left band - Sheets	8.25	4.75	
W105a		Left band - Vertical coil	£20	£12	£18
W106	2½d	**Carmine red** (Type II) - Sheets	1.50	1.00	1.20
W106a		Book pane BP138	7.50	4.50	
W107	3d	**Deep violet** - Sheets	1.00	65	75
W107a		Book pane BP139	1.25	70	
W108	4d	**Ultramarine**	5.75	3.00	4.50
W109	6d	**Claret** - Sheets	2.75	1.50	2.50
W110	1s 3d	**Deep green** - Sheets	6.50	3.50	3.50

Multiple Crowns Watermark Inverted
Green Phosphor

No.		Description	U/M	M/M	F/U
W102i	½d	**Orange red** - Book pane BP135a	5.00	2.70	3.75
W103i	1d	**Deep ultramarine** - Book pane BP136a	5.00	2.70	3.75
W104i	1½d	**Green** - Book pane BP137a	£10	6.00	5.00
W106i	2½d	**Carmine red** (Type II) - Book pane BP138a	£115	£65	£60
W107i	3d	**Deep violet** - Book pane BP139a	75	45	50

Multiple Crowns Watermark
Blue Phosphor - Cream Paper

No.		Description	U/M	M/M	F/U
W111	½d	**Orange red** - Sheets	20	12	10
W111a		Book pane BP140	65	35	
W111b		Vertical coil	1.50	85	
W112	1d	**Deep ultramarine** - Sheets	75	40	40
W112a		Book pane BP142	1.00	60	
W112b		Vertical coil	1.75	95	
W113	1½d	**Green** - Sheets	50	25	40
W113a		Book pane BP144	1.75	90	
W114	2d	**LB Light red brown** (Photo) - Sheets	£20	£13	£18
W114a		Vertical coil	£30	£16	
W115	2d	**2B Light red brown** (Typo) - Sheets	5.00	2.70	2.50
W115a		Narrow band left - Sheets (Typo)	10.50		
W115b		Narrow band left - Sheets (Typo)	10.50		
W115c		(Photo) - Sheets	1.20	70	
W115d		(Photo) - Vertical coil			
W116	2½d	**2B Carmine red** (Type II) (Photo) - Sheets	3.50	2.00	1.50
W116a		Book pane BP146	7.50	4.00	
W117	2½d	**LB Carmine red** (Type II) (Typo) - Sheets	2.00	1.30	2.00
W117a		(Photo) - Sheets	5.00	2.80	
W117b		Book pane BP147	7.50	4.00	
W118	2½d	**LB Carmine red** (Type I) (Typo) - Sheets	23.50	£15	£21
W119	3d	**Deep violet** - Sheets	1.00	60	80
W119a		Book pane BP148	65	35	
W119b		Vertical coil	3.00	1.60	
W120	4d	**Ultramarine** - Sheets	1.85	90	1.30
W121	4½d	**Chestnut** (Typo) - Sheets	2.75	1.50	1.25
W121a		Narrow band left (Typo) - Sheets	8.50		
W121b		Narrow band right (Typo) - Sheets	8.50		
W121c		(Photo) - Sheets	15.00	8.25	7.00
W122	6d	**Claret** (Typo) - Sheets	£300		
W122a		Narrow band left (Typo) - Sheets			
W122b		Narrow band right (typo) - Sheets			
W122c		(Photo) - Sheets	4.00	2.00	2.00
W123	1s 3d	**Deep green** - Sheets	£20	£12	6.50

Multiple Crowns Watermark Sideways Left
Blue Phosphor - Cream Paper

No.		Description	U/M	M/M	F/U
W111sl	½d	**Orange red** - Book pane BP141	6.50	4.00	6.00
W112sl	1d	**Deep ultramarine** - Book pane BP143	3.00	1.60	2.00
W113sl	1½d	**Green** - Book pane BP145	6.50	3.50	6.00
W119sl	3d	**Deep violet** - Book pane BP149	3.50	1.80	1.50

Multiple Crowns Watermark Sideways Right
Blue Phosphor - Cream Paper

No.		Description	U/M	M/M	F/U
W111sr	½d	**Orange red** - Book pane BP141a	6.50	4.00	6.00
W112sr	1d	**Deep ultramarine** - Book pane BP143a	3.00	1.60	2.00
W113sr	1½d	**Green** - Book pane BP145a	6.50	3.50	6.00
W119sr	3d	**Deep violet** - Book pane BP149a	3.50	1.80	1.50

Multiple Crowns Watermark Inverted
Blue Phosphor - Cream Paper

No.		Description	U/M	M/M	F/U
W111i	½d	**Orange red** - Book pane BP140a	55	30	65
W112i	1d	**Deep ultramarine** - Book pane BP142a	75	45	50
W113i	1½d	**Green** - Book pane BP144a	9.00	5.25	5.25
W116i	2½d	**2B Carmine red** (Type II) - Book pane BP146a	£125	£70	£75
W117i	2½d	**LB Carmine red** (Type II) - Book pane BP147a	£30	£15	£12
W119i	3d	**Deep violet** - Book pane BP148a	50	30	50

Multiple Crowns Watermark
Blue Phosphor - Whiter Paper

No.		U/M	M/M	F/U
W124	½d **Orange red** - Sheets	10	5	10
W124a	Book pane BP150	2.00	1.20	
W124b	Vertical coil	75	45	
W125	1d **Deep ultramarine** - Sheets	85	45	50
W125a	Book pane BP152	1.25	70	
W125b	Vertical coil	1.25	70	
W126	1½d **Green** - Sheets	12	7	20
W126a	Book pane BP156	5.50	3.00	
W127	2d **2B Light red brown** - Sheets	6.00	3.50	5.00
W127a	Vertical coil	£10	6.50	
W128	2½d **2B Carmine red** (Type II)			
	Photo - Sheets	30		35
W128a	Typo - Sheets	£850		
W128b	Narrow band left (Typo) - Sheets			
W128c	Narrow band right (Typo) - Sheets	£1250		
W129	2½d **LB Carmine red** (Type II)			
	Typo - Sheets	£175		
W129a	Photo - Sheets	30	17	60
W129b	Photo - Book pane BP158	4.50	2.50	
W130	3d **2B Deep violet** - Sheets	40	25	35
W130a	Book pane BP159	1.00	60	
W130b	Vertical coil	3.50	2.25	
W131	3d **LB Deep violet** - Sheets	2.25	1.30	2.00
W131a	Vertical coil	4.50	2.70	
W132	3d **RB Deep violet** - Sheets	2.25	1.35	2.00
W132a	Vertical coil	5.50	3.00	
W133	4d **Deep ultramarine** - Sheets	65	35	45
W133a	Book pane BP161	1.50	85	
W134	4½d **Chestnut** (Typo) - Sheets	1.75	95	65
W134a	Narrow band left (Typo) - Sheets	5.00		
W134b	Narrow band right (Typo) - Sheets	5.00		
W134c	(Photo) - Sheets	10	5	
W135	6d **Claret** (Typo) - Sheets	£285		
W135a	Narrow band left (Typo) - Sheets			
W135b	Narrow band left (Typo) - Sheets			
W135c	(Photo) - Sheets	50	35	45
W136	1s 3d **Deep green** - Sheets	2.00	50	1.10

Multiple Crowns Watermark Sideways Left
Blue Phosphor - Whiter Paper

No.		U/M	M/M	F/U
W124sl	½d **Orange red** - Book pane BP151	8.00	5.00	8.00
W125sl	1d **Deep ultramarine** -			
	Book pane BP153 (matt surface)	3.00	1.60	1.75
W125sla	Book pane BP154/BP155			
	(glossy surface)	3.00	1.60	1.75
W126sl	1½d **Green** - Book pane BP157	8.00	5.00	8.00
W130sl	3d **2B Deep violet** - Book pane BP160	3.50	1.90	1.50
W131sl	3d **LB Deep violet** - Book pane BP154	£25	£14	£17
W132sl	3d **RB Deep violet** - Book pane BP155	£25	£14	£17
W133sl	4d **Deep ultramarine** - Book pane BP162			
		2.00	1.20	1.50

Multiple Crowns Watermark Sideways Right
Blue Phosphor - Whiter Paper

No.		U/M	M/M	F/U
W124sr	½d **Orange red** - Book pane BP151a	7.50	4.20	7.00
W125sr	1d **Deep ultramarine** - Book pane			
	BP1533a (matt surface)	2.75	1.50	1.50
W125sra	Book pane BP154a/ BP155a			
	(glossy surface)	2.75	1.50	1.50
W126sr	1½d **Green** - Book pane BP157a	7.50	4.00	7.00
W130sr	3d **2B Deep violet** - Book pane BP160a	3.50	1.90	1.40
W131sr	3d **LB Deep violet** - Book pane BP154a	£25	£15	£20
W132sr	3d **RB Deep violet** - Book pane BP155a	£25	£15	£20
W133sr	4d **Deep ultramarine** - Book pane BP162a			
		2.00	1.20	1.50

Multiple Crowns Watermark Inverted
Blue Phosphor - Whiter Paper

No.		U/M	M/M	F/U
W124i	½d **Orange red** - Book pane BP150a	1.25	70	75
W125i	1d **Deep ultramarine** - Book pane BP152a			
		75	40	50
W126i	1½d **Green** - Book pane BP156a	£25	£14	£11
W129i	2½d **LB Carmine red** (Type II) - Book pane			
	BP158a	£30	£15	£14
W130i	3d **Deep violet** - Book pane BP159a	25	15	30
W133i	4d **Deep ultramarine** - Book pane BP161a	1.25	70	55

Multiple Crowns Watermark
Violet Phosphor - 8mm Bands

— 13mm —

No.		U/M	M/M	F/U
W137	½d **Orange red** (Typo) - Sheets	35	20	18
W137a	Narrow band left (Typo) - Sheets	3.50		
W137b	Narrow band right (Typo) - Sheets	3.50		
W137c	(Photo) - Vertical coil	1.00	45	40
W138	1d **Deep ultramarine** (Typo) - Sheets	17.50	9.00	£7
W138a	Narrow band left (Typo) - Sheets	£70		
W138b	Narrow band right (Typo) - Sheets	£70		
W138c	(Photo) - Sheets	45	25	25
W138d	Book pane BP163	2.00	1.20	
W138e	Vertical coil	1.25	70	
W139	1½d **Green** - Sheets	90	50	75
W139a	Narrow band left (Typo) - Sheets	4.25		
W139b	Narrow band right (Typo) - Sheets	4.25		
W140	2d **2B Light red brown** - Sheets	80	50	35
W140a	Vertical coil			

Wilding Definitives

No.			U/M	M/M	F/U
W141	**3d LB Deep violet** - Sheets		35	20	45
W141a	Book pane BP166		6.50	3.60	
W141b	Vertical coil		4.00	1.90	
W142	**3d RB Deep violet** - Sheets		35	25	50
W142a	Book pane BP166		1.25	70	
W142b	Vertical coil		4.00	1.90	
W143	**4d Deep ultramarine** - Sheets		50	30	40
W143a	Book pane BP167		1.00	60	
W144	**6d Claret** (Typo) - Sheets		7.50	4.00	5.00
W144a	Narrow band left (Typo) - Sheets		£20		
W144b	Narrow band right (Typo) - Sheets		£20		
W145	**1s 3d Deep green** (Typo) - Sheets		£15	8.00	6.50
W145a	Narrow band left (Typo) - Sheets		£30		
W145b	Narrow band right (Typo) - Sheets		£30		
W145c	(Photo) - Sheets		6.00	3.50	3.50

Multiple Crowns Watermark Sideways Left
Violet Phosphor - 8mm Bands

 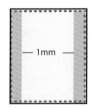

No.			U/M	M/M	F/U
W138sl	**1d Deep ultramarine** - Book pane				
	BP164-BP165		1.25	70	75
W141sl	**3d LB Deep violet** - Book pane BP164		2.75	1.85	2.40
W142sl	**3d RB Deep violet** - Book pane BP165		2.75	1.85	2.40
W143sl	**4d Deep ultramarine** (Photo)				
	Book pane BP168		60	35	40
W143sla	(Typo) - Book pane BP168b		£10	6.50	£10

Multiple Crowns Watermark Sideways Right
Violet Phosphor - 8mm Bands

 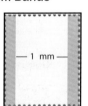

No.			U/M	M/M	F/U
W138sr	**1d Deep ultramarine** - Book pane				
	BP164a-BP165a		1.25	70	75
W141sr	**3d LB Deep violet** - Book pane BP164a		2.75	1.85	2.40
W142sr	**3d RB Deep violet** - Book pane BP165a		2.75	1.85	2.40
W143sr	**4d Deep ultramarine** (Photo) -				
	Book pane BP168a		60	35	40
W143sra	(Typo) - Book pane BP110c		£10	6.50	£10

Multiple Crowns Watermark Inverted
Violet Phosphor - 8mm Bands

 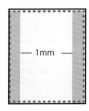

Queen Elizabeth II

No.			U/M	M/M	F/U
W138i	**1d Deep ultramarine** - Book pane				
	BP163a		75	40	25
W141i	**3d LB Deep violet** - Book pane BP166a		£35	£23	£35
W142i	**3d RB Deep violet** - Book pane BP166a		3.75	1.90	1.75
W143i	**4d Deep ultramarine** - Book pane BP167a				
			35	20	25

Multiple Crowns Watermark
Violet Phosphor - 9.5mm Bands

No.			U/M	M/M	F/U
W146	**1d Deep ultramarine** - Sheets		10	5	5
W146a	Book pane BP169		50	30	
W146b	Vertical coil		1.00	60	
W147	**2d 2B Light red brown** - Sheets		10	5	5
W147a	Vertical coil		75	45	
W148	**3d CB Deep violet** - Sheets		25	15	20
W148a	Book pane BP172		75	40	
W148b	Vertical coil				
W150	**4d Deep ultramarine** - Sheets		10	5	8
W150a	Book pane BP173		30	18	
W151	**5d Brown** - Sheets		12	8	10
W152	**6d Claret** - Sheets		15	12	10
W152a	Vertical coil		2.50	1.85	
W153	**7d Pastel green** - Sheets		25	13	10
W154	**8d Cerise** - Sheets		25	13	15
W155	**9d Greyish green** - Sheets		30	18	15
W156	**10d Deep blue** - Sheets		30	18	15
W157	**1s Bistre brown** - Sheets		25	15	15
W158	**1s3d Deep green** - Sheets		6.50	3.75	2.00
W159	**1s6d Grey blue** - Sheets		1.35	85	40

Multiple Crowns Watermark Sideways Left
Violet Phosphor - 9.5mm Bands

Violet Phosphor - 9.5mm Band Crown to Left

No.			U/M	M/M	F/U
W146sl	**1d Deep ultramarine** - Book panes				
	BP170-BP171		25	14	20
W147sl	**2d 2B Light red brown** - Sideways coil		18	10	35
W148sl	**3d CB Deep violet** - Sideways coil		40	25	70
W149sl	**3d 2B Deep violet** - Book panes				
	BP170-BP171		65	40	65
W150sl	**4d Deep ultramarine** - Sideways coil		35	19	25
W150sla	Book pane BP174		15	8	10

Multiple Crowns Watermark Sideways Right
Violet Phosphor - 9.5mm Bands

—11.5mm—

			U/M	M/M	F/U
W146sr	**1d Deep ultramarine** - Book pane BP170a-BP171a		25	13	20
W149sr	**3d 2B Deep violet** - Book pane BP170a-BP171a		65	40	65
W150sr	**4d Deep ultramarine** - Book pane BP174a		15	8	**10**

Multiple Crowns Watermark Inverted
Violet Phosphor - 9.5mm Bands

—11.5mm—

			U/M	M/M	F/U
W146i	**1d Deep ultramarine** - Book pane BP169a		20	12	20
W148i	**3d CB Deep violet** - Book pane BP172a	1.90	1.25	1.90
W150i	**4d Deep ultramarine** - Book pane BP173a		15	10	12

Coil Strips of Five

Watermark Tudor Crown Upright

				U/M
WCS1	½d	**Orange red**	Vertical	5.00
WCS1a	½d	**Orange red**	Horizontal	7.50
WCS2	1d	**Ultramarine**	Vertical	£25
WCS2a	1d	**Ultramarine**	Horizontal	£15
WCS3	1½d	**Green**	Vertical	7.50
WCS4	2d	**Red brown**	Vertical	£12
WCS5	3d	**Deep violet**	Vertical	
WCS5a	3d	**Deep violet**	Horizontal	
WCS6	4d	**Deep Ultramarine**	Horizontal	£25
WCS	6d	**Red purple**	Vertical	

Watermark Tudor Crown Sideways

				U/M
WCS7	1½d	**Green**	Sideways	90
WCS8	2d	**Red brown**	Sideways	1.80
WCS9	2½d	**Carmine-red** Type II	Sideways	13.75

Watermark St. Edwards Crown Upright

				U/M
WCS10	½d	**Orange red**	Vertical	5.00
WCS10a	½d	**Orange red**	Horizontal	5.00
WCS11	1d	**Ultramarine**	Vertical	£15
WCS11a	1d	**Ultramarine**	Horizontal	£15
WCS12	1½d	**Green**	Vertical	£15
WCS13	2d	**Red brown**	Vertical	£15
WCS13a	2d	**Light Red brown**	Vertical	£20
WCS14	2½d	**Carmine-red** Type II	Vertical	£10
WCS15	3d	**Deep violet**	Vertical	
WCS	3d	**Deep violet**	Horizontal	
WCS16	4d	**Deep Ultramarine**	Vertical	
WCS16a	4d	**Deep Ultramarine**	Horizontal	£25
WCS17	6d	**Red purple**	Vertical	
WCS17a	6d	**Deep Claret**	Vertical	

Watermark St. Edwards Crown Sideways

				U/M
WCS18	1½d	**Green**	Sideways	2.00
WCS19	2d	**Red brown**	Sideways	2.00
WCS19a	2d	**Light red-brown**	Sideways	15.50
WCS20	2½d	**Carmine-red** Type I	Sideways	2.40
WCS21	3d	**Deep violet**	Sideways	£32

Watermark St. Edwards Crown
Graphite Lined Issue

				U/M
WCS22	½d	**Orange red**	Vertical	1.50
WCS23	1d	**Ultramarine**	Vertical	2.70
WCS24	1½d	**Green**	Horizontal	5.00
WCS25	2d	**Light Red brown**	Vertical	£16
WCS25a	2d	**Light Red brown**	Horizontal	22.50
WCS26	2½d	**Carmine-red**	Horizontal	32.50
WCS27	3d	**Deep violet**	Horizontal	6.00

Multiple Crowns Watermark Upright
Cream Paper

				U/M
WCS28	½d	**Orange red**	Vertical	3.00
WCS28a	½d	**Orange red**	Horizontal	3.00
WCS29	1d	**Ultramarine**	Vertical	4.00
WCS29a	1d	**Ultramarine**	Horizontal	4.50
WCS30	1½d	**Green**	Vertical	6.00
WCS31	2d	**Light Red brown**	Vertical	£1
WCS32	2½d	**Carmine-red** Type I	Sideways	
WCS33	3d	**Deep violet**	Vertical	£1
WCS34	4d	**Deep Ultramarine**	Vertical	
WCS34a	4d	**Deep Ultramarine**	Horizontal	£2
WCS35	6d	**Red purple**	Vertical	£2

Wilding Definitives

Multiple Crowns Watermark Sideways Left
Cream Paper

WCS36	2d Light Red brown	Sideways	3.00
WCS37	2½d Carmine-red Type I	Sideways	2.50
WCS38	3d Ultramarine	Sideways	6.00

Multiple Crowns Watermark Upright
Whiter Paper

WCS39	½d Orange red	Vertical	3.00
WCS40	1d Ultramarine	Vertical	3.00
WCS41	1d Ultramarine	Horizontal	3.00
WCS42	1½d Green	Horizontal	5.00
WCS43	2d Light Red brown	Vertical	9.00
WCS44	2½d Carmine-red Type I	Vertical	3.00
WCS45	3d Deep violet	Vertical	5.00
WCS46	4d Deep Ultramarine	Vertical	
WCS47	6d Deep claret	Vertical	8.75

Multiple Crowns Watermark Sideways Left
Whiter Paper

WCS48	2d Light Red brown	Sideways	40
WCS49	2½d Carmine-red Type I	Sideways	50
WCS49a	2½d Carmine-red Type II	Sideways	£10
WCS50	3d Deep violet	Sideways	1.25
WCS51	4d Deep ultramarine	Sideways	3.00

Multiple Crowns Watermark
Graphite Lined

Displaced graphite lines as viewed from the back of the stamps.

WCS52	½d Orange red	Vertical	32.50
WCS53	1d Ultramarine	Vertical	3.25
WCS53a	1d Ultramarine - 2 lines at left	Vertical	3.00
WCS53b	1d Ultramarine - 2 lines at right	Vertical	3.00
WCS53c	1d Ultramarine - 1 line at left	Vertical	3.00
WCS53c	1d Ultramarine - 1 line at right	Vertical	£70
WCS53d	1d Ultramarine - 3 lines	Vertical	£20
WCS54	2d Light Red brown	Vertical	
WCS55	3d Deep violet	Vertical	£60
WCS55	3d Deep violet	Horizontal	

Multiple Crowns Watermark
Green Phosphor

WCS56	½d Orange red	Vertical	£15
WCS57	1d Ultramarine	Vertical	£15
WCS58	2d LB Light Red brown	Vertical	£90

Coil Strips

Queen Elizabeth II

Multiple Crowns Watermark
Blue Phosphor - Cream Paper

WCS59	½d Orange red	Vertical	6.00
WCS60	1d Ultramarine	Vertical	7.50
WCS61	2d 2B Light Red brown	Vertical	
WCS61	2d LB Light Red brown	Vertical	£100
WCS62	3d Deep violet	Vertical	12.50

Multiple Crowns Watermark
Blue Phosphor - Whiter Paper

WCS63	½d Orange red	Vertical	5.00
WCS64	1d Ultramarine	Vertical	5.00
WCS65	2d 2B Light Red brown	Vertical	£50
WCS66	3d 2B Deep violet	Vertical	£14
WCS66a	3d LB Deep violet	Vertical	£25
WCS66b	3d RB Deep violet	Vertical	£25

Multiple Crowns Watermark
Violet Phosphor - 8mm Bands

WCS67	½d Orange red (photo)	Vertical	3.00
WCS68	1d Ultramarine (photo)	Vertical	£10
WCS69	2d 2B Light Red brown	Vertical	
WCS70	3d LB Deep violet	Vertical	£20
WCS70a	3d RB Deep violet	Vertical	20.00

Multiple Crowns Watermark
Violet Phosphor - 9.5mm Bands

WCS71	1d Ultramarine	Vertical	3.00
WCS72	2d Light Red brown	Vertical	5.00
WCS73	3d CB Deep violet	Vertical	
WCS74	6d Claret	Vertical	£15
WCS74a	6d Claret, cream paper	Vertical	

Multiple Crowns Watermark Sideways Left
Violet Phosphor - 9.5mm Bands

WCS75	2d Light Red brown	Sideways	1.50
WCS76	3d CB Deep violet	Sideways	2.00
WCS77	4d Ultramarine	Sideways	1.50

Wilding Definitives
No.   U/M

Coil Joins
No.   U/M

Queen Elizabeth II
                                             U/M

Coil Joins

Please note that (2) or (4) indicated length of strip - two stamps or four - with the join at the centre.

Watermark Tudor Crown Upright

WCJ1	½d **Orange red (2)**	Horizontal	2.00
WCJ2	1d **Ultramarine (2)**	Horizontal	7.50
WCJ8	3d **Deep violet**	Vertical	
WCJ8a	3d **Deep violet**	Horizontal	
WCJ9	4d **Deep Ultramarine (2)**	Horizontal	£15
WCJ11	6d **Red purple**	Vertical	

Watermark St. Edwards Crown Upright

WCJ20	½d **Orange red (4)**	Horizontal	2.00
WCJ21	1d **Ultramarine (4)**	Horizontal	17.50
WCJ28	3d **Deep violet (4)**	Horizontal	17.50
WCJ29	4d **Deep Ultramarine (4)**	Horizontal	£20
WCJ31	6d **Red purple (2)**	Vertical	12.50
WCJ32	6d **Deep Claret (2)**	Vertical	**9.50**

Watermark St. Edwards Crown Graphite Lined Issue

WCJ43	1½d **Green (4)**	Horizontal	8.75
WCJ44	2d **Light Red brown (4)**	Vertical	£20
WCJ44a	2d **Light Red brown (4)**	Horizontal	18.75
WCJ45	2½d **Carmine-red (4)**	Horizontal	37.50
WCJ46	3d **Deep violet**	Horizontal	8.75

Multiple Crowns Watermark Upright Cream Paper

WCJ47	½d **Orange red (4)**	Horizontal	1.75
WCJ48	1d **Ultramarine**	Horizontal	
WCJ49	1½d **Green**	Vertical	
WCJ55	4d **Deep Ultramarine**	Vertical	
WCJ55a	4d **Deep Ultramarine**	Horizontal	
WCJ58	6d **Red purple**	Vertical	

Multiple Crowns Watermark Upright Whiter Paper

WCJ67	1d **Ultramarine (4)**	Horizontal	3.25
WCJ69	1½d **Green**	Horizontal	3.75
WCJ74	4d **Deep Ultramarine**	Vertical	
WCJ74a	4d **Deep Ultramarine**	Horizontal	
WCJ78	6d **Deep claret (4)**	Vertical	8.25

Multiple Crowns Watermark Graphite Lined

Displaced graphite lines as viewed from the back of the stamps.

WCJ89	2d **Light Red brown**	Vertical	
WCJ91	3d **Deep violet**	Horizontal	

Multiple Crowns Watermark Green Phosphor

WCJ102	½d **Orange red (4)**	Vertical	12.50
WCJ105	2d **LB Light Red brown (4)**	Vertical	£100

Cylinder Block Perforation Types

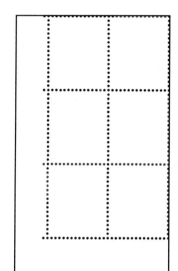

Type A
No dot and Dot
Type H No dot

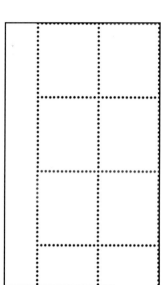

Type B
Left No dot

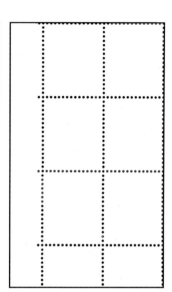

Type C
Right Dot

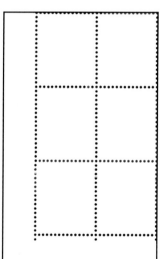

Type F(L)
No dot

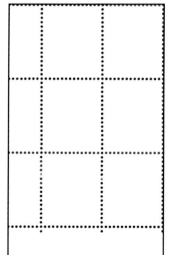

Type F(L)
Dot

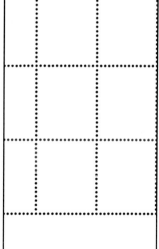

Type H
Dot

Wilding Definitives   Cylinder Blocks   Queen Elizabeth II

Watermark Tudor Crown Upright

No.	Perf.	Cyl.	No Dot	Dot
½d Orange red				
	B/C	1	6.25	6.25
	A	1	3.00	3.00
	A	3	3.50	3.00
1d Deep Ultramarine				
	B/C	1	3.25	3.25
	A	2	18.00	4.75
1½d Green				
	A	1	2.00	2.00
	A	2	2.00	2.00
	A	4	2.00	2.00
	A	5	2.00	2.00
	A	6	3.25	3.75
	A	8	4.50	4.50
	A	9	1.75	1.75
	A	10	1.75	1.75
	A	11	1.75	1.75
	A	12	1.75	1.75
	A	13	3.25	3.25
	B/C	1	£20	£20
	B/C	2	£20	£20
	B/C	6	£20	£20
	B/C	9	£20	£20
2d Red brown				
	A	1	6.50	6.50
	A	2	6.50	6.50
	A	3	6.00	6.00
	A	4	4.00	4.00
2½d Carmine red TI				
	A	2	2.50	2.50
	A	4	2.50	2.50
	A	5	2.75	2.75
	A	6	2.50	2.50
	A	7	2.50	2.50
	A	8	£11	3.00
	A	9	2.50	2.50
	A	10	2.50	2.50
	A	11	2.50	2.50
	A	12	2.50	2.50
	A	13	4.50	4.50
	A	14	2.50	2.50
	A	15	2.75	2.75
	A	16	2.50	2.50
	A	17	2.50	2.50
	A	18	2.50	2.50
	A	19	2.50	2.50
	A	22	2.50	2.50
	A	23	2.50	2.50
	A	24	2.50	2.5
	A	25	4.50	4.50
	A	27	2.50	2.50
	B/C	14	£10	£10
	B/C	24	£10	£10
3d Deep violet				
	A	3	8.50	8.50
	B/C	3	9.00	9.00
4d Ultramarine	A	1	£30	£30
	B/C	3	£26	£26
5d Brown	A	1	8.00	8.00

No.	Perf.	Cyl.	No Dot	Dot
6d Red purple				
	B	1	£33	-
	C	1	£34	-
	F(L)	1	£33	-
7d Pastel green				
	A	2	£75	£75
	B/C	2	£75	£75
8d Cerise				
	A	3	8.00	8.00
	B/C	3	8.00	8.00
9d Greyish green	A	1	£150	£150
	B/C	3	£150	£150
10d Deep blue				
	A	1	£125	£125
	B/C	1	£125	£125
11d Plum				
	B/C	1	£220	£220
1s Bistre brown				
	A	1	8.50	8.50
	A	2	£30	£30
	B/C	1	£20	£20
1s 3d Deep green				
	A	1	£37	£37
	B/C	1	£60	£60
1s 6d Grey blue				
	A	1	£100	£115
	B/C	1	£100	£115

Watermark St Edwards Crown Upright

No.	Perf.	Cyl.	No Dot	Dot
½d Orange red				
	B/C	1	3.50	3.50
	A	2	3.50	9.50
	A	3	4.50	4.50
1d Ultramarine				
	A	1	3.75	3.75
	A	2	17.50	17.50
	A	4	3.75	3.75
	B/C	4	6.50	6.50
1½d Green				
	A	11	2.75	3.25
	A	13	2.75	£14
	A	14	2.75	3.25
	A	15	2.75	3.25
2d Red brown				
	A	3	3.75	3.75
	A	4	3.75	3.75
	A	6	3.75	3.75
	A	7	3.75	3.75
	A	9	£20	£20

Wilding Definitives   Cylinder Blocks   Queen Elizabeth II

No.	Perf.	Cyl.	No Dot	Dot
2d Light red brown				
	A	6	3.25	3.25
	A	7	3.25	3.25
	A	8	3.25	3.25
	A	9	3.25	3.25
	A	10	8.50	3.25
	A	11	3.25	3.25
	A	12	3.25	3.25
	A	13	3.25	3.25
	A	14	3.25	3.25
	A	15	3.25	3.25
	A	16	3.25	3.25
	E	7	£35	-
	E	9	£35	-
2½d Carmine red TI				
	A	22	5.00	3.50
	A	24	3.50	£850
	A	25	3.50	5.00
	A	27	3.50	3.50
	A	30	3.50	3.50
	A	32	3.50	3.50
	A	33	3.50	3.50
	A	34	3.50	17.50
	A	37	3.50	3.50
	A	38	3.50	3.50
	A	39	3.50	3.50
	A	40	3.50	3.50
	A	42	3.50	3.50
	A	43	3.50	3.50
	A	44	3.50	3.50
	A	45	£65	£65
	E	32	£20	3.50
	E	37	£20	3.50
2½d Carmine red TII				
	A	46	3.50	3.50
3d Deep violet				
	A	2	2.75	2.75
	A	3	2.75	2.75
	A	4	2.75	2.75
	A	5	2.75	2.75
	A	9	2.75	2.75
	A	10	2.75	2.75
	A	15	2.75	2.75
	A	16	2.75	2.75
	A	17	2.75	2.75
	B/C	2	9.00	9.00
	B/C	3	9.00	9.00
	F(L)	5	£75	£75
d Ultramarine				
	A	1	£16	£16
	A	3	£20	£20
	B/C	1	10.50	£15
d Brown				
	A	1	£48	£48
d Red purple				
	B	1	37.50	-
	B	2	37.50	-
	C	1	£35	-
	C	2	£35	-
d Deep claret				
	B	2	37.50	-
	B	3	37.50	-
	C	2	£35	-
	C	3	£33	-
	F(L)	3	£50	-
d Pastel green				
	A	2	£320	£320

No.	Perf.	Cyl.	No Dot	Dot
8d Cerise				
	A	3	£55	£55
9d Greyish green				
	A	1	£150	£150
	B/C	1	£175	£175
10d deep blue				
	A	1	£165	£165
11d Plum				
	A	1	4.75	4.75
	B/C	1	4.75	4.75
1s Bistre brown				
	A	2	£160	£160
	A	3	£160	£160
	A	4	£200	£200
1s 3d Deep green				
	A	1	£210	£210
1s 6d Grey blue				
	A	1	£150	£175
	B/C	1	£175	£175

Graphite Lined Watermark St Edwards Crown Upright

No.	Perf.	Cyl.	No Dot	Dot
½d Orange red				
	B	4	4.75	-
	C	4	4.75	-
	B	5	£10	-
	C	5	6.00	-
1d Deep ultramarine				
	B	7	5.50	-
	C	7	5.50	-
	B	8	£11	-
	C	8	£11	-
1½d Green				
	B	21	9.00	-
	C	21	9.00	-
2d Light red brown				
	B	17	17.50	-
	C	17	17.50	-
2½d Carmine red TII				
	B	49	£60	-
	C	49	£60	-
3d Deep violet				
	B	7	£10	-
	C	7	£10	-
	B	11	£10	-
	C	11	£10	-

No.	Perf.	Cyl.	No Dot	Dot
½d Orange red				
	B/C	1	3.75	3.75
	B/C	3	3.50	3.50
	A	2	5.25	9.50
	A	3	5.25	5.25
1d Deep ultramarine				
	A	4	4.00	4.00
	A	5	4.00	4.00
	B/C	4	5.25	5.25
1½d Green				
	A	15	3.75	3.75
2d Light red brown				
	A	15	3.75	3.75
	A	19	3.75	3.75
	A	20	3.75	3.75
	A	21	3.75	3.75
	A	22	3.75	3.75
	A	23	3.75	3.75
	A	24	3.75	3.75
	A	25	3.75	3.75
	A	27	3.75	3.75
	A	29	3.75	3.75
	A	30	3.75	3.75
2½d Carmine red TI				
	A	42	£25	£25
	B/C	42	£850	£850
2½d Carmine red TII				
	A	50	5.00	5.00
	A	51	5.00	5.00
	A	52	5.00	5.00
	A	53	5.00	5.00
	A	54	5.00	5.00
	B/C	50	£12	£12
	B/C	51	£12	£12
	B/C	52	£12	£12
3d Deep violet				
	H	31	-	£40
	H	36	-	£40
	H	37	-	£40
	H	41	-	£40
	A	15	4.25	4.25
	A	16	£45	£45
	A	22	3.50	3.50
	A	25	3.50	3.50
	A	26	3.50	3.50
	A	28	3.50	3.50
	A	29	3.50	3.50
	A	30	3.50	3.50
	A	31	3.50	3.50
	A	33	3.50	3.50
	A	36	3.50	3.50
	A	37	3.50	3.50
	A	41	3.50	3.50
	A	46	3.50	3.50
	A	47	3.50	3.50
	A	49	3.50	3.50
	A	51	3.50	3.50
	A	52	3.50	3.50

Watermark Crowns Cream Paper

No.	Perf.	Cyl.	No Dot	Dot
	A	53	3.50	3.50
	A	54	3.50	3.50
	A	55	3.50	3.50
	A	58	3.50	3.50
	A	60	5.00	5.00
	A	61	5.00	5.00
	A	62	5.00	5.00
	A	64	5.00	5.00
	B/C	28	5.50	5.50
	B/C	41	£75	-
	B/C	51	£15	£15
	B/C	52	£15	£15
	B/C	54	£15	£15
	H	31	3.50	3.50
	H	36	3.50	3.50
	H	37	3.50	3.50
	H	41	3.50	3.50
4d Ultramarine				
	A	1	£13	£13
	A	6	£13	£13
	A	8	£13	£13
4½d Chestnut red				
	A	2	8.00	8.00
	A	6	8.00	8.00
	A	7	4.75	4.75
5d Brown				
	A	1	£22	£22
	A	2	£22	£22
6d Deep claret				
	B	2	£11	-
	B	3	£11	-
	C	2	£11	-
	C	3	£11	-
	B/C	5	£30	£30
	B/C	7	£11	£11
	A	7	£11	£11
	A	8	£11	£11
7d Pastel green				
	A	1	£20	£20
	A	2	£20	£20
	B/C	2	£20	£20
8d Cerise				
	A	3	£30	£30
9d Greyish green				
	A	1	£30	£30
	A	2	£30	£40
10d Deep blue				
	A	1	£30	£30
	B/C	1	£30	£30
1s Bistre brown				
	A	2	£27	£27
	A	3	£27	£27
	A	4	£27	£27
1s 3d Deep green				
	A	1	£23	£23
1s 6d Grey blue				
	A	1	£95	£120
	A	3	£95	£95
	B/C	1	£95	£120
	B/C	3	£95	£95

No.	Perf.	Cyl.	No Dot	Dot	No.	Perf.	Cyl.	No Dot	Dot

**Watermark
Crowns
Whiter Paper**

4d Deep ultramarine

	Perf.	Cyl.	No Dot	Dot
	A	12	2.25	2.25
	A	13	2.25	2.25
	A	16	2.25	2.25
	A	18	2.25	2.25
	A	20	2.25	2.25
	A	23	2.25	2.25
	A	25	2.25	2.25
	A	26	2.25	2.25
	A	27	2.25	2.25

4½d Chestnut red

	A	7	2.00	2.00
	A	8	2.00	2.00

½d Orange red

	A	1	3.00	3.00
	A	3	3.00	3.00

5d Brown

	A	1	3.25	3.25
	F(L)	1		

1d Deep Ultramarine

	A	4	4.00	4.00
	A	5	4.00	4.00

6d Deep claret

	A	8	3.50	3.50
	A	10	3.50	3.50
	A	11	£45	£45
	F(L)	10	5.25	5.25

1½d Green

	A	15	2.00	2.00
	A	22	2.75	2.75

2d Light red brown

	A	23	2.50	2.50
	A	25	2.50	2.50
	A	27	2.50	2.50
	A	30	2.50	2.50

7d Pastel green

	A	1	4.75	4.75
	A	2	4.75	4.75
	F(L)	1	£500	£500

2½d Carmine red TI

	A	42	£60	£60

8d Cerise

	A	3	8.00	6.00
	A	4	8.00	6.00
	F(L)	4		

2½d Carmine red TII

	A	50	2.00	2.00
	A	51	2.00	2.00
	A	52	2.00	2.00
	A	53	2.00	2.00
	A	54	2.00	2.00
	A	55	2.00	2.00
	A	56	2.00	2.00
	A	57	2.00	2.00
	A	58	2.00	2.00
	A	59	2.00	2.00
	B/C	51	£15	£15
	B/C	52	£15	£15

9d Greyish green

	A	2	5.00	5.00

10d Deep blue

	A	1	8.00	8.00
	F(L)	4		-

1s Bistre brown

	A	2	4.75	4.75
	A	3	4.75	4.75
	A	4	4.75	4.75

3d Deep violet

	A	51	1.75	1.75
	A	52	1.75	1.75
	A	54	1.75	1.75
	A	58	1.75	1.75
	A	60	1.75	1.75
	A	61	1.75	1.75
	A	62	1.75	1.75
	A	63	1.75	1.75
	A	64	1.75	1.75
	A	66	1.75	1.75
	A	67	1.75	1.75
	A	68	1.75	1.75
	A	69	1.75	1.75
	A	70	1.75	1.75
	A	71	1.75	1.75
	A	72	1.75	1.75
	A	73	1.75	1.75
	A	75	1.75	1.75
	A	78	1.75	1.75
	A	79	1.75	1.75
	A	80	1.75	1.75
	A	81	1.75	1.75
	A	82	1.75	1.75

1s 3d Deep green

	A	1	4.00	4.00
	A	2	4.00	4.00

1s 6d Grey blue

	A	1	£35	£40

**Phosphor/Graphite
Watermark
St. Edwards
Crown**

These are all single pane printings i.e. No Dot only blocks exist

½d Orange red

	B	5	£40	-
	C	5	£30	-

4d Ultramarine

	A	8	4.75	4.75

1d Deep Ultramarine

	B	8	£75	-
	C	8	£75	-

1½d Green

	B	21	£30	-
	C	21	£30	-

Graphite Watermark Crowns

No.	Perf.	Cyl.	No Dot	Dot
2d Light red brown				
	B	17	£45	-
	C	17	£45	-
2½d Carmine red TII				
	B	49	£85	-
	C	49	£85	-
3d Deep violet				
	B	11	£10	-
	C	11	£10	-
4d Ultramarine				
	A	6	£45	£45
4½d Chestnut				
	A	6	£50	£50

Phosphor/Graphite Watermark Crowns

No.	Perf.	Cyl.	No Dot	Dot
2d Light red brown				
	B	17	£70	-
	C	17	£70	-
Error St Edwards Crown	B	17	£1100	-
	C	17	£1100	-
2½d Carmine red TII				
	B	49	£130	-
	C	49	£130	-
3d Deep violet				
	B	11	£75	-
	C	11	£75	-
4d Ultramarine				
	A	6	£150	£125
4½d Chestnut				
	A	6	£225	£225

Watermark Crowns Green Phosphor

No.	Perf.	Cyl.	No Dot	Dot
½d Orange red				
	B/C	1	£15	£15
1d Deep ultramarine				
	B/C	5	£11	£11
1½d Green				
	B/C	15	£15	£15
2d Light red brown				
	B	17	£140	-
	C	17	£175	-
2½d Carmine red TII				
	B/C	50	£15	£15
3d Deep violet				
	B/C	41	£15	£15
4d Ultramarine				
	B/C	8	£75	£75
6d Claret				
	B	2	£24	-
	C	2	£24	-
1s 3d Deep green				
	B/C	1	£75	£55

Watermark Crowns Blue Phosphor Cream Paper

No.	Perf.	Cyl.	No Dot	Dot
½d Orange red				
	A	1	3.75	3.75
1d Deep ultramarine				
	B/C	5	7.50	7.50
1½d Green				
	B/C	15	7.50	7.50
2d LB Light red brown				
	A	29	£250	£250
	B/C	29	£250	£250
2d 2B Light red brown Typo				
	A	25	£100	-
	A	27	-	£75
	A	29	£100	£75
	A	30	£75	£75
2d 2B Light red brown Photo				
	A	30	16.50	16.50

Wilding Definitives   Cylinder Blocks   Queen Elizabeth II

No.	Perf.	Cyl.	No Dot	Dot
2½d 2B Carmine red TII				
	A	50	£42	£42
2½d LB Carmine red TII				
Typo	A	50	£130	£30
Photo	B/C	50	£90	£90
Photo	B/C	53	£120	£120
2½d LB Carmine red TI				
Typo	A	42	£325	£325
3d Deep violet				
	B/C	52	9.00	9.00
	B/C	60	9.00	9.00
4d Deep ultramarine				
	B/C	8	£30	£30
4½d Chestnut				
Typo	A	7	£40	£40
Photo	B/C	7	£150	£150
6d Claret				
Photo	A	7	£37	£37
Typo	A	8		
1s 3d Deep green				
	A	1	£130	£130

No.	Perf.	Cyl.	No Dot	Dot
3d Side bands Deep violet				
	A	67	£30	£30
	A	68	£30	£30
	A	71	£30	£30
	A	72	£30	£30
4d Deep ultramarine				
	A	12	6.00	6.00
	A	13	6.00	6.00
	A	18	6.00	6.00
	A	20	6.00	6.00
4½d Chestnut				
Photo	A	7	3.25	3.25
Photo	A	8	2.75	2.75
Typo	A	8	£25	£25
6d Claret				
Photo	A	8	£13	£10
Photo	A	10	£10	£10
Typo	A	8	£2750	£2750
1s 3d Deep green				
	A	1	£16	£16
	A	2	£16	£16

Watermark Crowns Blue Phosphor Whiter Paper

Watermark Crowns 8mm Violet Phosphor Whiter Paper

No.	Perf.	Cyl.	No Dot	Dot
½d Orange red				
	A	1	3.00	3.00
1d Deep ultramarine				
	A	4	6.00	6.00
1½d Green				
	A	15	2.25	2.25
	A	22	3.30	3.30
2d Light red brown				
	A	25	£45	£45
2½d LB Carmine red TII				
Photo	A	51	5.00	5.00
Photo	A	52	5.00	5.00
Photo	A	54	5.00	5.00
Photo	A	56	5.00	5.00
Photo	A	57	5.00	5.00
Typo	A	50		
2½d 2B Carmine red TII				
Photo	A	57	3.30	3.30
3d Deep violet				
	A	60	5.25	5.25
	A	61	5.25	5.25
	A	62	5.25	5.25
	A	64	5.25	5.25
	A	67	5.25	5.25
	A	71	5.25	5.25

No.	Perf.	Cyl.	No Dot	Dot
½d Orange red				
	A	1	£15	£16
1d Deep ultramarine				
Typo	A	5	£350	£385
Photo	A	5	5.25	5.25
1½d Green	A	15	£20	£20
2d Light red brown				
	A	27		£1400
	A	30	8.00	8.00
3d Side bands Deep violet				
	A	67	5.00	5.00
	A	71	5.00	5.00
	A	72	5.00	5.00
	A	81	5.00	5.00
	A	82	5.00	5.00
3d CB Deep violet				
	A	78	3.75	3.75
	A	79	3.75	3.75
	A	81	3.75	3.75
	A	82	3.75	3.75
4d Deep ultramarine				
	A	18	5.50	5.50
	A	20	5.50	5.50
6d Claret				
	A	8	£80	£80
1s 3d Deep green				
Typo	A	2	£160	£160
Photo	A	2	£50	£50

No.	Perf.	Cyl.	No Dot	Dot	No.	Perf.	Cyl.	No Dot	Dot

Watermark Crowns 9.5mm Violet Phosphor Whiter Paper

—11.5mm—

1d Deep ultramarine

| | F(L) | 4 | 2.00 | 2.00 |
| | A | 5 | 2.00 | 2.00 |

2d Light red brown

| | F(L) | 25 | 2.20 | 2.20 |
| | A | 27 | 2.20 | 2.20 |

4d Deep ultramarine

	A	16	3.00	3.00
	A	18	3.00	3.00
	A	23	3.00	3.00
	A	26	3.00	3.00
	A	27	3.00	3.00

5d Brown

| | A | 1 | 3.00 | 3.00 |
| | F(L) | 1 | 3.00 | 3.00 |

6d Claret

	A	10	£11	£11
	A	11	5.50	5.50
	F(L)	10	5.50	5.50

7d Pastel green

| | F(L) | 1 | 8.50 | 8.50 |
| | A | 2 | 5.50 | 5.50 |

8d Cerise

| | A | 4 | 6.50 | 3.50 |
| | F(L) | 4 | 6.50 | 3.50 |

9d Greyish green

| | A | 2 | 5.50 | 5.50 |

10d Deep blue

| | A | 1 | 6.00 | 6.00 |
| | F(L) | 1 | 6.00 | 6.00 |

1s Bistre brown

| | F(L) | 4 | 4.50 | 4.50 |

1s 3d Deep green

| | A | 2 | £70 | £70 |

1s 6d Grey blue

| | A | 1 | £17 | £22 |
| | F(L) | 8 | £22 | £22 |

The Castle High Values

To make the distinctions between the three printers as clear as possible we include this chart and comparison guide, which will enable collectors to detect the difference between the printers more easily. Where shades are mentioned we have endeavoured to describe the shades clearly according to the catalogue list. However, where there is a small but distinct difference this has been noted on the chart as a further aid in distinguishing the printers. The basic steps are as follows:

1. Sort by watermark. All those with St. Edward's Crown (1st) are either Waterlow or De La Rue, and those with Multiple Crown Watermarks (2nd) are either the second De La Rue or Bradbury Wilkinson. Those without watermark are Bradbury.

2. Check the Waterlow and De La Rue first watermark against the list below.

3. It is relatively easy to sort the De La Rue from the Bradbury in the Multiple Crown watermark series by the way the paper curls when the face is breathed upon. This is due to the method of printing on the paper web. On De La Rue printings the paper curls vertically, that is top and bottom pull together, whereas on the Bradbury it will curl horizontally, e.g. left and right sides pull together.

4. If used, examples with dated postmarks can be a great help. If difficulties are still experienced the list below should readily solve them. For an inexpensive exercise to help gain experience it is suggested a quantity of good used 2/6d values are obtained for study.

	Wmks.	Waterlow	De La Rue	Bradbury Wilkinson
Paper Type		Cream/lightish cream	Light cream/white	White/chalky
Paper Characteristics		Curls vertically	Curls vertically	Curls horizontally
Watermarks	1st	St. Edwards Crown	St. Edwards Crown	
	2nd		Multiple Crown	Multiple Crown
	Without			None
Perforations	1st	Thick tooth top right	Thin tooth top right	
	2nd		Vert. perf 11.8	Vert. perf 11.9 to 12
Shades				
2s 6d value	1st	Blackish brown	Blackish brown (less blackish tinge)	
	2nd		Blackish brown	Deep black brown
	Without			Deep black brown
5s value	1st	Rose carmine	Rose carmine (noticeably less carmine)	
	2nd		Red	Brownish red
	Without			Brownish red
10s value	1st	Ultramarine	Dull blue	
	2nd		Dull blue	Bright ultramarine
	Without			Bright ultramarine
£1 value	1st	Black	Deep greyish black	
	2nd		Greyish black	Intense black
	Without			Intense black
Print Impression		Very deep, slightly blurred	Soft and sharp	Deep with more detail in diadem

Notes

Some plates of the De La Rue 2nd Watermark had either 1 or 2 coloured plate dots in the bottom margin, row 10, stamp No.1. These marginal pieces are worth 150% premium.

Waterlow and **De La Rue** both used guide marks.

Waterlow - small guide lines 2-3mm at top and bottom, centre and centre left and right of each sheet.

De La Rue - only on the side margins between rows 5 and 6, usually as a 'T' or a cross, which marked a guide 'pinhole'.

Bradbury Wilkinson also used guide holes, row 6, left and right.

Castle High Values

Recess Printings

Original '£'

1955 (1 Sept.) Wmk. St. Edward's Crown. Perf. 11 x 12
Printer: Waterlow & Sons in Recess

			U/M	M/M	F/U
H1	**2s6d**	**Blackish brown** (23.9.55)	9.75	3.00	1.00
H2	**5s**	**Rose carmine** (23.9.55)	£22	7.50	2.00
H3	**10s**	**Ultramarine**	£52	£18	6.50
H4	**£1**	**Black**	£70	£25	£17
		Set of 4	£135	£48	23.50

1957 (17 July) - 58 Wmk. St. Edward's Crown. Perf. 11 x 12
Printer: De La Rue (1st) in Recess

H5	**2s6d**	**Blackish brown**	£19	9.50	1.75
H6	**5s**	**Rose carmine** (30.4.58)	£30	£19	5.70
H7	**10s**	**Dull blue** (25.4.58)	£140	£55	10.75
H8	**£1**	**Black** (28.4.58)	£190	£94	£20
		Set of 4	£340	£180	£35

1959 (15 June) Wmk. Multiple Crowns. Perf. 11 x 12
Printer: De L Rue (2nd) in Recess

H9	**2s6d**	**Blackish brown** (22.7.59)	6.00	3.25	20
H10	**5s**	**Red**	£22	£12	35
H11	**10s**	**Blue** (21.7.59)	£22	8.50	1.20
H12	**£1**	**Black** (23.6.59)5	£47	£25	6.00
		Set of 4	£84	42.50	7.50
		Presentation Pack	£350		
		Presentation Pack '£1.18s'	£350		
		Presentation Pack '$6.50'	£400		

1963 (1 July) Wmk. Multiple Crowns. Perf. 11 x 12
Printer: Bradbury Wilkinson & Co. in Recess

H13	**2s6d**	**Blackish brown**	20	12	15
H13a		Wmk. inverted	£175	£85	£35
H13b		Chalky paper (30.5.68)	30	15	40
H14	**5s**	**Red** (3.9.63)	1.00	60	30
H14a		Light brownish red	1.20	60	50
H14b		Wmk. inverted	£125	£60	£30
H15	**10s**	**Ultramarine** (16.10.63)	3.50	1.30	90
H16	**£1**	**Black** (14.11.63)	7.00	4.00	4.50
		Set of 4	8.95	5.75	4.75

1967 (4 Dec.) - 68 No watermark. Perf. 11 x 12
Printer: Bradbury Wilkinson & Co. in Recess

H17	**2s6d**	**Blackish brown** (1.7.68)	25	15	13
H18	**5s**	**Brownish red** (10.4.68)	1.00	50	26
H19	**10s**	**Ultramarine** (10.4.68)	4.00	2.00	5.00
H20	**£1**	**Black**	4.00	2.50	2.70
		Set of 4	8.50	4.90	7.50

1969 (5 March) No watermark. Perf. 12
Printer: Bradbury Wilkinson & Co. in Recess
PVA Gum

			U/M	M/M	F/U
H21	**2s6d**	**Brown**	20	10	20
H22	**5s**	**Red**	70	40	40
H23	**10s**	**Blue**	2.20	1.50	2.95
H24	**£1**	**Black**	2.80	1.70	70
		Set of 4	5.20	3.30	3.90
		First Day Cover			6.25
		Presentation Pack 7	£5		
		German Presentation Pack	£40		

Redrawn '£'

Photogravure Printings

1970 (17 July) - 74. No watermark. Perf. 12
Printer: Bradbury Wilkinson & Co. in Recess

A. Post Office paper. PVA Gum

			U/M	F/U
H25	**10p**	**Cerise** ('all over' phosphor)	40	50
H26	**20p**	**Olive green**	75	15
H27	**50p**	**Blue**	1.25	30
H27a		Uncoated paper	32.50	
H27b		Blue ('all over' phosphor) (1.2.73)	1.10	1.25
H28	**£1**	**Black** (6.12.72)	2.50	60
		Set of 4	4.50	1.20
		First Day Cover (10p-50p)		2.75
		Presentation Pack 18 (10p-50p)	4.00	
		First Day Cover (£1)		3.50

B. Bradbury paper. PVA Gum

H29	**20p**	**Olive green** (30.11.73)	35	20
H30	**50p**	**Greyish blue** (20.2.74)	75	25
H31	**£1**	**Black** (27.9.73)	1.70	60
		Set of 3	2.70	1.00
		Presentation Pack 38 (20p - £1, any) (25.11.71)	6.00	

Post Office paper is thick and slightly creamy, whereas Bradbury paper is thinner and whiter.

1977 (2 Feb.) - 87 Large format. No watermark. Perf. 14 x 15
Printer: Harrison & Sons in Photogravure
Fluorescent Coated Paper. PVA Dextrin Gum

			U/M	F/U
H32	**£1**	**Olive green & pale yellow**	1.60	15
H33	**£1.30**	**Blue green & pale drab** (3.8.83)	3.50	3.50
H34	**£1.33**	**Grey black & pale mauve** (28.8.84)	3.20	3.50
H35	**£1.41**	**Blue green & pale drab** (17.9.85)	4.60	4.00
H36	**£1.50**	**Grey black & pale mauve** (2.9.86)	3.20	2.00
H37	**£1.60**	**Blue green & pale drab** (15.9.87)	3.20	3.00
H38	**£2**	**Purple brown & pale green**	3.20	40
H39	**£5**	**Royal blue & pale pink**	7.50	1.20
		Set of 8	£24	17.50
		Gutter pairs (£1, £2, £5)	£25	
		Gutter pair (1.30)	8.00	
		Gutter pair (£1.33)	£10	
		Gutter pair (£1.41)	9.00	
		Gutter pair (£1.50)	7.00	
		Gutter pair (£1.60)	7.50	
		Traffic Light Gutter pairs (£1, £2, £5)	£30	
		Traffic Light Gutter pair (£1.30)	£11	
		Traffic Light Gutter pair (£1.33)	£12	
		Traffic Light Gutter pair (£1.41)	£12	
		Traffic Light Gutter pair (£1.50)	8.50	
		Traffic Light Gutter pair (£1.60)	9.00	
		First Day Cover (1.60)		3.50
		First Day Cover (£1, £2, £5)		£10
		First Day Cover (£1.30)		6.00
		First Day Cover (£1.33)		5.00
		First Day Cover (£1.41)		4.50
		First Day Cover (£1.50)		4.00
		Presentation Pack 91 (£1, £2, £5)	£15	
		Presentation Pack 13 (£1, £2 & £5) (3.3.87)	£18	
		Presentation Pack 14 (£1.60)	4.75	

Castles Series

1988 (18 Oct.) Historic Castles. No watermark. Perf. 15 x 14
Printer: Harrison & Sons in Recess
Fluorescent Coated Paper. PVA Dextrin Gum

H40	£1	Green	1.50	15
H41	£1.50	Burgundy	2.30	60
H42	£2	Blue	3.00	40
H43	£5	Brown	8.50	2.50
		Set of 4	£14	3.00
		Gutter pairs (horizontal)	£35	
		Gutter pairs (vertical)	£35	
		Gutter blocks of four	£75	
		First Day Cover		£25
		Presentation Pack 18	£16	

1992 (24 March)–97. Castles series. Perf 15 x 14 (elliptical).   Printed by engraving and recess-printing, with Queen's head in optically variable ink. The four Castles high-value stamps, which all have the silhouetted Queen's head printed in optically variable ink in the top right corner, were first issued, printed by Harrisons (now De La Rue), on 24 March 1992. Re-etched versions of the four, also by Harrisons, appeared at various times during 1994. Examined side by side with the originals, the re-etched Castles give the impression of denser, sharper, more solid images.

Original   Re-engraved

To identify a single stamp as original or re-engraved when there is nothing to compare it with, study the Queen's head under about 10x magnification. You will find that it is made up of a dense array of fine, crosshatched lines: if the crosshatching forms a mass of diamond patterns, it is the original design; if the patterns are square, it is re-etched. There is also much more detail visible especially around the windows and all the re-engraved issues are slightly deeper in colour as shown below.

Original   Re-engraved

The Carrickfergus Castle design was used for the £1 until 22 August 1995 when it was transferred to the new £3; on the same date a £1 Machin definitive, printed by Enschedé, was issued.

The four designs were engraved afresh in 1997 by Enschedé, whose printing superseded those of Harrisons on 29 July of that year. Comparison of the two printers' work shows the Enschedé versions to be more delicate, refined and finely detailed. Single stamps may be distinguished as Harrison or Enschedé products by close scrutiny of the capital "C" wherever it occurs: the Harrison "C" a upper serif only, the Enschedé "C" has an upper and a lower serif.

Harrison   Enschede

1992 (24 March) Historic Castles.
Printer: Harrison & Sons in Recess
*OBA Free Non Phosphor paper. PVA Dextrin Gum or * PVA Layflat Gum*

			U/M	F/U
H44	**£1**	**Green and gold**	1.90	20
H44a	**£1**	Green and gold (re-etched, 2 Dec 94)	3.50	2.00
H45	**£1.50**	**Burgundy and gold**	2.70	50
H45a		Bright magenta and gold (colour error)	£20	
H45b	**£1.50**	Burgundy and gold (re-etched, 26 Oct 94)	3.00	70
H45c	**£1.50**	Burgundy and gold (re-etched, 5 Mar 96) *	3.00	50
H45ca		Creamy opaque paper and brown PVA gum	£18	
H46	**£2**	**Blue and gold**	4.50	45
H46a		Complete offset of blue on gummed side	£45	
H46b		Bright blue and gold (colour error)	£35	
H46c	**£2**	Blue and gold (re-etched, 5 Nov 94)	3.50	65
H46ca		Bright blue and gold (colour error)	£45	
H46d	**£2**	Blue and gold (re-etched, 2 May 96) *	3.50	75
H46da		Ultra-translucent white paper	£10	
H47	**£5**	**Brown and gold**	7.50	2.25
H47a	**£5**	Brown and gold (re-etched, Aug 94)	9.50	1.50
H47aa		Missing Gold (Queen's head)	£275	
H47b	**£5**	Brown and gold (re-etched, 17 Sep 96) *	8.50	2.25
		Set of 4	£22	3.70
		Gutter pairs (horizontal)	£30	
		Gutter pairs (vertical)	£30	
		Gutter blocks of four	£60	
		First Day Cover		£20
		Presentation Pack 25	£15	

1995 (22 August) Historic Castles.
Printer: Harrison & Sons in Recess
OBA Free Non Phosphor paper. PVA Dextrin Gum

			U/M	F/U
H48	**£3**	**Violet**	4.50	75
H48a		Complete offset of violet on the gummed side	£25	

1997 (29 July) Historic Castles. No watermark.
Printer: Enschedé in Recess
Optical Free Non Phosphor paper. PVA Dextrin Gum

			U/M	F/U
H49	**£1.50**	**Burgundy and gold**	9.50	3.00
H50	**£2**	**Blue and gold**	7.50	2.20
H51	**£3**	**Violet and gold**	15.50	1.50
H51a		Missing Gold (Queen's head)	£650	
H52	**£5**	**Brown and gold**	17.50	4.00
H52a		Missing Gold (Queen's head)	£3,500	
		Set of 4	42.50	8.90
		Gutter pairs (horizontal)	£90	
		Gutter pairs (vertical)	£90	
		Gutter blocks of four	£180	

Britannia Issue

Britannia series. Perf 15 x 14 (two elliptical holes on each horizontal edge). Embossed with braille characters. The £10 stamp has paper with fluorescent coloured fibres and fluorescent ink, which both react under ultra-violet light. On all stamps the fluorescent ink can be seen on the shield, where it appears bright yellow-green. On stamps from part of the printing the wording "TEN POUNDS", which is printed in green ink underneath the value in figures in the lower right corner, has also been printed in fluorescent ink.

1993 (2 March) 'Britannia'. No watermark.
Printer: House of Questa in Litho
OBA-free non-phosphor paper with fluorescent fibres. PVA gum

			U/M	F/U
H53	**£10**	**Multicoloured**	£17	7.50
H53a		'TEN POUNDS' in fluorescent ink	£25	
H53aa	**£10**	Missing Silver (Queen's head)	£2500	
		First Day Cover		£18 ✓
		Presentation Pack 28	£16	
		PHQ Card	30	£20

Small Format Machin Head

There are many differences between the Enschedé and De La Rue printings. The image is much coarser on De La Rue and the paper is also whiter. Furthermore the gum on the De La Rue printing is whiter, whereas on the Enschedé version the gum has a matt appearance.

Enschedé   De La Rue

1999 (9 Mar.) Small Format Machin Head
Printer: Enschedé in Intaglio
OBA-free non-phosphor paper. PVA gum

			U/M	F/U
H54	**£1.50**	**Rust-red**	4.00	1.25
H55	**£2**	**Indigo**	4.50	1.25
H56	**£3**	**Purple**	5.50	75
H57	**£5**	**Sepia**	8.00	3.25

2000 (11 Apr.) Small Format Machin Head
Printer: De La Rue in Intaglio
OBA-free non-phosphor paper. PVA gum

			U/M	F/U
H58	**£1.50**	**Rust-red**	3.00	60
H59	**£2**	**Indigo**	3.50	60
H60	**£3**	**Purple**	5.50	30
H61	**£5**	**Sepia**	8.50	2.25

Introductory Notes

These notes are taken from the Machin Collectors Club Specialised Machin catalogue. They have been abbreviated to cover the listings here and give an excellent introduction to readers who may be interested in taking their interest in Machins further.

The design

The Machin definitives depict a plaster bas-relief of H.M the Queen, sculpted by Arnold Machin, OBE, RA, which was based on photographs taken by Lord Snowdon, supplemented with a number of sittings. This was photographed to produce master negatives used in the production of printing cylinders and plates.

The printers

Between 1967 and December 1979 all the small format Machin definitives were printed in photogravure by Harrison & Sons Ltd. On 12th December 1979 8p stamps printed in photogravure by Joh Enschedé en Zonen of Holland were released and during 1980 stamps printed in offset-lithography by the House of Questa & John Waddington Ltd. appeared. From 1989 onwards offset-lithographed stamps by Walsall Security Printers Ltd. were issued. In 1991 with the 18p value and then between 1993 and 1996 for the 'make-up' values, Joh. Enschedé was the first printer to use computer engraved gravure (its worth noting, however, that these printings did not use the digitally re-mastered head).

A major change occurred during 1997 when a digitally re-mastered head was introduced. In conjunction to this, Royal Mail required all printers to adopt gravure for printing low value definitives. Furthermore, the most famous of the printers of British stamps, since before the first world war, Harrison & Sons Ltd. of High Wycombe, was absorbed into the De La Rue organisation.

In 2003 Questa was absorbed with the De La Rue organisation. The plant at High Wycombe was closed down and the complete operation, including paper stock, presses etc. was transferred to the Questa plant at Byfleet in Surrey. De La Rue have now moved their operation to Dunstable in Bedfordshire.

A further change took place with the demise of the large format high value stamps. At the start of the Machin series the high value series were recess-printed by Bradbury, Wilkinson & Co. Ltd. These were followed by the photogravure Machin head series by Harrison & Sons Ltd. between 1977 and 1988, and then by the Castles first and second issues from Harrison & Sons Ltd which were Recess printed. The re-engraved stamps from Enschedé followed in 1994. In 1999 the Castle high values were then replaced by the normal sized 'Machins' printed by Recess.

All these changes are reflected in the various sections of this catalogue with useful tips on aids to identification.

For clarity the printers are referred to as De La Rue, Harrison, Enschedé, Questa, Waddington and Walsall throughout this catalogue.

Photogravure

This was the main process used for printing Machin definitives until the introduction of computer engraved cylinders (see below) in 1991. Photogravure is an intaglio process, which means the stamp image is etched below the surface of the copper-printing cylinder. The printing area on the copper cylinder consists of minute cells of uniformed size and shape. These cells are all etched to different depths but the background area surrounding the cells is level. On the printing press the surface of the cylinder passes through a duct of liquid ink which fills the cells and also covers the non-printing areas.

As the curved surface of the cylinder emerges from the duct the background is cleaned by a steel (doctor) blade, which scrapes the surplus ink from the surface and allows it to fall back into the ink duct. The surface of the cylinder is then brought into contact with the paper. Although not visible to the naked eye the photogravure-printed stamps have a distinctive screen pattern. When viewed under a magnifying glass, they will reveal line as well as tone made up of minute dots of uniformed size and shape, as a result of the cells depositing a quantity of ink on the paper. Gradations of tone are obtained by etching the cells to different depths, so that more or less ink is carried by the cells and transferred to the paper according to their depth.

So, in photogravure, the screen dots are the same size but the volume of ink deposited on the paper by each cell varies in thickness. In the highlights and middle tones, the thinner films of ink allow more of the white paper to show through. Therefore it appears lighter than the darker areas, which are more deeply etched and deposit a thicker film of ink on the paper. Although photogravure cylinders have a very long life span a back-up cylinder will be made and in some cases such as first and second class issues, several backup cylinders will be produced. Photogravure cylinders are very expensive to produce and to prolong their life even further are often chromium plated. The backup cylinder will come in to use if the original cylinder has to be taken off for repair or to be re-chromed. When repaired the original cylinder will usually go back in to use.

Gravure

In this process the image is directly engraved onto the cylinder by a diamond stylus or laser instead of using a photographic plus acid etching method. The printing process itself is as described above but the resultant image is easily recognised as can be seen from the scans on Page G - 4. Various names have been given to this new system. 'New image' by the Post Office, 'gravure', 'electro mechanical engraving' and 'computer engraved'. As the main difference is in the actual engraving of the cylinder we refer to it as 'gravure'. The term photogravure is no longer used since the 'photo' part is no longer appropriate.

Offset Lithography

This process of printing was, until the introduction of computer engraved cylinders, used by Walsall Security Printers and The House of Questa for the printing of book panes, although Harrison & Sons do use the lithographic process for the printing of their book covers.

Lithography is a planographic printing process where the printing image and the non-printing background are in the same plane, and not raised in relief as in the case of letterpress printing (sometimes referred to as typographic), nor etched into the surface as in photogravure. It can also be referred to as a chemical printing process because it uses the natural repulsion of oil or grease by water as a means of determining which parts of a printing surface shall be inked and which parts remain uninked.

Lithographic plates used for stamp printing are made of a metal, this being either zinc or aluminium. These metal plates are reasonably cheap to produce. Since their life span is fairly short compared to photogravure cylinders, they are easily replaced. This is the main reason why there are so many plate combinations on lithography printed stamps.

The stamp image is put on to the plate photographically, and is done by photographing the original artwork for the stamp. This is then made up into the pane size of either four or ten stamps. The negative is next printed on to the metal plate, which has a thin film of light-sensitive coating on its surface. When exposed to light the coating hardens and on development in water the areas unaffected by light are washed away, leaving the water-insoluble coating as the image printing areas. The negative is correctly positioned and exposed on to the metal plate the required number of times by a 'step and repeat' camera.

The term 'offset lithography' literally means that the image on the plate, (when on the press and inked up), is transferred or offset on to a rubber blanket and then from this blanket the image is transferred to the paper. This is done to give some flexibility between the plate and the paper.

Stamps printed by lithography when only printed in one colour, as with some Regional issues, are very flat with little tonal range, when compared to their photogravure counterparts. For this reason more than one plate is normally used and can be up to four plates, although Walsall used three plates for their first class stamps and Questa used two. Both of these printers used two plates for their second class stamps. Each plate prints a slightly different shade of the colour required and also prints a different part of the stamp. The background is on one plate, the head on a second plate and the background and head combined on a third plate. This third combined plate prints different parts of the head to the second plate.

The blue of the second class stamps only requires two plates to produce the same stamp as that printed by photogravure, these being one plate for the background and the other plate for the head. The direction of printing on lithographic stamps cannot be identified but it would normally be upright or inverted.

Stamps printed by photogravure are very easy to distinguish from the lithographic printed stamps. The simplest way to determine them is under magnification using a x10 glass. The edge of the stamp frame on a photogravure printing has spikes pointing in the direction which it was printed. This will only appear on one edge and will also help to distinguish the direction of print which can be either left, right, upright or inverted. Stamps printed by offset lithography normally have a straight clean edge on all four sides.

The information produced here on the printing of Machin definitives is only very brief but we hope will give an insight into the printing of our stamps and will also help to identify stamps printed by either photogravure or lithography.

It was always intended that Machin's sculpted bust should be reproduced only in photogravure, and many people feel that no completely satisfactory lithographic reproduction has yet been achieved. Offset-lithography is however a much cheaper process, but is also a less secure process i.e. can be forged more easily then gravure.

It is important to remember that for the first twelve years of the design's life, and whilst collectors were developing most of the terminology in use today, Harrisons printed all the small format stamps. When discussing technical aspects of stamp production comparisons are all too often made with the Harrison standard. Lithography is a completely different process and such comparisons are not always valid. In the notes following it may be assumed that references to offset lithography are common to Questa, Waddington & Walsall, those to photogravure are to both Harrisons & Enschedé. Many descriptions are common to both processes but comparisons between actual stamps should be drawn with care. (The computer engraved gravure process is common to all printers).

Recess

This printing process is also referred to as either Intaglio or line engraved. Recess printing falls into the same group of printing methods as gravure in that the design will be cut/etched into the printing plate/cylinder. This is achieved by :-

      Recess - engraved lines and dots   Gravure - screened image etching / engraving

Initially, the design will be engraved onto a master die in soft steel. Depending on the complexity of the design this can take many weeks and requires a highly skilled craftsman. This is why the method is generally associated with 'High' values. Once engraved the master die will be hardened. Various methods of taking the master die to the printing plate have been employed for the Machin recess printed stamps :-

£.s.d

From the master die a transfer roller was made and this was used to 'roll' out multiple images onto the printing plate. This consisted of 160 stamp images, arranged into four panes of 40 (5 x 8).

Decimal 'High' values 1970-1977

Again, the master die was used to create a transfer roller which was used to 'roll' out multiple images onto a 'Master' printing plate. This consisted of 100 stamp images, arranged in one pane of 10 x 10. The 'Master' plate is then used to create the working / printing plates. Many printing plates can be created from the 'Master'. This procedure was later revised to produce double pane printing plates.

Decimal small format 'High' values 1999-2003

The small format 'High' values introduced in 1999 used the world renowned master engraver Czeslaw Slania to create the die master for these issues. The value tablet position on the die master was not engraved which enabled the same head to be used for each of the four values - separate engravings were made for each of the value tablets. The same Slania die master was used by both Enschedé and De La Rue. Different techniques were used to manufacture the 'Master' and working plates - a detail account used by De La Rue can be found in the British Philatelic Bulletin June 2001 (Vol 38 No.10). The printing plates were in the main double pane consisting of 100 (10 x 10) in each pane. The Giori press used four of these plates concurrently during printing.

Letterpress

This printing process is also referred to as typography, surface printed or relief printed. The process is effectively the opposite of Recess in that the design is raised above the surface of the printing plate. This method can be described in terms of woodblock printing whereby the parts of the design not to be printed is cut away. This leaves the parts to be printed as raised surfaces which take the ink (the design is in reverse), the woodblock is then pressed against the paper.

It has only been used once to produce the Machin definitive in a booklet pane from the 'Profile on Print' prestige book issued in 1999 (the pane containing 4 x 1st Black NVI and printed by Harrison - the phosphor bands were printed in Litho).

Embossing

The process creates a raised profile of the design in relief by making an impression in the paper, a corollary is the head on a coin or medal. It is not necessary for a coloured ink to be used with this method although one often is.

This process has only been used to produce the Machin definitive in a booklet pane from the 'Profile on Print' prestige book issued in 1999 (the self adhesive pane containing 4 x 1st NVI and printed by Walsall - the value tablet in grey and the phosphor was printed in Litho).

Head Types

Photogravure and Gravure

Four distinct types and several sub-types of varying importance exist. For the stamps with solid backgrounds types A & B have been adopted. Head A shows a flat base to the portrait, head B shows it curved. There are also numerous minor variations between the two types.

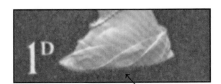 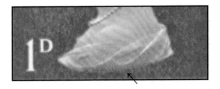

Head A with 'Flat' base   Head B with 'Curved' base

For stamps with a light coloured background which varies in density across the width of the stamp (e.g. the 6p value), head type C is used. For stamps which show evenly toned, light coloured, backgrounds (e.g. the 13p value) head D is used. Head B exists in two major types:- 'B1', the so-called 'small head' used for both the pre-decimal and the decimal issues and 'B2', 'large head'. This was first seen in 1976 and which is very similar except that the portrait is set lower, so that the tip of the bust is much nearer the lower frame line.

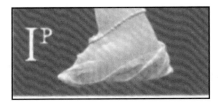

Head B2 with portrait set lower

There is also a missing photogravure-screening dot on the lower frame line near the left corner, common to all 'head B1' printings, which has been 'repaired'. Head C exists in two types - the standard 'head C' was used throughout except for two printings showing the portrait set lower, but as good a variety as 'head B2' above. Head D is consistent throughout except that some show a screen dot missing on the lower frame line, approx. 6.5mm from the left corner. Reduced size versions of all of the above were used for Regional issues, together with a variation of head D which shows a shaded space in the top of the central cross.

The gravure printed normal stamps are the B2 Head but are computer engraved.

     Head C with graduated background   Head D with solid line at base

The Millennium head stamps were introduced in the year 2000. Printed by De La Rue, Questa and Walsall, each printer's stamps can be identified without any philatelic aid. Walsall printings show three clear jewels at back of the crown, whilst Questa printings show the top of the crown cut off. Many other differences exist.

    De La Rue   Questa   Walsall

Lithography

The situation here is much more confused. The way in which the plastic plates are made has permitted a lot of minor variations and versions of head types A, B, C, D, both full size and reduced for Regional issues. In no case so far, however, has more than one obvious variation been used on any particular value and we list only the basic types, which should be recognisable from the Photogravure illustrations above.

Screened values

A number of printings show 'screened values', the result of the (unintentional) presence of photogravure screening dots in the white value area, or, occasionally, 'screened borders' where the inter-stamp gutters were inadequately masked out during production of the cylinder. Occasionally the whole of a printing is affected. A magnifying glass (x10) is required to detect these popular variations.

Phosphors

Many of the Machin issues have phosphor bands; either one or two set vertically at the centre or side(s) of the stamps. Bands are usually 4mm or from 9.5mm (across pair of stamps), but there have been exceptions, which are shown in the text. Harrison & Enschedé bands were applied by screened photogravure cylinders; Waddington's bands by unscreened typographic plates, and Questa's and Walsall's lithographic stamps by unscreened lithographic plates. All bands are now printed gravure and are unscreened.

From 1967 to 1993 all phosphor had Terephthalic acid as the activator. Harrisons call this Lettalite B3; philatelists generally refer to it as 'violet' or 'B3'. Under UV the phosphorescence is violet. Two errors occurred. A 2½p printing was made using green 'B1' phosphor in error, and the so-called 'jet' printings (see below) are a mixture of violet and green reacting inks, which glow a dirty yellow under the lamp.

From 1986 onwards Harrison's used a new phosphor, similar to 'B3' but using a different, almost transparent, solvent, which makes the bands much less obvious under natural light. This is described as 'A' Phosphor.

All phosphors show some fluorescence as well as phosphorescence. In 1991 a further new phosphor was introduced having strong yellow fluorescence and violet/blue phosphorescence. This is described as 'C'. The level of reaction of the yellow fluorescence varied from a very bright yellow to a pale greyish-yellow.

1995 saw a further change with the phosphor having blue fluorescence and blue/violet phosphorescence. This is described as 'D'. The changes to fluorescence, changes to adhesives from blue to white, and variations in the amount of optical brightening agent in the stamp paper means all collectors need to be vigilant at all times. Regular contact with your suppliers is essential if you wish to maintain the completeness of your collection.

All phosphors, excepting the 'blue' of the Wilding era and errors, have stronger phosphorescence at short wave than long wave. In 1994 a phosphor, which has stronger phosphorescence, such that it can easily be detected with long wave UV lamp was observed. Known, as 'Novaglo', the name of the company understood to manufacture the phosphor. Note that many other stamps show long wave phosphorescence, but are less bright.

For the identification of all different paper and phosphor types short wave and long wave ultraviolet lamps are essential. There are many models available, both battery operated and mains operated. Dual versions (interchangeable short & long wave tubes) are also available. Each lamp type has its own benefits and disadvantages.

Both the short wave and long wave versions are available with and without optical filters. In checking fluorescence of the B3 and 'A' phosphors a short wave with filter version is needed. In checking fluorescence of later phosphors a long wave version (without filter) is preferable.

Phosphor Bands

Normal phosphor banded stamps can have either a single band placed at the centre, left or right or two bands placed at either side. However the width of these can vary depending on several factors. Centre bands can be either 4mm or 4.5mm in width. Two band stamps are usually derived from 9.5mm bands printed across the perforations. Therefore each band (in theory) should be 4.75mm in width. However, as the registraion is not always accurate, the space *between* each band should be measured. As the small format stamps are 21mm wide and, in this case, the bands are 9.5mm wide the resulting space between the bands is 11.5mm.

Phosphor screens

Phosphor screens of 150, 250 and for the 1991 Enschedé stamps only 300 dots per linear inch screens have been used. Both 150 and 250 screens were used for a number of printings and these may be readily identified, with practice, using a x10 or x15 magnifier in good light. The 250 screen is very fine, the 150 much coarser by comparison. In both cases one normally sees a grid (you are seeing the 'streets', not the 'houses'), and it is the density of the grid which is important. Occasionally 150 screens can be seen with the naked eye. Conversely the screen may be 'clogged' in printing. These can be very difficult to distinguish without some experience.

'JET' phosphors

Named after its discoverer, Mr. J.E. Thompson, this is the result of the contamination of violet phosphor with green phosphor ink not intended for stamps. It glows a dirty yellow colour under long wave UV, but is more easily identified by viewing the stamp through a thin film of plastic, such as the front of a Prinz or Hawid mount. This gives a good reaction to long wave UV which is not found on normal 'B3' stamps.

Phosphor under Ink

Much the simplest (and the only reliable non-chemical) method for the identification of these is to hold the stamp up to the light and to look from the gummed side. In the area covered by the phosphor band the stamp is actually lighter than in the non-phosphor area. This is caused by the fact that the first layer of ink (be it colour or phosphor) effectively seals the surface, so that subsequent layers do not soak in well and in consequence more of the ink evaporates off. This effect is best seen on the lighter stamps - 4½p, 6p etc., but is visible on other values.

Short band, Inset and Stepped Bands

Where phosphor bands are short, inset or stepped they are described as such in the text. Please note that all short and inset bands must be clear of the normal perforations (not necessarily the elliptical perforations) to qualify for inclusion in this catalogue.

Perforations

Various perforation gauges have been employed and the main ones are given below:
* Harrison, and De La Rue, stamps are perforated 14¾ x 14;
* The Questa, Walsall and Waddington litho issues were originally perf. 13½ x 14 but this was later changed to perf 14¾ x 14,
* A printing of the Walsall litho 1st class N.V.I. book is known perforated 12¾ x 13 in error,
* The Questa gravure issues are perf. 14 x 14,
* The Walsall gravure sheet printings are perf. 14¾ x 14, whilst the gravure Prestige books are perf. 14 x14, with the Label books being perf 14¾ x 14, but with smaller holes and ellipses,
* The Bradbury Wilkinson High Value issues are perforated 12 x 12,
* The Harrison 'Machin' photogravure high values are 14 x 15.
* The decimal 'Castles' are perforated 15 x 14, as is the £10 'Britannia'.

Unfortunately no two authorities on this subject ever quote quite the same set of figures for the above. We show those most commonly used by collectors.

Perforators

A number of different techniques exist for producing the actual perforation holes. These are broadly as follows:

The 'Comb' perforator

The original type of perforator is still in use after 140 years. These use precisely engineered male and female dies. Perforation is slow but the results are excellent, with perfectly formed 'flat' holes. Minor errors in spacing at the intersection of one strike with another are often noticed.

The 'Kampf' perforator

This perforated the stamps 'in the web' and comprised a precisely engineered 'male' drum, with rows of pins projecting outwards, whilst the female die was a similar drum, but without the pins and blanketed with a thick rubber sheet. The method may be quite crude but it is very effective. The holes, being punched through at speed, are not perfectly circular and the individual discs of paper are frequently not punched out completely and so cling to the edges of the holes.

The Swedish 'Lawnmower' and APS Perforators

These draw the paper over raised 'pimples' to produce the holes in relief and the tops of these are then shaved or ground off with abrasives, from the gummed side. The holes are perfectly circular but 'debris' of paper and gum normally surrounds all or part of the holes and occasionally they are not cut through completely, so that a thin film covers each. This type of perforator has been in use since the late 1960s and Harrison's Ab Produktion Svenska (APS) machine is the latest development.

Straight sided and elliptically perforated stamps

During 1987 the first issues appeared with officially sanctioned straight edges on one or more sides. Since 1993 stamps showing elliptical perforations, as an anti-forgery 'security' measure, have appeared and are now included on almost every issue.

Straight Edge stamps

The vast majority of Machin issues have perforations to which we are all accustomed. Straight edged stamps, which only had a short life span, can therefore be described as imperforate and this is the term that is used throughout this catalogue.

Direction of printing (DOP), Photogravure and Gravure issues only.

This is beyond the scope of this catalogue but can be found in the Machin Collectors Club Specialised catalogue..

Papers

Paper variations have occurred on both the pre-decimal and decimal issues. On the Decimal issue the first type used was OCP (Original Coated Paper), which is off-white to cream in appearance and dull under UV light. FCP (Fluorescent Coated Paper) was introduced during 1971 and is much whiter and more fluorescent under UV light.
Experiments incorporating the phosphor into the paper coating go back to 1968 but large-scale production did not begin until 1979. Five different types are recognised:

* PCP (Phosphor Coated Paper): A largely experimental stock with some minor variations in finish but broadly similar to PCP1 (below) except for the weaker afterglow.
* PCP1 (Phosphor Coated Paper 1): A semi-shiny surface with a strong afterglow.
* PCP2: A highly glossy surface generally producing richly coloured stamps.
* ACP (Advanced Coated Paper): A semi-shiny surface, similar to PCP1, but with a very strong afterglow and appearing bright under UV (as bright as FCP - by comparison PCP/PCP1/PCP2 are as dull as OCP).
* PPP (Phosphor Pre-printed Paper): FCP paper to which an overall phosphor coating (150 screen) was applied under the ink. The surface is very matt and the stamp printing often blotchy.

During 1993 the decision was taken to remove all Optical Brightening Agents from the papers (these are significant pollutants) and three new papers have appeared in consequence.

* OFNP/SA (OBA Free Non-phosphor Paper): This is a paper/gum term and is used in all self-adhesive issues. Reaction to long wave UV light similar to that of OFNP, although the paper texture appears smoother. Note that whilst this is described as coated paper, other papers are also coated.
* OFNP (OBA Free Non-phosphor Paper): Used in conjunction with phosphor bands this replaced FCP.
* OFPP (OBA Free Phosphorised Paper): Replaced PCP/ACP.

Paper varieties

Varnished paper

Varnish was applied to sub standard paper both under and over the phosphor ink (on the 9p violet FCP/PVAD stamp) and was also used on the ½p (Cylinder 8 FCP/PVAD) and the Scottish 12½ p (plate 7A 7B). These two varieties can be easily distinguished by holding the stamp at an angle to the light. Where the phosphor has been applied over the varnish, the bands are quite visible, but where applied under the varnish, they are barely visible.

Translucent paper

Some books have appeared on both 'normal' and translucent papers with some falling in between. To determine the degree of translucency, lay the stamp side face down on a dark surface. Under normal lighting conditions the image will appear clear, if the paper is of the translucent type. It is very difficult to describe in print more accurately than this - comparison is always far more conclusive.

Thin paper

As paper thickness can vary in a normal production run, only those with a marked difference from the normal are listed. As with translucent paper, comparison is recommended for positive identification.

Silicone Coated Paper

This was an experimental coating designed to prevent coil stamps in vending machines sticking together. They can be distinguished (by comparison to a normal stamp) by holding them at an angle to the light looking across the phosphor bands, where they (the phosphor bands) appear much less distinct.

Uncoated Paper

Normal paper has a chalk coating which enhances the printed image. Where this has been omitted the stamp has a flatter appearance, shows no UV reaction and does not respond to the 'silver' test.

Glazed Paper

These stamps show a marked shiny effect most noticeable between the phosphor bands, and are easily recognised when compared to the normal stamp.

Adhesives

The identification of the adhesives used for the Decimal series should prove no problem to you. They are best described as follows: -

GA - Gum Arabic

This is always shiny in appearance and can be verified by looking at the back of the stamp with a x10 glass. You will notice a 'crazy paving' appearance in the adhesive. Gum Arabic also has a tendency to curl very easily and can be confirmed by placing the stamp on your palm - The warmth and moisture from your hand will soon make it curl.

PVA - Polyvinyl Alcohol

PVA is normally matt in appearance although it can sometimes appear with sheen but it lacks the 'crazy paving' effect of Gum Arabic. It does not curl as readily as GA either. The colour of PVA ranges from near white to a light brown but with the differences mentioned above should be easily identified.
In 1994 Harrisons issued some sheets of the 19p on Cylinder 3 using a new formulation of PVA with no dextrin added giving a matt and creamy appearance. It was also noticed that a further printing from Cylinder 3, shortly afterwards, appeared translucent and more white. It was later established that the cause of this was in fact a change of paper thickness and NOT a change to the additive in the adhesive.

PVA (Lay flat) - Non Curl

Introduced gradually since 1996 this adhesive has the property of resisting curling in conditions of high humidity. It is generally very matt in appearance and slightly cream in colour, it is often referred to as 'lay flat'.

PVAD - Polyvinyl Alcohol with Dextrin added

PVAD with the very familiar bluish-green tint has been used in the vast majority of Machin issues; it frequently appears ribbed or mottled. Some printings by the House of Questa have been on paper supplied by Henry Leigh Slater, which has Dextrine adhesive, but with the greenish dye omitted. This reacts chemically as Dextrine (it still contains the starch) but looks very much like PVA. When checking adhesives it is preferable to do so in natural daylight (not direct sunlight), although the modern Halogen hobby lamps may be useful.

Forgeries

Between 1872 and 1993 it seems that no GB stamp was forged, at least not on a commercial basis, or perhaps the forgers were never detected. In the Summer of 1993, copies of the then recently issued 24p rust stamp, which was then the current first class rate, began to appear in the South East of England. The forgers, it seems, had taken advantage of Royal Mail's decision to sell stamps at a discount to retail outlets and gone into business themselves.

We understand that stamps were sold in sheets, or part sheets, and not books, at 20p per stamp. This discount was much greater than that offered by Royal Mail and was obviously attractive to retailers who were not too concerned about buying stamps in this way.

The forged stamps can be easily distinguished by the following characteristics:

* They are perforated gauge 11, instead of the normal 14 or 15,
* The perforated stamps show a peculiar arrangement of holes at the corners of the stamps
* The gum is very shiny,
* The paper quality is very poor,
* The stamps were non-phosphor, which caused letters to be rejected at sorting centres.

About one year later another forgery appeared which was markedly superior to the 24p. This was the so-called 'Questa' 2nd class NVI. This stamp, unlike its predecessor, appeared in books (the covers of which were also forged) and loose panes.

The book and stamps have variously been attributed as rejected Questa printings, or trials, or the result of some nefarious unauthorised activities by an employee or employees at Questa. The House of Questa had always vehemently denied this.

The stamps themselves were produced to a remarkably high standard. The perforations were of the correct gauge, although these extended much further into the wider margin than is usual on normal Questa books. The elliptical security perforations, which must have caused the forgers considerable difficulties, invariably slope to the right.

On some stamps within the pane they are placed slightly higher than on others. The stamps have a central phosphor band, but this produces no afterglow under UV light, although there is some yellow fluorescence under the lamp. On the examples seen, the stamps are a paler blue than the originals and have a blurred appearance. The forgers apparently did not attempt to produce the familiar Questa logo as no plate books have ever been found. The book covers are good enough to fool the general public (with no disrespect!) but again are easily distinguishable as fakes.

The cover is 50mm wide against the normal 48mm and on a thin card. The locking tab is the right shape and in the right place, but slightly larger. The colours used on the outside of the cover are close to the original, although there are minor differences. The facsimile stamp is much darker and again blurred in appearance. This is the most obvious visible sign. Inside, the cover is shiny instead of being matt and those troublesome glue spots, characteristic of all Questa books, are absent.

Although Royal Mail's enquiry's into these forgeries continued for a while, it now seems unlikely, given the time that has passed, that any prosecutions will be made, or indeed whether further information will be made available.

Source Identification

Source

There can be a considerable difference in the value of any single stamp through its source. This guide is NOT comprehensive, but using other attributes such as value, colour, paper/gum combination and phosphor bands, positive source identification should hold no difficulties. Identifying a stamps source is achieved by looking at the perforations on each edge which can be either torn or guillotined.

Guillotined perforations   **Torn perforations with fibrous ends**

Follow these guidelines and the task is normally straighforward - The arrows on the following illustrations indicate *guillotined* edges.

1. On Sheet stamps all four sides are always torn.
3. On Horizontal coils stamps both the top and bottom sides are guillotined.
2. On Vertical coil stamps both the left and right sides are guillotined.

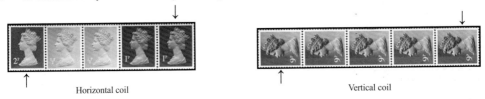

Horizontal coil   Vertical coil

4. On Machine (Vending) books the left and right sides of the *pane* are guillotined i.e. on any individual stamp either the left or right side is guillotined. The bottom stamps can be either torn or guillotined

5. On Counter books the top, bottom and right edges of the *pane* are guillotined i.e. on any single stamp *either* the top or bottom is guillotined and other sides are torn or, if they are from the end of the pane opposite the selvedge then two adjacent sides are guillotined.

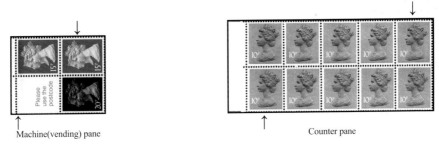

Machine(vending) pane   Counter pane

6. On Prestige panes (below right) if the stamps are totally separated from the original pane then all four sides would be torn and this could cause difficulty if there are no other attributes to consider. It is recommended therefore that, whenever possible, stamps from Prestige books be collected with the adjacent selvedge to prove its source.

Basic Machin Collecting

This additional listing had been introduced following requests from readers of the 13th Edition of the Stoneham catalogue.
It lists all the *basic* machins from this highly successful and long running series. A more comprehensive listing will be found on following pages for readers who wish
to extend their interests of this fascinating series. Any reader who is interested in studying Machins is highly recommended to join the Machin Collectors Club. See
their advertisments throughout this catalogue.

Pre-Decimal Machin - Basic Set

No.		U/M	F/U
½d	Orange	10	15
1d	2B Olive	5	10
1d	CB Olive	25	35
2d	2B Lake brown Type I	15	20
2d	2B Lake brown Type II	10	15
2d	CB Lake brown Type II	30	45
3d	CB Violet	5	10
3d	2B Violet	15	25
4d	2B Sepia	5	10
4d	2B Deep olive	5	10
4d	CB Vermilion	5	10
4d	LB Vermilion	70	90
4d	RB Vermilion	1.00	1.45
5d	2B Dark blue	6	10
6d	2B Reddish purple	12	15
7d	2B Bright emerald	30	35
8d	2B Vermilion	8	20
8d	2B Light blue	20	30
9d	2B Deep green	15	15
10d	2B Drab	20	25
1s	2B Violet	15	20
1s 6d	2B Pale blue & Deep blue	20	20
1s 9d	2B Bright orange & Black	25	20
	Full set as above	5.00	5.75
	Basic set 16 values	1.20	2.00

For illustration of different 2d types see page G - 13

Decimal Machin - Basic Sets

Photogravure printed by Harrison with phosphor bands

No.		U/M	F/U
½p	2B Turquoise	10	15
½p	LB Turquoise	£34	£17
½p	CB Turquoise	15	20
1p	2B Crimson	5	15
1p	CB Crimson	15	15
1p	Crimson All over phosphor	15	15
1p	LB Crimson	60	75
1p	RB Crimson	1.60	1.60
1½p	2B Black	15	15
2p	2B Green	15	15
2p	Green All over phosphor	15	15
2½p	CB Magenta	10	15
2½p	LB Magenta	60	70
2½p	RB Magenta	70	80
2½p	2B Magenta	15	20
2½p	2B Rose red	20	25
3p	2B Ultramarine	15	15
3p	CB Ultramarine	15	20
3p	2B Magenta	15	20
3½p	2B Olive-grey	15	20
3½p	CB Olive-grey	15	20
3½p	CB Purple-brown	60	65
4p	2B Ochre-brown	15	15
4p	2B Greenish-blue	65	75
4p	CB Pale Greenish-blue	60	65
4p	RB Greenish-blue	75	80
4p	LB Greenish-blue	75	85
4½p	2B Deep steel blue	15	15
5p	2B Pale violet	15	15
5p	CB Claret	90	65
5½p	2B Deep purple	20	20
5½p	CB Deep purple	15	20

No.		U/M	F/U
6p	2B Light green	20	20
6½p	2B Greenish-blue	25	30
6½p	CB Greenish-blue	20	15
6½p	LB Greenish-blue	35	40
6½p	RB Greenish-blue	40	40
7p	2B Purple-brown	15	10
7p	CB Purple-brown	15	15
7p	LB Purple-brown	20	30
7p	RB Purple-brown	30	35
7½p	2B Pale chestnut	20	15
8p	2B Red	15	10
8p	CB Red	15	15
8p	LB Red	30	35
8p	RB Red	30	35
8½p	2B Light yellow-green	20	15
9p	2B Black & Orange	30	25
9p	2B Violet	20	20
9½p	2B Purple	25	25
10p	2B Orange & Deep brown	20	15
10p	2B Light orange	20	10
10p	2B Light orange Type II Redrawn	12.50	13.00
10p	Light orange All over phosphor	20	25
10p	CB Light orange	20	20
10p	LB Light orange	30	35
10p	RB Light orange	30	35
10½p	2B Yellow	20	20
10½	2B Dull blue	30	25
11p	2B Brown-red	25	20
11½p	CB Drab	25	15
11½p	LB Drab	30	35
11½p	RB Drab	30	35
12p	2B Yelow-green	25	25
12p	CB Emerald	25	20
12p	LB Emerald	35	35
12p	RB Emerald	35	35
12½p	CB Light emerald	25	20
12½p	LB Light emerald	30	30
12½p	RB Light emerald	30	30
13p	CB Chestnut	30	25
13p	LB Chestnut	35	35
13p	RB Chestnut	35	35
14p	2B Grey-blue	35	40
14p	CB Dark blue	20	20
14p	RB Dark blue	2.00	2.10
15p	CB Blue	25	25
15p	LB Blue	1.90	2.00
15p	RB Blue	1.50	1.40
15½p	2B Pale violet	30	35
16p	2B Drab	80	85
17p	2B Grey-blue	35	40
17p	CB Deep blue	25	30
17p	LB Deep blue	1.00	1.90
1/p	RB Deep blue	1.10	1.15
18p	2B Dull olive-grey	35	40
18p	2B Bright green	35	35
19p	2B Orange-red	85	90
20p	2B Dull purple	50	45
20p	2B Black	80	80
22p	2B Orange	60	60
25p	2B Salmon pink	2.00	2 10
26p	2B Rosine	4.50	4.75
31p	2B Mauve	8.50	8.70
34p	2B Ochre-brown	4.20	4.50
50p	2B Ochre	1.00	25
50p	2B Sand	2.50	2.90
	Full set as listed above	90.00	72.00

Non-elliptical

No.   U/M   F/U

Basic Sets

No.

Machin Definitives

            U/M   F/U

Photogravure printed by Harrison on phosphorised paper

		U/M	F/U
½p	Turquoise	10	10
1p	Crimson	10	10
2p	Myrtle green	10	10
2p	Deep green - Redrawn value	10	10
2p	Myrtle green - Redrawn value	1.50	1.50
2½p	Rose red	10	12
3p	Magenta	10	10
3p	Magenta - Redrawn value	30	30
3½p	Dull chestnut	25	25
4p	Greenish-blue	10	15
4p	Pale greenish-blue	15	20
4p	New blue	10	15
5p	Pale violet	20	15
5p	Dull red-brown	10	15
6p	Lime green	10	15
7p	Brick red	85	90
8½p	Yellow-green	20	30
10p	Orange-brown	20	20
10p	Light tan - Redrawn value	50	40
11p	Orange-pink	40	40
11½p	Ochre-brown	30	30
12p	Yellow-green	25	25
13p	Olive-grey	30	30
13½p	Purple-brown	35	30
14p	Grey-blue	25	20
15p	Ultramarine	30	25
15½p	Pale violet	30	25
16p	Pale drab	30	20
16½p	Pale chestnut	45	30
17p	Light emerald	35	30
17p	Slate blue	30	15
17½p	Pale chestnut	40	45
18p	Violet	35	30
18p	Olive grey	35	25
19p	Orange-red	40	30
19½p	Olive grey	90	90
20p	Dull purple	45	20
20p	Sea-green	35	35
20p	Black	30	30
20½p	Ultramarine	65	65
22p	Blue	40	20
22p	Yellow-green	40	30
22p	Orange	35	35
23p	Brown-red	70	60
23p	Bright green	45	50
24p	Violet	75	80
24p	Indian red	80	80
24p	Red-brown	40	40
25p	Dull purple	50	30
26p	Rosine Type I	50	35
26p	Rosine Type II Re-drawn value	1.40	2.00
26p	Stone	50	55
27p	Rust brown	60	65
27p	Violet	65	70
28p	Dull violet	60	65
28p	Yellow ochre	1.10	1.10
28p	Slate	70	70
29p	Ochre-brown	1.20	1.25
29p	Purple	1.20	1.25
30p	Sage green	60	65
31p	Mauve	60	65
31p	Blue	70	70
32p	Dark turquoise	70	75
33p	Emerald	65	70
34p	Ochre-brown	80	85
34p	Slate	70	75
34p	Purple	90	90
35p	Dark brown	80	85
35p	Deep yellow	75	80
37p	Red	70	70
39p	Bright mauve	85	90

Photogravure printed by Harrison on ordinary paper
(No phosphor reaction under long wave ultra violet light)

		U/M	F/U
50p	Drab ochre	95	40
50p	Ochre Re-drawn value	95	40
75p	Black Re-drawn value	2.00	80
	Full set as listed above - 74 values	£30	£31

Litho printed by Waddington Perf 13½ x 14

		U/M	F/U
4p	2B Greenish blue	12	15
4p	Greenish blue All over phosphor	22	22
20p	2B Deep purple & Dull purple	60	60
20p	Deep purple & Dull purple All over phosphor	80	75

Litho printed by Questa
All are Perf 15 x 14 unless stated otherwise

		U/M	F/U
2p	Green Perf 13½ x 14	25	25
2p	Green	25	20
2p	Green Re-drawn value	40	40
4p	Greenish-blue	30	20
5p	Pale violet Perf 13½ x 14	20	25
5p	Claret Perf 13½ x 14	35	35
5p	Claret	35	35
13p	CB Pale chestnut	40	50
13p	LB Pale chestnut	50	55
13p	RB Pale chestnut	50	55
14p	CBar Dark blue	95	1.00
17p	CB Dark blue	45	50
18p	Grey-olive All over phosphor	35	40
18p	2B Grey-olive	4.20	4.30
18p	CB Bright green	70	75
18p	LB Bright green	1.40	1.60
18p	RB Bright green	1.00	1.10
19p	Orange-red All over phosphor	1.50	1.30
20p	Deep sepia & purple All over phosphor	65	70
22p	2B Bright yellow-green	5.50	6.00
22p	Orange All over phosphor	45	50
24p	Chestnut All over phosphor	45	50
24p	2B Chestnut	45	50
33p	Emerald All over phosphor	1.25	1.35
33p	2B Emerald	1.00	1.10
34p	2B Ochre-brown	5.00	5.50
39p	2B Bright mauve	1.00	1.00
75p	Non phosphor Black Perf 13½ x 14	2.10	45
75p	Non phosphor Black	2.25	65
75p	Black Re-drawn value	5.50	5.50

Litho printed by Walsall
All are Perf 14 and imperforate on one or more sides

		U/M	F/U
2p	Deep green	75	80
14p	RB Dark blue - Imperf at left	1.95	2.20
19p	2B Orange-red - Imperf at right	1.50	1.50
24p	Brown	55	60
29p	2B Purple	2.50	2.70
29p	Purple All over phosphor	2.70	3.00
31p	Blue	1.00	1.10
33p	Emerald	70	75
39p	Bright mauve	80	80
	Full set as listed above - 43 values	£48	£4

1840 Anniversary Issues

Photogravure printed by Harrison

		U/M	F/U
15p	**CB Blue**	40	40
15p	**CB Blue** Imperforate top	45	44
15p	**CB Blue** Imperforate bottom	45	45
15p	**LB Blue**	1.95	1.95
15p	**RB Blue**	1.40	1.50
20p	**Black** ACP Imperforate top	60	55
20p	**Black** ACP Imperforate bottom	60	55
20p	**Black** ACP Imperforate top & right	1.00	95
20p	**Black** ACP Imperforate bottom & right	90	95
20p	**Black** ACP Imperforate left	65	70
20p	**Black** ACP Imperforate right	50	55
20p	**2B Black**	1.50	1.50
29p	**Purple** ACP	80	85
29p	**2B Purple**	4.25	4.40
34p	**Slate** ACP	90	90
37p	**Red** ACP	90	90

Litho printed by Walsall

		U/M	F/U
15p	**CB Blue** Imperforate top	70	70
15p	**CB Blue** Imperforate bottom	70	70
15p	**CB Blue** Imperforate top & right	1.10	1.15
15p	**CB Blue** Imperforate bottom & right	1.10	1.15
20p	**Black** ACP Imperforate top	75	75
20p	**Black** ACP Imperforate bottom	75	75
20p	**Black** ACP Imperforate top & right	95	95
20p	**Black** ACP Imperforate bottom & right	95	95
20p	**Black** ACP Imperforate right	1.00	1.00
20p	**Black** ACP Imperforate left	1.50	1.60

Litho printed by Questa

		U/M	F/U
15p	**CB Blue**	1.15	1.20
20p	**Black ACP**	1.25	1.50
1st	**Black**	70	75

NVI Non Value Indicator Issues

Photogravure printed by Harrison

		U/M	F/U
2nd	**CB Blue** Imperforate top	50	55
2nd	**CB Blue** Imperforate bottom	50	55
2nd	**CB Blue** Imperforate top & right	5.00	5.00
2nd	**CB Blue** Imperforate bottom & right	5.00	5.00
2nd	**RB Blue** Normal perfs	1.30	1.35
1st	**Black ACP** Imperforate top	65	70
1st	**Black ACP** Imperforate bottom	65	70
1st	**Black ACP** Imperforate top & right	6.50	6.50
1st	**Black ACP** Imperforate bottom & right	6.50	6.50
1st	**2B Black** Nor,mal perfs	1.30	1.35
2nd	**CB Dark blue** Imperforate top	50	55
2nd	**CB Dark blue** Imperforate bottom	50	55
1st	**Orange-red** Imperforate top	70	75
1st	**Orange-red** Imperforate bottom	70	75

Litho printed by Walsall

		U/M	F/U
2nd	**CB Blue** Imperforate top	50	60
2nd	**CB Blue** Imperforate bottom	50	60
2nd	**CB Blue** Imperforate top & right	65	75
2nd	**CB Blue** Imperforate bottom & right	65	75
1st	**2B Black** Imperforate top	1.25	1.25
1st	**2B Black** Imperforate bottom	1.25	1.25
1st	**2B Black** Imperforate top & right	1.25	1.25
1st	**2B Black** Imperforate bottom & right	1.25	1.25
2nd	**CB Dark blue** Imperforate top	50	50
2nd	**CB Dark blue** Imperforate bottom	50	50
1st	**Orange-red** ACP Perf 14 Imperforate top	60	65
1st	**Orange-red** ACP Perf 14 Imperforate bottom	60	65
1st	**Orange-red** ACP Perf 13 Imperforate top	1.10	1.20
1st	**Orange-red** ACP Perf 13 Imperforate bottom	1.10	1.20

Litho printed by Questa

		U/M	F/U
2nd	CB Bright blue	60	65
2nd	RB Bright blue	1.50	1.50
2nd	LB Bright blue	1.50	1.50
1st	Black ACP	1.25	1.25
2nd	CB Dark blue	1.00	1.10
1st	Orange-red ACP	50	55
1st	2B Orange-red	70	70

Elliptical
No.

Basic Sets
U/M F/U No.

Machin Definitives
U/M F/U

Elliptical Issues

Photogravure/Gravure printed
All are perf 15 x 14 unless stated otherwise

		U/M	F/U
1p	2B Crimson	10	10
2p	2B Deep green	10	12
4p	2B New blue	10	12
5p	2B Dull Red-brown	10	15
6p	2B Yellow-olive	30	35
7p	2B Grey	3.00	3.10
7p	2B Magenta	15	20
8p	2B Yellow	15	30
9p	2B Yellow-orange	20	20
10p	2B Dull orange	20	25
10p	2B Dull orange Perf 14	1.20	1.30
12p	2B Greenish-blue	20	25
14p	2B Salmon pink	22	27
16p	2B Pink	25	30
19p	CB Bistre	40	45
19p	RB Bistre Perf 14	1.20	1.30
20p	2B Turquoise-green	60	70
20p	CB Bright green	40	45
20p	RB Bright green	90	95
20p	2B Bright green	50	55
25p	Rose-red AOP	60	65
25p	2B Rose-red	60	65
26p	2B Red-brown	70	65
26p	2B Gold	60	70
29p	2B Grey	75	80
30p	2B Deep olive-grey	65	70
31p	2B Deep mauve	70	75
33p	2B Grey-green	80	80
34p	2B Lime-green	1.60	1.70
35p	2B Yellow	95	1.00
35p	Yellow AOP	4.50	4.10
35p	2B Sepia	70	70
35p	2B Yellow-olive	50	60
36p	2B Ultramarine	80	85
37p	2B Bright mauve	80	80
37p	2B Grey	60	65
38p	2B Rosine	70	75
38p	2B Ultramarine	1.00	1.10
38p	2B Ultramarine Perf 14	3.90	4.00
39p	2B Bright magenta	1.15	1.15
39p	2B Grey	80	95
40p	2B Deep azure	90	80
40p	2B Turquoise	70	75
41p	2B Grey-brown	90	95
41p	2B Stone AOP	5.50	5.50
41p	2B Rosine	1.00	1.00
42p	2B Deep olive-grey	85	90
43p	2B Deep Olive-brown	90	90
43p	2B Sepia brown	2.20	2.20
43p	2B Sepia Perf 14	1.60	1.65
43p	2B Pale Emerald	90	90
44p	2B Grey-brown	2.20	2.50
44p	2B Ultramarine	70	75
45p	2B Bright mauve	1.20	1.20
46p	2B Old gold	70	75
47p	2B Sea green	1.20	1.25
48p	2B Rhododendron	75	80
49p	2B Rust	75	80
50p	2B Ochre	90	95
50p	2B Grey	80	85
54p	2B Rust	85	90
63p	2B Emerald	1.50	1.50
64p	2B Turquoise-green	1.50	1.50
65p	2B Greenish-blue	1.70	1.80
68p	2B Grey-brown	1.20	1.30
72p	2B Red	1.10	1.15
78p	2B Emerald green	1.20	1.30
£1	2B Violet	1.50	1.50
£1	2B Ruby	1.50	1.60
£1.50	2B Rust-red	2.50	2.20
£2	2B Indigo	3.00	3.00
£3	2B Purple	4.50	4.00
£5	2B Slate-blue	6.50	5.50

Litho Printed
All are perf 15 x 14 unless stated otherwise

		U/M	F/U
1p	2B Lake	90	95
6p	2B Yellow-olive	6.50	6.60
10p	2B Dull orange	3.00	3.10
19p	LB Bistre	1.30	1.35
19p	RB Bistre	1.30	1.40
20p	CB Bright green	1.40	1.45
25p	2B Red	70	75
26p	2B Chestnut	60	65
30p	2B Olive-grey	2.50	2.70
35p	2B Yellow Questa	1.00	1.05
35p	2B Yellow Walsall	65	70
37p	2B Mauve	1.80	1.80
41p	2B Drab Walsall	95	1.00
41p	2B Grey-brown Questa	2.50	2.55
60p	2B Blue-grey	1.60	1.70
63p	2B Light emerald	1.80	1.90

Pre Decimal Machins

M10	1s 2B Pale violet - Sheets (5.6.67)	35
M10a	Missing phosphor	£80
M10b	Left band omitted	£130
M10c	Right band omitted	£130
M10d	Bright violet - Sheets (6.68)	1.25
M11	1s6d 2B Blue-green & Dark blue - Sheets (8.8.67)	70
M11a	Missing phosphor	£15
M11b	Blue-green omitted	£130
M11c	Pale & Dark blue - Sheets (12.67)	75
M11d	Pale & Dark blue, missing phosphor - Sheets (12.67)	£15
M12	1s9d 2B Dull orange & Black - Sheets (5.6.67)	1.00
M12a	Missing phosphor	£60
M12b	Bright orange & black - Sheets (5.6.67)	1.50
	First Day Cover 4d, 1s, 1s9d (5.6.67)	1.00
	First Day Cover 3d, 9d, 1s6d (8.8.67)	1.00

2d Type I	2d Type II
Value close to frame edge	Value wide of frame edge

1967 (5 June) - 71. Machin series. No wmk. Perf. 15 x 14. Head types are only shown where relevant. Screen values are not included in these lists, but are to be found in the MCC Specialised catalogue.
Printer: Harrison & Sons in photogravure

Gum Arabic

M1	1d CB Yellow-olive - Coil (27.8.69)	50
M2	2d CB Lake brown, Type II - Sheets (27.8.69)	35
M3	3d CB Deep Violet, Head A - Sheets (8.8.67)	30
M3a	Missing phosphor - Sheets	1.25
M3b	Horizontal coil (2.10.67)	1.50
M3c	Violet - Sheets	30
M4	3d CB Reddish violet, Head B - MV coil (27.8.69)	50
M5	4d 2B Sepia, Head A - Sheets (5.6.67)	40
M5a	Missing phosphor - Sheets, BP175c	4.00
M5b	Left band omitted - Sheets	£90
M5c	Right band omitted - Sheets	£80
M5d	Pane BP175 (21.9.67)	75
M5e	Vertical coil (15.5.68)	
M5f	Horizontal coil	1.00
M5g	Broad band left - Horizontal coil	£50
M5h	Broad band right - Horizontal coil	£35
M6	4d 2B Sepia, Head B1 - Sheets (.8.68)	£1500
M7	4d CB Vermilion, Head A Pane BP176 (20.2.69)	£20
M7a	Missing phosphor	£1000
M8	4d CB Vermilion, Head B - M/V coil	50
M9	9d 2B Deep green - Sheets (8.8.67)	40
M9a	Missing phosphor	£30

PVA Gum

M13	½d 2B Orange-brown - Sheets (5.2.68)	15	10
M13a	Missing phosphor	£45	
M14	1d 2B Olive, Head A - Sheets (5.2.68)	15	10
M14a	Missing phosphor	£10	
M15	1d 2B Dull olive, Head B1 - Sheets (.10.68)	25	
M15a	Left band omitted - Sheets	£80	
M15b	Vertical coil	25	
M15c	Olive - Pane BP177 (25.3.68)	35	
M15d	Missing phosphor - Sheets, coil & pane	2.00	
M16	1d 2B Yellow-olive - Panes BP179, BP180, BP181 & SP4	35	25
M16a	Missing phosphor - Panes BP180b, BP181b	6.00	
M16b	Uncoated paper - Pane SP4b (£1 Cook book)	£90	
M17	1d CB Yellow-olive, Head B2 - Pane BP178 (16.9.68)	40	25
M17a	Missing phosphor	5.00	
M18	2d 2B Lake brown, Type I. Head A - Sheets (5.2.68)	25	10
M18a	Missing phosphor	£30	
M19	2d 2B Lake brown, Type II. Head B1 - Sheets (2.69)	25	10
M19a	Vertical coil	£10	
M19b	Broad band right - Vertical coil		
M19c	Missing phosphor - Sheets	1.00	
M19d	Horizontal coil	4.00	
M20	3d CB Violet, Head A - Sheets (12.3.68)	20	10
M20a	Missing phosphor - Sheets	3.50	
M20b	Horizontal coil	£35	
M21	3d CB Violet, Head B1 - Pane BP182 (25.3.68)	5.00	
M21a	Missing phosphor - Pane BP182a	£300	
M22	3d 2B Violet, Head A - Sheets (20.8.69)	30	20
M22a	Vertical coil	1.50	
M22b	Uncoated paper - Sheets		
M22c	Missing phosphor - Vertical coil	£35	
M23	3d 2B Violet, Head B1 - Vertical coil (.3.69)	3.00	
M23a	Missing phosphor - Vertical coil	£275	
M23b	Panes BP180, BP181	50	
M23c	Broad band centre - Panes BP180a, BP181a	4.00	
M23d	Missing phosphor - Panes BP180b, BP181b	£275	
M24	4d 2B Deep olive-brown, Head A - Sheets (22.1.68)	25	5
M24a	Missing phosphor - Sheets	£15	
M24b	Pane BP183	30	
M24c	Missing phosphor - Pane BP183b	£15	

No.			U/M	F/U
M25	**4d**	**2B Deep olive-sepia**, Head B2 - Sheets		
		(.4.68)	25	5
M25a		Missing phosphor - Sheets	2.50	
M25b		Pane BP185	35	
M25c		Broad band left - Pane BP185a	4.50	
M25d		Broad band right - Pane BP185a	4.50	
M25e		Broad band centre - Pane BP185a	4.50	
M25f		Missing phosphor - Pane BP185b	7.00	
M26	**4d**	**CB Deep olive-brown**, Head A - Sheets		
		(16.9.68)	15	5
M26a		Vertical coil		
M26b		Pane BP184 (16.9.68)	35	
M26c		Missing phosphor - BP184		
M26d		Horizontal coil	2.50	
M27	**4d**	**CB Deep olive-brown**, Head B1 - Sheets		
		(16.9.68)	15	15
M27a		Missing phosphor - Sheets	£15	
M27b		Panes BP186, BP187		
M27c		Missing phosphor - Pane BP187a		
M28	**4d**	**CB Vermilion**, Head A - Pane BP188		
		(6.1.69)	50	10
M28a		Missing phosphor - Pane BP158a	5.00	
M28b		Sheets (.5.69)	20	
M28c		Missing phosphor	1.00	
M28d		Vertical coil	7.50	
M28e		Horizontal coil	17.50	
M29	**4d**	**CB Vermilion**, Head B2 - Sheets (6.1.69)	15	
M29a		Missing phosphor - Sheets		
M29b		Pane BP189, BP190 (6.1.69)	35	10
M29c		Missing phosphor - Pane BP189a, BP190a		
M29d		Horizontal coil		
M29e		£1 Cook book - Pane SP2/3 (£1 Cook book)		
		(1.12.69)	25	
M29f		Missing phosphor	£10	
M29g		Uncoated paper	12.50	
M30	**4d**	**LB Vermilion**, Head B2 - Pane BP179 (6.1.69)	75	1.25
M31	**4d**	**LB Vermilion**, Head B2 - Pane SP4		
		(£1 Cook book) (1.12.69)	1.50	1.25
M31a		Uncoated paper	£150	
M32	**4d**	**RB Vermilion**, Head B2 - Pane SP4		
		(£1 Cook book) (1.12.69)	2.25	2.00
M32a		Uncoated paper	£150	

No.			U/M	F/U
M33	**5d**	**2B Dark blue** Head A - Sheets (1.7.68)	40	30
M33a		Missing phosphor	3.00	
M34	**5d**	**2B Deep blue**, Head B1 - Sheets (.3.69)	20	15
M34a		Missing phosphor - Sheets	3.50	
M34b		Pane BP191 (.3.69)	30	20
M34c		Missing phosphor - Pane BP191a	£10	
M34d		Vertical coil	5.00	2.95
M34e		Horizontal coil	4.00	2.50
M34f		£1 Cook book - Panes SP1/4 (1.12.69)	15	
M34g		Uncoated paper - Panes SP1/4 (1.12.69)	£15	
M34h		Missing phosphor - Panes SP1/4 (1.12.69)	£50	
M35	**6d**	**2B Reddish purple**, Head A - Sheets (5.2.68)	20	15
M35a		Missing phosphor	£15	
M35b		Bright magenta - Sheets	2.00	1.00
M35c		Claret - Sheets (.4.69)	75	20
M35d		Claret, Missing phosphor	£35	
M35e		Magenta, Head B - Vertical coil	£10	4.00
M35f		Claret, Head B - Vertical coil (9.70)	£85	£15
M36	**7d**	**2B Bright emerald** - Sheets (1.7.68)	50	25
M36a		Missing phosphor	£95	

No.			U/M	F/U
M37	**8d**	**2B Vermilion**, Head A - Sheets (1.7.68)	40	20
M37a		Missing phosphor	£275	
M38	**8d**	**2B Light blue**, Head B - Sheets (6.1.69)	75	40
M38a		Missing phosphor	£80	
M39	**9d**	**2B Deep green** - Sheets (29.11.68)	45	12
M39a		Missing phosphor	£60	
M40	**10d**	**2B Drab** - Sheets (1.7.68)	75	35
M40a		Missing phosphor	£50	
M40b		Uncoated paper	£20	
M41	**1s**	**2B Pale violet** - Sheets (26.4.68)	50	10
M41a		Missing phosphor	4.00	
M42	**1s6d**	**2B Pale blue & Deep blue** - Sheets		
		(29.8.68)	50	10
M42a		Missing phosphor	£25	
M42b		Missing Pale blue	£110	
M42c		Broad band centre	£85	
M42d		Broad band left	£14	
M42e		Broad band right	£14	
M43	**1s6d**	**Prussian blue & indigo** - Sheets (.5.70)	1.75	15
M43a		Missing phosphor	£30	
M44	**1s9d**	**2B Bright orange & black** - **Sheets**		
		(16.11.70)	1.00	20
M44a		Phosphor wash	£75	
		First Day Cover (½d, 1d, 2d, 6d) (5.2.68)		50
		First Day Cover (5d, 7d, 8d, 10d) (1.7.68)		75
		Presentation Pack (No.8) (5.3.69).		
		Contents: ½d, 1d, 2d, 3d, 4d red, 5d, 6d, 7d, 8d blue,		
		9d, 10d, 1s, 1s6d, 1s9d (14v)	6.00	
		German Presentation Pack	£30	

All Over Phosphor (PCP) PVA Gum

No.			U/M	F/U
M45	**5d**	**Deep Blue** (2B), Head B (1970)	£275	
M46	**1s6d**	**Prussian blue & indigo** (10.12.69)	45	45

Coil Strip

1969 (27 Aug.) No watermark. Perf. 15 x 14. One phosphor CB.
Gum Arabic

MV1	**1s**	**Coil strip** *Contents:* 2 x 2d, 3d, 1d and 4d		
		vermilion se-tenant.	75	1.00

Non-elliptical
No.

Decimal - OCP/PVA
U/M   F/U   No.

Machin Definitives
U/M   F/U

Decimal Machins

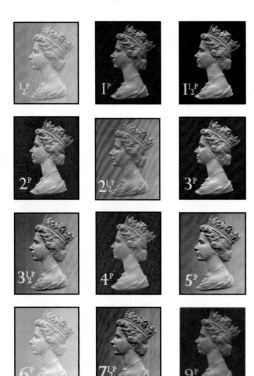

1971 (15 Feb.) - 91. Decimal Machin series.
All are perf. 15 x 14

Printers: Harrison & Sons in Photogravure, except the 8p which was printed in Photogravure and 18p in Gravure both printed by Enschedé.

Original Coated Paper - Gum Arabic
(OCP/GA)

No.				U/M	F/U
M47	½p	**2B Turquoise**), Head C, MV coil (15.2.71)		30	
M47a		Wide band left		6.00	
M47b		Wide band right		£30	
M47c		Missing phosphor		£65	
M47d		Missing phosphor (screened)		12.50	
M47e		Silicone coated		£40	
M48	1p	**2B Crimson**, Head B1, MV coil (15.2.71)		25	
M48a		Wide band left		6.00	
M48a		Wide band right		£35	
M48b		Missing phosphor		£65	
M48c		Missing phosphor (screened)		12.50	
M48d		Silicone coated		£40	
M49	2p	**2B Dark green**, Head B1, MV coil (15.2.71)	1.00		
M49a		Wide band left		22.50	
M49b		Wide band right		£125	
M49c		Missing phosphor		£175	
M49d		Missing phosphor (screened)		£30	
M49c		Silicone coated		£150	
M50	3p	**2B Ultramarine**, Head B1. Type II Horizontal coil (2.73)		£45	

Original Coated Paper - PVA Gum
(OCP/PVA)

No.				U/M	F/U
M51	½p	**2B Turquoise**, Head C - Sheets (15.2.71)		15	10
M51a		Missing phosphor - Sheets		35	
M51b		Pane MP4		1.75	
M51c		Broad band left - Pane MP4a		£40	
M51d		Broad band right - Pane MP4a		£45	
M51e		Broad band centre - Pane MP4a		£80	
M51f		Missing phosphor -Panes MP4a, MP1, MP3a		£35	
M51g		LB omitted - Pane MP3		£50	
M51h		RB omitted - Pane MP3		£50	
M52	½p	**2B Deep Turquoise,** Thick value Pane MP5 (14.4.71)		6.00	1.00
M52a		Broad band left - Pane MP5a		£300	
M52b		Broad band right - Pane MP5a		£375	
M52c		Broad band centre - Pane MP5a		£325	
M52d		Missing phosphor - Pane MP5b		£250	
M53	1p	**2B Dull crimson**, Head B1 - Panes MP6, MP7 (15.2.71)		90	10
M53a		Broad band right - Panes MP6a, MP7a		£45	
M53b		Broad band left - Panes MP6a, MP7a		£55	
M53c		Vertical coil		60	
M53d		Missing phosphor - Vertical coil		£350	
M53e		Thin paper - Vertical coil		£20	
M53f		Very thin value - S/T coil		1.50	
M54	1p	**2B Crimson** - Sheets		15	
M54a		Missing phosphor - Sheets		6.00	
M54b		Left band omitted		£400	
M54c		Right band omitted		£125	
M55	1½p	**2B Black**, Head B1 - Sheets (15.2.71)		20	10
M55a		Missing phosphor - Sheets		£20	
M55b		Uncoated paper - Sheets		£100	
M55c		Panes MP6, MP7		70	
M55d		Broad band left - Panes MP6a, MP7a		£110	
M55e		Broad band right - Panes MP6a, MP7a		£100	
M56	2p	**2B Dark green** - Sheets (15.2.71)		15	15
M56a		Missing phosphor - Sheets		£40	
M56b		Panes MP4, MP5		1.00	
M56c		Broad band left - Panes MP4a, MP5a		£40	
M56d		Broad band right - Panes MP4a, MP5a		£40	
M56e		Broad band centre - Panes MP4a, MP5a		£55	
M56f		Missing phosphor - Panes MP4b, MP5b		£70	
M56g		MV coil		1.00	
M57	2½p	**CB Magenta**, Head C - Sheets (15.2.71)		15	10
M57a		Missing phosphor		£10	
M57b		Thin higher set value - Sheets (Cyl 8)		1.25	
M57c		Missing phosphor - Sheets (Cyl 8)		£70	
M57d		Vertical coil		5.00	
M57e		Horizontal coil		3.50	
M57f		Panes MP8 to MP12		75	
M57g		Missing phosphor - Panes MP8a, MP9a, MP12a		£85	
M58	2½p	**LB Magenta**, Pane MP13		5.25	
M58a		Missing phosphor - Pane MP13a		£80	
M59	3p	**2B Ultramarine**, Head B1, Thin value Sheets (15.2.71)		30	10
M59a		Missing phosphor - Sheets		2.50	
M59b		Panes MP13, MP14, MP16		40	
M59c		Broad band left - Panes MP14, MP16		£200	
M59d		Broad band right - Panes MP14a, MP16a		£200	
M59e		Broad band centre - Panes MP14a, MP16a		£225	
M59f		Left band omitted - Pane MP14		£150	
M59g		Missing phosphor - Pane MP13a, MP16b		£85	
M60	3p	**2B Ultramarine**, Head B1, Thick value Horizontal coil		11.00	
M60a		Vertical coil		4.50	
M61	3½p	**2B Pale olive-grey**, Head C - Sheets		25	30
M61a		Missing phosphor		5.50	
M62	4p	**2B Ochre-brown**, Head B1 - Sheets (15.2.71)		25	15
M62a		Missing phosphor		£35	
M62b		Missing phosphor (screened)		£10	
M62c		LB omitted		£75	
M62d		RB omitted		£55	

No.			U/M	F/U
M63	5p	**2B Pale violet**, Head C - Sheets (15.2.71)	25	15
M63a		Missing phosphor	£225	
M64	6p	**2B Light green**, Head C - Sheets (15.2.71)	20	15
M64a		Missing phosphor	£50	
M64b		Uncoated paper	£15	
M64c		Very thin value, S/T coil (3.77)	1.50	1.00
M65	7½p	**2B Pale chestnut**, Head C - Sheets (15.2.71)	25	40
M65a		Missing phosphor	£15	
M66	9p	**2B Orange and black**, Head B1 - Sheets (15.2.71)	1.00	45
M66a		Missing phosphor	£80	
M66b		Screened value	1.50	
M66c		Missing phosphor - Screened value	£110	

Original Coated Paper - PVA Dextrin gum.
(OCP/PVAD)

			U/M	F/U
M67	3½p	**2B Deep olive-green**, Head C. Glazed paper. Paper error. (7.1.74)	£175	£50

Fluorescent Coated Paper - Gum Arabic
(FCP/GA)

No.			U/M	F/U
M68	½p	**2B Turquoise**, Head C - Sheets(22.9.72)	15	30
M68a		MV Coil	20	
M68b		Silicone coated - MV coil (22.9.72)	40	
M69	1p	**2B Bright crimson**, Head B1 - MV coil		
		Silicone coated (22.9.72)	30	30
M69a		Silicone omitted	£15	
M69b		Vertical coil	60	
M70	2p	**2B Green**, Head B1 - MV coil		
		Silicone coated (22.9.72)	2.00	75
M70a		Silicone omitted	£40	
M71	2½p	**CB Magenta**, Head C - Sheets, Comb perf (13.9.72)	20	10
M71a		Deep magenta. APS perf.	35	
M71b		Horizontal coil	£22	
M72	3p	**2B Ultramarine**, Head B1 - Sheets (23.8.72)	2.50	85
M72a		Missing phosphor	£20	
M72b		Horizontal coil	£22	
M73	3p	**CB Ultramarine** - Sheets (10.9.73)	1.00	10
M73a		Missing phosphor	£250	
M74	3p	**CB Deep Ultramarine**, Wider set value - Sheets (Cyls 24,31)	25	10

No.			U/M	F/U
M75	4p	**2B Ochre-brown**, Head B1 - Sheets (1.11.72)	30	35
M75a		JET phosphor	£20	
M76	6p	**2B Pale green**, Head C, JET phosphor - Sheets (6.6.73)	1.50	40

Fluorescent Coated Paper - PVA Gum.
(FCP/PVA)

			U/M	F/U
M77	½p	**2B Bright turquoise**, Head C - Sheets (17.9.71)	30	30
M77a		Missing phosphor - Sheets	£125	
M77b		Pane MP17, MP18	45	
M77c		RB Omitted - Pane MP18	£1000	
M77d		2B + AOP - Pane MP18	£150	
M77e		JET Phosphor - Pane MP18c	£10	
M78	½p	**2B Bright turquoise**, Thick value - Pane MP19	75	45
M78a		Broad band centre - Pane MP19a	£40	
M78b		Missing phosphor - Pane MP19b	£180	
M78c		JET Phosphor - Pane MP19c	5.00	
M79	½p	**2B Pale turquoise**, Thin value - Panes SP7, SP8 (£1 Wedgwood)	65	60
M79a		Broad band left, Panes SP7, SP8	£300	
M79b		Broad band right, Panes SP7, SP8	£300	
M79c		Broad band centre, Panes SP7, SP8	£300	
M79d		Bands front and back, Pane SP8	£200	
M79e		Missing phosphor, Panes SP7, SP8	£325	
M80	½p	**LB Turquoise** Pane SP8 (24.5.72)	£39	£20
M81	1p	**2B Deep crimson**, Head B1 - Sheets (6.10.71)	90	30
M81a		Missing phosphor - Sheets	£65	
M81b		Pane MP20	1.00	
M81c		Missing phosphor - Pane MP20b	£30	
M81d		Broad band left - Pane MP20a	£200	
M81e		Broad band right - Pane MP20a	£200	
M81f		JET Phosphor - Pane MP20c	6.00	
M82	1p	**2B Bright Crimson** - Sheets (Cyl. 1)	1.75	35
M82a		Missing phosphor - Sheets	£35	
M82b		Pane MP20	1.75	
M83	1½p	**2B Black**, Head B1 - Sheets (6.10.71)	75	35
M83a		Missing phosphor - Sheets	£75	
M83b		Pane MP20	1.00	
M83c		Broad band left - Pane MP20a	£195	
M83d		Broad band right - Pane MP20a	£200	
M83e		Missing phosphor - Pane MP20b	£30	
M83f		JET Phosphor - MP20c	6.00	
M84	2p	**2B Green**, Head B1 - Sheets (6.10.71)	1.75	30
M84a		Missing phosphor - Sheets	£300	
M84b		Pane MP19	75	
M84c		Broad band centre - Pane MP19a	£35	
M84d		JET Phosphor - Pane MP19c	6.00	

No.   U/M   F/U   No.   U/M   F/U

Thin value   Thick value   Very thin value

No.			U/M	F/U
M85	2½p	**CB Bright Magenta**, Head C, Thin value - Sheets(10.71)	1.50	30
M85a		Missing phosphor - Sheets	£20	
M85b		Pane MP25	2.50	
M85c		Pane SP6 (£1 Wedgwood)	2.50	
M85d		Missing phosphor - Pane SP6	£130	
M86	2½p	**CB Bright Magenta**, Thick value - Panes MP21, MP23, MP24	50	35
M86a		Missing phosphor - Panes MP21a, MP23a MP24a	9.00	
M86b		JET Phosphor - Pane MP23b	£10	
M87	2½p	**CB Pale Bright Magenta**, Thin value - Sheets	60	30
M87a		Missing phosphor - Sheets	£10	
M87b		JET Phosphor	£10	
M87c		Green phosphor - Sheets	5.00	
M88	2½p	**CB Pale Bright Magenta**, Very thin value - Pane SP7 (£1 Wedgwood)	2.50	1.00
M88a		Broad band left - Pane SP7c	£350	
M88b		Broad band right - Pane SP7c	£350	
M88c		Broad band centre - Pane SP7c	£300	
M88d		Missing phosphor - Pane SP7a	£200	
M89	2½p	**LB Magenta** - Thick value - Pane MP13 (24.5.72)	2.50	1.00
M89a		Missing phosphor - Pane MP13a	£35	
M89b		JET Phosphor - Pane MP13b	£45	
M89c		Very thin value - Panes SP7, SP8 (£1 Wedgwood)	2.00	2.00
M89d		Broad band left - Pane SP8a	£395	
M89e		Missing phosphor - Pane SP8b	£400	
M90	2½p	**RB Pale Magenta** - Thin value - Pane SP6 (24.5.72)	2.00	1.00
M90a		Missing phosphor - Pane SP6a	£85	
M90b		Broad band left - Pane SP6b	£350	
M90c		Broad band right - Pane SP6b	£350	
M90d		Broad band centre - Pane SP6b	£300	
M91	2½p	**RB Pale Magenta** - Very thin value - Pane SP7 (24.5.72)	3.50	1.00
M91a		Missing phosphor - Pane SP7a	£200	
M91b		Broad band left - Pane SP7b	£350	
M91c		Broad band right - Pane SP7b	£350	
M91d		Broad band centre - Pane SP7b	£275	
M92	3p	**2B Ultramarine**, Head B1 - Sheets (17.9.71)	60	15
M92a		Missing phosphor - Sheets	£10	
M92b		Panes MP13, MP14, MP16	60	
M92c		Broad band left - Pane MP14a	£150	
M92d		Broad band right - Pane MP14a	£150	
M92e		Missing phosphor - Panes MP13a, MP14b	£10	
M92f		Left band omitted - Pane MP13	£45	
M92g		Right band omitted - Pane MP13	£45	
M92h		JET Phosphor - Sheets	4.50	
M92i		JET Phosphor - Panes MP13b, MP16c	4.50	
M93	3p	**2B Ultramarine**, Thin paper - Sheets	5.00	3.50
M93a		Left band omitted - Sheets	£40	
M93b		Right band omitted - Sheets	£45	
M93c		Missing phosphor - Sheets	£25	
M93d		Pane MP27b	4.00	
M94	3p	**2B Dull Ultramarine** - Panes SP5, SP6 (£1 Wedgwood) (4.7.03)	75	50
M94a		Broad band left - Panes SP5, SP6	£25	
M94s		Broad band right - Panes SP5, SP6	£125	
M94d		Broad band centre - Panes SP5, SP6	£70	
M94d		Missing phosphor - Panes SP5, SP6	£45	
M94e		Wider bands (11mm) - Pane SP6	£10	
M94f		Broad band left - Pane SP6	£250	
M95	3p	**CB Bluish ultramarine** - Sheets (1.74)	60	30
M95a		Pane MP28 (14.11.73)	1.50	
M95b		Thin paper - Pane MP28	2.50	

No.			U/M	F/U
M96	3½p	**2B Bronze green**, Head C - Sheets (7.73)	1.75	
M96a		Pane MP30	1.00	
M96b		Missing phosphor - Pane MP30	£1500	
M97	4p	**2B Ochre-brown**, Head B1 - Sheets (18.7.73)	2.50	
M98	5p	**2B Pale violet** - Sheets 1971)	4.00	
M98a		Missing phosphor - Sheets	£450	
M98b		Right band omitted - Sheets	£1000	
M99	6p	**2B Light green**, Head C - Sheets (18.7.73)	£17	
M100	6½p	**CB Greenish blue**, Head B1 - Sheets (12.75)	£23	
M101	7½p	**2B Pale chestnut**, Head C - Sheets (1971)	2.75	
M101a		Missing phosphor - Sheets	£225	
M102	9p	**2B Orange and sepia**, Head B1 - Sheets (11.71)	2.50	
M102a		Broad band right	£30	
M102b		Missing phosphor	£70	
M103	10p	**2B Orange-brown and deep brown** - Sheets (11.8.71)	50	15
M103a		Missing orange-brown	£175	
M103b		Missing phosphor	£8	
M103b		Left band omitted	£175	
M104	10p	**2B Orange and Butter yellow** - Sheets (11.8.71)	£10	

FCP/PVAD

Several two banded stamps were derived from 8mm bands instead of the normal 9.5mm. To easily distinguish these measure the space *between* the bands as illustrated below.

All are B3 phosphor unless stated otherwise. Colours as before.

 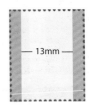

—11.5mm—   —13mm—

2B stamps from   2B stamps from
9.5mm bands   8mm bands

Thin value   Thick value

No.			U/M	F/U
M105	½p	**2B Turquoise**, Thin value, Head C - Sheets (10.9.73)	10	10
M105a		Missing phosphor - Sheets	1.00	
M105b		Left band omitted - Sheets	£60	
M105c		Right band omitted - Sheets	£60	
M105d		MV Coil	15	
M105e		Broad band centre - MV Coil	75	
M105f		Pane MP31	25	
M105g		Broad band left MP31a	£10	
M105h		Broad band right MP31a	1.50	
M105i		Broad band centre MP31a	1.25	
M106	½p	**2B Bright turquoise** Thick value - Pane MP31 (4.74)	25	30
M106a		Broad band left MP31a	£10	
M106b		Broad band right MP31a	£10	
M106i		Broad band centre MP31a	£150	

No.			U/M	F/U
M107	½p	**2B Deep turquoise** Thin value - MV Coil	25	25
M107a		Broad band centre - MV Coil	£15	
M107b		Missing phosphor - MV Coil	1.50	
M107c		Varnished paper - Sheets	50	
M108	½p	**2B, 8mm Bright Turquoise** Thin value - Pane FP39, FP40	25	15
M108a		Ribbed - Panes FP39, FP40	3.00	
M109	½p	**2B, 8mm Turquoise** Thin value, Panes FP16, FP17	50	30
M109a		Missing phosphor - Pane FP16b, FP17b	5.00	
M110	½p	**2B, 8mm Pale turquoise** Thick value (1.2.82) Panes FP24. FP25	10	15
M111	½p	**CB Bright Turquoise** Thin value - MV Coil (14.12.77)	10	15
M111a		Thick paper - MV Coil	£12	
M112	½p	**CB Bright Turquoise** Thick value - Pane FP15 (8.2.78)	10	15
M112a		Missing phosphor - Pane FP15	£10	

Original value   Redrawn value

No.			U/M	F/U
M113	1p	**2B Crimson**, Head B1 Narrow value - Sheets (10.9.73)	10	10
M113a		Glazed paper - Sheets	1.25	
M113b		Pane MP32	20	
M113c		Broad band left - Pane MP32a	£50	
M113d		Broad band right - Pane MP32a	£30	
M113e		Broad band centre - Pane MP32a	£10	
M113e		Missing phosphor - Pane MP32b		
M113g		Imperf. pair - Sheets	£800	
M113h		MV Coil	10	
M113i		Missing phosphor - MV Coil	5.00	
M114	1p	**2B Crimson**, Head B1 Very thin value - MV Coil (3.12.75)	10	10
M114a		Broad band left - MV Coil		
M114b		Broad band centre	1.00	
M115	1p	**2B Crimson**, Head B2 Very thin value - Pane FP13 (10.3.76)	30	10
M115a		Broad band left - Pane FP13	8.00	
M115b		Broad band right - Pane FP13	£10	
M116	1p	**2B, 8mm Crimson**, Head B2 Narrow value Panes FP16, FP17, FP39, FP40 (26.1.77)	60	35
M116a		Missing phosphor - Panes FP16b, FP17b	£7	
M117	1p	**CB Crimson**, Head B1. Very thin value - MV Coil (14.12.77)	10	10
M117a		Thick paper - MV Coil	£10	
M118	1p	**CB Crimson**, Head B1. Thick value - Pane FP1	50	40
M119	1p	**CB Crimson**, Head B2. Very thin value - Pane FP15	65	60
M119a		Missing phosphor - Pane FP15c	5.00	
M120	1p	**CB Crimson**, Head B2. Thick value - Pane FP26	65	60
M120a		Missing phosphor - Pane FP26a	£10	
M121	1p	**CB Crimson**, Head B2. Wide spaced value - Pane FP2	50	45
M122	1p	**RB Crimson A Phosphor** - Pane SP35 (P & O Prestige book)	2.50	1.90

Redrawn Numerals

No.			U/M	F/U
M123	1p	**CB 4mm Crimson** - Pane FP27	40	20
M123a		Missing phosphor Pane FP27a	£35	
M123b		Imperf. left - Pane FP 19	1.00	
M123c		Imperf. left, Missing phosphor - Pane FP19a	£95	
M124	1p	**CB 4.5mm Crimson** - Panes FP18 FP27	1.75	75

No.			U/M	F/U
M125	1p	**LB Crimson** - Pane FP3 (20.10.86)	40	20
M125a		Broad band left - Pane FP3	£180	
M125b		Missing phosphor - Pane FP3a	£18	
M126	1p	**RB Crimson - Error** - Pane FP3b	£30	
M127	1½p	**2B Black**, Head B1 - Sheets (12.11.73)	10	10
M127a		Glazed paper - Sheets	1.00	
M127b		Pane MP32	50	
M127c		Broad band left - Pane MP32a	£80	
M127d		Broad band right - Pane MP32a	£50	
M127e		Missing phosphor - Pane MP32b	£275	
M128	2p	**2B Green**, Head B1 - Sheets (10.9.73)	10	10
M128a		Missing phosphor - Sheets	£10	
M128b		Glazed paper - Sheets	1.50	
M128c		MV Coil	15	
M128d		Missing phosphor - MV Coil	£10	
M128e		Broad band left - MV Coil	£10	
M128f		Broad band right - MV Coil	£15	
M128g		Thin paper - MV Coil	£35	
M128h		Pane MP31 (12.11.73)	30	
M128i		Broad band left - MP31a	£10	
M128j		Broad band right - MP31a	£15	
M129	2p	**2B Myrtle green**, Head B2, Value set high - Panes SP11, SP12 (£3 Wedgwood) (16.4.80)	15	15
M129a		6mm Broad band left - Pane SP11a	£80	
M129b		6mm Broad band centre - Pane SP11a	£35	
M129c		9.5mm Broad band left - Pane SP11a	£55	
M129d		9.5mm Broad band centre - Pane SP11a	£35	
M129e		Bands front and back - Panes SP9c, SP12b	£110	
M129f		Missing phosphor - Panes SP11b, SP12a	£20	
M130	2p	**2B Myrtle green**, Head B2, Value set low - Pane SP15 (SG Prestige book) (28.8.79)	1.00	75
M130a		Broad band left - Pane SP15	£70	
M130b		Broad band right - Pane SP15	£75	
M130c		Broad band centre - Pane SP15	£70	
M130d		Bands front and back - Pane SP15	£300	
M130e		Missing phosphor - Pane SP15	£30	
M131	2p	**2B 8mm Myrtle green**, - Panes FP30, FP31 (29.8.79)	30	10
M131a		Short bands at top - Pane FP30	2.50	
M131b		Short band at bottom left - Pane FP30	2.50	
M131c		Short band at bottom right - Pane FP31	2.50	
M131d		Inset left band - Pane FP30	7.50	
M131e		Inset right band - Pane FP31	7.50	
M132	2p	**2B 8mm Myrtle green**, Value set high - Panes FP32, FP33 (4.2.80)	75	25
M132a		Short bands at top - Pane FP32	5.00	
M132b		Short band at bottom left - Pane FP32	5.00	
M132c		Short band at bottom right - Pane FP34	£15	
M132d		Inset left band - Pane FP32	7.50	
M132e		Inset right band - Pane FP34	7.50	
M132f		Broad band left - Pane FP34	£15	
M132g		Broad band right- Pane FP33	£15	
M132h		Missing phosphor - Pane FP33a	7.50	
M133	2½p	**CB Magenta**, Head C - Sheets (8.8.73)	10	10
M134	2½p	**2B Magenta**, Head C - Sheets (21.5.75)	20	30
M135	2½p	**2B 8mm Rose-red** - Panes FP36, FP36a (26.8.81)	25	30
M136	3p	**CB Ultramarine**, Head B1, Thin value - Sheets (10.9.73)	15	20
M136a		Missing phosphor - Sheets	£10	
M137	3p	**CB Ultramarine**, Head B1, Very thin value - Sheets (14.11.73) - Pane MP33	2.50	50

Decimal - FCP/PVAD

No.		Description	U/M	F/U
M138	**3p**	**CB Ultramarine**, Head B1, Thick value		
		- Horizontal coil (11.73)	7.00	1.50
M138a		Band at left (Displaced)	8.00	
M138b		Vertical coil (.4.74)	7.50	
M139	**3p**	**2B 8mm Bright magenta**, Head B1 -		
		Pane FP24, FP25 (1.2.82)	25	20
M139a		Missing phosphor - Panes FP24a, FP25a	£500	
M139b		All over phosphor - Panes FP24, FP25	£85	
M140	**3p**	**2B Bright magenta**, Head B2 - Pane SP15		
		(SG Prestige book) (19.5.82)	1.00	50
M140a		Broad band left - Pane SP15a	£150	
M140b		Broad band right - Pane SP15a	£250	
M140c		Broad band centre - Pane SP15a	£225	
M140d		Missing phosphor - Pane SP15b	£120	
M140e		Bands front and back - Pane SP15c	£650	
M141	**3½p**	**2B Bronze green**, Head C - Sheets (22.8.73) 40	10	15
M141a		Missing phosphor - Sheets	7.50	
M141b		Right band omitted - Sheets	£130	
M141c		Pane MP34	75	
M141d		Missing phosphor - Pane MP34a	7.50	
M141e		Vertical coil	£11	
M141f		Horizontal coil (.2.74)	2.00	
M142	**3½p**	**2B Deep Olive-brown**, Head C		
		- Error of colour - Sheets	£700	
M143	**3½p**	**CB Bronze green**, Head C - Sheets		
		(24.6.74)	30	10
M143a		Side band left (Displaced) - Sheets	5.00	
M143b		Missing phosphor - Sheets	7.50	
M143c		Pane MP35 (23.10.74)	50	
M143d		Missing phosphor - Pane MP35b	£20	
M143e		Horizontal coil (.12.74)	1.00	

No.		Description	U/M	F/U
M144	**3½p**	**CB Dull chestnut**, Head D - Pane FP26		
		(5.4.83)	80	75
M144a		Missing phosphor - Pane FP26a	5.00	

Original value		Re-drawn value		
M145	**4p**	**2B Light ochre**, Head B1 - Sheets (24.6.74)	25	10
M145a		Glazed paper	75	
M146	**4p**	**2B 8mm Greenish blue** Head B1		
		- Panes FP36, FP37 (26.8.81)	1.00	1.00
M146a		Short band at bottom left - Pane FP37	3.50	
M146b		Short band at bottom right - Pane FP37		3.50

4p Re-drawn value

No.		Description	U/M	F/U
M147	**4p**	**CB Pale greenish blue** - Pane FP27 (3.9.84)	75	75
M147a		Missing phosphor - Pane FP27a	£75	
M148	**4p**	**LB Greenish blue** - Pane SP27		
		(The Times Prestige book) (8.1.85)	1.00	75
M148a		Broad band at left - Pane SP25a	£450	
M148b		Missing phosphor - Pane SP25b	£500	
M148c		Bands front and back - Pane SP25c	£375	
M149	**4p**	**RB Greenish blue** - Pane SP25 (8.1.85)	1.00	1.10
M149a		Bands front and back - Pane SP25c	£375	
M150	**4½p**	**2B Light grey-blue**, Head D - Sheets		
		(24.10.73)	7.00	15
M151	**4½p**	**2B Deep steel-blue**, Head D - Sheets		
		(24.10.73)	50	30
M151a		Broad band right - Sheets	8.00	
M151b		Missing phosphor - Sheets	6.00	
M151c		Imperf. pair - Sheets	£300	
M151d		PUI - Phosphor under ink - Sheets	2.00	
M151e		Horizontal coil	75	
M151f		Pane MP36	1.00	
M151g		Missing phosphor - Pane MP36a	£250	
M151h		PUI - Phosphor under ink -Pane MP36b	£35	
M152	**5p**	**2B Pale violet**, Head C - Sheets (5.6.74)	20	10
M152a		All over phosphor - Sheets	£160	
M152b		Broad band left - Sheets	£10	
M153	**5p**	**2B Claret**, Head C - Pane FP18 (20.10.86)	1.00	35
M154	**5p**	**2B Claret**, Head C, 'A' phosphor 4.5mm -		
		Pane FP18a (27.1.87)	1.00	1.00
M154b		Imperf. at left, 4.5mm band - Pane FP19	70	40
M154c		Imperf. at left, 4mm band - Pane FP19b		
		(30.10.87)	1.20	75
M154d		Imperf. at left, missing phosphor - PaneFP19a	£85	

No.		Description	U/M	F/U
M155	**5½p**	**2B Deep purple**, Head B1 - Sheets (24.10.73)	30	15
M156	**5½p**	**CB Deep purple** - Sheets (17.3.75)	30	15
M156a		Missing phosphor	£10	
M156b		Uncoated paper	£350	
M156c		Glazed paper	1.50	
M157	**6p**	**2B Light green**, Thin value - Sheets Head C	25	15
		(10.10.73)		
M157a		Missing phosphor - Sheets	£350	
M157b		PUI - Phosphor under ink - Sheets	1.75	
M157c		Glazed paper - Sheets	2.00	
M158	**6p**	**2B Light green**, Very thin value - MV coil	60	25
M158a		Broad band right - MV coil	2.00	
M158b		Broad band centre - MV coil	7.50	
M159	**6p**	**2B Light green**, Thick value - PUI		
		Phosphor under ink - Sheets (31.10.77)	50	15
M160	**6½p**	**2B Greenish blue**, Head B1 - Sheets (4.9.74)	30	15
M160a		Thin translcent paper - Sheets	2.50	
M160b		All over phosphor - Thin translucent paper		
		- Sheets	£150	
M161	**6½p**	**CB Greenish blue**, Head B1 - Sheets		
		(24.9.75)	30	10
M161a		Imperf. pair - Sheets	£200	
M161b		Missing phosphor - Sheets	£10	
M161c		Uncoated paper - Sheets	£170	
M161d		Horizontal coil	1.00	
M162	**6½p**	**CB Greenish blue** , Head B2 - Sheets	30	15
M162a		Imperf. pair - Sheets	£300	
M162b		Panes FP41, FP42	45	20
M162c		Vertical coil	1.00	
M163	**6½p**	**LB Greenish blue** - Pane FP40 (26.1.77)	30	40
M164	**6½p**	**RB Greenish blue** - Pane FP39 (26.1.77)	50	40

No.			U/M	F/U
M165	**7p**	**2B Purple-brown**, Head B1		
		- Sheets (15.1.75)	30	10
M165a		Missing phosphor - Sheets	5.00	
M165b		Imperf. pair	£300	
M165c		PUI - Phosphor under ink - Sheets	1.00	
M165d		PUI - Missing phosphor	2.50	
M165e		Glazed paper	60	
M166	**7p**	**CB Purple-brown**, Head B1, Thin value		
		- Sheets (13.6.77)	40	10
M166a		All over phosphor	£750	
M166b		Imperf. pair	£750	
M166c		Horizontal coil (16.11.77),		
M166d		MV coil (14.12.77)	40	
M166e		Thick paper - MV coil (14.12.77)	£20	
M167	**7p**	**CB Purple-brown** (CB), Head B2, Thin value		
		- Sheets (13.6.77)	20	15
M167a		Imperf. pair	£100	
M167b		Imperf. at top (marginal)	£150	
M167c		Vertical coil (13.6.77)	50	
M167d		Panes FP43, FP44	60	
M168	**7p**	**CB Chocolate brown** (CB), Head B2,		
		PUI - Phosphor under ink - Sheets	50	20
M169	**7p**	**CB Purple-brown** (CB), Head B2, Thick value		
		- Pane FP15 (8.2.78)	50	20
		Missing phosphor - Pane FP15c	5.00	

Thin value   Very thin value

No.			U/M	F/U
M170	**7p**	**LB Red-brown**, Head B2 - Thin value		
		Pane FP29 (13.6.77)	50	25
M170a		Very thin value	1.00	
M170b		Centre *Bar* - Pane FP79 (Christmas book)	50	25
M170c		Centre *Bar* - Plus2 x 1.5mm short bands at top		
		- Pane FP79 (Christmas book)	5.00	
M171	**7p**	**RB Red-brown**, Head B2 - Thin value		
		Pane FP28 (13.6.77)	50	25
M171a		Very thin value	1.50	
M172	**7½p**	**2B Pale chestnut**, Head C, Thick value		
		- Sheets (30.4.74)	1.25	50
M172a		Broad band left - Sheets	£300	
M173	**7½p**	**2B Pale chestnut**, Head C, Thin value		
		- Sheets (30.4.74)	50	40

M180

No.			U/M	F/U
M174	**8p**	**2B Red**, Head B1 - Sheets (24.10.73)	20	15
M174a		Uncoated paper - Sheets	9.00	
M174b		Glazed paper - Sheets	80	
M174c		PUI - Phosphor under ink - Sheets	3.50	
M175	**8p**	**CB Red**, Head B1 - Sheets (20.8.79)	25	10
M175a		Imperf. pair - Sheets	£700	
M175b		Uncoated paper - Sheets	£600	
M176	**8p**	**CB Bright red**, Head B1, Value set right		
		- Pane FP1	25	15
M176a		Short band at top - Pane FP1	2.50	
M176b		MV coil	25	
M176c		All over phosphor wash - MV coil	£375	

No.			U/M	F/U
M177	**8p**	**CB Bright red**, Head B2 - Pane FP2		
		(Chambon)	40	25
M177a		Short band at top - Pane FP2	5.00	
M178	**8p**	**CB Red**, Head B2, value set high		
		Sheets	30	20
M178a		Panes FP45, FP46	60	
M178b		Vertical coil	60	
M179	**8p**	**CB Red**, Head B1, value set left		
		- Sheets (Halley press)	85	50
M179a		Missing phosphor - Sheets (Halley press)	£500	
M180	**8p**	**CB Red**, Enschedé printing (sloping 'p')		
		- Sheets (12.12.79)	25	25
M180a		Missing phosphor - Sheets	£180	
M181	**8p**	**LB 8mm Red**, Head B2 - Pane FP31		
		(28.8.79)	35	35
M182	**8p**	**RB 8mm Red**, Head B2 - Pane FP30		
		(28.8.79)	35	35
M183	**8p**	**CBar Red**, Head B2 - Pane FP80		
		(Christmas book) (14.11.79)	60	45
M184	**8½p**	**2B Light yellow-green**, Head C - Sheets		
		(24.9.75)	40	15
M184a		Left band omitted - Sheets	£200	
M184b		Broad band left - Sheets	£250	
M184c		Imperf. pair - Sheets	£1300	
M184d		Missing phosphor - Sheets	2.50	
		Glazed paper - Sheets	1.25	
M185	**8½p**	**2B 8mm Yellow green** - Panes FP39, FP40		
		(26.1.77)	40	20

No.			U/M	F/U
M186	**9p**	**2B Dull orange and black**, Head B1 - Sheets		
		(22.3.74)	75	15
M186a		Broad band right - Sheets	£40	
M186b		Missing phosphor - Sheets	£100	
M187	**9p**	**2B Bright orange and black**, Head B1		
		- Sheets	75	20
M187a		Broad band right - Sheets	2.50	
M187b		Missing phosphor - Sheets	£100	
M187c		Left band omitted - Sheets	£40	
M187d		Right band omitted - Sheets	£40	
M188	**9p**	**2B Bright violet**, Head C - Sheets (25.2.76)	50	15
M188a		Missing phosphor - Sheets	2.00	
M188b		All over phosphor - Sheets	£85	
M188c		Vertical coil	60	25
M188d		Horizontal coil	60	25
M189	**9p**	**2B Bright violet**, Head C, Varnish over		
		phosphor - Sheets	2.00	25
M190	**9p**	**2B Bright violet**, Head C, Varnish under		
		phosphor - Sheets	1.00	20
M190a		Missing phosphor - Sheets		
M191	**9p**	**2B Dull violet**, Head C - Sheets	50	15
M191a		Imperf. pair - Sheets	£250	
M192	**9p**	**2B Dull violet**, Head C, PUI - Phosphor		
		under ink - Sheets	50	15
M192a		Imperf. pair - Sheets	£250	
M193	**9p**	**2B 8mm Violet**, Head C - Panes FP28,		
		FP29	40	15
M194	**9p**	**2B Bluish violet**, Head C - Sheets	60	15
M194a		All over phosphor wash - Sheets	£10	
M194b		Left band omitted - Sheets	£35	
M194c		Right band omitted - Sheets	£35	
M194d		Missing phosphor - Sheets	6.00	
M194e		Panes FP49, FP50	60	
M195	**9p**	**2Bar Pale bluish violet**, Head C - Pane FP79		
		(Christmas book)	50	20
M195a		Additional CB at top - Pane FP79	4.00	

No.			U/M	F/U
M196	**9½p**	**2B Purple**, Head C - Sheets (25.2.76)	25	15
M196a		Missing phosphor - Sheets	£15	
M196b		Left band omitted - Sheets	£25	
M196c		Right band omitted - Sheets	£25	
M196d		Bright purple magenta. Error of colour	£2500	
M197	**10p**	**2B Orange and deep brown**, Head B1		
		- Sheets Cyl 8A (12.11.73)	40	15
M198	**10p**	**2B Light orange and deep brown**, Head B1		
		- Sheets, Cyl 5A (12.11.73)	1.00	25
M198a		Imperf. pair - Sheets, Cyl 5A	£2000	

Original value   Redrawn value

No.			U/M	F/U
M199	**10p**	**2B Light orange**, Head D - Sheets (25.2.76)	40	20
M199a		Imperf. pair - Sheets	£250	
M199b		All over phosphor wash - Sheets	£40	
M199c		Broad band at right - Sheets	£10	
M200	**10p**	**2B Light orange**, Head D - PUI (Phosphor under		
		ink) - Sheets (25.2.76)	50	25
M200a		Imperf. top marginal pair	£500	
M201	**10p**	**2B 10mm Light orange**, Head D, Chambon		
		printing - Sheets	45	25
M201a		Missing phosphor - Sheets	1.75	
M201b		Gutter pair - Sheets	1.20	
M201c		Gutter pair, Missing phosphor - Sheets	£20	
M201d		Left band omitted - Sheets	£85	
M201e		Right band omitted - Sheets	£85	
M202	**10p**	**2B 8mm Light orange**, Head D		
		- Panes FP30, FP31	35	15
M202a		Missing phosphor - Panes FP30a, FP31a	4.50	
M203	**10p**	**CBar Light orange**, Head D - Pane FP80		
		(Christmas book)	75	
M204	**10p**	**CB Light orange** - Sheets (4.2.80)	30	15
M204a		Imperf. pair	£225	
M204b		Missing phosphor	5.00	
M204c		All over phosphor wash	£50	
M204d		Solid all over phosphor	£300	
M204e		Imperf. pair	£250	
M204f		Panes FP51, FP52	40	
M204g		Panes SP10, SP12 (£3 Wedgwood)	40	
M204h		Broad band left - Pane SP12	£550	
M204i		Bands front and back - Pane SP12b	£150	
M205	**10p**	**LB 8mm Light orange** Pane FP33		
		(4.2.80)	50	35
M205a		Missing phosphor - Pane FP33a	5.00	
M206	**10p**	**LB Light orange** Pane SP12		
		(£3 Wedgwood)	1.50	25
M206a		Bands front and back - Pane SP12b	£350	
M207	**10p**	**RB 8mm Light orange** - Pane FP32		
		(4.2.80)	50	35
M207a		Broad band left - Pane FP32	7.50	
M207b		Broad band right - Pane FP32	7.50	
M207c		Missing phosphor - Pane FP 33a	5.00	
M208	**10p**	**CBar Light orange**, Head D		
		- Pane FP81 (Christmas book)	50	20
M208a		Missing phosphor - Pane FP81a	£10	

Redrawn value

No.			U/M	F/U
M209	**10p**	**2B Light orange** - Pane SP23		
		(Christian Heritage prestige book)	£10	4.90
M209a		Bands front and back - Pane SP23	£900	
M209b		Missing phosphor - Pane SP23a	£1750	

No.			U/M	F/U
M210	**10½p**	**2B Yellow**, Head D - Sheets (25.2.76)	40	20
M210a		All over phosphor error	5.50	
M211	**10½p**	**2B Dull blue** - Sheets (26.4.78)	35	30
M211a	**11p**	**2B Brown red**, Head D - Sheets (25.2.76)	35	10
M211b		Imperf. pair - Sheets	£1500	
M211c		Missing phosphor - Sheets	4.50	
M211d		PUI (Phosphor under ink) - Sheets	1.00	

No.			U/M	F/U
M212	**11½p**	**CB Drab**, Head B2 - Sheets (14.1.81)	50	20
M212a		Imperf. pair - Sheets	£300	
M212b		Panes FP54, FP55	60	
M212c		Phosphor wash - Pane FP55	£60	
M212d		Vertical coil	1.00	
M213	**11½p**	**CBar Drab**, Head B2 - Pane FP82		
		(Christmas book)	50	20
M214	**11½p**	**LB 8mm Drab**, Head B1 - Pane FP37		
		(26.8.81)	40	30
M215	**11½p**	**LB 8mm Drab**, Head B2 - Pane FP17		
		(26.1.81)	40	30
M215a		Missing phosphor - Pane FP17b	£10	
M215b		Pane FP56 (6.5.81)	40	30
M216	**11½p**	**RB 8mm Drab**, Head B1 - Pane FP36		
		(26.8.81)	40	40
M217	**11½p**	**RB 8mm Drab**, Head B2 - Pane FP16		
		(26.1.81)	40	30
M217a		Missing phosphor - Pane FP16b	£10	
M217b		Pane FP56 (6.5.81)	40	30
M218	**12p**	**2B Yellow green**, Head C - Panes SP9, SP12		
		(£3 wedgwood) (16.4.80)	40	20
M218a		6mm Broad band left - Panes SP9, SP12	£50	
M218b		6mm Broad band right - Panes SP9, SP12	£100	
M218c		6mm Broad band centre - Panes SP9, SP12	£35	
M218d		9.5mm Broad band left - Panes SP9, SP12	£45	
M218e		9.5mm Broad band right - Panes SP9, SP12	£70	
M218f		9.5mm Broad band centre - Panes SP9, SP12	£25	
M218g		Bands front and back - Panes SP9, SP12	£85	
M218h		Missing phosphor - Panes SP9, SP12	7.50	
M219	**12p**	**2B 8mm Yellow green**, Head C - Pane FP33		
		(25.6.80)	40	25
M219a		Broad band left - Pane FP33	7.50	
M219b		Broad band right - Pane FP33	7.50	
M219c		Missing phosphor - Pane FP33a	7.50	
M220	**12p**	**2B 8mm Yellow green**, Value set high		
		- Panes FP32, FP34	75	30
M221	**12p**	**2Bar Yellow green**, Head C - Pane FP81		
		(Christmas book)	65	
M221a		Missing phosphor - Pane FP81a	£10	
M221b		Left band omitted - Pane FP81	£50	
M221c		Right band omitted - Pane FP81	£60	
M222	**12p**	**CB 4mm Emerald green**, Head B2 - Sheets		
		(29.10.85)	30	15
M222a		Missing phosphor - Sheets	8.00	
M222b		'A' phosphor - Sheets (.6.86)	45	
M222c		All over phosphor wash - Sheets	£10	
M222d		Panes FP58, FP59	50	
M222e		Missing phosphor - Panes FP58a, FP59a	8.00	
M222f		Pane FP20	50	
M222g		Vertical coil	50	
M222h		Horizontal coil	50	

No.			U/M	F/U
M223	12p	**CB 4.5mm Emerald green**, Head B2		
		- Pane SP30 (B. Rail book) (29.10.85)	50	25
M223a		Missing phosphor - Pane SP30a	£30	
M223b		CB displaced to right - Pane SP30	7.50	
M224	12p	**CB 4.5mm Emerald green**, Head B2, 5 point		
		star underprint - Sheets (29.10.85)	50	25
M224a		Band displaced right - Sheets	9.50	
M225	12p	**LB Emerald green** - Panes FP60, FP61		
		(14.1.86)	75	50
M225a		Pane SP31 (B. Rail book)	75	
M225b		Broad band left - Pane SP31a	£200	
M225c		Missing phosphor - Pane SP31b	£70	
M225d		Bands front and back - Pane SP31c	£400	
M226	12p	**RB Emerald green** - Panes FP60, FP61		
		(14.1.86)	75	50
M226a		Pane SP31 (B. Rail book)	75	
M226b		Bands front and back - Pane SP31	£400	

M232/M245    M230

No.			U/M	F/U
M227	12½p	**CB Light emerald**, Thin value, Head D		
		- Sheets (27.1.82)	25	10
M227a		Missing phosphor - Sheets	7.00	
M227b		Imperf. pair - Sheets	£100	
M228	12½p	**CB Light emerald**, Thin value, Head D,		
		PUI (Phosphor under ink) - Sheets	50	25
M228a		Phosphor wash - Sheets	7.50	
M228b		Band displaced left - Sheets	1.50	
M228c		Band displaced right - Sheets	7.50	
M228d		Two narrow bands - Sheets	7.50	
M228e		Imperf. pair - Sheets	£375	
M229	12½p	**CB Light emerald**, (short band bottom),		
		Thin value, Head D - Pane SP15 (SG Book)	1.50	35
M229a		Broad band left - Pane SP15a	£50	
M229b		Broad band right - Pane SP15a	£110	
M229c		Broad band centre - Pane SP15a	£100	
M229d		Bands front and back - Pane SP15c	£275	
M229e		Missing phosphor - Pane SP15b	£12	
M230	12½p	**CBar Light emerald**, Thin value, 10 point		
		star underprint - Pane FP83 (Christmas book)	60	
M230a		Missing phosphor - Pane FP83a	£75	
M231	12½p	**CB Light emerald**, Thick value, Head D,		
		- Vertical coil (1.2.82)	60	25
M231a		Panes FP62, FP63	60	
M231b		Missing phosphor - Panes FP62a, FP63a	5.00	
M231c		Pane FP26	60	
M231d		Missing phosphor - Pane FP26a	5.00	
M232	12½p	**CB Light emerald**, Thick value, Head D,		
		5 star underprint - Pane FP84 (Christmas book)	60	25
M233	12½p	**LB Light emerald**, Thin value - Pane SP14		
		(SG book) (19.5.82)	50	30
M233a		Broad band left - Pane SP14a	£70	
M233b		Broad band right - Pane SP14a	£75	
M233c		Broad band centre - Pane SP14a	£70	
M233d		Pane FP66, FP67	50	
M233e		Missing phosphor - Pane FP66a, FP67a	£10	
M233f		Panes SP17, SP18 (Royal Mint book)	60	
M233g		Bands front and back - Panes SP17c, SP18c	£100	
M234	12½p	**LB Light emerald**, Short band at top,		
		Thin value - Pane SP15 (SG book)	1.25	35
M234a		Bands on front and back - Pane SP15c	£300	
M235	12½p	**LB Light emerald**, Thin value set high		
		- Pane SP17 (SG book)	1.50	40
M235a		Missing phosphor - Pane SP17b	£140	
M236	12½p	**RB Light emerald**, Thin value - Pane SP14		
		(SG book) (19.5.82)	50	30
M236a		Pane FP66, FP67 (5.4.83)	50	
M236b		Missing phosphor - Pane FP66a, FP67a	£10	
M236c		Panes SP17, SP18 (Royal Mint book) (14.9.93)	60	
M236d		Bands front and back - Panes FP17c, FP18c	£100	

No.			U/M	F/U
M237	12½p	**RB Light emerald**, Thin value set high		
		- Pane SP17 (Royal Mint book)	1.50	75
M238	12½p	**LB 8mm Light emerald**, Thin value		
		- Panes FP24, FP25	50	30
M238a		Pane SP14 (SG book)	50	
M238b		8mm Broad band left - Pane SP14a	£35	
M238c		8mm Broad band right - Pane SP14a	£35	
M238d		8mm Broad band centre - Pane SP14a	£150	
M238e		Bands front and back - Pane SP14c	£80	
M238f		Missing phosphor - Pane SP14b	£10	
M239	12½p	**LB 8mm Light emerald**, Thick value		
		- Panes FP64, FP65	50	25
M239a		Missing phosphor - Panes FP64a, FP65a	£300	
M240	12½p	**RB 8mm Light emerald**, Thin value		
		- Panes FP24, FP25	50	25
M240a		Missing phosphor - Pane FP24a, FP25a	£375	
M240b		Pane SP14 (SG book)	50	
M240c		Bands front and back - Pane SP14c	£100	
M241	12½p	**RB 8mm Light emerald**, Thick value		
		- Panes FP64, FP65	50	25
M241a		Missing phosphor - Panes FP64a, FP65a	£300	

> 8mm side banded stamps are best collected se-tenant to distinguish from the normal 9.5mm derived types

No.			U/M	F/U
	12½p	**2B Light emerald** - Error pane		
M242		Left band short at top and bottom		
		- Panes FP64b, FP65b	£25	
M242a		Right band short at top and bottom		
		- Panes FP64b, FP65b	£25	

No.			U/M	F/U
M243	13p	**CB 4mm Chestnut** - Sheets		
		(28.88.84)	30	20
M243a		Imperf. pair - Sheets	£1000	
M243b		Pane FP27	30	
M243c		Missing phosphor - Pane FP27a	6.00	
M243d		Panes FP68, FP70	30	
M243e		Missing phosphor - Panes FP68b, FP70b	6.00	
M243f		Pane FP18	30	
M243g		Horizontal coil	30	
M243h		Band at right - Horizontal coil	7.50	
M243i		Vertical coil	30	
M244	13p	**CB 5mm Chestnut** - Pane SP26		
		(The Times book)	60	30
M244a		Missing phosphor - Pane SP26a	£75	
M244b		Bands front and back - Pane SP26b	£100	
M245	13p	**CB Chestnut** - 5 point star underprint		
		- Panes FP69, FP71 (Christmas book)		
		(1.12.86)	50	30
		Missing phosphor - Panes FP69a, FP71a	£1400	
M246	13p	**LB Chestnut** - Panes FP73, FP74		
		(3.9.84)	60	30
M246a		Panes SP22, SP23, SP24 (Heritage book)		
		(4.9.84), SP27 (Times book) (8.1.85)	70	
M246b		Missing phosphor - SP22a, SP23a, SP24b		
		(4.9.84), SP27b (Times book) (8.1.85)	£50	
M246c		Broad band left - Pane SP24a	£100	
M246d		Broad band right - Pane SP24a	£140	
M246e		Broad band centre - Pane SP24a	£100	
M246f		Pane FP21	60	
M246g		Error Pane, Pane FP3b	60	

No.			U/M	F/U
M247	13p	**RB Chestnut** - Panes FP73, FP74 (3.9.84)	60	25
M247a		Panes SP22, SP24 (Heritage book) (4.9.84), SP25 (Times book) (8.1.85)	70	
M247b		Missing phosphor - SP22a, SP23b, SP24b (4.9.84), SP25b (Times book) (8.1.85)	£50	
M247c		Pane FP3	60	
M247d		Missing phosphor - Pane FP3a	£40	
M248	13p	**2B Chestnut** - Error panes FP73a, FP74a Left band short at top and bottom	7.50	
M248a		Right band short at top and bottom	7.50	
M249	13p	**CB 4.5mm Chestnut**, 'A' phosphor, Pane FP18a	50	25
M249a		Imperf. at right - Pane FP19	50	
M249b		Missing phosphor - Pane FP19a	£25	
M250	13p	**CB 4mm Chestnut**, 'A' phosphor, Sheets (27.1.87)	40	25
M250a		Imperf. pair - Sheets	£900	
M250b		Missing phosphor - Sheets	7.50	
M250c		Panes FP68a, FP70a	40	
M250d		Missing phosphor - FP68b, FP70b	7.50	
M250e		Screened value - FP68a , FP70a	1.00	
M250f		Panes SP34, SP35 (P & O book) (3.3.87)	40	
M250g		Pane FP4, FP72 Window books (4.8.87)	40	
M250h		Imperf. at right - Pane FP19b (20.10.87)	1.00	
M251	13p	**LB 4mm Chestnut**, 'A' phosphor - Pane FP21a (27.1.87)	1.00	35
M251a		Pane FP3e	1.00	
M251b		Imperf. at left - Pane FP22	2.50	
M251c		Displaced bands giving 2B stamps - Pane FP22	£15	
M252	13p	**RB 4mm Chestnut**, 'A' phosphor - Pane FP3c (27.1.87)	1.00	35
M252a		Missing phosphor - Pane FC3d	£15	
M252b		Pane SP35	1.00	
M253	14p	**2B 8mm Grey blue** - Panes FP16, FP17 (26.1.81)	50	30
M253a		Missing phosphor - Pane FP16b, FP17b	£40	
M253b		Left band omitted - Pane FP16, FP17	£70	
M253c		Right bad omitted - Pane FP16, FP17	£70	
M253d		Panes FP56, FP57	50	
M253e		Left band short at top and bottom, Panes FP56, FP57	1.00	
M253f		Right band short at top and bottom, Panes FP56, FP57	1.00	
M254	14p	**2Bar Grey blue** - Pane FP82 (Christmas book)	1.00	35
M255	14p	**CB Dark blue**, 'A' phosphor - Sheets (23.8.88)	45	25
M255a		AOP wash - Sheets	£10	
M255a		Pane FP5, FP110	45	
M255b		Panes FP75, FP76	45	
M255c		Missing phosphor - Panes FP75a, FP76a	£35	
M255d		Imperf. at top, Panes FP6, FP78	60	25
M255e		Imperf. at top, Missing phosphor - Pane FP6a, FP78a	£10	
M255f		Imperf. at bottom, Panes FP6, FP78	60	25
M255g		Imperf. at bottom, Missing phosphor - Pane FP6a, FP78a	£10	
M255h		Imperf. at top and right - Pane FP7	7.50	
M255i		Imperf. at top and right, Missing phosphor - Pane FP7a	£10	
M255j		Imperf. at bottom and right - Pane FP7	7.50	
M255k		Imperf. at bottom and right, Missing phosphor - Pane FP7	£10	
M256	14p	**RB Dark blue**, 'A' phosphor Imperf. at left - Pane FP23	75	35
M256a		Imperf. at left, Missing phosphor - Pane FP23a	£300	
M257	14p	**RB Dark blue**, 'A' phosphor, Comb perf - Pane FP8	1.50	85
M257a		APS perf - Pane FP8	1.50	
M257b		Missing phosphor - Pane FP8b	7.50	

No.			U/M	F/U
M258	15p	**CB Light blue** - Sheets (26.9.89)	45	30
M258a		Imperf. pair - Sheets	£450	
M258b		Missing phosphor - Sheets	£12	
M258c		Vertical coil	50	
M258d		Horizontal coil	1.50	
M259	15p	**LB Light blue** - Pane FP9	1.25	45
M259a		Missing phosphor - Pane FP9a	£150	
M259b		Inset band - Pane FP9	2.00	
M259c		Stepped band at top - Pane FP9	2.50	
M260	15p	**RB Light blue** - Pane SP47 (London Life book) (20.3.90)	1.25	1.10
M261	15½p	**2B 8mm Pale violet**, Thick value - Panes FP64, FP65 1.2.82)	45	40
M261a		Left band short at top -Panes FP64, FP65	1.50	
M261b		Left band short at bottom -Panes FP64, FP65	1.50	
M261c		Left band short at top -Panes FP64, FP65	1.50	
M261d		Right band short at top -Panes FP64, FP65	1.50	
M261e		Right band short at bottom -Panes FP64, FP65	1.50	
M261f		Left band short at top and bottom - Panes FP64, FP65	1.00	
M261g		Right band short at top and bottom - Panes FP64, FP65	1.00	
M261h		Missing phosphor - Pane FP64a, FP65a		
M262	15½p	**2B 9.5mm Pale violet**, Thin value - Panes SP13, SP16 (SG Book)	50	45
M262a		6mm Broad band left - Panes SP13a, SP16a	£50	
M262b		6mm Broad band right - Panes SP13a, SP16a	£50	
M262c		6mm Broad band centre - Panes SP13a, SP16a	£50	
M262d		9.5mm Broad band left - Panes SP13a, SP16a	£50	
M262e		9.5mm Broad band right - Panes SP13a, SP16a	£50	
M262f		9.5mm Broad band centre - Panes SP13a, SP16a	£50	
M262g		Bands front and back - Panes SP13c, SP16c	£250	
M262h		Missing phosphor - Panes SP13b, SP16b	£10	
M262i		Solid AOP - Pane SP13	£125	
M263	15½p	**2Bar Pale violet**, Thick value, 10 point star underprint - Pane FP83 (Christmas book)	50	45
M263a		Missing phosphor - Pane FP83a	£100	
M263b		Left band omitted -Pane FP83	£175	
M263c		Right band omitted - Pane FP83	£175	
M264	15½p	**LB 8mm Pale violet**, Error panes FP64b, FP65b	£60	
M265	15½p	**RB 8mm Pale violet**, Error panes FP64b, FP65b	£60	
M266	16p	**2B Drab** - Panes FP66, FP67 (5.4.83)	1.00	50
M266a		Left band short top and bottom - Panes FP66, FP67	1.25	
M266b		Right band short top and bottom - Panes FP66, FP67	1.25	
M266c		Missing phosphor - Panes FP66a, FP67a	£70	
M266d		Left band omitted, Pane FP66	£60	
M266e		Right band omitted, Pane FP66	£60	

M271

No.				U/M	F/U
M267	17p	**2B Grey blue** - Panes FP60, FP61, FP73, FP74 (3.9.84)		60	30
M267a		Left band short at top and bottom - Panes FP60, FP61, FP73, FP74		1.00	
M267b		Right band short at top and bottom - Panes FP60, FP61, FP73, FP74		1.00	
M267c		Left band short at top - Panes FP60, FP61		2.50	
M267d		Left band short at bottom - Panes FP60, FP61		2.50	
M267e		Left band short at top and bottom - Panes FP73, FP74		1.25	
M267f		Right band short at top and bottom - Panes FP73, FP74		1.25	
M267g		Panes SP23, SP27 (Heritage, Times panes respectively), SP31, SP32 (B. Rail book)		60	
M267h		Missing phosphor - Panes SP23a, SP27b, SP31b		£300	
M267i		Broad band left - Panes SP27a, SP31a		£300	
M267j		Bands front and back - Panes SP23a, SP27c, SP31c		£300	
M267k		Right band short at top - Pane SP23		2.00	
M267l		Right band short at bottom - Pane SP23		2.00	
M268	17p	**2B Grey blue** 250 Screen - Pane FP10		75	30
M268a		Short bands at top - Pane FP10		3.50	
M269	17p	**LB Grey blue**, Error panes FP73a, FP74a		£13	
M270	17p	**RB Grey blue**, Error panes FP73a, FP74a		£13	
M271		**2B Grey blue**, Multiple star underprint - Pane FP11 (4.11.85)		50	
M271a		Short bands at top - Pane FP11		1.50	
M271b		Left band stepped at top - Pane FP11		2.50	
M271c		Left band inset - Pane FP11		2.25	
M271d		Short bands at bottom - Pane FP11		£10	
M271e		Left band omitted - Pane FP11		£50	
M271f		Right band omitted - Pane FP11		£45	
M271g		Missing phosphor - Pane FP11a		£12	
M272	17p	**CB Dark blue** - Sheets (4.9.90)		50	40
M272a		Screened value - Sheets		45	
M272b		Imperf. pair - Sheets		£1000	
M272c		Vertical coil		50	
M273	17p	**LB Dark blue** Pane FP12 (4.9.90)		50	50
M273a		Missing phosphor - Pane FP12a		£10	
M273b		Stepped band at top - Pane FP12		50	
M273c		Short band bottom - Pane FP12		2.50	
M274	17p	**RB Dark blue** - Pane FP12 (4.9.90)		1.00	65
M274a		Short band bottom - Pane FP12		6.00	
M274b		Imperf. at left - Pane FP38		75	
M274c		Imperf. at left - Short band top - Pane FP38		1.00	
M274d		Imperf. at left - Missing phosphor - Pane FP38a		£25	
M275	18p	**2B Dull olive grey** - Pane FP21 (20.10.86)		1.00	35
M275a		Short band at top left - Pane FP3		2.00	
M275b		Short band at top right - FP3, FP21		1.50	
M275c		Left band stepped at top - Pane FP21		1.75	
M275d		Left band inset - Pane FP21		1.75	
M275e		Broad band left - Pane FP3		£275	
M275f		Missing phosphor - Pane FP3a		£25	
M276	18p	**2B Dull olive grey**, Screened value - Pane FP21 (20.10.86)		6.00	4.50
M276a		Left band short at top - Pane FP21		£15	
M276b		Left band stepped at top - Pane FP21		17.50	
M276c		Left band inset - Pane FP21		£20	
M276d		Right band short at top - Panes FP3, FP21		£15	

No.				U/M	F/U
M277	18p	**2B Dull olive grey**, 'A' phosphor - Panes FP21a, SP35 (P&O book)		1.00	60
M277a		Left band short at top - Panes FP3b, FP3c		1.00	
M277b		Left band stepped at top - Pane FP21a		1.50	
M277c		Left band inset - Pane FP21a		1.50	
M277d		Right band short at top - Panes FP3b, FP3c		1.00	
M277e		Broad band left - FP7c		£275	
M277f		Missing phosphor Pane FP3a		£28	
M278	18p	**2B Dull olive grey**, Screened value , 'A' phosphor - Pane FP21a		£10	
M278a		Left band short at top - Pane FP3c		£15	
M278b		Left band stepped at top - Pane FP21a		£15	
M278c		Left band inset - Pane FP21a		£15	
M278d		Right band short at top - Pane FP3c FP21a		£15	
M278e		Imperf. at left - Pane FP22		1.50	
M278f		Imperf. at left, Right band short at top - Pane FP22		1.75	
M278g		Imperf. at right - Pane FP22		1.00	
M278h		Imperf. at right, Right band short at top - Pane FP22		1.25	
M278i		Imperf. at right, Left band inset - Pane FP22		1.25	

No.				U/M	F/U
M279	18p	**CB (Offset left) Bright green** - Sheets		40	25
M279a		Imperf. pair - Sheets (10.9.91)		£325	
M279b		Screened value - Sheets		1.00	
M279c		Vertical coil (16.9.91)		40	
M279d		Missing phosphor - Vertical coil		£15	
M280	18p	**CB (Offset left) Deep bright green** - Sheets		2.00	95
M281	19p	**2B Orange red**, APS perf , Inset bands, - Panes FP8, FP8a (5.9.88)		85	50
M281a		Comb perf, Inset bands - Panes FP8, FP8a		85	50
M281b		Missing phosphor - Pane FP8b		4.50	
M281c		Right band inset, left band stepped at top APS perf - Pane FP8		1.00	
M281d		Right band inset, left band stepped at top Comb perf - Pane FP8		1.00	
M281e		Right band inset - Pane FP8		2.00	
M281f		Bands short at bottom - Pane FP8		2.00	
M281g		Imperf. at right - Pane FP23		1.00	
M281h		Imperf. at right, Right band stepped at top - Pane FP23		3.00	
M281i		Imperf. at right, Right band inset - Pane FP23		1.00	
M281j		Imperf. at right, Missing phosphor - Pane FP23a		£350	
M282	20p	**2B Dull purple** - Sheets (25.2.76)		55	25
M282a		Broad band		£18	

No.				U/M	F/U
M283	20p	**2B Black** - Pane SP47 (London Life book)		1.00	90
		Left band inset - Pane FP9		1.50	
		Left band inset and both bands short at top - Pane FP9		2.00	
		Missing phosphor - Pane FP9a		£475	
M284	22p	**2B (RB 4mm and inset) Orange**			
		Imperf. at right - Pane FP38 (4.9.90)		75	60
		Right band stepped at top - Pane FP38		1.50	
		Missing phosphor - Pane FP38a		£13	

M285	22p	**2B (Both bands 4mm and inset) Orange**		
		Pane FP38 (4.9.90)	1.25	55
		Short bands at top - Pane FP38	1.50	
M286	22p	**2B (RB 5mm and inset) Orange**		
		Pane FP38	75	45
		Left band stepped at top - Pane FP38	1.50	
M285	22p	**2B (Both bands 5mm and inset) Orange**		
		Pane FP38	1.50	60
		Short bands at top - Pane FP38	3.00	
M286	26p	**2B Rosine, 'A' Phosphor** - Pane SP35		
		(P & O book) (3.3.87)	5.00	3.00
M287	31p	**2B Mauve** - Pane SP31 (B. Rail book)		
		(18.3.86)	6.00	4.00
M287a		Broad band left - Pane SP31a	£1000	
M287b		Bands front and back - Pane SP31c	£850	
M287c		Missing phosphor - Pane SP31b	£900	
M288	34p	**2B Ochre brown**, - Pane SP27 (Times book)		
		(8.1.85)	5.00	4.00
M288a		Broad band left - Pane SP27a	£1000	
M288b		Bands front and back - Pane SP27c	£1000	
M288c		Missing phosphor - Pane SP27b	£900	
M289	50p	**2B Ochre** - Sheets (2.2.77)	1.25	25
M289a		Imperf. pair - Sheets	£550	
M290	50p	**Drab ochre**, (Non phosphor) - Sheets		
		(21.5.80)	1.25	40
M290a		Imperf. pair - Sheets	£450	
M291	50p	**Ochre** - Sheets (Cyl 35) (13.3.90)	1.25	50
M291a		Deep yellow-ochre (Cyl 36) (.10.90)	1.50	
M292	50p	**2B Bistre** - Pane SP47 (London Life book)		
		(20.3.90)	3.00	2.00
M293	75p	**Grey black**, Head B2 - Sheets (26.7.88)	1.25	1.25
M293a		Screened value - Sheets	2.50	

Phosphor Pre-printed Paper-PVA Dextrin Gum
(PPP/PVAD)

M294	1p	**Crimson**, Head B1 - Sheets (10.10.79)	20	10
M295	2p	**Myrtle green**, Head B2 - Sheets (10.10.79)	20	10
M295a		Missing phosphor	£200	
M296	10p	**Orange brown**, Head D - Sheets (3.10.79)	50	30
M296a		Missing phosphor in pair with normal	£375	
M296b		Panes FP85, FP86 (3.10.79)	50	
M296c		Pale orange brown - Panes FP85, FP86	2.50	50
M296d		Vertical coil (14.11.79)	50	

Phosphor Coated Paper-PVA Dextrin Gum
(PCP/PVAD)

This was an experimental coating and has a very short lived afterglow.

| M297 | 4½p | **2B Grey blue** - Sheets (13.11.74) | 50 | 30 |
| M299 | 8½p | **Yellow green**, Head C (24.3.76) | 40 | 30 |

PCP1-PVA Dextrin Gum
(PCP1/PVAD)

M300	½p	**Turquoise**, Head C - Sheets (10.12.80)	15	10
M300a		Imperf. pair -Sheets	£250	
M300b		RD coil	15	
M300c		Fluorescent brightener omitted - RD coil	£950	
M301	1p	**Crimson**, Head B1 - Sheets (12.12.79)	15	10
M302	1p	**Crimson**, Head B2 -Sheets	15	10
M302a		Thick value - RD 13p coil	20	
M303	2p	**Pale green**, Head B2 - Sheets	20	10
M303a		Imperf. pair - Sheets	£1300	

M304	2½p	**Rose red**, Head C. - Sheets (14.1.81)	40	15
M304a		Bright rose red - RD 11½p coil (6.81)	30	
M304b		Fluorescent Brightener omitted	£25	
M305	3p	**Bright magenta**, Head B1 - Sheets		
		(22.10.80)	20	10
M305a		Imperf. pair	£1000	
M305b		Phosphor missing from coating - Sheets	£130	
M306	3p	**Magenta**, Head B2 - Sheets	20	10
M307	3p	**Pink**, Head B1 - RD 11½p coil	25	10
M307a		Fluorescenet brightener omitted - RD coil	5.00	
M308	3½p	**Dull chestnut**, Head D - Sheets (30.3.83)	30	20

M309	4p	**Greenish blue**, Head B1 - RD 12½p coil		
		(30.12.81)	15	10
M309a		Fluorescent Brightener omitted		
		- RD 12½p coil	£350	
M310	4p	**Pale greenish blue**, Head B2		
		- RD 13p coil (14.4.84)	30	10
M311	5p	**Pale violet**, Head C - Sheets (10.10.79)	30	15
M312	7p	**Brick red**, Head B2 - Sheets (29.10.85)	1.50	1.25

M313	10p	**2B Orange brown** (Chambon printing),		
		Head D - Sheets (20.8.79)	35	2
M313a		Gutter pair	1.50	
		Missing phosphor - Sheets	£100	

No.			U/M	F/U
M313	10p	**Orange brown,** Head D - Sheets (10.10.79)	23	20
M314	10p	**CB Orange brown** - Sheets (4.2.80)	75	30
M314a	11p	**Orange-pink** - Sheets (.7.80)	40	40
M315	11½p	**Ochre brown,** Head B2 - Sheets (15.8.79)	50	20
M316	12p	**Yellow green,** Head C - Sheets (30.1.80)	40	25
M316a		Panes FP89, FP90	40	
M316b		Vertical coil	40	

No.			U/M	F/U
M318	13p	**Olive grey,** Head C - Sheets (15.8.79)	45	25
M319	13½p	**Reddish brown,** Head B2 - Sheets (30.1.80)	45	30
M320	14p	**Grey-blue,** Head D - Sheets (14.1.81)	40	20
M320a		Panes FP91, FP92 (26.1.81)	40	
M320b		Fluorescent Brightener omitted - Panes FP91a, FP92a	2.50	

M322b/M329

M320a	15p	**Ultramarine,** Head B2 - Sheets (15.8.79)	40	20
M321	15½p	**Pale violet,** Head C - Sheets (14.1.81)	40	20
M321a		Imperf. pair	£300	
M321b		Fluorescent Brightener omitted	£14	
M321c		Vertical coil	50	25
M322	16p	**Pale drab,** Head D - Panes FP95, FP97 (5.4.83)	40	25
M322a		Vertical coil	40	
M322b		'D' underprint in blue - Panes FP96, FP98 (10.8.83)	55	

M323	16½p	**Pale chestnut,** Head D - Sheets (27.1.82)	50	40
M324	17p	**Light emerald,** Head D - Sheets (30.1.80)	45	20
M324a		Fluorescent Brightener omitted - Sheets	1.25	
M325	17p	**Slate blue,** Head D - Sheets (30.3.83)	50	25
M326		Panes FP99, FP101	50	
M327		Pane FP88	50	
M328		Vertical coil	50	
M329		'D' underprint in blue - Panes FP100, FP102 (5.3.85)	60	
M330	17p	**2B Slate blue** (Paper error) - Pane FP87	£65	
M331		Short bands at top - Pane FP87	£130	
M332	17½p	**Pale chestnut,** Head D - Sheets (30.1.80)	50	35

No.			U/M	F/U
M333	18p	**Violet,** Head C - Sheets (14.1.81)	50	40
M334	18p	**Olive grey,** Head C - Panes FP103, FP104 (27.1.82)	60	30
M334a		Vertical coil	60	
M335	19½p	**Olive grey,** Head C - Sheets (27.1.82)	1.50	1.00

M336	20p	**Dull purple,** Head D - Sheets (10.10.79)	60	
M337	20½p	**Ultramarine,** Head B2 - Sheets (30.3.83)	1.00	50
M337a		Imperf. pair - Sheets	£1200	
M338	22p	**Blue,** Head B2 - Sheets (22.10.82)	55	20
M338a		Imperf. pair - Sheets	£225	
M338b		Missing phosphor - Sheets	£650	
M338c		Experimental (ribbed) coating - Sheets	1.00	

M339	23p	**Brown red,** Head D - Sheets (30.3.84)	1.00	40
M339a		Imperf. pair -Sheets	£1300	
M340	25p	**Dull purple,** Head C - Sheets (12.80)	1.50	
M341	26p	**Red,** Head B2 - Sheets (27.1.82)	70	

M342	28p	**Deep violet,** Head C - Sheets (30.3.83)	75	
M342a		Imperf. pair - Sheets	£1100	
M343	29p	**Ochre brown,** Head B2 - Sheets (27.1.82)	2.00	75
M344	31p	**Mauve,** Head C - Sheets (30.3.83)	1.00	
M345	34p	**Ochre brown,** Head B2 - Sheets (28.8.84)	1.00	

PCP2-PVA Dextrin Gum (PCP2/PVAD)
Colours are as PCP1

No.			U/M	F/U
M346	½p	Turquoise, Head C - Sheets	25	15
M346a		Imperf. pair - Sheets	£175	
M346b		RD coil	25	
M347	1p	Deep crimson, Head B1 - Sheets (.12.79)	20	10
M348	1p	Deep crimson, Head B2 - Sheets (.83)	£10	10
M349	2p	Deep green, Head B2 - Sheets (.12.79)	20	10
M350	2p	Pale green, Head B2 - Sheets (.80)	35	15
M350a		Imperf. pair - Sheets	£1250	
M351	2½p	Rose red, Head C - Sheets	20	10
M352	3p	Bright magenta, Head B1 - Sheets	30	15
M352a		Imperf. pair - Sheets	£1250	
M353	4p	Greenish blue, Head B1 - RD coil	£275	
M354	5p	Pale lilac, Head C - Sheets (.11.80)	30	15
M355	12p	Lime green, Head C - Sheets (.7.80)	1.50	75
M355a		Bright Lime green - Sheets	80	70
M356	14p	Grey, Head D - Sheets (14.1.81)	50	30
M356a		Panes FP106, FP107 (26.1.81)	50	
M356b		Phantom CB - Panes FP106, FP107	3.50	
M356c		Vertical coil (11.3.81)	50	
M357	15p	Ultramarine, Head B2 - Sheets (1.80)	1.50	75
M357a		Deep ultramarine - Sheets (1980)	55	25
M358	15½p	Dull violet, Head C - Sheets (14.1.81)	50	35
M359a		Panes FP108, FP109	2.50	
M360	16½p	Deep chestnut, Head D - Sheets (27.1.82)	2.00	75
M361	17p	Bright emerald, Head D - Sheets (30.1.80)	2.25	
M362	17½p	Light brown, Head D - Sheets (30.1.80)	1.50	
M363	18p	Deep violet, Head C - Sheets (14.1.81)	50	35
M364	20p	Deep dull purple, Head D - Sheets (10.10.79)	50	20
M365	22p	Deep blue, Head B2 - Sheets (22.10.80)	60	25
M366	25p	Deep purple, Head B2 - Sheets (14.1.81)	70	50
M367	29p	Olive-sepia - Sheets (.82)	4.50	3.50

Advanced Coated Paper-PVA Dextrin Gum (ACP/PVAD)

No.			U/M	F/U
M368	1p	Claret, Head B1 - Sheets Experimental coating (short afterglow)	2.50	2.50
M369		Normal afterglow	65	
M370	1p	Claret, Head B2, Narrow value set high - Sheets (7.1.86)	25	10
M371	1p	Claret, Head B2, Thick value set high Horizontal coil (23.6.87)	35	20
M372	1p	Claret, Head B2, Thick value - RD coil (18.3.88)	50	25
M373	1p	Claret, Head B2, Very thin value - Sheets (Cyls 15,17) (.9.88)	25	10
M373a		Imperf. pair - Sheets	£1000	

Re-drawn value

No.			U/M	F/U
M374	1p	Claret - Vertical coil (26.7.88)	35	
		Pane FP112 (10.9.91)	35	

Re-drawn value

No.			U/M	F/U
M375	2p	Deep green, Head B2 - Sheets (26.7.88)	15	10
M375a		Imperf. pair		
M375b		Screend value (26.7.88)	65	
M375c		RD 14p coil (5.9.88)	1.50	1.60
M376	2p	Deep green, Head B2. Imperf. at left - Pane FP113 (10.9.91)	45	20
M377	2p	Deep green, Head B2. Imperf. at right - Pane FP113 (10.9.91)	45	20

No.			U/M	F/U
M378	3p	Magenta, Head B2 - Sheets	40	25
M378a		Pane SP19 (Royal mint book) (14.9.93)	1.25	
M379	3p	Bright magenta, Head B1 - Sheets	25	10

Re-drawn value

No.			U/M	F/U
M380	3p	Bright magenta, Sheets (21.1.92)	30	**15**
M381		RD 15p coil (10.10.89)	85	
M382		Thin paper - RD 15p coil	2.50	

No.			U/M	F/U
M383	3½p	Dull chestnut, Head D - Pane SP19 - Royal Mint book (14.9.83)	90	40
M384	4p	Greenish blue, Head B2 - RD 13p & 14p coils (18.3.88)	30	15

Re-drawn value

No.			U/M	F/U
M385	4p	New blue - RD 18p coil (1.10.93)	35	15
M386	4p	New blue, Screened value - Sheets	25	15
M386a		Imperf. pair - Sheets	£1500	
M386b		RD 15p & 17p coils ((10.10.89)	25	
		Thin paper RD 15p coil	1.00	
M387	5p	Dull red brown, Head B2 - Sheets (26.7.88)	25	10
M387a		Screened value - Sheets	65	
M387b		Imperf. pair - Sheets	£1500	
M387c		RD 17p & 18p coils (27.11.90)	25	

No.			U/M	F/U
M388	6p	Lime green - Sheets (10.9.91)	25	15
M389	10p	Orange brown, - Sheets (16.7.85)	30	15

Re-drawn value

No.			U/M	F/U
M390	10p	Light tan, Head B2 (4.9.90)	25	25

No.			U/M	F/U
M391	15½p	Pale violet, Head C - Sheets (1983)	3.00	1.00
M392	16p	Drab, Head D - Sheets (30.3.83)	40	15
M392a		Imperf. pair - Sheets	£125	
		Panes SP19, SP20 (Royal Mint book)	40	
M393	17p	Grey blue, Head D - Sheets (19.6.84)	45	20
M393a		Imperf. pair - Sheets	£250	
M393b		Panes SP21, SP28, SP29 (Heritage, Times and B. Rail books respectively)	45	

No.			U/M	F/U
M394	**18p**	**Olive green**, Head B2 - Sheets (28.8.84)	50	30
M394a		Screened value - Sheets	3.00	
M394b		Imperf. pair (Screened value) - Sheets	£80	
M394c		Pane SP33 (P&O book)	50	
M394d		Panes FP122, FP123	50	
M394e		Pane FP114, FP124	50	
M394f		Vertical coil	50	
M395	**19p**	**Dull orange red**, Head B2 - Sheets (23.8.88)	40	25
M395a		Imperf. pair - Sheets	£500	
M395b		Panes FP115, FP127	40	
M395c		Pane FP125	40	
M395d		Vertical coil	40	
M396	**19p**	**Dull orange red**, - Imperf. at top		
		- Panes FP116, FP117, FP128	75	35
M397	**19p**	**Dull orange red**, - Imperf. at bottom		
		- Panes FP116, FP117, FP128	75	35
M398	**19p**	**Dull orange red**, - Imperf. at top		
		and right - Pane FP117 (24.1.89)	6.50	4.50
M399	**19p**	**Dull orange red**, - Imperf. at right		
		and bottom - Pane FP117 (24.1.89)	6.50	
M400	**20p**	**Turquoise green**, Head B2 - Sheets (23.8.88)	35	30
M401	**20p**	**Black**, Head B2 APS perf. - Sheets (2.10.89)	35	35
M401a		Imperf. pair -Sheets	£600	
M410b		Screened value - Sheets	2.75	
M401c		Horizontal coil	35	
M401d		Vertical coil	35	
M402	**20p**	**Black**, Imperf. at left - Pane FP121	1.00	75
M402a		Screened value - Pane FP121	3.00	
M403	**20p**	**Black**, Imperf. at right - Pane FP121	1.00	75
M403a		Screened value - Pane FP121	3.00	

No.			U/M	F/U
M404	**22p**	**Dark blue** - Experimental coating -Sheets	2.50	1.75
M405	**22p**	**Bright green**, Head B2 - Sheets (28.8.84)	40	35
M405a		Screened value - Sheets	1.25	
M405b		Imperf. pair	£1000	
M406	**22p**	**Orange**, - Sheets (4.9.90)	50	30
M406a		Screened value - Sheets	70	
M406b		Imperf. pair, Screened value - Sheets	£400	
M406c		Vertical coil	50	
M406d		Low OBA - Sheets	3.50	
M406e		Low OBA, Screened value - Sheets	2.50	
M407	**23p**	**Light green**, Head B2 - Sheets (23.8.88)	70	25

No.			U/M	F/U
M408	**24p**	**Violet**, Head B2 - Sheets (28.8.84)	1.25	45
		Screened value - Sheets	2.25	
M409	**24p**	**Indian red**, Head B2 - Sheets (26.9.89)	75	65
M409a		Imperf. pair - Sheets	£1800	
M410	**24p**	**Brown**, Head B2 - Sheets (10.9.91)	2.00	90
M410a		Low OBA, screened value - Sheets	1.50	
M410b		Imperf. pair - Sheets	£700	
M410c		Pane FP112 (10.9.91)	45	45
M411	**24p**	**Brown**, Imperf. at left - Pane FP113	60	35
M412	**24p**	**Brown**, Imperf. at right - Pane FP113	60	35

26p Type I   26p Type II

No.			U/M	F/U
M413	**26p**	**Red**, Head B2, Type I - Sheets (1984)	65	25
M413a		Imperf. pair - Sheets (1984)	£550	
M414		Type II - Pane FP118 (4.8.87)	3.50	1.75
M414a		Screened value - FP118	6.50	
M415	**26p**	**Stone**, Head B2 - Sheets (4.9.90)	65	45

No.			U/M	F/U
M416	**27p**	**Rust brown**, Head B2 - Sheets (23.8.88)	1.00	40
M416a		Screened value (part) - Sheets	4.50	
M417	**27p**	**Rust brown**, Imperf. at top (11.10.88)		
		- Pane FP120	4.00	2.50
M418	**27p**	**Rust brown**, Imperf. at bottom		
		- Pane FP120	4.00	
M419	**27p**	**Mauve**, Head B2 - Sheets (4.9.90)	55	50
M420	**28p**	**Dull violet**, Head C - Sheets (21.10.86)	80	60

No.			U/M	F/U
M421	**28p**	**Yellow ochre**, Head B2 - Sheets (23.8.88)	65	50
M422	**28p**	**Slate**, Head B2 - Sheets (10.9.91)	55	50
M423	**29p**	**Purple**, Head B2 - Sheets (26.9.89)	1.25	50

No.			U/M	F/U
M424	**30p**	**Sage green**, Head B2 - Sheets (26.9.89)	2.25	75
M242a		Screened value - Sheets	90	
M425	**31p**	**Mauve**, Head C - Sheets (17.9.85)	90	65
M425a		Imperf. pair -Sheets	£1100	
M426	**31p**	**Blue**, Head B2 - Sheets (4.9.90)	85	75

No.			U/M	F/U
M427	**32p**	**Dark turquoise**, Head B2 - Sheets (23.8.88)	6.50	4.50
M427a		Screened value - Sheets	85	
M427b		Imperf. pair, screened value - Sheets	£1600	

No.			U/M	F/U
M428	**33p**	**Emerald**, Head B2 - Sheets (4.9.90)	70	55
		Vertical coil	70	
M429	**34p**	**Ochre brown**, Head B2 - Sheets (24.6.86)	1.00	50

M430	**34p**	**Slate**, Head B2 - Sheets (26.9.89)	90	70
M431	**34p**	**Purple**, Head B2 - Sheets (10.9.91)	65	60
M432	**35p**	**Dark brown**, Head B2 - Sheets (23.8.88)	9.00	
M432a		Screened value - Sheets	1.00	65
M432b		Imperf. pair, screened value - Sheets	£1300	

M433	**35p**	**Deep yellow**, Head B2 - Sheets (10.9.91)	80	80
M433a		Deep bright yellow - Sheets	1.00	90
M434	**37p**	**Red** - Sheets (26.9.89)	1.25	90
M435	**39p**	**Bright mauve**, Head B2 - Sheets (10.9.91)	90	65
M435a		Screened value - Sheets	1.75	
M435b		Vertical coil (11.2.92)	90	
M436	**50p**	**Sand**, Head B2 - Sheets (21.1.92)	1.25	50
M436a		Imperf. pair - Sheets	£1500	

1996 (6 February). Perf. 15 x 14. Two phosphor bands
Printer: Harrison & Sons in photogravure

OFPP/PVAD

M437	**4p**	**New blue** - RD 19p coil (30.1.95)	30	30
M438	**5p**	**Claret** - RD coil (30.1.95)	35	30

OFNP/PVAD

M439	**25p**	**Salmon pink** - RD coil (16.1.96)	4.00	

Litho Printings

Photogravure   Litho
Image tends to look 'flat'

Printed by Waddington in Lithography

1980 (30 Jan.) - 86. No watermark.

FCP/PVA - Perf. 13½ x 14

LM1	**4p**	**2B Greenish blue**, - Sheets (30.1.80)	15	20
LM1a		Missing phosphor - Sheets	£1300	
LM1b		Imperforated right marginal - Sheets		
LM2	**20p**	**2B Deep purple and dull purple**		
		- Sheets (21.5.80)	75	25
LM2a		Dull purple and dull purple. Error of colour		
		(stamp appears in one colour)	£350	

PCP/PVAD - Perf. 13½ x 14

LM3	**4p**	**Greenish blue** - Sheets (11.81)	20	10
LM4	**20p**	**Deep purple and dull purple** - Sheets (11.81)	85	20
LM4a		Deep purple brown and dull purple - Sheets		
		(10.85)	1.75	50

ACP/PVAD - Perf. 13½ x 14

LM5	**4p**	**Greenish blue** - Sheets (2.86)	6.50	4.50
LM6	**20p**	**Deep purple and dull purple** - Sheets (.2.86)	4.50	3.50

Printed by Questa in Lithography

FCP/PVAD - Perf. 13½ x 14

LM7	**75p**	**Black** - Sheets (30.1.80)	2.50	1.00
LM7a		Imperf. at right (marginal)	£225	

PCP/PVA - Perf. 13½ x 14

LM8	**5p**	**Pale lilac** - Sheets (10.81)	35	20
LM8a		Imperf. at right (marginal)	£450	

PCP/PVAD - Perf. 13½ x 14

LM9	**2p**	**Green**, Type I - Sheets (21.5.80)	20	10
LM10	**5p**	**Pale lilac** - Sheets (21.5.80)	20	10
LM11	**5p**	**Pale lake brown** - Sheets (21.1.82)	35	15

OCP/PVA - Perf. 15 x 14

LM12	**75p**	**Black** - Sheets (28.2.84)	2.25	1.00

FCP/PVA - Perf. 15 x 14

LM13	**13p**	**CB Pale chestnut** - Pane SP38 (FT book) (9.2.88)	50	35
LM14	**13p**	**LB Pale chestnut** - Pane SP39 (FT book) (9.2.88)	50	35

LM15	**13p**	**RB Pale chestnut** - Pane SP39 (FT book) (9.2.88)	50	35
LM16	**14p**	**CBar Dark blue** - Pane LP1 (11.10.88)	1.40	55
LM16a		Short bar at top - Pane LP1	2.50	
LM16b		Short bar at bottom - Pane LP1	2.50	
LM17	**17p**	**CB Dark blue** - Panes SP49, SP52 (Agatha Christie book) (19.3.91)	55	45
LM17a		Missing phosphor - Panes SP49a, SP52a	£200	

LM18	**18p**	**2B Grey olive** - Pane SP39 (FT book) (9.2.88)	3.50	3.50
LM18a		Double print (various degrees) - SP39	£600	
LM18b		Blackish olive - Pane SP39	£35	
LM19	**18p**	**CB Bright green** - Pane SP58 (Tolkien book) (27.10.92)	65	35
LM20	**18p**	**RB Bright green** - Pane SP59 (27.10.92)	85	50
LM20a		Short additional band upper left - Pane SP59	4.00	
LM21	**22p**	**2B Bright yellow green** - Pane SP39 (9.2.88)	4.50	4.50

LM22	**24p**	**2B Chestnut** - Pane SP59 (Tolkien book) (27.10.92)	1.00	75
LM22a		Left band short at top - Pane SP59	4.00	
LM23	**33p**	**2B Emerald** - Panes SP55 (Wales book) (25.9.92)	1.00	75
		Missing phosphor - Pane SP55a	£550	
LM24	**34p**	**2B Ochre brown** - Pane SP39 (FT book) (9.2.88)	3.50	3.50

75p Type I   75p Type II

LM25	**39p**	**2B Bright mauve** - Pane SP59 (Tolkien book) (27.10.92)	1.00	1.00
LM25a		Short bands at top - Pane SP59	4.50	
LM26	**75p**	**Black**. Type I - Sheets (7.10.86)	2.50	2.25
LM27	**75p**	**Black and pale grey brown**. Type II - Sheets (23.2.88)	7.00	4.00

FCP/PVAD - Perf. 15 x 14

LM28	**75p**	**Black**. Type I - Sheets (19.2.85)	3.00	2.00

PCP/PVAD - Perf. 15 x 14

LM29	**2p**	**Deep green** - Sheets (10.7.84)	20	10
LM30	**5p**	**Pale lake brown** - Sheets (21.2.84)	40	15

Non-elliptical
No.
       U/M F/U

Decimal - Questa Litho
No.

Machin Definitives
       U/M F/U

ACP/PVA - Perf. 15 x 14

			U/M	F/U
LM31	**2p**	**Deep green and light yellow green** - Sheets (23.2.88)	40	35
LM32	**19p**	**Orange red**, - Pane LP2 (11.10.88)	1.00	75
LM33	**22p**	**Orange red** - Pane SP51 (Agatha Christie book) (19.3.91)	60	45
LM34	**24p**	**Chestnut** - Panes SP57, SP60 (Tolkien book) (27.10.92)	60	45
LM35	**33p**	**Emerald** - SP51 (Agatha Christie book) (19.3.91)	1.20	1.00

ACP/PVAD - Perf. 15 x 14

			U/M	F/U
LM36	**2p**	**Deep green** - Sheets (25.2.86)	20	10
LM37	**4p**	**Greenish blue** - Sheets (13.5.86)	40	40
LM37a		Double impression - Sheets	£500	
LM38	**5p**	**Pale lake brown** - Sheets	40	10
LM39	**18p**	**Grey olive** - Panes SP37, SP40 (FT book) (9.2.88)	60	40
LM40	**20p**	**Deep sepia and purple** - Sheets (13.5.86)	85	45

OFNP/PVA - Perf. 15 x 14

			U/M	F/U
LM41	**33p**	**2B Emerald** - Pane SP64 (Beatrix Potter book) (10.10.93)	1.00	1.00
LM42	**39p**	**2B Bright mauve** - Pane SP64 (Beatrix Potter book) (10.10.93)	1.25	1.25

OFNP/PVA - C (Yellow) fluor phosphor

			U/M	F/U
LM43	**18p**	**LB Bright green** - Pane SP64 (B. Potter book) (10.8.93)	1.50	1.50
LM43a		Short band at top left	4.00	4.00
LM43b		Short band at bottom left	4.00	4.00
LM43c		Two side bands		
LM43d		Side band right		
LM43e		CB offset left		
LM43f		Missing phosphor	£300	£300
LM44	**33p**	**2B Light emerald** - Pane SP64 (B. Potter book) (10.8.93)	1.25	1.25
LM44a		Short band at top right	4.00	4.50
LM44b		Short band at bottom right	4.00	4.50
LM44c		Broad band left		
LM44d		Broad band right		
LM44e		Missing phosphor	£375	£375
LM45	**39p**	**2B Bright mauve** - Pane SP64 (B. Potter book) (10.8.93)	1.50	1.50
LM45a		Short band at top right	4.50	4.50
LM45b		Short band at bottom right	4.50	4.50
LM45c		Single 4mm CB		
LM45d		Single 4mm LB		
LM45e		Double impression		
LM45f		Missing phosphor	£475	£475

Printed by Walsall in Lithography

ACP/PVA - Perf 14

FCP/PVA - Perf 14

No.			U/M	F/U
LM53	29p	**Purple,** Imperf. at top - Pane LP6 (17.4.90)	2.50	2.00
LM54	29p	**Purple,** Imperf. at bottom - Pane LP6 (17.4.90)	2.50	2.00
LM55	29p	**Purple,** Imperf. at top and right - Pane LP6 (17.4.90)	2.50	2.00
LM56	29p	**Purple,** Imperf. at right and bottom - Pane LP6 (17.4.90)	2.50	2.00
LM57	31p	**Blue,** Imperf. at top - Pane LP7 (17.9.90)	1.00	65
LM57a		Low OBA - Pane LP7a	1.10	
LM58	31p	**Blue,** Imperf. at bottom - Pane LP7 (17.9.90)	1.00	65
LM58a		Low OBA - Pane LP7a	1.10	
LM59	33p	**Emerald,** Imperf. at top - Pane LP8 (16.9.91)	85	80
LM60	33p	**Emerald,** Imperf. at bottom - Pane LP8 (16.9.91)	85	80
LM61	39p	**Bright mauve,** Imperf. at top - Panes LP9, LP10 (16.9.91)	90	80
LM62	39p	**Bright mauve,** Imperf. at bottom - Panes LP9, LP10 (16.9.91)	90	80

No.			U/M	F/U
LM46	14p	**RB Dark blue,** Imperf. at left - Pane LP3 (25.4.89)	1.00	1.00
LM46a		Missing phosphor - Pane LP3a	£225	
LM47	19p	**2B Orange red,** Imperf. at left - Pane LP3 (25.4.89)	1.50	1.50
LM47a		Band short at bottom, LB short at top - Pane LP3	2.00	
LM47b		Missing phosphor - Pane LP3a	£350	
LM48	19p	**2B Orange red,** Imperf. at right - Pane LP3a (25.4.89)	1.00	1.00
LM48a		Bands short at top - Pane LP3	2.00	
LM48b		Bands short at bottom - Pane LP3	2.50	
LM48c		Missing phosphor - Pane LP3a	£175	
LM49	29p	**2B Purple,** Imperf. at top - Pane LP4 (2.10.89)	2.50	1.50
LM50	29p	**2B Purple,** Imperf. at bottom - Pane LP4 (2.10.89)	2.50	1.50
LM51	29p	**2B Purple,** Imperf. at top and right - Pane LP4 (2.10.89)	2.50	1.50
LM52	29p	**2B Purple,** Imperf. at right and bottom - Pane LP4 (2.10.89)	2.50	1.50

ACP/PVAD - Perf 14

No.			U/M	F/U
LM63	2p	**Deep green,** Imperf. at left - Pane LP5 (9.2.93)	60	40
LM64	2p	**Deep green,** Imperf. at right - Pane LP5 (9.2.93)	60	40
LM65	24p	**Brown,** Imperf. at left - Pane LP5 (9.2.93)	60	50
LM66	24p	**Brown,** Imperf. at right - Pane LP5 (9.2.93)	60	50
LM67	33p	**Emerald,** Imperf. at top - Pane LP11 (8.9.92)	1.50	1.00
LM68	33p	**Emerald,** Imperf. at bottom - Pane LP11 (8.9.92)	1.50	1.00

Elliptical
No.   U/M F/U

Harrison Photo
No.

Machin definitives
    U/M F/U

Printed by Harrison in Photogravure

Perf. 15 x 14 elliptical.

OFPP/PVAD

			U/M	F/U
SM1	**25p**	**Salmon-pink** - Sheets	55	55
SM1a		Imperforate pair - Sheets	£400	
SM1b		Panes EP1, EP2, EP3 ((1.11.94)	60	
SM1c		Vertical coil	75	
SM2	**35p**	**Deep yellow** - Vertical coil (1.11.93)	4.50	4.10
SM3	**41p**	**Stone** - Vertical coil (1.11.93)	5.50	5.50

OFNP/PVAD - C (yellow) fluor

			U/M	F/U
SM4	**19p**	**CB Olive-green** - Sheets	60	45
SM4a		Imperforate pair - Sheets	£250	
SM4b		Missing phosphor - Sheets	£100	
SM4c		Two narrow side bands - Sheets	£120	
SM4d		Narrow band at right	£175	
SM4e		Vertical coil	75	
SM4f		Bottom of value filled in - Vertical coil	2.75	
SM4g		Deep olive-green - Sheets (Cyl 4)	1.00	
SM5	**19p**	**CB Deep Olive-green,** Thick opaque paper - Sheets	3.50	
SM6	**25p**	**2B Salmon-pink** - Sheets (20.12.94)	65	55
SM6a		Panes EP4, EP5 and EP6	65	
SM6b		Short bands at top - Pane EP5 (6.6.95)	1.25	
SM6c		Translucent paper - Sheets	1.25	
SM6d		Broad band at left - Translucent paper	£25	
SM6e		Vertical coil (16.5.95)	1.25	

OFNP/PVA(Layflat) - C (yellow) fluor phosphor

			U/M	F/U
SM7	**19p**	**CB Olive-green** (19.7.94)	75	55
SM7a		Thinner paper, whiter gum	1.25	

OFNP/PVAD - D (blue) fluor

			U/M	F/U
SM8	**19p**	**CB Olive-green** - Sheets (28.7.95)	50	45
SM8a		Screened value - Sheets	3.00	
SM8b		Vertical coil (.10.95)	55	
SM9	**19p**	**CB Deep olive-green,** Opaque paper - Sheets	90	
SM9a		Translucent paper - Sheets	65	
SM10	**20p**	**CB Bright green** - Sheets (25.6.95)	45	45
SM10a		Imperforate pair - Sheets	£325	
SM10b		Value set high (Cyl 14) - Sheets	60	
SM11	**25p**	**2B Salmon-pink** - Sheets (.8.95)	65	65
SM11a		Panes EP5a, EP6a	65	
SM11b		Short bands at top - Pane EP5a	4.00	
SM11c		Missing phosphor	£22	
SM11d		Vertical coil	5.00	
SM12	**26p**	**2B Reddish brown** - Sheets (25.6.96)	60	55
SM12a		Screened value - Sheets	4.00	
SM13	**26p**	**2B Deep reddish brown** - Sheets	1.25	75

— 11 mm —   — 12.5mm —

There are two varieties of phosphor bands on the 37p, 43p and 63p Vertical coil stamps. For simplicity these are described as either 11mm or 12.5mm which refers to the space *between* the bands as shown above.

			U/M	F/U
SM14	**37p**	**2B 11mm Amethyst** - Vertical coil (8.7.96)	1.00	1.00
SM14a		**2B 12.5mm** - Vertical coil	2.75	
SM15	**43p**	**2B 11mm Chocolate-brown** - Vertical coil (8.7.96)	1.00	1.00
SM15a		**2B 12.5 mm** - Vertical coil	2.50	
SM16	**63p**	**2B 11mm Light emerald** - Vertical coil (12.12.96)	1.25	1.25
SM16a		**2B 12.5mm** - Vertical coil (12.12.96)	3.50	

OFNP/PVA(Layflat) - D (blue) fluor phosphor

			U/M	F/U
SM17	**20p**	**CB Bright green** - Sheets (1.2.97)	1.25	1.00
SM18	**25p**	**2B Salmon-pink** - Sheets (.8.95)	9.00	5.00
SM19	**26p**	**2B Pale reddish brown** - Sheets (28.2.97)	1.25	1.25
SM19a		Reddish brown - Sheets (Cyl 6)	2.00	

Printed by Harrison/De La Rue in Gravure

OFNP/PVA - D (blue) fluor

No.			U/M	F/U
SM20	1p	**2B Reddish crimson** - Sheets (1.4.97)	10	10
SM21	2p	**2B Deep grey-green** - Sheets (27.5.97)	15	10
SM21a		Pane SP160 (Machin Anniversary) (5.6.07)	25	30
SM22	4p	**2B New blue** - Sheets (27.5.97)	20	15

SM23	5p	**2B Claret** - Sheets (27.5.97)	25	20
SM23a		Pane SP157 (World of Invention) (1.3.07)	40	45
SM24	6p	**2B Lime green** - Sheets (1.4.97)	30	25
SM25	7p	**2B Light grey** - Sheets (20.4.99)	30	25
		Imperforate pair - Sheets	£1000	

SM26	8p	**2B Deep yellow** - Sheets (25.4.00	30	25
SM27	10p	**2B Deep orange** - Sheets (27.5.97)	30	35
SM27a		Dull Brownish-orange - Sheets	85	
SM28	19p	**CB Yellowish olive** - Sheets (20.4.99)	40	35
SM28a		Additional narrow band at left - Sheets	3.00	
SM28b		Additional narrow band at right - Sheets	3.00	
SM29	19p	**CB Deep olive** - Sheets (.4.99)	90	50
SM30	19p	**CB Olive-green** - Sheets (9.8.99)	90	50

SM31	20p	**CB Bright green** - Sheets (29.4.97)	45	40
SM31a		Imperforate pair - Sheets	£350	
		Pale bright green - Sheets	1.00	
SM32	20p	**RB Bright green** - Pane SP78 (BBC book) (23.9.97)	95	80
SM33	20p	**2B Bright green** - Sheets (.2.98)	40	35

No.			U/M	F/U
SM34	26p	**2B Reddish brown** - Sheets	50	40
SM34a		Imperforate pair - Sheets	£290	
SM34b		Pane SP78 (BBC book) (23.9.97)	55	65
SM35	26p	**Chocolate brown** (18.4.98)	1.10	75
SM36	26p	**2B Gold** - Sheets (29.4.97)	60	55
SM36a		Imperforate pair - Sheets	£2000	
SM36b		Pane SP77 (BBC book) (23.9.97)	60	
SM36c		Short bands at top - Pane SP77	2.50	
SM36d		Short bands at bottom - Pane SP77	2.50	
SM36e		Left band inset - Pane SP77	1.95	
SM36f		Right band inset - Pane SP77	1.95	

SM37	30p	**2B Olive-grey** - Sheets (12.5.97)	60	55
SM38	30p	**2B Deep Olive-grey** - Sheets (24.7.98)	1.50	
SM38a		Imperforate pair - Sheets		
SM39	31p	**2B Royal purple** - Sheets (7.8.97)	60	55
SM40	33p	**2B Slate blue** - Sheets (25.4.00)	55	

SM41	37p	**2B Bright mauve** - Sheets (7.8.97)	75	75
SM41a		Vertical coil (26.8.97)	75	
SM42	37p	**2B Grey-black** , Dull fluor - Sheets (4.7.02)	75	60
SM42a		Bright fluor - Pane SP135 (Letters by night book) (16.3.04)	1.25	
SM43	38p	**2B Ultramarine** - Sheets (20.4.99)	65	55

SM44	39p	**2B Bright magenta** - Sheets (27.5.97)	75	75
SM44a		Imperforate pair - Sheets	£750	
SM45	40p	**2B Greyish blue** - Sheets (20.4.99)	70	65
SM46	41p	**2B Rosine** - Sheets (20.4.99)	95	80

SM47	42p	**2B Grey-green** - Sheets (4.7.02)	85	75
SM48	43p	**2B Sepia brown** - Sheets (1.4.97)	80	80
SM48a		Vertical coil (26.8.97)	1.00	
SM49	44p	**2B Stone** - Sheets (20.4.99)	85	75

No.			U/M	F/U
SM50	45p	2B Bright mauve - Sheets (20.4.99)	75	55
SM50a	46p	2B Old gold - Pane SP160 (Machin Anniversary) (5.6.07)	1.00	1.10
SM51	47p	2B Sea green - Sheets (4.7.02)	95	75
SM51a	48p	2B Rhododendron - Pane SP160 (Machin Anniversary) (5.6.07)	1.10	1.20
SM52	50p	2B Ochre - Sheets (1.4.97)	1.00	95

No.			U/M	F/U
SM53	63p	2B Light emerald - Sheets (13.8.97)	1.10	1.00
SM54	64p	2B Sea-green - Sheets (20.4.99)	1.10	1.00
SM55	65p	2B Greenish-blue - Sheets (25.4.00)	1.10	1.00

No.			U/M	F/U
SM56	68p	2B Stone - Sheets (06.02)	1.15	1.00
SM57	£1	2B Bluish violet - Sheets (1.4.97)	1.75	1.75
SM57a		Imperforate pair - Sheets	£650	
SM57b	£1	2B Ruby - Pane SP160 (Machin Anniversary) (5.6.07)	1.80	1.90

OFPP/PVA(Layflat)
All from Jeffrey Matthews Miniature Sheet

No.			U/M
SM58	4p	New blue (22.5.00)	50
SM59	5p	Claret	50
SM60	6p	Lime green	60
SM61	10p	Deep orange	70
SM62	31p	Royal purple	1.10
SM63	39p	Bright magenta	1.30
SM64	64p	Sea green	2.50
SM65	£1	Bluish-violet	3.50

Printed by Enschedé in Gravure

OFNP/PVAD

No.			U/M	F/U
E18a	18p	CB Bright green (Yellow phosphor - Non elliptical))	40	45

OFNP/PVA - C (yellow) fluor phosphor

No.			U/M	F/U
EE1	1p	2B Crimson (unvarnished) (8.6.93)	30	30
EE1a		4 mm varnish bands (20.4.94)	80	
EE1b		2 mm varnish bands	80	
EE2	2p	2B Deep green (2 mm varnish bands) (11.4.95)	30	30
EE4	4p	2B New blue (4 mm varnish bands) (14.12.93)	35	35
EE4a		2 mm varnish bands (13.9.94)	1.00	

No.			U/M	F/U
EE5	5p	2B Claret (unvarnished) (8.6.93)	35	35
EE5aa		2 mm varnish bands	1.00	
EE6	6p	2B Lime green (unvarnished) (27.4.93)	35	35
EE6a		Wide left band and narrow right band	1.50	
EE6b		2 mm varnish bands	1.00	
EE6c		Missing phosphor	-	
EE10	10p	2B Orange (unvarnished) (8.6.93)	40	40
EE10a		Deep orange, 4 mm varnish bands	1.00	
EE10b		Deep orange, 2 mm varnish bands (14.2.95)	1.00	

No.			U/M	F/U
EE20	20p	2B Sea-green (4 mm varnish bands) (14.12.93)	45	45
EE20a		2 mm varnish bands (28.8.94)	1.10	
EE29	29p	2B Light grey (unvarnished) (26.10.93)	60	60
EE29a		4 mm varnish bands (25.4.94)	1.20	
EE29b		2 mm varnish bands (31.3.95)	1.20	

Elliptical
No.   U/M F/U

Enschedé Gravure
No.   U/M F/U

Machin Definitives
U/M F/U

EE30	30p	2B Grey-green (unvarnished) (27.7.93)	60	60
EE30a		4 mm varnish bands	1.25	
EE30b		2 mm varnish bands (23.11.94)	1.25	

OFNP/PVA White - D (blue) fluor phosphor

(25p unvarnished, others with 2 mm varnish bands)

EE1d	1p	2B Crimson (29.4.96)	50	25
EE2b	2p	2B Deep green (25.5.96)	35	55
EE4c	4p	2B New blue (1.8.96)	40	40
EE5c	5p	2B Claret (4.10.96)	50	40
EE5d		Deep reddish claret, mottled background	75	
EE6d	6p	2B Lime green (26.3.96)	40	35
EE10d	10p	2B Deep orange (13.9.96)	80	45
EE20	20p	2B Sea-green (26.3.96)	1.30	1.10
EE25	25p	2B Deep salmon-pink (20.10.95)	90	65
EE30d	30p	2B Grey-green (26.3.96)	1.00	1.00
EE31	31p	2B Deep purple (25.6.96)	70	65
EE37	37p	2B Amethyst (25.6.96)	75	70
EE39	39p	2B Bright magenta (25.6.96)	80	75

EE35	35p	2B Deep yellow (unvarnished) (17.8.93)	65	65
EE35a		4 mm varnish bands (9.6.94)	1.40	
EE35b		2 mm varnish bands (28.6.95)	1.40	
EE35c	35p	CB Lime green	85	75
EE36	36p	2B Ultramarine (unvarnished) (26.10.93)	70	70
EE36a		4 mm varnish bands	1.40	
EE36b		2 mm varnish bands (12.5.95)	1.40	

EE43a	43p	2B Chocolate-brown (25.6.96)	1.00	95
EE50d	50p	2B Ochre (14.11.96)	1.50	1.20
EE63	63p	2B Light emerald (25.6.96)	1.20	1.10
EE100a	£1	2B Bluish violet (fluorescent ink) and Iriodin ink (27.6.96)	2.50	2.00
EE100b		Bluish violet (without fluorescence)	3.25	
EE100c		Iriodin ink stops short of base of design	5.50	

EE38	38p	2B Rosine (unvarnished) (26.10.93)	75	75
EE38a		2 mm varnish bands (25.1.94)	1.40	
EE38b		Imperf. pair	£175	
EE38c		2 mm varnish bands, Novaglo phosphor	2.75	
EE41	41p	2B Stone (unvarnished) (26.10.93)	75	75
EE41a		Drab (2 mm varnish bands) (23.6.94)	1.25	
EE50	50p	2B Ochre (4 mm varnish bands) (14.12.93)	1.00	1.00
EE50a		2 mm varnish bands (14.7.94)	1.50	

OFNP/PVA Tinted - D (blue) fluor phosphor

(25p unvarnished, others with 2 mm varnish bands)

EE1c	1p	2B Crimson (15.2.96)	30	25
EE2a	2p	2B Deep green (16.11.95)	30	55
EE1b	4p	2B New blue (2.11.95)	45	40
EE5b	5p	2B Claret (14.3.96)	40	40
EE10c	10p	2B Deep orange (10.1.96)	50	45
EE25	25p	2B Bright salmon-pink (10.10.95)	75	65
EE25a		'Rogue' Layflat paper	7.50	
EE29c	29p	2B Light grey (18.1.96)	1.00	85
EE30c	30p	2B Grey-green (26.3.96)	1.25	1.00
EE35d	35p	2B Deep yellow (18.12.95)	1.00	90
EE38d	38p	2B Rosine (8.1.96)	1.00	90
EE41b	41p	2B Stone (11.8.95)	1.20	1.00
EE41c		Pale grey-brown (2.5.96)	1.75	
EE43	43p	2B Rosine (25.6.96)	1.25	1.00
EE50b	50p	2B Stone (21.2.96)	1.50	1.20
EE50c		Imperf. pair	-	
EE100	£1	2B Bluish violet and Iriodin ink (22.8.95)	2.50	2.00

Printer: Enschedé in Gravure

EEG1	1p	2B Crimson - Pane SP166 (Army Uniforms)	30	35
EEG35	35p	CB Lime green - Pane SP151 (Brunel) (23.2.06)	85	95
EEG40	40p	2B Greenish-blue - Pane SP151 (Brunel) (23.2.06)	85	95
EEG42	42p	2B Sage green - Pane SP136 (Glory of the Garden book) (25.5.04)	1.50	1.60
EEG46	46p	2B Old gold - Pane SP166 (Army Uniforms)	1.10	1.20
EEG47	47p	2B Sea green - Pane SP136 (Glory of the Garden book) (25.5.04)	1.65	1.70
EEG54	54p	2B Rust - Pane SP166 (Army Uniforms)	1.70	1.80

Printer: Enschedé in Litho

| EEL50 | 50p | 2B Ochre - Pane SP154 (Victoria Cross) (21.9.06) | 1.50 | 1.60 |
| EEL1st | 1st | 2B PiP Gold - Pane SP154 (Victoria Cross) (21.9.06) | 1.20 | 1.30 |

Elliptical
No.   U/M   F/U

Questa Litho/Gravure
No.   U/M   F/U

Machin Definitives
U/M   F/U

Printed by Questa in lithography

On the Questa Litho printings with elliptical perfs there are two types of ellipse - A(r) and B(s) - and also two fluor types. These are beyond the scope of this work, but full details may be found in the MCC Specialised Machin catalogue.

Colours similar to Enschedé Printings

OFNP/PVA - C (yellow) fluor phosphor

			U/M	F/U
EQL6	**6p**	**2B Lime green** - Pane SP66 (N. Ireland book)		
		(26.7.94)	5.00	4.00
EQL10	**10p**	**2B Deep orange** - Pane SP70		
		(Nat. Trust book) (25.4.95)	2.50	2.00
EQL10a		Short bands at bottom	4.75	
EQL18	**18p**	**LB Bright green** - Pane SP64 ·		
		(B. Potter book) (10.8.93)	2.00	1.50
		Short band at top - Pane SP64	8.00	
		Short band at bottom -Pane SP64	8.00	
		Two side bands - Pane SP64		
		Missing phosphor - Pane SP64a	£350	
EQL19	**19p**	**LB 4mm Olive-green** - Panes SP66		
		(N. Ireland book) (26.7.94), SP70 (Nat.		
		Trust book) (25.4.95)	1.00	90
EQL19a		Short additional band at bottom right		
		- Pane SP70	3.25	
EQL19b		4.75 mm left band - Pane SP72 (25.4.95)	75	
EQL19c	**19p**	**RB 4mm Olive-green** - Pane SP70 (Nat.		
		Trust book) (25.4.95)	1.00	90
EQL19d		Short additional band at bottom left		
		- Pane SP70	3.25	
EQL19e		4.75 mm right band - SP72 (Nat.		
		Trust book) (25.4.95)	75	
EQL25	**25p**	**2B Salmon-pink** - Panes SP66		
		(N. Ireland book) (26.7.94), SP70 (Nat.		
		Trust book) (25.4.95)	80	70
EQL25a		Short band at top right - Pane SP66	4.00	
EQL25b		Left band inset - Pane SP70	6.00	
EQL30	**30p**	**2B Grey-green** - Pane SP70 (Nat. Trust book)		
		(25.4.95)	2.60	2.25
		Left band inset - Pane SP70	£15	
EQL33	**33p**	**2B Light emerald** - Pane SP64		
		(B. Potter book) (10.8.93)	1.75	
EQL33a		Right band short at top - Pane SP64	9.00	
EQL33b		Right band short at bottom - Pane SP64	9.00	
EQL33c		Missing phosphor - Pane SP64a	£450	
EQL35	**35p**	**2B Deep yellow** - Pane SP70 (Nat. Trust book)		
		(25.4.95)	1.50	1.3
EQL35a		Short bands at top	£13	
EQL39	**39p**	**Bright mauve** - Pane SP64 (B. Potter book)		
		(10.8.93)	1.90	
EQL39a		Right band short at top - Pane SP64	9.00	
EQL39b		Right band short at bottom - Pane SP64	9.00	
EQL39c		Double/triple impression - Pane SP64	£300	
EQL39d		Missing phosphor - Pane SP64a	£500	
EQL41	**41p**	**2B Drab** - Pane SP70 (Nat. Trust book)		
		(25.4.95)	1.75	1.50

OFNP/PVA - D (blue) fluor phosphor

			U/M	F/U
EQL1	**1p**	**2B Crimson** - Pane EP14 (8.7.96)	50	30
EQL1a		Short bands at top - Pane EP14		
EQL1b		Short bands at bottom - Pane EP14	5.50	
EQL1c		Broad band at right - Pane EP14	£150	
EQL1d		Missing phosphor - Pane EP14a	£500	
EQL20	**20p**	**CB Bright green** - Panes EP14, EP16		
		(8.7.96)	1.00	90
EQL20a		Short bands at top - Panes EP14, EP16	£15	
EQL20b		Short bands at bottom - Pane EP14	£12	
EQL20c		Missing phosphor - Pane EP14a, EP16a	£175	
EQL20d		Narrow band at left - Pane EP14	£125	
EQL25	**25p**	**2B Salmon-pink** - Panes EP13, EP15		
		(19.12.95)	65	55
EQL25a		Pane SP77 (Euro '96 book)	3.50	
EQL25b		Broad band left - Pane SP77	£500	
EQL26	**26p**	**2B Red-brown** - Panes EP14, EP16		
		(8.7.96)	60	55
EQL26a		Short bands at top - Panes EP14, EP16	£15	
EQL26b		Short bands at bottom - Panes EP14	£15	
EQL26c		Inset left band - Panes EP14	£15	
EQL26d		Inset right band - Panes EP14	£15	
EQL26e		Broad band at right- Panes EP14	£150	
EQL26f		Missing phosphor	£45	

Printed by Questa in Gravure

OFNP/PVA - C (yellow) fluor phosphor

			U/M	F/U
EQG1	**1p**	**2B Crimson** - Pane EP21 (1.12.98)	50	35
EQG1a		'Invisible' phosphor - Pane EP21	£10	
EQG1b	**1p**	**2B Deep Crimson** - Pane EP22 (26.4.99)	50	35
EQG1c		Short bands at top - Pane EP22	3.00	
EQG1d		Short bands at bottom and additional		
		Short CB at bottom	7.50	
EQG1f	**1p**	**2B (10mm) Crimson** - Pane SP98		
		(World Changers book) (21.9.99)	1.25	1.00
EQG1g		Short bands at top - Pane SP98	55	
EQG1h		Right band inset and short bands at top		
		- SP98	3.25	
EQG1i		Right band inset - Pane SP98	5.00	
EQG1j	**1p**	**2B Crimson (Added OBA)** - Pane EP22	1.50	90
EQG1k		Short bands at top - Pane EP22	5.00	
EQG2	**2p**	**2B Green** - Pane EP22 (26.4.99)	50	35
EQG2a		Short bands at top - Pane EP22	3.25	
EQG2b	**2p**	**2B Green (Added OBA)** - Pane EP22		
		(31.7.99)	1.50	90
EQG2c		Short bands at top - Pane EP22	5.00	
EQG19	**19p**	**CB Olive-green** - Panes EP22, EP24	75	50
EQG19a		Additional narrow band at left - Pane EP22	£12	
EQG19b		Additional narrow band at right - Pane EP22	£12	
EQG19c	**19p**	**CB 5mm Bistre** - Pane SP98	1.00	75
EQG19d	**19p**	**CB Olive-green (Added OBA)**		
		- Panes EP22, EP24 (31.7.89)	1.50	1.00
EQG19e		Additional narrow band at left - Pane EP22	£12	
EQG19f		Additional narrow band at right - Pane EP22	£12	
EQG20	**20p**	**CB Bright green** - Panes EP21, EP23		
		(1.12.98)	1.25	90
EQG20a		Short band at top - Pane EP23	4.50	
EQG20b		'Invisible' phosphor - Pane EP23	£25	
EQG26	**26p**	**2B Red-brown** - Pane EP21	65	45
EQG26a		Short bands at bottom - Pane EP21	£15	
EQG26b		Right band inset - Pane EP21	5.00	
EQG26c		'Invisible' phosphor - Pane EP21	7.50	
EQG26A	**26p**	**2B 10mm Chestnut** - Pane SP98		
		(World Changers book)	2.00	1.50
EQG26Aa		Right band inset	5.00	
EQG26B	**26p**	**2R Red-brown (Added OBA)** - Pane EP22		
		(31.7.99)	1.25	90
EQG26Ba		Left band inset - Pane EP22	5.00	
EQG26Bb		Right band inset - Pane EP22	£15	

Elliptical
No.

Walsall Litho/Gravure
U/M   F/U   No.

Machin Definitives
U/M   F/U

Printed by Walsall in Lithography

OFNP/PVA (Cream)
- C (yellow) fluor phosphor

			U/M	F/U
EWL25	25p	2B (Inset) Deep salmon-pink - Pane EP7		
		(1.11.93)	1.00	90
EWL25a		Short bands at top - Pane EP7	5.00	
EWL25b		Short bands at bottom - Pane EP7	5.00	
EWL25c		Double broad bands at right - Pane EP7	£65	
EWL25d		One narrow band at right - Pane EP7	£175	
EWL25e		One band at left, two bands at right - Pane EP7	£40	
EWL35	35p	2B (Inset) Deep yellow - Pane EP8		
		(1.11.93)	1.10	1.00
EWL35a		Inset left band - Pane EP8	4.00	
EWL35b		Inset right band - Pane EP8	4.50	
EWL35c		Two Full bands - Pane EP8	£10	
EWL41	41p	2B (Inset) Stone - Pane EP10 (1.11.93)	1.15	1.00
EWL41a		Left band inset - Pane EP10	£18	
EWL41b		Right band inset - Pane EP10	£18	
EWL41c		Missing phosphor		
EWL41d		One band at left, two bands at right	-	
EWL60	60p	2B Slate-blue (Inset left band) - Pane EP11		
		(9.8.94)	2.50	1.75
EWL60a		Inset right band - Pane EP11 (9.8.94)	4.00	
EWL60b		Full bands - pane EP11 (16.9.95)	5.50	

OFNP/PVA (White)
- C (yellow) fluor phosphor

			U/M	F/U
EWL35d	35p	2B Deep yellow - Pane EP8	3.00	1.00
EWL41e	41p	2B Stone - Pane EP10	2.00	1.00
EWL41f		4mm CB (OR) - Pane EP10	£500	
EWL41g		Broad band left - Pane EP10	£500	
EWL60c	60p	2B Slate-blue - Pane EP11	2.25	1.75

OFNP/PVA (White)
- D (blue) fluor phosphor

			U/M	F/U
EWL35e	35p	2B Deep yellow - Pane EP8a (20.10.95)	1.25	75
EWL35f		Left band inset - Pane EP8a (19.3.96)	1.30	
EWL35g		Right band inset - Pane EP8a (19.3.96)	1.30	
EWL37	37p	2B Amethyst - Pane EP9 (8.7.96)	4.50	3.50
EWL37a		Right band inset - Pane EP9 (8.7.96)	1.75	
EWL37b		Left band inset - Pane EP9 (8.7.96)	1.75	
EWL41h	41p	2B Stone - Pane EP10a (19.3.96)	4.50	1.50
EWL41i		Left band inset - Pane EP10a (19.3.96)	1.50	
EWL41j		Right band inset - Pane EP10a	1.50	
EWL60d	60p	2B Slate-blue - Pane EP11a (19.3.96)	4.50	1.90
EWL60e		Left band inset - Pane EP11a(19.3.96)	2.00	
EWL60f		Right band inset - Pane EP11a	2.00	
EWL63	63p	2B Light emerald - Pane EP12 (8.7.96)	1.00	1.00
EWL63a		Left band inset - Pane EP12 (8 7 96)	1.00	
EWL63b		Right band inset - Pane EP12	4.50	
EWL63c		Missing phosphor -Pane EP12a	£500	

Printed by Walsall in Gravure

OFNP/PVA - D (blue) fluor phosphor

			U/M	F/U
EWG10	10p	2B Deep orange - Pane SP88		
		(Breaking Barriers book) (13.10.98)	1.25	1.00
EWG10a		Short bands at top - Pane SP88	7.50	
EWG10b		Short bands at bottom - Pane SP88	£22	
EWG19	19p	RB Bistre - Pane SP101		
		(Special by Design book) (15.2.00)	1.00	95
EWG19a		Short band at top - Pane SP101	6.50	
EWG19b		Right band inset - Pane SP101	4.00	
EWG19c		Right band inset and Short band at top - Pane SP101	7.50	
EWG30	30p	2B Grey-green - Pane EP17 (5.5.98)	50	50
EWG37	37p	2B Amethyst - Pane EP18 (26.8.97)	80	75
EWG37a		Shiny printing - Pane EP18 (5.5.98)	1.10	
EWG38	38p	2B Ultramarine - Pane EP19 (26.4.99)	80	70
EWG38a	38p	2B Ultramarine (Smaller design) - Pane SP101		
		(Special by Design book) (15.2.00)	5.00	4.00
EWG38b		Left band short at top - Pane SP101	1.25	
EWG38c		Right band inset - Pane SP101	£25	
EWG38d		Right band inset and Left band short at top - Pane SP101	8.00	
EWG39	39p	2B Light grey - Pane SP140 (Bronte sisters book) (24.2.05)	1.75	1.30
EWG40	40p	2B Greyish-blue - Pane EP20	80	60
EWG42	42p	2B Sage green - Pane SP140 (Bronte sisters book) (24.2.05)	1.80	1.50
EWG43	43p	2B Chocolate-brown - Pane SP88		
		(Breaking Barriers book) (13.10.98)	1.25	1.00
EWG43a		Short bands at top - Pane SP88	8.00	
EWG43b		Short bands at bottom - Pane SP88	£20	
EWG43c		Right band inset - Pane SP88	5.00	
EWG43d		Right band stepped at top - Pane SP88	£25	
EWG43e	43p	2B Sepia-brown - Pane SP86		
		(Breaking Barriers book) (13.10.98)	1.25	1.00
EWG43f		Short bands at bottom -Pane SP86	£20	
EWG43g		Left band inset - Pane SP86	£23	
EWG50	50p	2B Ochre - Pane·SP145 (Trafalgar book)		
		(18.10.05)	1.30	1.40
EWG63	63p	2B Light emerald - Pane EP21 (26.8.97)	1.25	1.00
EWG63a		Shiny printing	1.50	
EWG64	64p	2B Sea green - Pane EP22	1.25	1.20
EWG65	65p	2B Greenish-blue - Pane EP23	1.30	1.25
EWG68	68p	2B Stone - Pane SP145 (Trafalgar book)		
		(18.10.05)	1.30	1.40

Elliptical
No.   U/M   F/U

DLR - ATN
U/M   F/U   No.

Machin Definitives
U/M   F/U

De La Rue ATN Printings
(formerly known as Byfleet)

Printed by De La Rue on the ATN press in Gravure with Dlw phosphor/fluor.

These were formerly known as 'Byfleet' printings, and are easily differentiated from the earlier gravure printings by the bright blue fluorescence.

In co-operation with other Machin dealers, this catalogue, and the Machin Collectors Club, have now sub divided these further into three gum types. These are:-

                    ATN(l) Layflat gum
ATN (t) Tinted gum   ATN (c) Cream PVA gum

On the printings with tinted gum - ATN(t) - different papers are known which are variously described as Bright Intermediate or Dull, these descriptions meaning the reaction of the paper when viewed under long wave UV. However with single stamps it is virtually impossible to distinguish between the bright or intermediate papers *unless* you have a marginal example. In these listings we show single stamps as either Dull or Bright/Intermediate. For collectors who do collect marginal single stamps or who specialise in Cylinder or Date blocks you will find the complete listings of ALL paper varieties in the Machin Collectors Club specialised catalogue - and also a monthly update in the MCC's Newsletters.

Please note that prices for phosphor band varieties are difficult to determine with any accuracy at this time. However, all known varieties are listed, and with current prices where known.

ATN (l) - Layflat gum

No.			U/M	F/U
ATN(l)20	**20p**	**2B Bright green**	50	
ATN(l)20a		Left band inset	7.50	
ATN(l)20b		Right band inset		
ATN(l)20c		Short band top	6.00	
ATN(l)20d		Dark shade. from 04/03/03 printing		
ATN(l)20e		Phosphor/fluor wash from 04/03/03 printing		
ATN(l)33	**33p**	**2B Slate blue**	60	
ATN(l)33a		Left band inset	£12	
ATN(l)33b		Short band top		
ATN(l)35	**35p**	**2B Sepia-brown**	60	

No.			U/M	F/U
ATN(l)39	**39p**	**2B Light grey**	60	
ATN(l)39a		Left band inset	8.50	
ATN(l)39b		Right band inset		
ATN(l)39c		Short band bottom		
ATN(l)40	**40p**	**2B Greenish-blue**	80	
ATN(l)43	**43p**	**2B Pale emerald**	85	

ATN (t) - Tinted Gum

No.			U/M	F/U
ATN(t)1	**1p**	**2B Crimson - Bright/Inter. paper**	10	
ATN(t)1a		Left band inset	4.00	
ATN(t)1b		Right band inset	4.00	
ATN(t)1c		Short band at top	£10	
ATN(t)1d		Short band at bottom	5.00	
ATN(t)2	**2p**	**2B Deep green - Bright/Inter. paper**	15	
ATN(t)2a		Left band inset	3.50	
ATN(t)2b		Right band inset	7.00	
ATN(t)2c		Short band top	8.00	
ATN(t)4	**4p**	**2B New blue - Dull paper**	20	
ATN(t)4a		Left band inset		
ATN(t)4b		Right band inset		
ATN(t)4Aa	**4p**	**2B New blue - Bright/Inter. paper**	20	
ATN(t)4Ab		Left band inset	3.50	
ATN(t)4Ac		Right band inset		

No.			U/M	F/U
ATN(t)5	**5p**	**2B Claret - Dull paper**	25	
ATN(t)5a		Left band inset	9.00	
ATN(t)5b		Short band top	5.50	
ATN(t)5Aa	**5p**	**2B Claret - Bright/Inter. paper**	25	
ATN(t)5Ab		Left band inset	8.00	
ATN(t)5Ac		Short band top		
ATN(t)7	**7p**	**2B Bright magenta - Bright/Inter. paper**	30	
ATN(t)7a		Right band inset		
ATN(t)8	**8p**	**2B Deep yellow - Bright/Inter. paper**	30	
ATN(t)8a		Left band inset		
ATN(t)8b		Short band top		

No.			U/M	F/U
ATN(t)9	**9p**	**2B Orange - Bright/Inter. paper**	35	
ATN(t)9a		Left band inset	£11	
ATN(t)10	**10p**	**2B Deep orange - Bright/Inter. paper**	35	
ATN(t)10a		Left band inset		
ATN(t)10b		Right band inset	6.50	
ATN(t)10c		Short band bottom	4.50	
ATN(t)10a		Phosphor/fluor wash		
ATN(t)10b		Dark shade		
ATN(t)10c		Dark shade - Phosphor/fluor wash		

No.			U/M	F/U
ATN(t)20	**20p**	**2B Bright green** - Bright/Inter. paper	40	
ATN(t)20a		Left band inset	4.00	
ATN(t)20b		Right band inset		
ATN(t)20c		Short band top		
ATN(t)20d		Short band bottom		
ATN(t)20a		Dark shade		
ATN(t)20b		Pale shade		
ATN(t)20Aa	**20p**	**2B Bright green** - Dull paper	65	
ATN(t)20A		Left band inset		
ATN(t)33	**33p**	**2B Slate blue** - Bright paper	50	
ATN(t)33a		Left band inset	6.00	
ATN(t)34	**34p**	**2B Lime green** - Bright/Inter. paper	50	
ATN(t)34a		Left band inset	4.50	
ATN(t)34b		Right band inset		
ATN(t)34c		Short band top		
ATN(t)34Aa	**34p**	**2B Lime green** - Dull paper	75	
ATN(t)34Ab		Left band inset		
ATN(t)34Ac		Right band inset		
ATN(t)35	**35p**	**2B Sepia-brown** - Bright/Inter. paper	50	
ATN(t)35a		Left band inset	12.50	
ATN(t)35b		Short band top		
ATN(t)35Aa	**35p**	**CB Lime green** - Bright/Inter. paper	50	

No.			U/M	F/U
ATN(t)68	**68p**	**2B Stone** - Inter. paper		
ATN(t)68a		Left band inset	6.00	
ATN(t)68b		Short band top	6.00	
ATN(t)100	**£1**	**2B Bluish-violet** - Dull paper		
ATN(t)100Aa	**£1**	**2B Bluish-violet** - Bright/Inter. paper	1.80	
ATN(t)100Ab		Left band inset	8.00	
ATN(t)100Ac		Right band inset		
ATN(t)100Ad		Short band top		
ATN(t)150	**£1.50**	**2B Rust-red** - Inter. paper	2.50	
ATN(t)150a		Short band bottom	5.00	

£2 - Missing '£' sign

ATN(t)37	**37p**	**2B Grey-black** - Inter. paper	55	
ATN(t)37a		Short band top	6.00	
ATN(t)39	**39p**	**2B Light grey** - Inter. paper	60	
ATN(t)40	**40p**	**2B Greenish-blue** - Bright/Inter. paper	60	
ATN(t)40a		Left band inset	6.00	
ATN(t)41	**41p**	**2B Red** - Bright paper		
ATN(t)41a		Left band inset	5.00	
ATN(t)42	**42p**	**2B Grey-green** - Bright/Inter. paper	75	
ATN(t)42a		Left band inset		
ATN(t)43	**43p**	**2B Pale emerald** - Inter. paper	80	
ATN(t)43a		Right band inset		

ATN(t)200	**£2**	**2B Indigo** - Dull paper	3.75	
ATN(t)200a		Short band bottom		
ATN(t)200b		Missing £ - Stamp 18/1 No dot sheet	£100	
ATN(t)200Aa	**£2**	**2B Indigo** - Bright paper		
ATN(t)300	**£3**	**2B Purple** - Dull paper	6.00	
ATN(t)500	**£5**	**2B Slate-blue** - Inter. paper	8.50	

ATN(t)46	**46p**	**2B Old Gold** - Bright/Intermediate paper		
ATN(t)47	**47p**	**2B Sea green** - Dull paper		
ATN(t)47Aa	**47p**	**2B Sea green** - Bright/Intermediate paper		
		Left band inset	12.50	
ATN(t)50	**50p**	**2B Ochre** - Bright/Inter. paper	95	
ATN(t)50a		Left band inset		
ATN(t)50b		Right band inset		
ATN(t)50c		Short band top		
ATN(t)50d		Short band bottom	6.50	

Elliptical
No.   U/M   F/U

DLR - ATN
No.

Machin Definitives
U/M   F/U

ATN (c) - Cream PVA Gum

No.			U/M	F/U
ATN(c)100	**£1**	**2B Bluish-violet**	1.80	1.50
ATN(c)100a		Right band inset	12.50	
ATN(c)100A	**£1**	**2B Ruby**	1.80	1.75

The NVI printings on ATN (c) - Cream PVA Gum will be found on Page 139 at the bottom of column 1.

No.			U/M	F/U
ATN(c)1	**1p**	**2B Crimson**	15	15
ATN(c)1a		Left band inset	12.50	
ATN(c)1b		Right band inset	8.00	
ATN(c)1c		Short band top	8.00	
ATN(c)1d		Short band bottom	8.00	
ATN(c)2	**2p**	**2B Deep green**	15	15
ATN(c)2a		Left band inset	8.00	
ATN(c)2b		Right band inset	8.00	
ATN(c)2c		Short band top	8.50	
ATN(c)2d		Short band bottom	£10	
ATN(c)5	**5p**	**2B Claret**	0.20	25
ATN(c)5a		Left band inset	9.00	
ATN(c)5b		Right band inset	8.00	
ATN(c)5c		Short band top	6.00	
ATN(c)5d		Short band bottom	7.00	
ATN(c)9	**9p**	**2B Orange**	0.25	30
ATN(c)9a		Right band inset	8.00	
ATN(c)10	**10p**	**2B Deep orange**	0.30	35
ATN(c)12	**12p**	**2B Greenish-blue**	0.30	35
ATN(c)14	**14p**	**2B Salmon pink**	0.40	45
ATN(c)16	**16p**	**2B Pink**	0.40	45
ATN(c)20	**20p**	**2B Bright green**	0.40	45

No.			U/M	F/U
ATN(c)35	**35p**	**CB Lime green**	0.60	65
ATN(c)37	**37p**	**CB Brown-olive**	0.75	80
ATN(c)42	**42p**	**2B Grey-green**	0.75	80
ATN(c)44	**44p**	**2B Ultramarine**	0.75	80
ATN(c)44a		Short band bottom	12.50	
ATN(c)46	**46p**	**2B Old gold**	0.70	75
ATN(c)47	**47p**	**2B Sea green**	0.90	95
ATN(c)47a		Left band inset	£15	
ATN(c)48	**48p**	**2B Rhododendron**	0.80	85
ATN(c)49	**49p**	**2B Rust**	0.90	95
ATN(c)49a		Short band top	8.50	
ATN(c)50	**50p**	**2B Ochre**	90	95
ATN(c)50a		Right band inset	£10	
ATN(c)50A	**50p**	**2B Grey**	1.00	1.00
ATN(c)54	**54p**	**2B Rust**	1.10	1.00
ATN(c)72	**72p**	**2B Red**	1.20	1.30
ATN(c)72a		Left band inset	£15	
ATN(c)78	**78p**	**2B Emerald green**	1.30	1.40

Multi-Value Coil Strips

All coil stamps were printed by Harrisons

OCP/GA

MC1	**2 x ½p**	**2B Turquoise, 2 x 1p 2B Crimson and 2p 2B Green** (15.2.71)	95
MC1a		Broad band at left	£25
MC1b		Broad band at right	£125
MC1c		Missing phosphor (screened)	£30
MC1d		Silicone coated	£200

OCP/PVA

MC2	**2 x ½p**	**2B Turquoise, 1p 2B Crimson, 2p 2B Green and 6p 2B Light green** (3.77)	2.75

FCP/GA

MC3	**2 x ½p**	**2B Turquoise, 2 x 1p 2B Crimson and 2p 2B Myrtle-green** with silicone coating (9.72) As MC1	2.50
MC3a		Silicone omitted	£15

FCP/PVAD

MC4	**2 x ½p**	**2B Turquoise, 2 x 1p 2B Crimson and 2p 2B Green** (4.74) As MC1	50
MC4a		Broad band	£40
MC4b		Missing phosphor	7.50
MC4c		Thin paper	£40
MC5	**2 x ½p**	**2B Turquoise, 1p 2B Crimson, 2p 2B Dark green and 6p 2B Light green** (3.12.75) As MC2	65
MC5a		Broad band	2.00
MC5b		Broad band at right	7.00

MC6	**2 x ½p**	**CB Turquoise, 2 x 1p CB Crimson and 7p CB Purple-brown** (14.12.77)	55
MC6a		Screened value on 7p	9.50
MC6b		Thick paper	3.00

[image: strip with 8p, 1p, 1p, "be properly addressed", "use the postcode"]

MC7	**2 x 1p**	**CB Crimson, 8p CB Rosine** *plus* 2 x "be properly addressed" and "use the postcode" labels (16.1.80)	45
MC7a		'All over' phosphor error	£250

PCP1/PVAD

MC8	**½p**	**Turquoise and 3 x 4p Greenish blue** (30.12.81)	65
MC8a		Fluorescent Brightener Omitted (mounted)	£175
MC8b		FBO (unmounted mint)	£1500
MC8a		PCP2. Fluorescent Brightener Omitted (mounted)	£125

MC9	**1p**	**Crimson and 3 x 4p Greenish blue** (14.8.84)	65

MC10	**2½p**	**Rose-red and 3 x 3p Dull red magenta** (6.81)	65
MC10a		Fluorescent Brightener Omitted	£35

ACP/PVAD

MC11	**1p**	**Crimson and 3 x 4p Greenish blue** (18.3.88)	45

MC12	**2p**	**Green and 3 x 4p Pale blue** (5.9.88)	1.95

MC13	**3p**	**Bright magenta and 3 x 4p New blue** (10.10.89)	1.00

MC14   **5p**   **Dull red-brown** and **3 x 4p New blue**
            (27.11.90)   85

Single Value Coil Strip

SC1   **5 x 25p**   **Salmon pink** - Readers digest coil strip
                   (6.2.96)   £20

MC15   **2 x 5p**   **Dull red-brown** and **2 x 4p New blue**
            (1.10.91)   75

OFPP/PVAD

MC16   **3 x 5p**   **Dull red-brown** and **4p New blue**
            (31.1.95   75

Single Value Coil Strips

OCP/GA

CS3D	3p 2B Ultramarine - Horizontal	225.00

OCP/PVA

CS1A	1p 2B Crimson - Vertical	3.00
CS2.5A	2½p CB Magenta - Horizontal 250 screen	9.00
CS2.5C	2½p CB Magenta - Vertical 150 screen	23.00
CS3A	3p 2B Ultramarine - Horizontal 250 screen	125.00
CS3B	3p 2B Ultramarine - Horizontal 150 screen	150.00
CS3E	3p 2B Ultramarine - Vertical	40.00

FCP/GA

CS1B	1p 2B Crimson - Vertical	3.00
CS2.5B	2½p CB Magenta - Horizontal	112.50
CS3C	3p 2B Ultramarine - Horizontal	125.00

FCP/PVAD

CS3F	3p CB Ultramarine Horizontal 250 screen	37.50
CS3G	3p CB Ultramarine Vertical 150 screen	35.00
CS3.5A	3½p 2B Grey-green Horizontal	10.00
CS3.5B	3½p 2B Grey-green Vertical	55.00
CS3.5C	3½p CB Grey-green Horizontal	6.50
CS4.5A	4½p 2B Steel blue Vertical	4.00
CS6.5A	6½p CB Peacock-blue Vertical	5.00
CS6.5B	6½p CB Peacock-blue Horizontal	4.00
CS7A	7p CB Purple-brown Vertical	2.75
CS7B	7p CB Purple-brown Horizontal	4.50
CS8A	8p CB Post Office Red Vertical	3.00
CS8.5A	8½p 2B Yellowish-green Vertical	2.80
CS8.5B	8½p 2B Yellowish-green Horizontal	5.00
CS9A	9p 2B Blue-violet Vertical	4.50
CS9B	9p 2B Blue-violet Horizontal	7.50
CS10B	10p CB Orange-brown Vertical	3.80
CS11.5A	11½p CB Mushroom Vertical	3.80
CS12B	12p CB Emerald Vertical	3.30
CS12C	12p CB Emerald Horizontal	3.30
CS12.5A	12½p CB Light green Vertical	3.50
CS13A	13p CB Light chestnut Vertical	3.30
CS13B	13p CB Light chestnut Horizontal	3.80
CS13C	13p CB Light chestnut Horizontal - CB shifted to right	10.00
CS14B	14p CB Deep blue Horizontal	3.30
CS14C	14p CB Deep blue Vertical	3.30
CS15A	15p CB Bright blue Vertical	3.50
CS15B	15p CB Bright blue Horizontal	3.75
CS17A	17p CB Deep blue Vertical	3.50
CS18C	18p CB Bright green Vertical	2.50
CS18D	18p Bright green Vertical - Missing phosphor	67.50

PPP/PVAD

CS10A	10p Orange-brown Vertical	4.50

PCP1/PVAD

CS12A	12p Yellowish-green Vertical	3.80
CS15.5A	15½p Light violet Vertical	3.80
CS16A	16p Light mushroom Vertical	4.00
CS17A	17p Grey-blue Vertical	3.50
CS18A	18p Grey-green Vertical	10.00

PCP2/PVAD

CS14A	14p Steel-blue Vertical	4.00

ACP/PVAD

CS1C	1p Crimson - Horizontal	2.25
CS1D	1p Crimson Vertical	2.25
CS18B	18p Grey-green Vertical	7.50
CS19A	19p Orange red Vertical	3.50
CS20A	20p Black Vertical	3.50
CS20A	20p Black Horizontal	3.50
CS22A	22p Orange-red Vertical	4.00
CS24A	24p Red-brown Vertical	3.50
CS33A	33p Emerald Vertical	4.50
CS39A	39p Rhododendron Vertical	5.00

OFPP/PVAD

CS25A	25p Salmon pink Vertical	3.00
CS35A	35p Deep yellow Vertical	18.50
CS41A	41p Stone Vertical	20.00

OFNP/PVAD

CS19B	19p CB Olive green Vertical (Yellow fluor)	3.75
CS19C	19p CB Olive green Vertical (Blue fluor)	3.50
CS25B	25p 2B Salmon pink Vertical (Yellow fluor)	10.00
CS25C	25p 2B Salmon pink Vertical (Blue fluor)	4.00
CS37A	37p 2B Amethyst Vertical (11mm)	5.00
CS37B	37p 2B Amethyst Vertical (12½mm)	15.00
CS43A	43p 2B Chocolate brown Vertical (11mm)	5.00
CS43B	43p 2B Chocolate brown Vertical (12½mm)	15.00
CS63A	63p 2B Emerald green Vertical (11mm)	18.50
CS63B	63p 2B Emerald green Vertical (12½mm)	22.50

OFNP/PVA

CS37C	37p 2B Amethyst Vertical	5.00
CS43C	43p 2B Sepia Vertical	5.00

NVI Coil Strips

Photogravure - OFNP/PVAD

CS2ndA	2nd CB Bright blue Vertical	5.00
CS1stA	1st 2B Orange-red Vertical (11mm)	5.00
CS1stA	1st 2B Orange-red Vertical (12.5mm)	7.00

Gravure - OFNP/PVAD

CS2ndB	2nd CB Bright blue Vertical	15.00

Photogravure - OFNP/PVA

CS1stC	1st 2B Orange-red Vertical	6.00

Gravure - OFNP/PVA

CS2ndC	2nd CB Bright blue Vertical (Dsw fluor-Harrison)	5.00
CS2ndD	2nd CB Bright blue Horizontal	5.00
CS2ndE	2nd CB Bright blue Vertical (Dlw fluor - Enschedé)	12.50
CS2ndF	2nd CB Bright blue Vertical (Dlw fluor-Harrison)	5.00
CS2ndG	2nd PiP CB Bright blue Vertical	5.00
CS1stC	1st 2B Orange-red Vertical	5.00
CS1stD	1st 2B Orange-red Horizontal	6.00
CS1stE	1st 2B Gold Vertical (Enschedé)	6.00
CS1stF	1st 2B Gold Vertical (De La Rue)	6.00
CS1stG	1st PiP 2B Gold Vertical	6.00

Please see page 122 for explanation of 11mm and 12.5mm phosphor bands

Stamps inscribed 1st or 2nd class were issued on 22nd August 1989 for a trial period. Partly, their purpose was to avoid stock returns from retail outlets when postal rate changes came into operation.

1989 (22 Aug.) - 90

Printed by Harrison in Photogravure

Perf. 15 x 14

FCP/PVAD

No.		Description	U/M	F/U
HN1	2nd	CB Bright blue, Imperf. at top - Panes CP1, CP2	65	50
HN2	2nd	CB Bright blue, Imperf. at top and right, Pane CP1	3.00	2.00
HN3	2nd	CB Bright blue, Imperf. at bottom - Panes CP1, CP2	65	50
HN4	2nd	CB Bright blue. Imperf. at bottom and right - Panes CP1	3.00	2.00
HN5	2nd	RB Bright blue - Pane SP47 (London Life book) (20.3.90)	2.50	1.40
HN6	2nd	CB Dark blue Imperf. at top - Pane CP3 (7.8.90)	50	45
HN7	2nd	CB Dark blue ,Imperf. at bottom - Pane CP3	50	45
HN8	1st	2B Black Pane SP47 (London Life book) (20.3.90)	2.50	1.40

ACP/PVAD

No.		Description	U/M	F/U
HN9	1st	Black, Imperf. at top - Panes CP4, CP5	70	60
HN10	1st	Black, Imperf. at top and right - Pane CP4	4.00	5.00
HN11	1st	Black, Imperf. at bottom - Pane CP4, CP5	70	60
HN12	1st	Black, Imperf. at bottom and right - Pane CP4	4.00	5.00
HN13	1st	Orange-red, Imperf. at top - Pane CP6 (7.8.90)	50	50
HN14	1st	Orange-red, Imperf. at bottom - Pane CP6	50	50
		First Day Cover (22.8.89)		1.50

Printed by Questa in Lithography

Perf. 15 x 14

FCP/PVA

No.		Description	U/M	F/U
QN1	2nd	CBar Bright blue - Pane CP7, CP7a (19.8.89)	60	45
QN1a		Short band at top - Pane CP7	2.00	
QN1b		Short band at bottom - Pane CP7	2.00	
QN2	2nd	RB 4.5mm Bright blue - Pane SP55 (Wales book) (25.2.92)	95	85
QN2a		Missing phosphor - Pane SP55a	£700	
QN3	2nd	RB 3.5mm Bright blue - Pane SP59 (Tolkien book) (27.10.92)	1.00	85
QN3a		Short additional band at top left - Pane SP59	4.00	
QN4	2nd	CBar Dark blue - Pane CP8 (7.8.90)	75	85
QN4a		Short band at top - pane CP8	2.00	
QN4b		Short band at bottom - Pane CP8	2.00	
QN5	1st	2B Orange-red - Pane SP59 (Tolkien book) (27.10.92)	1.25	1.00
QN5a		Left band short at top - Pane SP59	4.50	
QN6	1st	2B Orange-red - Pane SP55 (Wales book) (25.2.92)	1.00	75
QN6a		Missing phosphor - Pane SP55	£750	

ACP/PVA

No.		Description	U/M	F/U
QN7	1st	Black - Panes CP9, CP9b (19.9.89)	1.00	1.10
QN7a		Low OBA -Panes CP9a, CP9c	1.40	
QN8	1st	Orange-red - Pane CP10 (6.8.91)	60	50

ACP/PVAD

No.		Description	U/M	F/U
QN9	1st	Orange-red - Pane CP11 (7.8.90)	40	

OFNP/PVA - C (Yellow) fluor

No.		Description	U/M	F/U
QN10	1st	2B Orange-red - Pane SP63 (B. Potter book) (10.8.93)	1.50	1.25
QN10a		Left band inset - Pane SP63	9.00	
QN11	2nd	LB Bright blue - Pane SP64 (B. Potter book) (10.8.93)	1.00	95
QN11a		Short additional band at top right - Pane SP64	2.50	
QN11b		Short additional band at bottom right - Pane SP64	2.50	
QN11c		Missing phosphor - Pane SP64a	£325	

Printed by Walsall in Lithography

Perf. 14

FCP/PVA

No.				U/M	F/U
WN1	2nd	CB Bright blue, Imperf. at top - Pane CP12			
		(22.8.89)		40	50
WN1a		Short band at top - Pane CP12		5.00	
WN2	2nd	CB Bright blue, Imperf. at top and right			
		- Pane CP12		1.25	70
WN3	2nd	CB Bright blue, Imperf. at bottom - Pane CP12	40		50
WN4	2nd	CB Bright blue, Imperf. at bottom and right			
		- Pane CP12		1.25	70
WN5	2nd	CB Dark blue, Imperf. at top - Panes CP13,			
		CP16 (7.8.90)		45	40
WN5a		Short band at top - pane CP13		£15	
WN6	2nd	CB Dark blue, Imperf. at bottom - Panes CP13,			
		CP16		45	40
WN6a		Short band at bottom - Pane CP16		5.00	
WN7	1st	2B Black, Imperf. at top - Pane CP15			
		(22.8.89)		1.00	1.00
WN7a		Missing phosphor - Pane CP15a		£150	
WN8	1st	2B Black, Imperf. at top and right			
		- pane CP15		1.25	1.00
WN8a		Missing phosphor - Pane CP15a		£150	
WN9	1st	2B Black, Imperf. at bottom - Pane CP15		1.00	1.00
WN9a		Missing phosphor - Pane CP15a		£150	
WN10	1st	2B Black, Imperf. at bottom and right			
		- Pane CP51		1.25	1.00
WN10a		Missing phosphor - Pane CP15a		£150	

FCP/PVAD

			U/M	F/U
WN11	2nd	CB Bright blue, Imperf. at top (16.3.93)	40	50
WN12	2nd	CB Bright blue, Imperf. at bottom	40	50

ACP/PVA

			U/M	F/U
WN13	1st	Orange-red Imperf. at top - Panes CP19, CP20		
		(7.8.90)	50	50
WN13a		Low OBA - Panes CP19a, CP20a	50	
WN14	1st	Orange-red, Imperf. at bottom - Panes CP19,		
		CP20	50	50
WN14a		Low OBA - Panes CP19a, CP20a	50	

Perf 13

			U/M	F/U
WN15	1st	Orange-red, Imperf. at top - Pane CP21		
		(10.90)	1.50	85
WN15a		Low OBA - Pane CP21a	1.75	
WN16	1st	Orange-red, Imperf. at bottom - Pane CP21	1.50	85
WN16a		Low OBA - Pane CP21a	1.75	
		First Day Cover (7.8.90)		1.50

ACP/PVAD

			U/M	F/U
WN17	1st	Orange-red Imperf. at top - Panes CP22,		
		CP23 (9.2.93)	50	30
WN18	1st	Orange-red, Imperf. at bottom - Panes CP22,		
		CP23	50	30

1993 (6 April). Perf 15 x 14 (elliptical).

Printed by Harrison in Photogravure

OFPP/PVAD

No.		Description	U/M	F/U
HNE1A	**1st Orange-red** - Panes CP27, CP28 (6.4.93)		55	30
HNE1Aa	Translucent paper		4.50	

OFNP/PVAD - C (Yellow) fluor

No.		Description	U/M	F/U
HNE2A	**2nd CB Bright blue** - Panes CP24 (7.9.93)		1.60	
HNE2Aa	Translucent paper - Pane CP24		50	25
HNE1B	**1st 2B Orange-red** - Pane CP26 (4.4.95)		65	30
HNE1Ba	Translucent paper - Pane CP26		2.00	

OFNP/PVAD - D (Blue) fluor

No.		Description	U/M	F/U
HNE2B	**2nd CB 4mm Bright blue** - Pane CP24a (28.7.95)		1.10	75
HNE2C	**2nd CB 4.5mm Bright blue** - Pane CP24a		90	70
HNE2Ca	Vertical coil (8.7.96)		90	
HNE2Cb	Translucent paper - Pane CP24a		2.50	
HNE2D	**2nd CB 4.5mm Deep bright blue** - Pane CP25		1.10	85
HNE2Da	Translucent paper - Pane CP25 (6.8.96)		2.00	

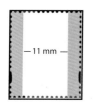 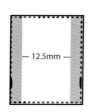

— 11 mm —   — 12.5mm —

There are two varieties of phosphor bands on the 1st Vertical coil stamps. For simplicity these are described as either 11mm or 12.5mm which refers to the space *between* the bands as shown above.

No.		Description	U/M	F/U
HNE1C	**1st 2B Orange-red** - Pane CP26a (28.7.95)		1.00	85
HNE1Ca	Translucent paper - CP26a		3.25	
HNE1Cb	Vertical coil, 11mm (8.7.96)		1.00	
HNE1Cc	Vertical coil, Screened value, 11mm (8.7.96)		7.00	
HNE1Cd	Vertical coil, 12.5mm		2.50	
HNE1Ce	Vertical coil, Screened value, 12.5mm		11.00	

OFNP/PVA (Layflat) - D (Blue) fluor

No.		Description	U/M	F/U
HNE2E	**2nd CB Bright blue** - Pane CP29 (.4.97)		3.00	70
HNE1D	**1st 2B Orange-red** - Pane CP30 (.4.97)		3.25	85

Printed by Walsall in Lithography

OFNP/PVA - C (Yellow) fluor

No.		Description	U/M	F/U
WNE2A	**2nd CB Bright blue**, Cream gum, - Panes CP35, CP36 (6.4.93)		60	45
WNE2Aa	Short band at bottom		£18	
WNE2B	**2nd CB Bright blue**, White gum - Pane CP35		1.75	
WNE1A	**1st 2B (Both inset) Orange-red**, Cream gum - Panes CP37, CP39 (6.4.93)		65	50
WNE1Aa	Bands short at bottom, Both bands inset - Pane CP39		4.75	
WNE1Ab	Right band inset - Pane CP39		£15	
WNE1Ac	Double broad band left - Panes CP37, CP39		£175	
WNE1Ad	Double broad band right - Panes CP37, CP39		£125	
WNE1Ae	One 4mm Centre band - Panes CP37, CP39		£200	
WNE1Af	Missing phosphor - Pane CP39a		£200	
WNE1Ag	One band at left, two bands at right - Pane CP39		£45	
WNE1B	**1st 2B (Left inset) Orange-red**, Cream gum - Panes CP37, CP39 (6.4.93)		1.95	1.50
WNE1C	**1st 2B (Right inset) Orange-red**, Cream gum - Panes CP37, (6.4.93)		1.95	1.50
WNE1D	**1st 2B Orange-red**, White gum - Panes CP37, CP39 (6.4.93)		1.00	
WNE1Da	Short bands at top - CP37, CP39		£10	
WNE1Db	Left band inset - Panes CP37, CP39		7.50	
WNE1Dc	Right band inset - Panes CP37, CP39		7.50	
WNE1Dd	Missing phosphor - Panes CP37, CP39		£175	

OFNP/PVA - D (Blue) fluor

No.		Description	U/M	F/U
WNE2C	**2nd CB Bright blue**, White gum - Pane CP35a		85	55
WNE1E	**1st 2B Orange-red**, Dull fluor - Panes CP38, CP40		85	65
WNE1Ea	Left band inset - Panes CP38, CP40		4.50	
WNE1Eb	Right band inset - Panes CP38, CP40		4.50	
WNE1F	**1st 2B Orange-red**, Bright fluor - Panes CP38, CP40		1.00	80
WNE1Fa	Short bands at bottom - Pane CP40		6.50	
WNE1Fb	Short bands at bottom, Right band inset - Pane CP40		£10	
WNE1Fc	Left band inset - Pane CP40		£10	
WNE1Fd	Right band inset - Pane CP40			

Printed by Questa in Lithography

Thick value   Thin value

Questa used two types of perforator which resulted in two distinct ellipse shapes as illustrated below. The first has a rounded or 'rugby ball' shape and is known as A(r), whereas the second is straighter or 'sausage' shaped and is known as B(s). A further difference on the Questa printings is the gum colour which is either cream or white. Either or both of these can make a considerable difference to the value of a stamp.

Ellipse Type A(r)   Ellipse Type B(s)

OFNP/PVA - C (Yellow) fluor

No.	Description	U/M	F/U
QNE2A	**2nd CBar Bright blue**, Cream gum, A(r) ellipse Sheets (6.4.93)	60	45
QNE2Aa	Pane CP31 - (6.4.93)	60	
QNE2Ab	Short band at top - Pane CP31	3.00	
QNE2Ac	Short band at bottom -Pane CP31	3.00	
QNE2Ad	Missing phosphor - CP31a	£175	
QNE2Ae	Very weak phosphor - CP31	4.50	
QNE2B	**2nd CBar Bright blue**, Cream gum, B(s) ellipse Sheets (.10.94)	£15	
QNE2Ba	Short band at bottom only - Sheets	£20	
QNE2C	**2nd CB Bright blue**, Cream gum, A(r) ellipse Pane CP32	60	45
QNE2D	**2nd CBar Bright blue**, White gum, B(s) ellipse Sheets (7.10.94)	1.50	
QNE2Da	Short band at top only - Sheets	3.75	
QNE2Db	Short band at bottom only - Sheets	7.50	
QNE2Dc	Reduced fluor - Pane CP32 (22.2.95)	£30	
QNE2E	**2nd CB Bright blue**, White gum, A(r) ellipse Pane CP32	1.75	1.50
QNE2Ea	Missing phosphor - Pane CP32	£175	
QNE2Eb	Reduced fluor - Pane CP32	2.00	
QNE1A	**1st 2B Orange-red**, Thin value, Cream gum, A(r) ellipse - Sheets & Boots M/S	60	45
QNE1Aa	Bands short at bottom - Sheets & Boots M/S	7.50	
QNE1Ab	Left band inset - Boots M/S	£15	
QNE1Ac	Right band inset - Boots M/S	£15	
QNE1Ad	Missing phosphor - Boots M/S	£850	
QNE1B	**1st 2B Orange-red**, Thick value, Cream gum, A(r) ellipse - Panes CP33, CP34	1.00	75
QNE1Ba	Short bands at top - Pane CP33	5.00	
QNE1Bb	Short bands at bottom - Pane CP33	7.50	
QNE1Bc	Left band inset - Pane CP33	£15	
QNE1Bd	Right band inset - Pane CP33	12.50	
QNE1Be	Missing phosphor - Pane CP34a		
QNE1C	**1st 2B Orange-red**, Thin value, Cream gum, B(s) ellipse - Boots M/S	£30	

No.	Description	U/M	F/U
QNE1D	**1st 2B Orange-red**, Thin value, White gum, A(r) ellipse - Pane CP33	1.00	
QNE1Da	Reduced fluor - Pane CP33	4.00	
QNE1E	**1st 2B Orange-red**, Thin value, White gum, B(s) ellipse - Pane CP33, Boots M/S	2.00	
QNE1Ea	Short bands at top - Boots M/S	£22	
QNE1Eb	Short bands at bottom - Pane CP33		
QNE1Ec	Left band inset - Boots M/S	£10	
QNE1Ed	Right band inset - Boots M/S	£15	

OFNP/PVA - D (Blue) fluor

No.	Description	U/M	F/U
QNE2F	**2nd CB 4mm Bright blue**, B(s) ellipse - Pane CP32a (28.7.95)	1.00	75
QNE2G	**2nd CB 4mm Bright blue**, A(r) ellipse - Pane CP32a	£30	
QNE2H	**2nd CBar 4mm Deep bright blue**, B(s) ellipse - Sheets (14.11.95)	1.00	85
QNE2Ha	Short band at bottom only - Sheets	£15	
QNE2I	**2nd CB 4mm Bright blue**, B(s) ellipse - Pane CP32a (20.4.96)	1.50	1.25
QNE2Ia	3.5mm Narrow weak phosphor band - Pane CP32a	5.00	
QNE2J	**2nd CB 4.5mm Bright blue**, B(s) ellipse - Sheets (5.10.96)	1.50	1.00
QNE2Ja	Short band at bottom - Sheets	£25	
QNE1F	**1st 2B Orange-red**, B(s) ellipse - Pane CP33a (28.7.95)	1.00	85
QNE1Fa	Sheets (14.11.95), Boots M/S (11.9.95)	1.00	
QNE1Fb	Left band inset - Boots M/S	£15	
QNE1Fc	Missing phosphor - Boos M/S	£600	
QNE1G	**1st 2B 8mm Orange-red**, B(s) ellipse - Pane CP33a (7.9.98)	1.00	85
QNE1Ga	Pane SP93 (Profile on Print book)	1.00	
QNE1Gb	Short bands at top - Pane SP93	£22	
QNE1H	**1st 2B 7mm Orange-red**, A(r) ellipse - Sheets	£10	
QNE1I	**1st 2B 8mm Orange-red**, A(r) ellipse - Pane SP93 (Profile on Print book)	1.50	1.25

Printer: Enschedé in Litho

OFNP/PVA - D (Blue) fluor

No.	Description	U/M	F/U
ENE1A	**1st 2B Orange-red**, Dull violet fluor - Unbranded M/S	75	50
ENE1B	**1st 2B Orange-red**, Bright violet fluor - Unbranded M/S	7.50	5.75
ENE1Ba	Short bands at top- Unbranded M/S	£20	
ENE1Bb	Short bands at bottom- Unbranded M/S	£20	
ENE1C	**1st 2B Orange-red**, Bright turquoise fluor - Unbranded M/S	£30	

Printed by Harrison/De La Rue in Gravure

OFNP/PVAD - D (Blue) fluor

No.			U/M	F/U
HNEG2A	2nd	**CB Bright blue** - Vertical coil (8.7.96)	2.50	2.00

OFNP/PVA Layflat - D (Blue) fluor

HNEG2B	2nd	**CB Bright blue** - Pane CP40	95	50
HNEG2Ba		Vertical coil (24.9.97)	95	
HNEG2C	2nd	**CB PiP Bright blue** - Pane SP163		
		(Machin Anniversary) (5.6.07)	90	1.00
HNEG2D	2nd	**2B Large PiP Bright blue** - Pane SP163		
		(Machin Anniversary) (5.6.07)	1.20	1.20
HNEG1A	1st	**2B Gold**, Dull fluor - Pane CP44 (21.4.97)	1.10	55
HNEG1Aa		Pane SP80 (BBC book) (23.9.97)	1.10	
HNEG1Ab		Left band stepped at top - Pane SP80	17.50	
HNEG1Ac		Left band stepped at bottom - Pane SP80	10.00	
HNEG1Ad		Right band stepped at top - Pane SP80	17.50	
HNEG1Ae		Right band stepped at bottom - Pane SP80	10.00	
HNEG1B	1st	**2B Gold**, Bright fluor - Pane SP135		
		(Letters by night book) (16.3.04)	1.00	55
HNEG1C	1st	**2B Orange-red** - Vertical coil (29.4.97)	1.00	
HNEG1Ca		Pane CP41(18.11.97)	1.00	
HNEG1D	1st	**2B Deep orange-red** - Pane SP89 (Profile		
		on Print book) (16.2.99)	1.00	55
HNEG1Da		Short bands at top - Pane SP89	6.00	
HNEG1Db		Short bands at bottom - Pane SP89	4.00	
HNEG1Dc		Left band inset - Pane SP89	3.00	
HNEG1Dd		Right band inset - Pane SP89	3.25	
HNEG1De		Left band stepped at top - Pane SP89	15.00	
HNEG1Df		Left band stepped at bottom - Pane SP89	17.50	
HNEG1Dg		Right band stepped at top - Pane SP89	15.00	
HNEG1Dh		Right band stepped at bottom - Pane SP89	25.00	
HNEG1Di		Broad band left - Pane SP89	£13	
HNEG1Dj		4.5mm CB OL - Pane SP89	£13	
HNEG1E	1st	**2B Millennium** - Sheets (6.1.00)	75	50
HNEG1F	1st	**2B PiP Gold** - Pane SP157		
		(World of Invention) (1.3.07),		
		Pane SP163 (Machin Anniversary) (5.6.07)	1.00	1.10
HNEG1G	1st	**2B Large PiP Gold** - Pane SP163		
		(Machin Anniversary) (5.6.07)	1.10	1.20

OFPP/PVAD - D (Blue) fluor

HNEG1F	1st	**2B Millennium** - Her Majesty's stamps		
		miniature sheet (23.5.00)	1.50	1.00

ATN (c) - Cream PVA Gum

ATN(c)1st	1st	**2B Gold**	70	55
ATN(c)1sta		Left band inset	9.00	
ATN(c)1stb		Right band inset	£10	
ATN(c)1stc		Short band top	12.50	
ATN(c)1std		Short band bottom	8.50	
ATN(c)1stA	1st	**2B PiP Gold**	70	55
ATN(c)1stB	1st	**2B PiP Large Gold**	70	55
ATN(c)2nd	2nd	**CB Bright blue**	40	45
ATN(c)2ndA	2nd	**CB PiP Bright blue**	50	55
ATN(c)2ndB	2nd	**2B PiP Large Bright blue**	70	75

Printed by Walsall in Gravure

On the Walsall Gravure printings there are two types of both the fluor level and the finish. The fluor level can be either Dull or Bright, and you will need a long wave UV lamp to detect this. The finish can either appear matt or glossy. Both these terms are used in the following Walsall listing. All are rotary perfs unless otherwise stated.

On some stamps there are also two types of Ellipse similar to the Questa types illustrated earlier.

OFNP/PVA - D (Blue) fluor

WNEG2A	2nd	**CB Bright blue**, Dull fluor, Matt finish		
		- Sheets (29.4.97)	75	50
WNEG2B	2nd	**CB Deep bright blue**, Dull fluor, Matt finish		
		- Pane CP45 (26.8.97)	1.00	
WNEG2C	2nd	**CB Bright blue**, Dull fluor, Matt finish,		
		Comb perfs - Pane CP45 (.10.97)	1.50	
WNEG2D	2nd	**CB Deep bright blue**, Bright fluor, Glossy		
		finish - Pane CP45 (.11.97)	75	
WNEG2E	2nd	**CB Deep bright blue**, Bright fluor, Glossy		
		finish, Comb perfs - Sheets	1.50	
WNEG2Ea		Pane CP45 (.11.97)	1.50	
WNEG2F	2nd	**CB Bright blue**, Bright fluor, Matt finish,		
		SP128 (Perfect Coronation book) (2.6.03),		
		SP140 (Bronte sisters book) (24.2.05)	95	
WNEG2G	2nd	**LB Bright blue**, Bright fluor, Glossy		
		finish, - Pane SP87 (Breaking barriers		
		book) (13.10.98)	1.00	75
WNEG2Ga		Short band at bottom - Pane SP87	8.50	
WNEG2Fb		Short band at bottom - Pane SP87	£20	
WNEG2H	2nd	**RB Bright blue**, Bright fluor, Glossy		
		finish, - Pane SP87 (Breaking barriers		
		book) (13.10.98)	1.20	75
WNEG2Ha		Short band at top - Pane SP87	£20	
WNEG2Hb		Short band at bottom - Pane SP87	£20	
WNEG2I	2nd	**2B Deep bright blue**, Bright fluor, Glossy		
		finish (Very pale Queen's head), A(r) ellipse		
		- Sheets (13.4.99)	1.10	60
WNEG2J	2nd	**2B Deep bright blue**, Bright fluor, Glossy		
		finish (Very pale Queen's head), B(s) ellipse		
		- Sheets (13.4.99)	1.10	
WNEG1A	1st	**2B Pale gold**, Head 1, Dull fluor,		
		Shiny finish - Sheets (21.4.97)	1.00	50
WNEG1B	1st	**2B Pale gold**, Head 2, Dull fluor,		
		Shiny finish - Pane CP48 (30.5.97)	2.00	95
WNEG1C	1st	**2B Pale gold**, Head 2, Bright fluor, Shiny		
		finish, Comb perfs - Pane CP48 (.10.97)	£20	
WNEG1D	1st	**2B Pale gold**, Head 2, Bright fluor, Shiny		
		finish - Pane CP48 (30.5.97)	2.50	1.20
WNEG1E	1st	**2B Deep gold**, Head 2, Dull fluor, Matt		
		finish - Pane CP48 (21.4.97)	1.50	75
WNEG1F	1st	**2B Deep gold**, Head 2, Bright fluor, Matt		
		finish - Sheets (21.4.97)	1.25	65
WNEG1Fa		Pane CP48 (21.4.97)	1.25	
WNEG1G	1st	**2B Gold** - Pane SP128 (Perfect		
		Coronation book) (2.6.03), Pane SP145		
		(Trafalgar book) (18.10.05)	1.25	1.30
WNEG1H	1st	**2B Pale orange-red**, Dull fluor, Matt		
		finish - Pane CP46 (26.8.97)	75	60
WNEG1Ha		Missing phosphor - Pane CP46a	£200	

No.		U/M	F/U
WNEG1I	**1st 2B Pale orange-red**, Dull fluor, Matt finish, Comb perfs - Pane CP46 (.10.97)	3.00	1.50
WNEG1J	**1st 2B Bright orange-red**, Dull fluor, Matt finish, Comb perfs - Pane CP49 (18.11.97)	1.25	75
WNEG1K	**1st 2B Bright orange-red**, Bright fluor, Matt finish - Sheets (18.11.97)	1.00	
WNEG1Ka	Pane CP46 (.11.97)	1.00	
WNEG1L	**1st 2B Bright orange-red**, Bright fluor, Matt finish, Comb perfs - Pane CP46 (10.97)	1.50	80
WNEG1La	Left band ommited - Pane CP46	£300	
WNEG1Lb	Missing phosphor - Pane CP46a	£600	
WNEG1M	**1st 2B Bright orange-red**, Bright fluor, Glossy finish, Comb perfs - Panes CP46, CP50 (3.98)	90	65
WNEG1N	**1st 2B Pale orange-red**, Bright fluor, Glossy finish, Comb perfs - Pane CP46 (.3.98)	1.50	
WNEG1Na	Left band inset - Pane CP46	£25	
WNEG1O	**1st 2B Pale orange-red**, Bright fluor, Glossy finish, A(r) ellipse, Very pale Queen's head - Panes CP41E, CP41F (.3.98)	1.25	75
WNEG1Oa	Short bands at bottom - Pane CP41F	£15	
WNEG1Ob	Left band inset - Pane CP41E	4.50	
WNEG1P	**1st 2B Pale orange-red**, Bright fluor, Glossy finish, B(s) ellipse, Very pale Queen's head - Sheets (25.5.99)	1.25	75
WNEG1Q	**1st 2B Millennium**, Perf 15 - Pane CP50	1.00	
WNEG1R	**1st 2B Millennium**, Dull fluor, Perf 14 - Pane SP99 (Special by Design book) (15.2.00)	1.00	75
WNEG1Ra	Bright fluor - Pane SP110 (Treasury of Trees book)	1.10	95
WNEG'E'A	**E 2B Deep blue**, Bright fluor, Glossy finish - Pane CP47 (19.1.99)	75	60

Printed by Questa in Gravure

No.		U/M	F/U
QNEG2A	**2nd CB Bright blue**, Perf 14, patchy uneven background - Pane CP51 (1.12.98)	95	75
QNEG2B	**2nd CB Deep bright blue**, Perf 14, smooth even background - Pane CP51	1.50	95
QNEG2C	**2nd CB Dull mid-blue**, Perf 14, smooth even background - Pane CP51	1.00	80
QNEG2D	**2nd CB Bright blue**, Perf 15 - Panes CP54, CP55 CP56 (27.4.00)	70	50
QNEG2Da	Short band at top - Panes CP54, CP55	4.50	
QNEG2Db	Additional narrow band at left - Pane CP54	£10	
QNEG2Dc	Additional narrow band at right - Pane CP54	£10	
QNEG2Dd	Narrow band at right - Pane CP55	8.00	
QNEG1A	**1st 2B Orange-red**, Perf 14 - Pane CP52 (1.12.98)	90	75
QNEG1B	**1st 2B Orange-red**, Perf 15 - Panes CP54, CP55, CP56 (27.4.00)	90	70
QNEG1Ba	Short bands at top - Pane CP54	4.50	
QNEG1Bb	Short bands at top, Left band inset - Pane CP54	5.50	
QNEG1Bc	Short bands at top, Right band inset - Pane CP54	6.50	
QNEG1Bd	Left band stepped at top -Pane CP54	£15	
QNEG1Be	Right band stepped at top - pane CP54	£15	
QNEG1Bf	Broad band left - Pane CP55a	£18	
QNEG1C	**1st 2B Millennium**, Perf 14 - Pane CP53	95	75
QNEG1Ca	Perf 15 - Pane SP104 (Life of the Century book) (4.8.00)	1.00	
QNEG1Cb	Left band inset - Pane SP104	£20	
QNEG1D	**1st 2B Gold** - Panes SP122 (Across the Universe book) (24.9.02),	1.25	75
QNEG'E'B	**E 2B Dark blue**, SP122 (Across the Universe book)	1.25	95

Printed by Enschedé in Gravure

No.		U/M	F/U
ENEG2A	**1st CB Bright blue** - Pane SP116 (Gracious Accession book) (6.02.02)	0.70	60
ENEG1A	**1st 2B Gold** - Panes SP125 (Microcosmos book) (25.2.03), SP136 (Glory of the Garden book) (25.5.04), SP151 (Brunel) (23.2.06)	1.00	75
ENEG'E'A	**E 2B Dark blue** - Pane SP116 (Gracious Accession book), Pane SP125 (Microcosmos book) (25.2.03)	1.30	1.20

Further single values are will be found in the self-adhesive section.

Greetings Card Miniature Sheets ('Boots Labels')

The greetings card miniature sheet, also known as the "Boots" label, consists of a single 1st class NVI at the centre of a rectangular pane that also bears informative and publicity text. It is rouletted from each bottom corner to the centre of the top edge to enable it to be folded round one corner of a greetings card. It was originally printed by Questa for Boots, with the Boots logo above the stamp, and presented in a sealed transparent pack with a Boots greetings card. Later versions were printed without the logo, first by Questa and then by Enschedé.

The Questa unbranded printings have either shorter spacing between the rouletting holes or longer spacing. The Questa version with Boots logo and blue fluor (SLMS3) only exists folded as it was always found with a greetings card, but all the others are known unfolded from philatelic outlets.

1994 (17 Aug.) Perf 15 x 14 (elliptical). Two phosphor bands.

Printed by Questa in Lithography
(Boots logo)

OFNP/PVA - C (Yellow) fluor

			U/M	F/U
SLMS1	1st	**2B Bright orange-red** (sheet 85 x 43 mm), A(r) Ellipse, Cream gum (17.8.94)	2.00	1.50
SLMS1a		Short band at bottom	£20	
SLMS1b		Left band inset	£15	
SLMS1c		Right band inset	£15	
SLMS1d		Missing phosphor	£800	
SLMS2	1st	**2B Bright orange-red** (sheet 85 x 42 mm), B(s) Ellipse, White gum (.10.94)	2.00	1.50
SLMS2a		Short bands at top	£20	
SLMS2b		Left band inset	£12	
SLMS2c		Right band inset	£17	
SLMS3	1st	**2B Bright orange-red** (sheet 85 x 42 mm), B(s) Ellipse, Cream gum (.10.94)	£30	

Printed by Questa in Lithography
(Boots logo)

OFNP/PVA - D (Blue) fluor

			U/M	F/U
SLMS4	1st	**2B Bright orange-red**, B(s) Ellipse, White gum (25.9.95)	5.00	5.00
SLMS4a		Right band inset	£15	
SLMS4b		Missing phosphor	£550	

1995 (11 Sep.) Perf 15 x 14 (elliptical). Two phosphor bands

Printed by Questa in Lithography
(Unbranded)

OFNP/PVA - D (Blue) fluor

			U/M	F/U
SLMS5	1st	**2B Bright orange-red**, Short spacing (11.9.95)	1.00	75
SLMS6	1st	**2B Bright orange-red**, Long spacing (10.98)	£10	75
SLMS6a		Mixed ellipses (B(s) to the left, A(r) to the right)	£80	

Printed by Enschedé in Lithography
(Unbranded)

OFNP/PVA - D (Blue) fluor

			U/M	F/U
SLMS7	1st	**2B Bright orange-red**, Dull fluor, violet tint to fluor (29.4.97)	90	90
SLMS8	1st	**2B Bright orange-red**, Bright fluor, violet tint to fluor (29.4.97)	9.00	
SLMS8a		Short bands at top	£20	
SLMS8b		Short bands at bottom	£20	
SLMS9	1st	**2B Bright orange-red**, Bright fluor, turquoise tint to fluor (29.4.97)	£30	

The Penny Black (1840) Anniversary Stamps

To mark the 150th Anniversary of the 1840 1d Black, special 'double head' design stamps were issued on 10 January 1990. The first five stamps were issued as commemoratives and for the next nine months also served as definitives, alongside the subsequent booklet stamps.

1990 (10 Jan.) Perf. 15 x 14

Printed by Harrison in Photogravure

FCP/PVAD

No.			U/M	F/U
PB1	15p	CB Light blue - Sheets (10.1.90)	65	30
PB1a		Screened value - Sheets	1.75	
PB1b		Imperforate pair - Sheets	£1250	
PB2		Imperf. top - Pane AP2 (30.1.90)	60	35
PB3		Imperf. bottom - Pane AP2 (30.1.90)	60	35
PB4	15p	LB Light blue - Pane AP1 (30.1.90)	1.50	1.50
PB4a		Left band clear of perfs -Pane AP1	2.00	1.75
		Left band stepped at top - Pane AP1	2.00	
PB5	15p	RB Light blue - Pane SP47 (London Life book) (20.3.90)	2.50	2.00
PB6	20p	2B Black and buff, - Pane AP1	1.50	1.00
PB6a		Left band inset - Pane AP1 (30.1.90)	2.00	1.80
PB6b		Short bands at top and Left band inset - Pane AP1	2.25	
PB7	29p	2B Purple - Pane SP47 (London Life book)	6.00	6.50

ACP/PVAD

No.			U/M	F/U
PB8	20p	Black and pale buff - Sheets	55	50
PB8a		Imperforate pair - Sheets	£1300	
PB8b		Low OBA - Sheets	1.00	
PB8c		Shift 2½mm to top of buff - Sheets	5.00	
PB8d		Shift 3mm to bottom of buff - Sheets	£10	
PB8e		Shift 5mm to bottom of buff - Sheets	£14	
PB9	20p	Imperf. at top - Panes AP3, AP5 (30.1.90)	80	60
PB10		Imperf. at top and right - Pane AP3 (17.4.90)	1.50	1.10
PB11		Imperf. at bottom - Panes AP3, AP5 (30.1.90)	50	60
PB12		Imperf. bottom and right - Pane AP3 (17.4.90)	1.50	1.10
PB13		Imperf. at left - Pane AP4 (30.1.90)	1.00	75
PB14		Imperf. at right - Pane AP4 (30.1.90)	85	65
PB15		Very dull paper - Pane SP48 (London Life book) (20.3.90)	£50	
PB16	29p	Mauve - Sheets (10.1.90)	1.10	80
PB17	34p	Slate - Sheets (10.1.90)	90	85
PB17a		Low OBA - Sheets	1.50	
PB18	37p	Red - Sheets	1.20	90
		Presentation Pack 204	3.75	

1990 (3 May) 'Stamp World 90', London Miniature Sheet
Printed in Photogravure and recess

No.			U/M	F/U
MS6	£1	Miniature sheet containing 20p stamp	3.00	2.75
MS6a		Missing Black (Recess printing)	£7500	
MS6b		Missing Cream (Recess printing)	£4000	
MS6c		Imperforate	£3500	
MS6d		Imperforate. First Day Cover	£3500	
MS6e		Recess printing inverted (background)	£4500	
		Souvenir Book	£20	

Printed by Questa in Lithography

Perf. 15 x 14

FCP/PVA

No.			U/M	F/U
PB19	15p	CBar Light blue - Pane AP6 (17.4.90)	1.25	1.10
PB19a		Short band at top - Pane AP6	3.00	
PB19b		Short band at bottom - Pane AP6	3.00	

ACP/PVAD

No.			U/M	F/U
PB20	20p	Black. Low OBA - Pane AP7 (17.4.90)	1.25	1.25
PB20a		Normal OBA - Pane AP7	£45	

Printed by Walsall in Lithography

Perf. 14

FCP/PVA

No.			U/M	F/U
PB21	15p	CB Light blue. Imperf. at top - Pane AP8 (30.1.90)	1.00	80
PB22		Imperf. at top and right - Pane AP8	1.00	1.30
PB23		Imperf. at bottom - Pane AP8	1.00	80
PB24		Imperf. at bottom and right - Pane AP8	1.00	1.30

ACP/PVA

No.			U/M	F/U
PB25	20p	Black and buff, Low OBA, Imperf. at left - Pane AP10 (30.1.90)	1.25	90
PB26		Low OBA, Imperf. at right - Pane AP10	1.00	75
PB27		Imperf. at top, Low OBA - Pane AP12 (30.1.90)	1.50	90
PB28		Imperf. at top and right, Low OBA - Pane AP12	1.50	1.20
PB29		Imperf. at bottom, Low OBA, - Pane AP12	1.50	75
PB30		Imperf. at bottom and right, Low OBA - Pane AP12	1.50	1.20

ACP/PVAD

No.			U/M	F/U
PB31	20p	Black and buff. Imperf. at top - Pane AP12 (30.1.90)	1.00	90
PB32		Imperf. at top and right- Pane AP12	1.75	1.20
PB33		Imperf. at bottom - Pane AP12	1.00	75
PB34		Imperf. at bottom and right - Pane AP12	1.75	1.20

Printer: Walsall Security Printers in Gravure

OFNP/PVA

No.			U/M	F/U
PB30	1st	2B Black and buff - Pane SP102 (Special by Design book) (15.2.00)	1.00	

'Wilding' Design Decimal Definitives, £1 Dulac, Wilding Castles Design

2000 (23 May) Her Majesty's Stamps miniature sheet - MS11

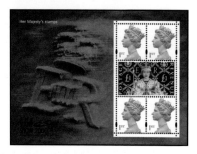

2002 (5 Dec.) Widlings Definitive Collection I - MS19

2003 (20 May.) Widlings Definitive Collection II - MS20

2003 (2 June) Pane from 'A Perfect Coronation' Prestige Book - SP131

Pane SP131 is on Watermarked paper

Wildings Definitive collection

No.			U/M	F/U
WD1	1p	**2B Orange** - 1st Wildings Min. sheet	30	40
WD2	2p	**2B Ultramarine** - 1st Wildings Min. sheet	30	40
WD4	4p	**2B Deep lilac** - 2nd Wildings Min. sheet	30	40
WD5	5p	**2B Brown** - 1st Wildings Min. sheet	30	40
WD8	8p	**2B Ultramarine** - 2nd Wildings Min. sheet	30	40
WD10	10p	**2B Purple** - 2nd Wildings Min. sheet	35	45
WD20	20p	**CB Bright green** - 2nd Wildings Min. sheet,	50	55
WD20a	20p	**LB Bright green** - SP82 & SP83 (Definitive Portrait book)	75	85
WD20a	20p	**RB Bright green** - SP82 & SP83 (Definitive Portrait book)	75	85
WD26	26p	**2B Brown** - SP81, SP83 & SP84 (Definitive Portrait book)	75	85
WD28	28p	**2B Bronze-green** - 2nd Wildings Min. sheet	75	90
WD33	33p	**2B Brown** - 1st Wildings Min. sheet	80	95
WD34	34p	**2B Brown-purple** - 2nd Wildings Min. sheet	95	1.10
WD37	37p	**2B Magenta** - 1st Wildings Min. sheet	1.10	1.30
WD37a	37p	**2B Red-purple** - SP83, SP84 (Definitive Portrait book)	1.20	1.40
WD42	42p	**2B Prussian blue** - 2nd Wildings Min. sheet	1.30	1.50
WD47	47p	**2B Bistre-brown** - 1st Wildings Min. sheet	1.50	1.70
WD47a		Pane SP131* (Perfect coronation book)	3.50	4.00
WD50	50p	**2B Green** - 1st Wildings Min. sheet	1.60	1.70
WD68	68p	**2B Grey-blue** - 2nd Wildings Min. sheet	2.00	2.25
WD68a		Pane SP131* (Perfect coronation book)	3.50	4.00
WD1st	1st	**2B Green** - 1st Wildings Min. sheet, (A Gracious Accession book)	1.00	1.25
WD2nd	2nd	**CB Carmine-red** - 1st Wildings Min. sheet, (A Gracious Accession book)	75	90
WD'E'	E	**2B Chestnut** - 2nd Wildings Min. sheet	1.10	1.30
WDM	1st	**Millennium** - Her Majesty's stamps miniature sheet	1.10	1.30
WD100	£1	**2B Dulac design** - Pane SP131* Watermarked paper (Perfect coronation book)	£25	£28
WD100a	£1	**Dulac design,** Unwatermarked, Phosphorised paper - Her Majesty's stamps miniature sheet	£6	£7

2005 (22 Mar.) Wilding Castles

WC50A	50p	**Blackish-brown**	1.00	1.40
WC50B	50p	**Black**	1.00	1.40
WC100A	£1	**Red**	2.00	2.50
WC100B	£1	**Ultramarine**	2.00	2.50

QE2 Commemorative (Special) Issues

Please note that prices for Cylinder Blocks, which include all the plate numbers, can be for blocks of four, six eight Etc. depending on the stamp format.

✓**1953 (3 June) Coronation.** Wmk. Tudor Crown.

No.			U/M	M/M	F/U
C1	2½d	Carmine red	15	10	10
C2	4d	Ultramarine	60	40	50
C3	1s3d	Olive green	3.60	1.80	1.80
C4	1s6d	Slate blue	5.00	3.10	3.10
		Set of 4	8.25	4.90	4.15
		Set of 4 Cylinder Blocks	£60		
		First Day Cover			£29

1957 (1 Aug.) World Scout Jubilee Jamboree

No.			U/M	M/M	F/U
C5	2½d	Rolling Hitch	10	5	10
C6	4d	'Coming to Britain'	35	15	40
C7	1s3d	Globe and Compass	2.75	1.60	2.75
		Set of 3	3.00	1.60	3.00
		Set of 3 Cylinder Blocks	£15		
		First Day Cover			12.50

1957 (12 Sept.) 46th Parliamentary Conference

No.			U/M	M/M	F/U
C8	4d	Light Blue	35	25	42
		First Day Cover			£80
		Cylinder Block	2.80		

✓**1958 (18 July) 6th British Empire and Commonwealth Games**

No.			U/M	M/M	F/U
C9	3d	Welsh Dragon	8	5	10
C9a	3d	'Specimen'		£20	
C10	6d	Flag and Emblem	25	18	25
C10a	6d	'Specimen'		£20	
C11	1s3d	Welsh Dragon	1.10	70	1.00
C11a	1s3d	'Specimen'		£20	
		Set of 3	1.20	80	1.10
		Set of 3 Cylinder Blocks	8.50		
		First Day Cover			£50

> **Multiple Crowns Watermark**
> This watermark was used for all commemoratives up to and including the 1967 Wild Flowers. From the 1967 British Paintings issue all commemoratives to date have been issued with no watermark, unless otherwise stated.

✓**1960 (7 July) Tercentenary of General Letter Office.** Perf. 14 x 15 (1s3d)

No.			U/M	M/M	F/U
C12	3d	Postbox of 1660	10	5	10
C12a		Chalky paper	60	30	50
C13	1s3d	Posthorn of 1660 (wmk sideways)	1.60	1.00	1.50
		Set of 2	1.60	1.25	1.30
		Set of 2 Cylinder Blocks	£11		
		First Day Cover			£24

✓**1960 (19 Sept.) 1st Anniversary European Postal and Telecommunications Conference**

No.			U/M	M/M	F/U
C14	6d	Green & reddish purple	40	30	30
C15	1s6d	Brown & deep blue	5.30	2.60	2.60
C15a	1s6d	Shift 3mm to bottom of brown	£35		
		Set of 2	5.60	2.70	2.70
		Set of 2 Cylinder Blocks	£40		
		First Day Cover			23.50

✓ **1961 (28 Aug.) Post Office Savings Bank Centenary Timson Press.**
Perf. 14 x 15 (2½d)

No.		Description	U/M	M/M	F/U
C16	2½d	**Thrift Plant** (wmk. sideways)	22	12	16
C16a		Missing Black (Queen's portrait)	£17000		
C16b		Black shift 1mm right	£500		
C17	3d	**Growth of Savings**	18	10	10
C17a		Perforated through side margin	£13		
C17b		Missing Orange-brown (squirrel, leaves etc.)	£195		£175
C18	1s6d	**Thrift Plant**	90	70	85
		Set of 3	1.00	75	75
		Set of 3 Cylinder Blocks	7.00		
		First Day Cover			£31

Thrissell Press

No.		Description	U/M	M/M	F/U
C19	2½d	**Thrift Plant** (wmk. sideways)	1.10	75	1.10
C19a		Missing Red	£4500		
C20	3d	**Growth of Savings**	20	15	30
C20a		Missing Orange-brown (squirrel, leaves etc.)	£750		£450

The 2½d Timson portrait is a dull olive-tinged black and is much more shaded. The portrait on the Thrissell is lighter and grey-black.

On the 3d Timson printing the portrait is distinct with highlights and deep shadows. On the 3d Thrissell printing the portrait shows a definite dullness and lacks any contrast.

✓ **1961 (18 Sept.) C.E.P.T. Conference, Torquay**

No.		Description	U/M	M/M	F/U
C21	2d	**C.E.P.T.**	10	8	10
C21a		Missing Orange	£8000		
C22	4d	**Doves and Emblem**	10	8	10
C23	10d	**Doves and Emblem**	13	10	20
C23a		Missing Yellow-green (doves)	£9750		
C23b		Missing Turquoise	£2500		
C23c		Pale green shift	£75		
C23d		Turquoise shift	£25		
		Set of 3	20	15	25
		Set of 3 Cylinder Blocks	2.00		
		First Day Cover			4.50

✓ **1961 (25 Sept.) Commonwealth Parliamentary Conference**
Perf. 14 x 15 (1s3d)

No.		Description	U/M	M/M	F/U
C24	6d	**Hammer Beam Roof**	17	10	20
C24a		Missing Gold (Beam Roof)	£750		
C25	1s3d	**Westminster** (wmk. sideways)	1.05	75	1.10
C25a		Missing Blue (Queen's portrait)	£12750		
C25b		Missing Green (dry print)	£12500		
		Set of 2	1.10	75	1.15
		Set of 2 Cylinder Blocks	8.00		
		First Day Cover			£18

> ## PHOSPHOR BANDS
> All the following issues were also printed on an experimental basis with 3 vertical phosphor bands or 1 phosphor band where indicated. These experimental issues were initially distributed only from Post Offices in the Southampton area.

✓ **1962 (14 Nov.) National Productivity Year.** On both the 2½d and 3d values, the watermark is normally inverted.

Ordinary

No.		Description	U/M	M/M	F/U
C26	2½d	**Units of Productivity**	10	5	10
C26a		Deep green & bright carmine-red	20	10	15
C26b		Olive green & carmine red	20	10	15
C27	3d	**National Productivity**	10	5	10
C27a		Missing Blue (Queen's portrait, etc.)	£1200		
C28	1s3d	**Unified Productivity**	90	60	1.00
C28a		Missing Blue (Queen's portrait, etc.)	£6500		
		Set of 3	1.10	70	1.00
		Set of 3 Cylinder Blocks	7.50		
		First Day Cover			£22

Phosphor

No.		Description	U/M	M/M	F/U
C29	2½d	**Units of Productivity** (1 band)	25	15	30
C30	3d	**National Productivity**	95	75	60
C30a		Missing left phosphor band	£40		
C31	1s3d	**Unified Productivity**	12.40	£10	£1
		Set of 3	£13	£10	11.2
		Set of 3 Cylinder Blocks			
		First Day Cover			£9

✓ **1963 (21 March) Freedom from Hunger**
Ordinary

No.		Description	U/M	M/M	F/U
C32	2½d	**Campaign Emblem**	10	5	1
C33	1s3d	**Children of Three Races**	90	60	9
		Set of 2	1.10	60	1.1
		Set of 2 Cylinder Blocks	£8		
		First Day Cover			£1

Phosphor

No.			U/M	M/M	F/U
C34	2½d	Campaign Emblem	1.00	50	1.00
C35	1s3d	Children of Three Races	12.50	8.25	£11
		Set of 2	12.70	£10	£11
		Set of 2 Cylinder Blocks	£120		
		First Day Cover			£22

1963 (7 May) Paris Postal Conference Centenary
The normal watermark on this issue is inverted.

Ordinary

C36	6d	Green & lilac	15	10	20
		First Day Cover			8.00
		Cylinder Block	1.30		

Phosphor

C37	6d	Green & lilac	3.10	2.30	3.10
C37a	6d	Missing Green (leaves)		£2250	£1000
		First Day Cover			17.50
		Cylinder Block	£24		

1963 (16 May) National Nature Week

Ordinary

C38	3d	Posy of Flowers	10	5	10
C39	4½d	Woodland Life	10	10	15
		Set of 2	15	12	20
		Set of 2 Cylinder Blocks	1.20		
		First Day Cover			9.25

Phosphor

C40	3d	Posy of Flowers	30	20	20
C41	4½d	Woodland Life	1.40	60	1.50
		Set of 2	1.40	70	1.50
		Set of 2 Cylinder Blocks	£11		
		First Day Cover			19.50

1963 (31 May) 9th International Lifeboat Conference

Ordinary

C42	2½d	Rescue at Sea	10	5	10
C43	4d	19th Century Lifeboat	30	20	40
C44	1s6d	Lifeboatmen	1.30	90	1.00
		Set of 3	1.40	1.00	1.20
		Set of 3 Cylinder Blocks	£10		
		First Day Cover			£18

Phosphor

No.			U/M	M/M	F/U
C45	2½d	Rescue at Sea	70	35	70
C46	4d	19th Century Lifeboat	60	40	60
C47	1s6d	Lifeboatmen	£21	£15	£12
		Set of 3	22.25	£15	12.20
		Set of 3 Cylinder Blocks	£180		
		First Day Cover			£28

1963 (15 Aug.) Red Cross Centenary Congress

Ordinary

C48	3d	Red & violet	10	5	10
C48a		Missing Red (Cross)	£5000		
C48b		Shift 2mm to bottom of Red	8.00		
C49	1s3d	Red, blue & grey	1.40	90	1.25
C50	1s6d	Red, blue & bistre	1.40	90	1.60
		Set of 3	2.40	1.70	2.75
		Set of 3 Cylinder Blocks	£19		
		First Day Cover			£18

Phosphor

C51	3d	Red & violet	85	60	60
C51a	3d	Missing Red (Cross)	£8000		
C52	1s3d	Red, blue & grey	£21	£11	£14
C53	1s6d	Red, blue & bistre	£15	£7	£12
		Set of 3	33.85	£25	£24
		Set of 3 Cylinder Blocks	£270		
		First Day Cover			£38

1963 (3 Dec.) Opening of C.O.M.P.A.C. Cable

Ordinary

C54	1s6d	Commonwealth Cable	1.00	85	1.00
C54a		Missing Black (cable)	£3500		
C54b		'Cancelled'			
		Cylinder Block	7.50		
		First Day Cover			£12

Phosphor

C55	1s6d	Commonwealth Cable	7.20	4.50	7.70
		Cylinder Block	£58		
		First Day Cover			22.50

		U/M	M/M	F/U
	Set of 4	1.70	1.10	1.80
	Set of 4 Cylinder Blocks	£13		
	First Day Cover			£11
	Presentation Pack	£85		

Phosphor

No.			U/M	M/M	F/U
C69	2½d	Urban (1 band)	25	15	30
C70	4d	Industrial	1.00	70	1.10
C71	8d	Forestry	2.20	1.60	2.00
C72	1s6d	Nuclear	£10	7.00	£9
		Set of 4	11.50	8.00	9.50
		Set of 4 Cylinder Blocks	£90		
		First Day Cover			£29

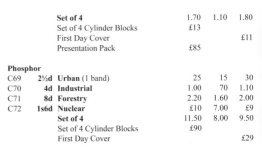

✓1964 (23 April) Shakespeare Festival

2s6d value recess printed by Bradbury, Wilkinson & Co. (Perf. 11 x 12)

Ordinary

No.			U/M	M/M	F/U
C56	3d	Midsummer Nights Dream	10	5	10
C57	6d	Twelfth Night	16	10	15
C58	1s3d	Romeo & Juliet	50	25	50
C58a		Wmk. inverted	£550		
C59	1s6d	Henry V	80	55	45
C59a		Wmk. inverted			£1250
C59b		White Knight. Shift 5mm to right of Violet	£125		
C60	2s6d	Hamlet	80	55	1.10
C60a		Wmk inverted	£335		
C60b		Black	£500		£200
		Set of 5	1.80	1.20	2.20
		Set of 5 Cylinder Blocks	£14		
		First Day Cover			£6
		Presentation Pack	£13		

Phosphor

No.			U/M	M/M	F/U
C61	3d	Midsummer Nights Dream	15	15	15
C62	6d	Twelfth Night	75	50	75
C63	1s3d	Romeo & Juliet	2.80	2.00	3.00
C63a		Wmk. inverted	£110	£30	£50
C64	1s6d	Henry V	3.00	2.00	3.20
		Set of 4	6.00	4.00	6.95
		Set of 4 Cylinder Blocks	£48		
		First Day Cover			£8

✓1964 (5 Aug.) International Botanical Congress

Ordinary

No.			U/M	M/M	F/U
C73	3d	Spring Gentian	10	5	10
C73a		Missing Blue	£5000		
C73b		Perf. shift 2.5mm to right	£30		
C73c		Missing Sage-green	£7250		
C74	6d	Dog Rose	20	15	20
C75	9d	Honeysuckle	70	50	1.00
C75a		Wmk. inverted	£40		
C75b		Missing Green (Leaves)	£6250	£4000	£2000
C76	1s3d	Waterlily	1.00	75	1.00
C76a		Wmk. inverted	£500		
C76b		Missing Yellow (flowers)	£30000		
		Set of 4	1.80	1.25	2.00
		Set of 4 Cylinder Blocks	£14		
		First Day Cover			£12
		Presentation Pack	£85		

Phosphor

No.			U/M	M/M	F/U
C77	3d	Spring Gentian	30	15	1
C78	6d	Dog Rose	1.70	1.20	1.50
C79	9d	Honeysuckle	2.00	1.50	3.00
C80	1s3d	Waterlily	£10	6.50	7.5
		Set of 4	12.50	8.50	10.50
		Set of 4 Cylinder Blocks	£95		
		First Day Cover			£2

✓ 1964 (1 July) 20th International Geographical Congress

Ordinary

No.			U/M	M/M	F/U
C65	2½d	Urban	10	5	10
C66	4d	Industrial	30	20	30
C66a		Wmk. inverted	£425		
C66b		Missing Violet (4d etc.)	£195		£110
C66c		Missing Red-brown	£5500		
C66d		Missing Violet and Red-brown	£290		
C66e		Shift 1mm to left of violet (4d, etc.)	£15		
C67	8d	Forestry	50	30	70
C67a		Wmk. inverted	£450		
C67b		Missing Green (grass)	£9750		£4000
C68	1s6d	Nuclear	1.60	90	1.25
C68a		Wmk. inverted	£20		

✓1964 (4 Sept.) Opening of the Forth Road Bridge

Ordinary

No.			U/M	M/M	F/U
C81	3d	Black, ultramarine & purple	10	5	1
C81a		Imperforate top margin	£700		
C82	6d	Black, blue & maroon	20	10	1
C82a		Wmk. inverted	1.00	80	1.00
C82b		Missing Blue	£2750		£100
		Set of 2	20	10	2
		Set of 2 Cylinder Blocks	1.50		
		First Day Cover			£
		Presentation Pack	£375		

Phosphor

No.		Description	U/M	M/M	F/U
C84	**3d**	**Black, ultramarine & purple**	40	30	35
C85	**6d**	**Black, blue & maroon**	2.20	1.40	2.35
C86		Wmk. inverted	£500	£350	
		Set of 2	2.20	1.50	2.20
		Set of 2 Cylinder Blocks	£17		
		First Day Cover			6.50

✓1965 (8 July) Sir Winston Churchill Memorial Issue

Ordinary

No.		Description	U/M	M/M	F/U
C87	**4d**	**Black & deep brown** (R)	10	5	10
C87a		Wmk. inverted	1.00	60	75
C87b		Black & deep brown (T)	10	5	10
C87c		Missing Queen's head			
		(due to paper fold)	£2500		
C87d		Missing Black	£2750		
C88	**1s3d**	**Black & slate grey**	16	10	25
C88a		Wmk. inverted	£70		
		Set of 2	20	12	25
		Set of 2 Cylinder Blocks	1.50		
		First Day Cover			2.20
		Presentation Pack	£35		

Phosphor

No.		Description	U/M	M/M	F/U
C89	**4d**	**Black & deep-brown**	20	15	20
C90	**1s3d**	**Black & slate grey**	1.10	75	1.20
		Set of 2	1.15	70	1.30
		Set of 2 Cylinder Blocks	£9		
		First Day Cover			3.50

(R) = Rembrandt Press   (T) = Timson Press

The Churchill 4d was printed by the Rembrandt and Timson machines. The Rembrandt shows a lack of detail on the face and the Queen's portrait appears dull and out of focus. On the Timson printing there is much more detail on the face and the left eyebrow is complete, while the Queen's portrait is much more clearly defined and lighter in shade.

1965 (19 July) 700th Anniversary of Parliament

Ordinary

No.		Description	U/M	M/M	F/U
C91	**6d**	**Simon de Montfort's Seal**	15	10	15
C91a		Imperf at top (marginal)	£700	£450	£400
C92	**2s6d**	**Parliament Buildings**	44	30	50
C92a		Wmk inverted	£15		
C92b		Shift 1mm to bottom of Ivory			
		(Queen's portrait)	£45		
		Set of 2	45	30	55
		Set of 2 Cylinder Blocks	3.50		
		First Day Cover			7.25
		Presentation Pack	£58		

Phosphor

No.		Description	U/M	M/M	F/U
C93	**6d**	**Simon de Montfort's Seal**	40	25	45
C93a		Missing phosphor	£100		
		First Day Cover			10.50
		Cylinder Block	£3		

✓1965 (9 Aug.) Centenary of the Salvation Army

Ordinary

No.		Description	U/M	M/M	F/U
C94	**3d**	**Bandsmen and Banner**	10	5	10
C95	**1s6d**	**Three Salvationists**	40	30	55
		Set of 2	45	30	55
		Set of 2 Cylinder Blocks	3.50		
		First Day Cover			£11

Phosphor

No.		Description	U/M	M/M	F/U
C96	**3d**	**Bandsmen and Banner** (1 band)	27	15	30
C97	**1s6d**	**Three Salvationists**	1.10	80	1.20
		Set of 2	1.15	80	1.30
		Set of 2 Cylinder Blocks	£9		
		First Day Cover			£14

1965 (1 Sept.) Commonwealth Arts Festival

Ordinary

No.		Description	U/M	M/M	F/U
C98	**6d**	**Trinidad Carnival Dancers**	14	5	15
C99	**1s6d**	**Canadian Folk Dancers**	45	35	65
		Set of 2	60	30	70
		Set of 2 Cylinder Blocks	£4		
		First Day Cover			£8

Phosphor

No.		Description	U/M	M/M	F/U
C100	**6d**	**Trinidad Carnival Dancers**	20	10	25
C101	**1s6d**	**Canadian Folk Dancers**	1.30	70	1.45
		Set of 2	1.35	70	1.45
		Set of 2 Cylinder Blocks	£10		
		First Day Cover			9.50

✓1965 (1 Sept.) Joseph Lister Centenary

Ordinary

No.		Description	U/M	M/M	F/U
C102	**4d**	**Carbolic Spray**	10	5	10
C102a		Missing Brown (tubing)	£295		£250
C102b		Missing Indigo	£4250		
C102c		Shift 2mm to left of Blue	£15		
C103	**1s**	**Chemical Symbols**	40	25	60
C104		Wmk. inverted	£325		
		Set of 2	40	25	60
		Set of 2 Cylinder Blocks	£3		
		First Day Cover			£7

Phosphor

No.		Description	U/M	M/M	F/U
C105	**4d**	**Carbolic Spray**	20	10	20
C105a		Missing Brown (tubing)	£2250		
C106	**1s**	**Chemical Symbols**	1.30	70	1.40
C106a		Wmk. inverted	£300		
		Set of 2	1.30	65	1.40
		Set of 2 Cylinder Blocks	£10		
		First Day Cover			£9

No.   U/M   M/M   F/U   No.   U/M   M/M   F/U

1965 (8 Oct.) Opening of Post Office Tower, London

Ordinary

No.			U/M	M/M	F/U
C123	**3d**	**Geogian Buildings**	10	5	10
C123a		Missing Yellow bistre (Tower)	£2250		$750
C124	**1s3d**	**Regents Park**	25	15	30
C124a		Wmk inverted	£45		
C124b		Shift 1mm to left of Green			
		(Queen's portrait, etc.)	£25		
		Set of 2	25	15	30
		Set of 2 Cylinder Blocks	1.50		
		First Day Cover			£4
		Presentation Pack	3.50		

Phosphor

C125	**3d**	**Geogian Buildings** (1 side band)	15	10	15
C126	**1s3d**	**Regents Park**	25	15	30
C126a		Wmk inverted	£25	£15	£1
		Set of 2	35	20	35
		Set of 2 Cylinder Blocks	1.50		
		First Day Cover			4.75
		Presentation Pack	3.00		

1965 (13 Sept.) 25th Anniversary of the Battle of Britain

Ordinary

No.			U/M	M/M	F/U
C107/112	**4d**	**Block of 6 se-tenant**	3.40	1.90	3.80
C107		Olive green & black (A)	50	30	50
C108		Olive green, grey & black (B)	50	30	50
C109		Olive green, red, blue & grey (C)	50	30	50
C110		Olive green, grey & black (D)	50	30	50
C111		Olive green, grey & black (E)	50	30	50
C112		Olive green, grey, blue & black (F)	50	30	50
C112a		Missing Blue			£4000
C113	**9d**	**Black, orange & purple**	70	40	80
C113a		Wmk. inverted	£50		
C114	**1s3d**	**Multicoloured**	60	35	90
C114a		Wmk. inverted	£20		
C114b		Shift 2mm to left of Blue (Sky)	£50		
C114c		Shift 2mm to right of pale grey			
		(St. Paul's, etc.)	£50		
C114d		Shift 12mm to bottom of Black			
		(Queen's portrait & 1s3d)	£150		
C114e		Shift 2mm to bottom left of Dark Grey	£30		
		Set of 8	3.80	2.10	3.90
		Set of 3 Cylinder Blocks	£30		
		First Day Cover			£11
		Presentation Pack	£42		

Phosphor

C115/20	**4d**	**Block of 6 se-tenant**	5.25	2.75	5.70
C115		Olive green & black (A)	85	15	95
C116		Olive green, grey & black (B)	85	15	95
C117		Olive green, red, blue & grey (C)	85	15	95
C118		Olive green, grey & black (D)	85	15	95
C119		Olive green, grey & black (E)	85	15	95
C120		Olive green, grey, blue & black (F)	85	15	95
C121	**9d**	**Black, orange & purple**	60	40	80
C122	**1s3d**	**Multicoloured**	70	40	90
C122a		Wmk. inverted	5.00		
		Set of 8	6.00	3.50	6.10
		Set of 3 Cylinder Blocks	£45		
		First Day Cover			£13

1965 (25 Oct.) 20th Anniversary of United Nations and International Co-operation Year

Ordinary

C127	**3d**	**UN Emblem**	10	5	10
C128	**1s6d**	**ICY Emblem**	45	20	47
C128a		Wmk. inverted			£1750
C128b		Shift 2.5mm to left of Black	£25		
C128c		Imperf. between stamp & top margin	£1500		
		Set of 2	45	20	50
		Set of 2 Cylinder Blocks	3.50		
		First Day Cover			£7

Phosphor

C129	**3d**	**UN Emblem** (1 band)	15	10	15
C130	**1s6d**	**ICY Emblem**	1.60	90	1.70
		Set of 2	1.70	80	1.65
		Set of 2 Cylinder Blocks	£13		
		First Day Cover			£8

1965 (15 Nov.) Centenary of International Telecommunications Union

Ordinary

C131	**9d**	**Telecommunications**	20	15	20
C131b		Shift 4mm to left of deep Violet	£55		
C131c		Shift 2mm to left of Blue	£45		
C131d		Shift 1mm to top of Red	£35		
C131a		Wmk. inverted	£15		

No.			U/M	M/M	F/U

C132	**1s6d**	**Radio Waves**	40	25	50
C132a		Wmk. inverted	£50		
C132b		Missing Pink (panel behind			
		Queen's portrait)	£1500		£1350
C132c		Shift 8mm to bottom of Pink (panel)	£40		
		Set of 2	55	35	60
		Set of 2 Cylinder Blocks	£4		
		First Day Cover			£8

Phosphor

C134	**9d**	**Telecommunications**	40	25	40
C134a		Wmk. inverted	£60		
C134b		Shift 1mm to left of Black			
		(inscription & Queen's portrait)	£20		
C135	**1s6d**	**Radio Waves**	2.50	1.50	2.70
		Set of 2	2.60	1.50	2.70
		Set of 2 Cylinder Blocks	18.50		
		First Day Cover			£10

1966 (25 Jan.) Robert Burns

Ordinary

C136	**4d**	**Black, violet & light blue**	10	5	10
C137	**1s3d**	**Black, slate blue & orange**	25	15	30
C137a		Shift 2mm to left of Slate-blue			
		(Background to Queen's portrait)	£65		
		Set of 2	22	15	30
		Set of 2 Cylinder Blocks	1.70		
		First Day Cover			2.50
		Presentation Pack	£36		

Phosphor

C138	**4d**	**Black, violet & light blue**	10	5	15
C139	**1s3d**	**Black, slate blue & orange**	1.10	60	1.15
		Set of 2	1.10	60	1.15
		Set of 2 Cylinder Blocks	8.50		
		First Day Cover			2.75

1966 (28 Feb.) 900th Anniversary of Westminster Abbey
2s6d value recess printed by Bradbury, Wilkinson & Co. (Perf 11 x 12)

Ordinary

C140	**3d**	**Westminster Abbey**	10	5	10
C140a		Shift 1mm to left of Chestnut	£20		
C141	**2s6d**	**Fan Vaulting**	25	20	40
		Set of 2	30	20	40
		Set of 2 Cylinder Blocks	1.70		
		First Day Cover			3.20
		Presentation Pack	£36		

Phosphor

C142	**3d**	**Westminster Abbey** (1 band)	10	5	10
		First Day Cover			6.50
		Cylinder Block	80		

 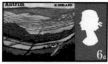

1966 (2 May) Landscapes of the British Isles

Ordinary

C143	**4d**	**Hassocks**	10	5	10
C144	**6d**	**Antrim**	10	8	10
C144a		Wmk. inverted	5.00		
C144b		Missing 'D' in 'AND (SONS)'	£10		
C144c		Shift 1mm to bottom of Emerald green			
		(Mountain tops)	£15		
C145	**1s3d**	**Harlech**	17	10	22
C146	**1s6d**	**Cairngorm**	17	13	25
C146a		Wmk. inverted	£10		
C146b		Shift 2mm to left of Black (trees)	£35		
C146c		Shift 2mm to left of Deep Blue			
		(panel behind Queen's head)	£35		
		Set of 4	35	30	60
		Set of 4 Cylinder Blocks	2.70		
		First Day Cover			£3

Phosphor

C147	**4d**	**Hassocks**	10	5	12
C148	**6d**	**Antrim**	10	5	10
C148a		Wmk. inverted	£30		
C148b		Missing 'D' in 'AND (SONS)'	5.00		
C149	**1s3d**	**Harlech**	17	10	22
C150	**1s6d**	**Cairngorm**	17	12	25
		Set of 4	45	25	60
		Set of 4 Cylinder Blocks	3.50		
		First Day Cover			3.20

1966 (1 June) World Cup Football Competition

Ordinary

C151	**4d**	**Players with Ball**	10	5	10
C152	**6d**	**Goalmouth Melee**	10	5	10
C152a		Wmk. inverted	1.00	60	75
C152b		Missing Black (Goalkeeper, etc.)	£125		£45
C152c		Missing Green (shorts & pitch)	£3250		£1500
C152d		Missing Red (left & right players)	£3750		
C152e		Shift 4mm to left of Black	£45		
C152f		Shift 4mm to left of Red	£125		

C153	**1s3d**	**Goalkeeper Saving**	15	10	20
C153a		Wmk. inverted	£100		
C153b		Missing Blue (stripes)	£160		
C153c		Shift 5mm to bottom of Blue (Arrow by ball)	£45		
C153d		Shift 3mm to left of Yellow (Two balls, etc.)	£20		
		Set of 3	30	15	35
		Set of 3 Cylinder Blocks	1.70		
		First Day Cover			£5
		Presentation Pack	9.00		

Phosphor

C154	**4d**	**Players with Ball**	10	5	10
C155	**6d**	**Goalmouth Melee**	10	5	10
C155a		Missing Black (Goalkeeper, etc.)	£550		
C156	**1s3d**	**Goalkeeper Saving**	15	10	20
C156a		Wmk. inverted	1.00	60	75
		Set of 3	25	15	30
		Set of 3 Cylinder Blocks	1.40		
		First Day Cover			7.50

1966 (18 Aug.) World Cup Football. England winners
Ordinary

C165	**4d**	**England Winners**	15	10	15
C165a	4d	Shift 2mm to right of blue, red & flesh	£75		
		Cylinder Block	80		
		First Day Cover			3.50

1966 (19 Sept.) British Technology
Ordinary

C166	**4d**	**Jodrell Bank**	10	5	10
C167	**6d**	**British Motor Cars**	10	5	10
C167a		Missing red (Minis)	£6000		
C167b		Double print of red (Minis)	£250		
C167c		Missing deep blue (Jaguar)	£4750		
C168	**1s3d**	**SRN6 Hovercraft**	10	5	20
C169	**1s6d**	**Windscale Reactor**	10	5	20
		Set of 4	27	15	50
		Set of 4 Cylinder Blocks	2.00		
		First Day Cover			1.50
		Presentation Pack	8.00		

Phosphor

C170	**4d**	**Jodrell Bank**	10	5	10
C171	**6d**	**British Motor Cars**	10	5	15
C172	**1s3d**	**SRN6 Hovercraft**	10	5	20
C173	**1s6d**	**Windscale Reactor**	10	5	20
		Set of 4	35	25	60
		Set of 4 Cylinder Blocks	2.50		
		First Day Cover			1.50

1966 (8 Aug.) British Birds
Ordinary

C157/60	**4d**	**Block of 4 se-tenant**	35	25	55
C157		Black Headed Gull (A)	12	8	15
C157a		Missing Black (A) Single	£7500		£3500
C158		Blue Tit (B)	12	8	15
C159		Robin (C)	12	8	15
C160		Blackbird (D)	12	8	15
C157/60a		Block of 4. Wmk. inverted	7.50	3.50	4.00
C157/60b		Missing Black, blue, bistre & brown	£6500		
C157/60c		Missing Greenish-yellow	£2250		
C157/60d		Missing Red (A & C)	£1500		
C157/60e		Missing Green (A, B & C)	£325		£225
C157/60f		Missing Blue (A & B)	£750		
C157/60g		Missing Bistre (A, B & C)	£375		
C157/60h		Missing Brown (C & D)	£150		
C157/60i		Shift 3mm to top of Red & green (A, B & C)	£225		
C157/60j		Shift 2mm to left of red (A & C)	£135		
		Cylinder Block	1.90		
		First Day Cover			3.45
		Presentation Pack	7.00		

Phosphor

C161/4	**4d**	**Block of 4 se-tenant**	32	25	55
C161		Black Headed Gull (A)	13	8	15
C162		Blue Tit (B)	13	8	15
C163		Robin (C)	13	8	15
C164		Blackbird (D)	13	8	15
		Cylinder Block			
C161/4a		Block of 4. Wmk. inverted	£35	£15	£25
C161/64b		Missing Green (A, B & C)	£325		
C161/64c		Missing Blue (A & B)	£7000		
C161/64d		Missing Bistre (A, B & C)	£8750		
C161/64e		Missing Brown (C & D)	£225		
C161/64f		Missing Greenish-yellow	£5500		
		Cylinder Block			
		First Day Cover			3.45

Prices are for blocks of four unless stated. Brackets indicate stamps affected.

E   F

No.			U/M	M/M	F/U
C190	**1s3d**	**Horsemen** (wmk. sideways)	20	15	20
C190a		Wmk. sideways inverted	£35		
C190b		Missing Lilac	£600		
C190c		Missing Gold	£450		
		Set of 8	80	60	1.20
		Set of 3 Cylinder Blocks	£6		
		First Day Cover			3.50

1966 (1 Dec.) Christmas 1966
Ordinary

No.			U/M	M/M	F/U
C191	**3d**	**King**	10	5	10
C191a		Missing 'T' in 'SHEMZA'	£2		
C191b		Missing Gold (Queen's head) *	£125		
C192	**1s6d**	**Snowman**	14	10	20
C192a		Wmk. inverted	£15		
C192b		Missing Pink (Hat)	£1500		
C192c		Missing Gold (Queen's head) *	£550		
		Set of 2	13	10	20
		Set of 2 Cylinder Blocks	1.00		
		First Day Cover			1.25
		Presentation Pack	4.00		

Phosphor

No.			U/M	M/M	F/U
C193	**3d**	**King** (1 side band)	10	5	10
C193a		Missing 'T' in 'SHEMZA'	£2		
C193b		Missing Gold (Queen's head) *	£525		
C194	**1s6d**	**Snowman** (2 bands)	14	10	20
C194a		Wmk. inverted	£40		
C194b		Missing Gold	£625		
		Set of 2	13	10	25
		Set of 2 Cylinder Blocks	1.00		
		First Day Cover			1.25

*   Only purchase with a certificate.

1966 (14 Oct.) 900th Anniversary of Battle of Hastings
Ordinary

No.			U/M	M/M	F/U
C175/80	**4d**	**Strip of 6 se-tenant**	60	30	1.20
C175		Battle Scene (A)	10	5	15
C176		Battle Scene (B)	10	5	15
C177		Battle Scene (C)	10	5	15
C178		Battle Scene (D)	10	5	15
C179		Battle Scene (E)	10	5	15
C179a		Missing Light blue and Grey			
		(single stamp on cover)			£5000
C180		Battle Scene (F)	10	5	15
C175/80a		Strip of 6. Wmk. inverted	£70		
C175/80b		Missing Olive-green	£375		
C175/80c		Missing Bistre	£375		
C175/80d		Missing Deep blue	£410		
C175/80e		Missing Orange (A, B, C, E & F)	£375		
C175/80f		Missing Magenta	£375		
C175/80g		Missing Green	£375		
C175/80h		Missing Blue	£375		
C175/80i		Missing Grey	£240		
C181	**6d**	**Norman Ship**	10	5	15
C181a		Wmk. inverted	£40		
C182	**1s3d**	**Horsemen** (wmk. sideways)	20	15	20
C182a		Wmk. sideways inverted	£35		
C182b		Missing Gold (Queen's head)	£125		
C182c		Missing Lilac	£400		
		Set of 8	80	45	1.20
		Set of 3 Cylinder Blocks	£6		
		First Day Cover			2.20
		Presentation Pack	3.50		

Phosphor

No.			U/M	M/M	F/U
C183/88	**4d**	**Strip of 6 se-tenant**	60	45	1.20
C183		Battle Scene (A)	15	10	20
C184		Battle Scene (B)	15	10	20
C185		Battle Scene (C)	15	10	20
C186		Battle Scene (D)	15	10	20
C187		Battle Scene (E)	15	10	20
C188		Battle Scene (F)	15	10	20
C183/88a		Strip of 6. Wmk. inverted	£35		
C183/88b		Missing Olive-green	£375		
C183/88c		Missing Bistre	£375		
C183/88d		Missing Deep blue	£410		
C183/88e		Missing Orange (A, B, C, E & F)	£375		
C183/88f		Missing Magenta	£375		
C183/88g		Missing Green	£300		
C183/88h		Missing Blue	£375		
C183/88i		Missing Grey	£300		
C189	**6d**	**Norman Ship**	10	5	15
C189a		Wmk. inverted	£50		

1967 (20 Feb.) European Free Trade Association
Ordinary

No.			U/M	M/M	F/U
C195	**9d**	**Multicoloured**	10	5	11
C195a		Wmk. inverted	£15	8.00	£10
C195b		Missing Black, Brown, Light			
		Blue & Yellow	£850		
C195c		Missing Lilac	£65		
C195d		Missing Green	£65		
C195e		Missing Brown	£50		
C195f		Missing Light Blue	£65		
C195g		Missing Yellow	£65		
C195h		Shift 3mm of Brown and 1mm of			
		Light Blue to bottom	£35		
C196	**1s6d**	**Multicoloured**	10	10	14
C196a		Missing Deep Blue	£350		
C196b		Missing Brown	£65		
C196c		Missing Light Blue	£65		
C196d		Missing Yellow	£65		
C196e		Missing Blue-grey	£65		

The 4d is usually collected in se-tenant strips of six as printed. The missing orange only affects Types A, B, C, E & F

No.			U/M	M/M	F/U
	Set of 2		10	8	15
	Set of 2 Cylinder Blocks		80		
	First Day Cover				1.25
	Presentation Pack		1.75		
Phosphor					
C197	**9d**	**Multicoloured**	10	5	11
C197a		Wmk. inverted	6.00	2.50	3.25
C197b		Missing Lilac	£150		
C197c		Missing Green	£65		
C197d		Missing Brown	£50		
C197e		Missing Light Blue	£65		
C197f		Missing Yellow	£65		
C198	**1s6d**	**Multicoloured**	10	10	14
C198a		Wmk. inverted	£15	8.00	£10
C198b		Missing Red	£6500		
C198c		Missing Deep Blue	£350		
C198d		Missing Brown	£50		
C198e		Missing Light Blue	£65		
C198f		Missing Blue-grey	£65		
	Set of 2		14	10	20
	Set of 2 Cylinder Blocks		1.20		
	First Day Cover				1.25

No.			U/M	M/M	F/U
C209	**9d**	**Dog Violet**	10	5	15
C210	**1s9d**	**Primroses**	13	10	17
	Set of 6		35	25	70
	Set of 3 Cylinder Blocks		2.60		
	First Day Cover				2.00
	Presentation Pack		3.50		

The 4d is usually collected in blocks of four as printed. With the missing colour varieties the stamps affected are shown in brackets.

1967 (10 July) British Paintings

No.			U/M	M/M	F/U
C211	**4d**	**Multicoloured**	10	5	10
C211a		Missing phosphor	£10		
C211b		Missing Gold (4d & Queen's head)	£225		
C211c		Missing Light Blue	£6000		
C211d		Shift 3.5mm to right of Gold	£45		
C212	**9d**	**Multicoloured**	10	5	15
C212a		Missing phosphor	£450		
C212b		One broad band	£15		
C212c		Missing Black (9d & Queen's head)	£550		£175
C212d		Missing Black (Queen's head), 9d at right	£750		
C212e		Shift 24mm to right of Black (Queen's head & 9d transposed)	£175		
C213	**1s6d**	**Multicoloured**	10	5	12
C213a		Missing phosphor	£300		
C213b		One broad band	5.00		
C213c		Missing Light Blue	£200		
C213d		Missing Grey	£55		
C213e		Missing Gold (Queen's head)	£6000		£3000
	Set of 3		15	10	27
	Set of 3 Cylinder Blocks		1.10		
	First Day Cover				1.20
	Presentation Pack		2.90		

A · 4d · B

C · 4d

· 4d · D

9d

1/9

1967 (24 April) British Wild Flowers

Ordinary

No.			U/M	M/M	F/U
C199/202	**4d**	**Block of 4 se-tenant**	40	30	60
C199		Hawthorn and Bramble (A)	10	10	10
C200		Bindweed (B)	10	10	10
C201		Ox-eye Daisy (C)	10	10	10
C202		Bluebell (D)	10	10	10
C199/202a		Block of 4 Wmk. inverted	£25		
C199/202b		Missing reddish-purple (D)	£950		
C199/202c		Missing red (A)	£2500		
C199/202d		Missing slate-purple (A)	£4250		
C203	**9d**	**Dog Violet**	10	5	15
C203a		Wmk. inverted	5.00		
C204	**1s9d**	**Primroses**	13	10	17
	Set of 6		55	40	75
	Set of 3 Cylinder Blocks		4.20		
	First Day Cover				2.00
	Presentation Pack		3.50		

Phosphor

No.			U/M	M/M	F/U
C205/8	**4d**	**Block of 4 se-tenant**	40	20	60
C205/8a		Block of 4 Wmk. inverted	£25		
C205/8b		4d Missing agate (A, B, C & D)	£7500		
C205/8c		4d Missing violet (B & D)	£10000		
C205/8d		4d Missing slate-purple (A)	£300		£500
C205		Hawthorn and Bramble (A)	10	5	15
C206		Bindweed (B)	10	5	15
C207		Ox-eye Daisy (C)	10	5	15
C208		Bluebell (D)	10	5	15

IMPORTANT NOTE

From this issue all stamps have only 2 vertical phosphor bands except where stated. The price column for Mounted Mint (M/M) is omitted from this date, as collectors prefer Unmounted Mint (U/M) in modern issues.

1967 (24 July) Sir Francis Chichester

No.			U/M	F/U
C214	1s9d	**Gypsy Moth** IV (3 bands)	10	12
		Cylinder Block	75	
		First Day Cover		60

1967 (19 Sept.) British Scientific Discoveries. Wmk. Multiple Crowns

			U/M	F/U
C215	4d	**Radar Screen** (3 bands)	10	10
C215a		Missing phosphor	5.00	
C216	1s	**Penicillium**	10	10
C216a		Missing phosphor	£15	
C216b		Wmk. inverted	£10	7.50
C217	1s6d	**VC10 Jet Engines**	10	12
C217a		Missing phosphor	£500	
C217b		Wmk. inverted	£30	£15
C218	1s9d	**Television** (wmk. sideways)	10	15
C218a		Missing phosphor	£500	
C218b		Missing Grey		£4500
		Set of 4	19	25
		Set of 4 Cylinder Blocks	1.50	
		First Day Cover		1.25
		Presentation Pack	1.80	

1967 (18 Oct.) Christmas 1967

			U/M	F/U
C219	3d	**Adoration of the Shepherds** (1 band) (27 Nov.)	10	10
C219a		Missing phosphor	1.00	
C219b		Printed on the gummed side	£400	
C219c		Missing Gold (3d & Queen's head)	£80	
C219d		Missing Rose	£2500	
C219e		Left margin imperforate	£500	
C219e		Missing Yellow	£4000	
C220	4d	**Madonna and Child**	10	10
C220a		Missing phosphor	£100	
C220b		Missing Gold (3d & Queen's head)	£60	£25
C220c		Missing Yellow	£6000	
C221	1s6d	**Adoration of the Shepherds** (27 Nov.)	10	15
C221a		Missing phosphor	£10	
C221b		One broad band	£30	
C221c		Missing Gold (Queen's head & value)	£2000	
C221d		Missing Ultramarine	£500	
C221e		Missing Lemon	£7500	
		Set of 3	20	25
		Set of 3 Cylinder Blocks	1.50	
		First Day Covers (2)		1.25

1967 (27 Nov.) Special Gift Pack

		U/M	F/U
YP1	Presentation Pack	1.00	

1968 (29 April) British Bridges

			U/M	F/U
C222	4d	**Tarr Steps, Exmoor**	10	10
C222a		Missing phosphor	5.00	
C222b		Printed on the gummed side	£20	
C223	9d	**Aberfeldy**	10	11
C223a		Missing phosphor	£15	
C223b		Broad Band	£15	
C223c		Missing Ultramarine		£4000
C223d		Missing Gold (Queen's head)	£175	
C224	1s6d	**Menai**	10	15
C224a		Missing phosphor	£16	
C224b		Missing Reddish orange	£185	
C224c		Missing Gold (Queen's head)	£185	
C224d		Shift 3mm to bottom of Turquoise-green	£55	
C224e		Shift 2mm to bottom of Gold (Queen's head)	£20	
C225	1s9d	**M4 Viaduct**	10	17
C225a		Missing phosphor	£10	
C225b		Broad Band	£10	
C225c		Missing Gold (Queen's head)	£185	
C225d		Missing Gold & phosphor	£3500	£1600
		Set of 4	19	30
		Set of 4 Cylinder Blocks	1.50	
		First Day Cover		1.20
		Presentation Pack	1.80	

1968 (29 May) British Anniversaries

No.			U/M	F/U
C226	4d	TUC	10	10
C226a		Missing phosphor	£10	
C227	9d	Emmeline Pankhurst	10	12
C227a		Missing phosphor	£10	
C228	1s	Sopwith Camel	10	15
C228a		Missing phosphor	£10	
C229	1s9d	Captain Cook	10	15
C229a		Missing phosphor	£150	
		Set of 4	19	30
		Set of 4 Cylinder Blocks	1.50	
		First Day Cover		2.20
		Presentation Pack 1	1.70	

1968 (12 Aug.) British Paintings 1968

No.			U/M	F/U
C230	4d	Queen Elizabeth I	10	10
C230a		Missing phosphor	1.00	
C230b		Missing Gold (Queen's head & 4d)	£200	
C230c		Missing Gold & phosphor	£200	
C230d		Missing Vermilion (face & hands)	£250	
C230e		Missing embossing	£80	
C231	1s	'Pinkie'	10	11
C231a		Missing phosphor	£10	
C231b		Missing Gold (Queen's head & 1s)	£4650	
C231c		Missing Gold & phosphor	£250	
C232	1s6d	'Ruins of St. Mary'	10	12
C232a		Missing phosphor	£10	
C232b		Missing Gold (Queen's head & 1/6)	£125	
C232c		Shift 7mm to top of Gold (Queen's head & 1/6)	£35	
C233	1s9d	'The Hay Wain'	10	15
C233a		Missing phosphor	£20	
C233b		Missing Gold, & phosphor	£550	
C233c		Missing Red *	£7500	£1500
C233d		Perf. shift 4mm to top	£45	
		Set of 4	20	25
		Set of 4 Cylinder Blocks	1.50	
		First Day Cover		1.25
		Presentation Pack 1	1.70	
		German Presentation Pack	8.50	

* This stamp is of uncertain origin.

1968 (16 Sept.) Collectors Pack 1968

No.		U/M	F/U
YP2	Presentation Pack	3.00	

The Post Office began numbering all Presentation Packs commencing with the 1968 British Paintings issue.

1968 (16 Sept.) Gift Pack 1968

No.		U/M	F/U
YP3	Presentation Pack 3	3.00	
YP3a	German Gift Pack	22.50	

1968 (25 Nov.) Christmas 1968

No.			U/M	F/U
C234	4d	Rocking Horse (1 band)	10	10
C234a		Missing phosphor	5.00	
C234b		Missing Vermilion	£225	
C234c		Missing Ultramarine & phosphor	£225	£200
C234d		Missing Gold (Queen's head)	£3500	
C234e		Missing Bistre brown	£3000	
C234f		Shift 2mm to top of Gold (Queen's head) & embossing	£45	
C234g		Shift 11.5mm to bottom of embossing	£35	
C234h		Shift 5mm to left of Ultramarine	£50	
C234i		Missing embossing	5.00	
C235	9d	Dolls House	10	12
C235a		Missing phosphor	£10	
C235b		Missing Yellow	£70	
C235c		Shift 2mm to bottom of embossing		
C235d		Missing embossing & phosphor	£10	
C235e		Missing embossing	5.00	
C236	1s6d	Train Set	10	12
C236a		Missing phosphor	£15	
C236b		Shift 5mm to bottom of embossing	£10	
		Set of 3	15	20
		Set of 3 Cylinder Blocks	80	
		First Day Cover		70
		Presentation Pack 4	1.70	
		German Presentation Pack	6.00	

The 4d value was printed on the Rembrandt and Thrissell machines. Either version is worth the same.

Rembrandt: If you imagine a line from the top of the boy's head to the top of the Queen's portrait it should be perfectly horizontal.

Thrissell: The Queen's head is normally lower and also the grey of the boy's pullover is mottled compared with the Rembrandt printing.

1969 (3 March) First Flight of Concorde

No.			U/M	F/U
C243	**4d**	**Concord in Flight**	15	10
C243a		Missing phosphor	1.00	
C243b		Missing Violet (4d, etc.)	£275	
C243c		Missing Orange (line of fuselage)	£300	£180
C243d		Missing Orange & phosphor	£300	£180
C243e		Shift 2mm to left of Green	£15	
C243f		Missing Violet	£300	£180
C244	**9d**	**Plan and Elevation Views**	20	20
C244a		Missing phosphor	£100	
C245	**1s6d**	**Concorde's Nose and Tail**	20	20
C245a		Missing phosphor	£10	
C245b		Missing Silver (Queen's head)	£300	£180
		Set of 3	50	50
		Set of 3 Cylinder Blocks	3.70	
		First Day Cover		3.00
		Presentation Pack 6	6.50	
		German Presentation Pack	24.50	

1969 (15 Jan.) British Ships

No.			U/M	F/U
C237	**5d**	Queen Elizabeth 2 (1 horizontal band)	10	10
C237a		Missing phosphor	5.00	
C237b		Missing Black (5d, Queen's head & hull)	£950	
C237c		Missing Grey (decks)	£70	
C237d		Missing Red (Cunard, etc.)	£85	
C237e		Missing Red & phosphor	£65	
C237f		Perf. shift 4mm to right ('5' at right)	£40	
C237g		Perf. shift 4mm to top (missing inscription)	£60	
C237h		Perf. shift 4mm to top (inscription above '5')	£35	
C237i		Perf. shift 2mm to top	£25	
C237j		Shift 1mm to top of Grey (superstructure in the sky)	£40	
C238/40	**9d**	**Strip of 3 se-tenant**	60	80
C238/40a		Missing phosphor	£35	
C238/40b		Missing Red and Blue	£1400	
C238/40c		Missing Blue	£1250	
C238/40d		Shift 5mm to top of Red (Bulwarks in the sky)	£150	
C238	9d	Elizabethan Galleon (A)	24	27
C238a		Missing phosphor	£10	
C239	9d	East Indiaman (B)	24	27
C239a		Missing phosphor	£10	
C240	9d	Cutty Sark (C)	24	27
C240a		Missing phosphor	£10	
C241/2	**1s**	**Pair se-tenant**	25	40
C241/2a		Missing phosphor	£75	
C241/2b		Missing Greenish-yellow	£2500	
C241/2c		Missing Green	£17500	
C241/2d		Missing Carmine (hull)	£15500	
C241/2e		Missing Red	£12500	
C241/2f		Missing Carmine & Red	£13500	
C241	1s	SS Great Britain (D)	13	13
C241a		Missing phosphor	£35	
C242	1s	RMS Mauretania (E)	13	13
C242a		Missing phosphor	£35	
		Set of 6	70	1.00
		Set of 3 Cylinder Blocks	5.00	
		First Day Cover		1.75
		Presentation Pack 5	2.30	
		German Presentation Pack	18.50	
		Cunard Presentation Pack	5.00	

1969 (2 April) British Anniversaries

No.			U/M	F/U
C246	**5d**	**Daily Mail/Vickers FB27**	10	10
C247	**9d**	**Europa and CEPT Emblems**	10	10
C247a		Missing phosphor	£20	
C247b		Uncoated paper	£1500	
C248	**1s**	**I.L.O. Emblem**	10	10
C248a		Missing phosphor	£10	
C249	**1s6d**	**Flags of N.A.T.O**	15	17
C249a		Missing phosphor	£10	
C249b		Missing Black	£75	
C249c		Missing Green	£55	
C249d		Missing Green & phosphor	£55	
C249e		Missing Lemon (FDC)		£3500
C250	**1s9d**	**Vickers FB-27**	15	20
C250a		Missing phosphor	5.00	
C250b		Uncoated paper	£200	
C250c		Shift 3mm to left of Green (globe)	£40	

	U/M	F/U
Set of 5	28	50
Set of 5 Cylinder Blocks	2.10	
First Day Cover		1.50
Presentation Pack 9	2.50	
German Presentation Pack	£45	

1969 (28 May) British Architecture. Cathedrals

No.			U/M	F/U
C251/4	5d	Block of 4 se-tenant	25	50
C251/4a		Missing Pale Bluish-violet	£7000	
C251/4b		Missing 'd' after value	£300	
C251/4c		Missing Green	£80	
C251/4d		Imperforate block of 4	£1250	
C251		Durham (A)	10	10
C252		York Minster (B)	10	10
C252a		Missing Violet (B)	£3000	
C253		St. Giles, Edinburgh (C)	10	10
C254		Canterbury (D)	10	10
C255	9d	St. Pauls	17	15
C255a		Missing phosphor	£45	
C255b		Missing Black (9d)	£75	
C255c		Shift 12mm to bottom of Black (9d)	£45	
C255d		Missing Black & Phosphor	£125	
C256	1s6d	Liverpool	20	20
C256a		Missing phosphor	£20	
C256b		Missing Black (1/6d)	£2500	
C256c		Shift 10mm to bottom of Black (1/6d)	£125	
C256d		Offset on reverse of Yellow-olive	£50	
		Set of 6	50	75
		Set of 3 Cylinder Blocks	5.00	
		First Day Cover		1.50
		Presentation Pack 10	2.50	
		German Presentation Pack	£16	

The 5d is usually collected in blocks of four as printed.

A   B   C

1969 (1 July) Investiture of HRH The Prince of Wales

No.			U/M	F/U
C257/9	5d	Strip of 3 se-tenant	20	50
C257/9a		Missing phosphor	£18	
C257/9b		Missing Black (5d and inscription)	£650	
C257/9c		Missing Red (Flags)	£1500	
C257/9d		Missing Deep grey (Windows, etc.)	£650	
C257/9e		Missing Green (Flags)	£1500	
C257/9f		Shift 4mm to bottom of Deep olive-grey (Queen's head)	£95	
C257/9g		Missing Pale grey	£12500	
C257		The Kings Gate (A)	10	15
C257a		Missing phosphor	6.00	
C258		The Eagle Tower (B)	10	15
C258a		Missing phosphor	6.00	
C258b		Missing Pale grey		£3750
C259		Queen Eleonor's Gate (C)	10	15
C259a		Missing phosphor	6.00	
C260	9d	Celtic Cross	15	14
C260a		Missing phosphor	£20	
C260b		Shift 9mm to bottom of Black (9d, Queen's head & inscription)	£80	
C261	1s	Prince Charles	15	14
C261a		Missing phosphor	£15	
C261b		One broad band	£30	
		Set of 5	35	65
		Set of 3 Cylinder Blocks	3.50	
		First Day Cover		1.50
		Presentation Pack 11	1.75	
		German Presentation Pack	£16	
		Welsh Presentation Pack	£24	

The 5d is usually collected in se-tenant strips of three as printed.

1969 (13 Aug.) Ghandi Centenary Year

No.			U/M	F/U
C262	1s6d	Mahatma Ghandi	10	14
C262a		Missing phosphor	5.00	
C262b		Printed on the gummed side	£400	
		Cylinder Block	75	
		First Day Cover		50

1969 (15 Sept.) Collectors Pack

No.		U/M	F/U
CP4	Collectors Year Pack 12	8.50	

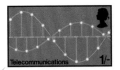

1969 (1 Oct.) Post Office Technology
Printer: De La Rue in Lithography. Perf. 13½ x 14

No.			U/M	F/U
C263	5d	National Giro	10	10
C263a		Missing phosphor	5.00	
C263b		One broad band	£15	
C264	9d	International Subscriber Dialling	10	15
C264a		One broad band	£15	
C264b		Perf. shift 4mm to right	£38	
C265	1s	Pulse Code Modulation	10	15
C265a		Missing phosphor	£300	
C265b		One broad band	£15	
C266	1s6d	Automatic Sorting	10	15
C266a		One broad band	£15	
		Set of 4	20	40
		Set of 4 Cylinder Blocks	1.50	
		First Day Cover		1.25
		Presentation Pack 13	1.60	

1969 (26 Nov.) Christmas 1969

No.			U/M	F/U
C267	4d	Herald Angel (one 8mm centre band)	10	10
C267a		One 4mm centre band	5	5
C267b		Missing Gold (Queen's head)	£4250	
C268	5d	The Three Shepherds	10	10
C268a		Missing phosphor	5.00	
C268b		Perforated right margin	£25	
C268c		Missing Olive brown		£3500
C268d		Missing Gold, Red and Olive brown	£7500	
C268e		Missing Green (centre Shepherd)	£175	
C268f		Missing Light Blue (sheep, etc.)	£65	
C268g		Missing Red (hat & leggings, etc.)	£650	
C268h		Missing Gold (Queen's head)	£425	
C268i		Missing embossing	£20	
C269	1s6d	The Three Kings	10	15
C269a		Missing phosphor	5.00	
C269b		Missing Deep slate	£275	
C269c		Missing Gold (Queen's head)	£85	
C269d		Missing Light Blue	£70	
C269e		Missing Yellow	£230	
C269f		Missing Violet		
C269g		Missing embossing	£10	
C269h		Missing embossing & phosphor	£10	
		Set of 3	13	20
		Set of 3 Cylinder Blocks	1.00	
		First Day Cover		60
		Presentation Pack 14	1.60	

1970 (11 Feb.) British Rural Architecture

No.			U/M	F/U
C270	5d	Fife Harding	10	10
C270a		Missing phosphor	5.00	
C270b		Missing Dark Grey	£7500	
C270c		Missing Grey (Queen's head)	£5000	
C270d		Missing Lemon	£75	
C270e		Missing Greenish-blue	£3500	
C270f		Shift 1mm to left of Greenish blue (door)	£25	
C271	9d	Cotswold Limestone	10	15
C271a		Missing phosphor	£10	
C271b		Shift 3mm to left of Grey (Queen's head)	£50	
C272	1s	Welsh Stucco	10	15
C272a		Missing phosphor	£15	
C272b		Missing Light blue	£100	
C273	1s6d	Ulster Thatch	10	15
C273a		Missing phosphor	5.00	
C273b		Missing Turquoise-blue (lawn)	£5000	
C273c		Shift 1mm to right of Lilac	£15	
		Set of 4	20	45
		Set of 4 Cylinder Blocks	1.50	
		First Day Cover		1.25
		Presentation Pack 15	2.50	

1970 (1 April) Anniversaries

No.			U/M	F/U
C274	5d	Declaration of Arbroath	10	10
C274a		Missing phosphor	£300	
C274b		Missing Emerald (tunics)	£175	
C274c		Missing Gold (Queen's head)	£650	
C274d		Shift 6mm to bottom of Gold (Queen's head)	£35	
C274e		Partial missing Gold (small Queen's head)		
C274f		Dry print of Emerald *	£20	

* Often mistaken for and sold as Missing Emerald

No.			U/M	F/U
C275	**9d**	**Florence Nightingale**	10	15
C275a		Missing phosphor	5.00	
C275b		Missing Ochre (bedding)	£175	
C275c		Missing embossing	£15	
C275d		Shift 2mm to left of Green (Grey dress)	£20	
C276	**1s**	**International Co-operative Alliance**	10	15
C276a		Missing phosphor	5.00	
C276b		Missing Brown	£135	
C276c		Missing Gold (Queen's head)	£55	
C276d		Missing Green (tablecloth)	£75	
C276e		Missing Green & embossing	£85	£45
C276f		Missing embossing	£15	
C276g		Missing embossing & phosphor	£20	
C277	**1s6d**	**Mayflower**	15	15
C277a		Missing phosphor	5.00	
C277b		Missing Emerald (under skirt at left)	£70	
C277d		Missing embossing	5.00	
C278	**1s9d**	**Royal Astronomical Society**	20	20
C278a		Missing phosphor	5.00	
C278b		Missing embossing	£75	
		Set of 5	25	48
		Set of 5 Cylinder Blocks	1.80	
		First Day Cover		1.50
		Presentation Pack 16	1.60	

A   B   C   D   E

✓**1970 (3 June) Literary Anniversaries**

C279/82	**5d**	**Block of 4 se-tenant**	40	60
C279/82a		Imperforate block of 4	£800	
C279/82b		Missing Silver	£11000	
C279/82c		Missing Yellow-bistre	£6000	
C279/82d		Missing Light Greenish-blue	£400	
C279/82e		Missing Light Greenish-blue & Silver	£12500	
C279		Multicoloured (A)	10	12
C280		Multicoloured (B)	10	12
C281		Multicoloured (C)	10	12
C282		Multicoloured (D)	10	12
C283	**1s6d**	**Multicoloured** (E)	15	25
C283a		Missing phosphor	5.00	
C283b		Missing Blue (1/6)	£7500	
C283c		Missing Gold (Queen's head)	£2500	£750
C283d		Missing Silver ('Grasmere')	£100	
C283e		Missing embossing	5.00	
C283f		Missing embossing & phosphor	£20	
		Set of 5	55	80
		Set of 3 Cylinder Blocks	3.00	
		First Day Cover		1.20
		Presentation Pack 17	1.80	

The 5d is usually collected in se-tenant blocks of four as printed.

✓**1970 (15 July) 9th Commonwealth Games**

Printer: De la Rue in lithography. Perf. 13½ x 14

			U/M	F/U
C284	**5d**	**Runners**	10	10
C284a		Missing phosphor	£200	
C284b		Missing Greenish-yellow	£7250	£2750
C285	**1s6d**	**Swimmers**	25	27
C285a		Missing phosphor	£60	
C286	**1s9d**	**Cyclists**	25	27
		Set of 3	50	50
		Set of 3 Cylinder Blocks	3.70	
		First Day Cover		1.25
		Presentation Pack 19	1.60	

1970 (14 Sept.) Collectors Year Pack 1970

CP5		Collectors Year Pack Pack 20	7.50	

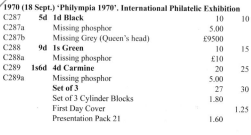

✓**1970 (18 Sept.) 'Philympia 1970'. International Philatelic Exhibition**

C287	**5d**	**1d Black**	10	10
C287a		Missing phosphor	5.00	
C287b		Missing Grey (Queen's head)	£9500	
C288	**9d**	**1s Green**	10	15
C288a		Missing phosphor	£10	
C289	**1s6d**	**4d Carmine**	20	25
C289a		Missing phosphor	5.00	
		Set of 3	27	30
		Set of 3 Cylinder Blocks	1.80	
		First Day Cover		1.25
		Presentation Pack 21	1.60	

1970 (25 Nov.) Christmas 1970

No.				U/M	F/U
C290	4d	**Multicoloured** (1 band)		10	10
C290a		Missing phosphor		£60	
C290b		Imperforate left margin		£650	
C290c		Missing embossing		£50	
C290d		Shift 15mm to left of embossing - also 2 phosphor bands instead of 1 band			
C291	5d	**Multicoloured**		10	10
C291a		Missing phosphor		5.00	
C291b		Imperforate pair		£250	
C291c		Missing Emerald		£55	
C291d		Missing Gold (Queen's head)			£3500
C291e		Missing embossing		£15	
C291f		Perf. shift 4mm to right			
C292	1s6d	**Multicoloured**		18	20
C292a		Missing phosphor		5.00	
C292b		Missing Salmon		£85	
C292c		Missing Ochre		£55	
C292d		Missing embossing		£35	
		Set of 3		19	25
		Set of 3 Cylinder Blocks		1.40	
		First Day Cover			70
		Presentation Pack 22		1.50	

1971 (28 July) Literary Anniversaries

C296	3p	**John Keats**	10	10
C296a		Missing phosphor	5.00	
C296b		Missing Gold (Queen's head)	£85	
C296c		Shift 4mm to right of embossing	5.00	
C297	5p	**Thomas Gray**	15	17
C297a		Missing phosphor	£30	
C297b		Missing Gold (Queen's head)	£325	
C298	7½p	**Sir Walter Scott**	20	25
C298a		Missing phosphor	£20	
C298b		Missing embossing	£35	
		Set of 3	40	50
		Set of 3 Cylinder Blocks	3.00	
		First Day Cover		1.40
		Presentation Pack 32	2.90	

Change to Decimal Currency

1971 (16 June) 'Ulster 71' Paintings

C293	3p	**A Mountain Road**	10	10
C293a		Missing phosphor	5.00	
C293b		Missing Venetian Red	£4000	
C294	7½p	**Deer's Meadow**	27	30
C294a		Missing phosphor	£20	
C294b		One broad band	5.00	
C294c		Missing Pale olive-grey	£85	
C294d		Offset on reverse of Grey-blue (panel, Queen's head and inscription)	£55	
C295	9p	**Slieve na Brock**	27	30
C295a		Missing phosphor	£20	
C295b		One broad band	£20	
C295c		Missing Orange	£1250	
C295d		Shift 4mm to bottom of Grey (sky)	£65	
		Set of 3	40	50
		Set of 3 Cylinder Blocks	3.00	
		First Day Cover		1.35
		Presentation Pack 26A	2.90	

1971 (25 Aug.) General Anniversaries

C299	3p	**British Legion**	10	10
C299a		Missing phosphor	5.00	
C299b		One broad band	6.00	
C299c		Missing Black	£11000	£4000
C299d		Missing Olive-brown (faces)	£250	
C299e		Missing Reddish-orange (Nurse's cape)	£275	
C299f		Missing Deep blue (sailor)	£550	
C299g		Shift 1mm to right of Deep Blue	£15	
C299h		Shift 1mm to bottom of Deep Blue	£20	
C300	7½p	**City of York**	30	35
C300a		Missing phosphor	£10	
C300b		One broad band	£15	
C300c		Missing Grey	£185	
C300d		Shift 8mm to right of Mauve	£75	
C300e		Shift 1.5mm to right of Black (shield)	£28	

No.			U/M	F/U	No.			U/M	F/U

No.			U/M	F/U
C301	**9p**	**Rugby Football**	30	35
C301a		Missing phosphor	£400	
C301b		One broad band	£10	
C301c		Missing Olive-brown	£110	
C301d		Missing Light blue	£4000	
C301e		Missing Myrtle green	£7500	£2000
C301f		Missing Lemon	£4000	
C301g		Shift 2mm to right of Yellow (shirts)	£35	
C301h		Shift 3mm to right of Brown (heads, ball and boots)	£75	
		Set of 3	50	60
		Set of 3 Cylinder Blocks	3.70	
		First Day Cover		1.40
		Presentation Pack 32A	2.90	

1971 (22 Sept.) British Architecture. Modern University Buildings

No.			U/M	F/U
C302	**3p**	**Aberystwyth**	10	10
C302a		Missing phosphor	5.00	
C302b		(Partial) Missing Black (windows)	£8500	
C302c		Shift of Lemon (appears missing)		£4000
C303	**5p**	**Southampton**	17	20
C303a		Missing phosphor	£60	
C303b		Larger value tablet, due to the use of Cylinder 1A, instead of 2A	£5000	
C304	**7½p**	**Leicester**	35	40
C304a		Missing phosphor	£10	
C305	**9p**	**Essex**	50	55
C305a		Missing phosphor	£15	
C305b		Pale Lilac Missing	£2500	
		Set of 4	80	95
		Set of 4 Cylinder Blocks	6.00	
		First Day Cover		1.35
		Presentation Pack 33	3.70	

1971 (29 Sept.) Collectors Pack

No.			U/M	F/U
CP6		Presentation Pack 34	£20	

1971 (13 Oct.) Christmas 1971

No.			U/M	F/U
C306	**2½p**	**Dream of the Wild** (1 band)	10	10
C306a		Imperf. pair	£400	
C307	**3p**	**Adoration of the Magi**	10	10
C307a		Missing phosphor	5.00	
C307b		Missing Light blue (sky)	£5500	
C307c		Missing Lemon	£135	
C307d		Missing Carmine-rose	£2750	£750
C307e		Missing Gold (Queen's head)	£575	
C307f		Missing Reddish violet	£3000	£750
C307g		Missing embossing	£10	
C307h		Missing embossing & phosphor	£65	
C307i		Shift 1mm to bottom of Blue (panel)	£15	
C307j		Missing Lemon and Carmine-rose		£5500
C308	**7½p**	**Ride of the Magi**	32	45
C308a		Missing phosphor	£10	
C308b		One broad band	£10	
C308c		Missing Lemon yellow		£4000
C308d		Missing Lilac	£575	
C308e		Missing Emerald	£295	
C308f		Missing Gold (Queen's head)	£135	
C308g		Missing embossing	£35	
C308h		Missing embossing & phosphor	£25	
C308i		Shift 3mm to bottom of Gold	£15	
C308j		Shift 2mm to right of Light blue	£18	
C308k		One broad band on back	£30	
C308l		One broad diagonal band	£30	
		Set of 3	35	50
		Set of 3 Cylinder Blocks	2.60	
		First Day Cover		1.25
		Presentation Pack 35	2.20	

1972 (16 Feb.) British Polar Explorers

No.			U/M	F/U
C309	**3p**	**Sir James Clark Ross**	10	10
C309a		Missing phosphor	5.00	
C309b		Missing Lemon	£6000	
C309c		Missing Slate black (hair)	£3000	
C309d		Missing Gold (Queen's head)	£90	
C309e		Missing Gold & embossing	£110	
C309f		Missing embossing	£30	
C309g		Missing embossing & phosphor	£25	
C309h		Shift 1mm to bottom of Blue (eyes)	£35	
C309i		Uncoated paper	£2000	
C310	**5p**	**Sir Martin Frobisher**	17	2
C310a		Missing phosphor	£10	
C310b		Missing Gold (Queen's head)	£90	
C310c		Missing Gold & phosphor	£110	
C310d		Missing embossing	£20	

			U/M	F/U
C311	7½p	Henry Hudson	35	40
C311a		Missing phosphor	£20	
C311b		Missing Gold (Queen's head)	£295	
C312	9p	Capt. Robert F. Scott	35	40
C312a		Missing phosphor	£275	
C312b		Perf. shift 2mm to left	£20	
		Set of 4	80	90
		Set of 4 Cylinder Blocks	6.00	
		First Day Cover		1.40
		Presentation Pack 39	2.50	

1972 (26 April) General Anniversaries

			U/M	F/U
C313	3p	Tutankhamun	10	10
C313a		Dry print of Black (inscription only)	£1500	
C313b		Imperforate between stamp and bottom margin	£650	
C314	7½p	Coastguard	25	27
C314a		Missing phosphor	£225	
C314b		Shift 2mm to bottom of Light blue (arms)	£35	
C315	9p	Ralph Vaughan Williams	25	27
C315a		Missing phosphor	£30	
C315b		Missing Brown (face, etc.)	£850	£450
C315c		Missing Gold (Queen's head)	£2500	£1500
C315d		Missing Deep slate	£6000	
		Set of 3	42	55
		Set of 3 Cylinder Blocks	3.15	
		First Day Cover		1.40
		Presentation Pack 40	2.20	

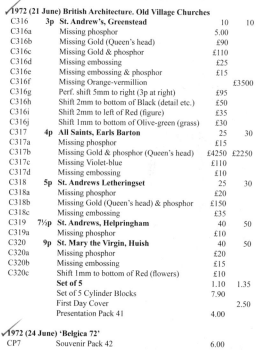

1972 (21 June) British Architecture. Old Village Churches

			U/M	F/U
C316	3p	St. Andrew's, Greenstead	10	10
C316a		Missing phosphor	5.00	
C316b		Missing Gold (Queen's head)	£90	
C316c		Missing Gold & phosphor	£110	
C316d		Missing embossing	£25	
C316e		Missing embossing & phosphor	£15	
C316f		Missing Orange-vermillion		£3500
C316g		Perf. shift 5mm to right (3p at right)	£95	
C316h		Shift 2mm to bottom of Black (detail etc.)	£50	
C316i		Shift 2mm to left of Red (figure)	£35	
C316j		Shift 1mm to bottom of Olive-green (grass)	£30	
C317	4p	All Saints, Earls Barton	25	30
C317a		Missing phosphor	£15	
C317b		Missing Gold & phosphor (Queen's head)	£4250	£2250
C317c		Missing Violet-blue	£110	
C317d		Missing embossing	£10	
C318	5p	St. Andrews Letheringset	25	30
C318a		Missing phosphor	£20	
C318b		Missing Gold (Queen's head) & phosphor	£150	
C318c		Missing embossing	£35	
C319	7½p	St. Andrews, Helpringham	40	50
C319a		Missing phosphor	£10	
C320	9p	St. Mary the Virgin, Huish	40	50
C320a		Missing phosphor	£20	
C320b		Missing embossing	£15	
C320c		Shift 1mm to bottom of Red (flowers)	£10	
		Set of 5	1.10	1.35
		Set of 5 Cylinder Blocks	7.90	
		First Day Cover		2.50
		Presentation Pack 41	4.00	

1972 (24 June) 'Belgica 72'

CP7		Souvenir Pack 42	6.00

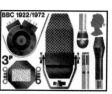

1972 (13 Sept.) British Broadcasting

			U/M	F/U
C321	3p	Microphone	10	10
C321a		Missing Yellow (terminals)	£4250	
C321b		Shift 2mm to bottom of Yellow (terminals) & Slate (Queen's head) *1	£20	

*1 This is often mistaken for the missing yellow.

No.   U/M   F/U   No.   U/M   F/U

No.			U/M	F/U
C322	5p	Loudspeaker	20	20
C322a		Missing phosphor	5.00	
C323	7½p	TV Camera	30	35
C323a		Missing phosphor	£10	
C323b		One broad band	£10	
C323c		Missing Slate (Queen's head) *2		£2750
C324	9p	Oscillator	30	40
C324a		Missing phosphor	£15	
C324b		One broad band	£25	
C324c		Missing Slate (Queen's head)	£2500	
C324d		Phosphor printed on gum side	£75	
		Set of 4	70	90
		Set of 4 Cylinder Blocks	5.20	
		First Day Cover		1.45
		Presentation Pack 43	2.20	
		BBC Staff Pack	£20	

*2 This stamp is known used on First Day Cover with Edinburgh FDI cancel.

1972 (18 Oct.) Christmas 1972

			U/M	F/U
C325	2½p	With Trumpet	10	10
C325a		Missing phosphor	£10	
C325b		Missing Gold	£300	
C325c		Missing Deep grey	£1500	
C325d		Missing embossing	£10	
C325e		Imperf. left margin	£650	
C325f		All colours missing	£50	
C326	3p	Playing Lute	7	10
C326a		Missing phosphor	£5	
C326b		Missing Bright green	£120	
C326c		Missing Red brown	£600	
C326d		Missing Blush violet	£120	
C326e		Missing Lavender	£8500	
C326f		Missing Gold	£550	
C326g		Missing embossing	5.00	
C326h		Missing embossing & phosphor	£10	
C326i		Shift 6mm to bottom left of Bright green	£15	
C326j		Imperforate between stamp and left margin	£650	
C327	7½p	Playing Harp	27	27
C327a		Missing phosphor	£10	
C327b		Missing Ochre	£90	
C327c		Missing embossing	£10	
C327d		Missing embossing & phosphor	£20	
C327e		Missing Blackish-violet	£6500	
		Set of 3	27	30
		Set of 3 Cylinder Blocks	1.90	
		First Day Cover		1.25
		Presentation Pack 44	2.20	

1972 (20 Nov.) Royal Silver Wedding
All over phosphor (3p) and without phosphor (20p)

Rembrandt Printing

			U/M	F/U
C328	3p	Silver, brown and steel blue	10	10
C328a		Missing phosphor	£30	

Jumelle Printing

			U/M	F/U
C328b	3p	Silver, brown and steel blue	13	13
		Gutter pair	20	20
		Gutter pair (Traffic Light)	£8	£8
C328c		Missing Silver ('Silver Wedding' & 3p)	£350	£200
C328d		Shift 4mm to right of Silver ('Silver Wedding' & 3p)	£30	
C329	20p	Silver, brown & purple	40	36
		Set of 2	50	37
		First Day Cover		1.25
		Presentation Pack 45	2.60	
		Japanese Pack	4.50	
		Souvenir Pack 46	2.20	

Printings The easiest way to identify the two printings is to examine the Duke's head. On the Jumelle printing it is distinct and a lighter shade of brownish-black, on the Rembrandt machine it appears slightly out of focus and is a deeper colour.

Gutter Pairs The Jumelle printing provided a plain gutter through the centre of the sheet - thus providing a new variety for collectors in the form of a gutter pair. This sheet form became standard for all Commemorative stamps from the Horse Chestnut Tree 10p issue of 27th February 1974, but both values of the Royal Wedding issued on 14th November 1973 were also printed with a gutter.

1972 (20 Nov.) Collectors Pack 1972

		U/M	F/U
CP8	Presentation Pack 42	13.50	

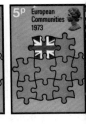

1973 (3 Jan.) Entry into The European Communities

			U/M	F/U
C330	3p	Multicoloured	10	1
C331/2	5p	Pair se-tenant	70	8
C331	5p	Multicoloured	35	4
C332	5p	Multicoloured	35	4
		Set of 3	65	8
		Set of 2 Cylinder Blocks	2.50	
		First Day Cover		1.2
		Presentation Pack 48	1.60	

No.   U/M   F/U   No.   U/M   F/U

1973 (28 Feb.) Tree Planting Year

No.			U/M	F/U
C333	**9p**	**Oak Tree** (2 band)	17	22
C333a		Missing phosphor	£85	
C333b		One broad band	£20	
C333c		Missing Black (9p and inscription)	£350	
C333d		Missing Grey (Queen's head)	£300	
		Cylinder Block	1.25	
		First Day Cover		1.25
		Presentation Pack 49	1.30	

From this issue, stamps were printed with 'all over' phosphor unless otherwise stated.

1973 (18 April) British Explorers

No.			U/M	F/U
C334/5	**3p**	**Pair se-tenant**	35	35
C334/5a		Pair missing phosphor	£40	
C334/5b		Missing Turquoise (oceans & inscription)	£750	
C334/5c		Missing Light Orange-brown	£700	
C334/5d		Missing Gold (Queen's head)	£110	
C334/5e		Missing Gold and phosphor	£110	
C334/5f		Missing embossing	£50	
C334/5g		Missing embossing and phosphor	£50	
C334	**3p**	**David Livingstone**	15	15
C334a		Missing phosphor	£18	
C335	**3p**	**H. M. Stanley**	15	15
C335a		Missing phosphor	£18	
C336	**5p**	**Sir Francis Drake**	30	26
C336a		Missing phosphor	£10	
C336b		Missing Grey-black	£625	
C336c		Missing Grey-black and phosphor	£625	
C336d		Missing Sepia (light hair)	£575	
C336e		Missing Gold (Queen's head)	£110	
C336f		Missing embossing	£10	
C336g		Missing embossing and phosphor	£30	

No.			U/M	F/U
C337	**7½p**	**Sir Walter Raleigh**	45	30
C337a		Missing phosphor	£200	
C337b		Missing Ultramarine (eyes)	£2750	
C337c		Missing Gold (Queen's head)	£2750	
C337d		Shift 2mm to left of Grey-black	£85	
C338	**9p**	**Charles Sturt**	45	30
C338a		Missing phosphor	£30	
C338b		Missing Greyish black	£1250	
C338c		Double print of Brown-grey (hair and facial features)	£800	£600
C338d		Missing Gold (Queen's head)	£110	£45
C338e		Brown-red missing	£500	
C338f		Flesh tones missing	£1000	
C338g		Missing embossing	£30	
		Set of 5	80	90
		Set of 4 Cylinder Blocks	9.50	
		First Day Cover		1.40
		Presentation Pack 50	1.80	

1973 (16 May) County Cricket Centenary

No.			U/M	F/U
C339	**3p**	**Ochre, black and gold**	10	10
C339a		Two phosphor bands **		
C339b		Missing Gold (Queen's head)	£2250	
C339c		Missing embossing	310	
C340	**7½p**	**Green, black and gold**	30	40
C340a		Missing phosphor	£80	
C340b		Two phosphor bands **		
C340c		Missing embossing	£20	
C341	**9p**	**Blue, black and gold**	40	45
C341a		Two phosphor bands **		
C341b		Missing embossing	£60	
		Set of 3	75	80
		Set of 3 with two phosphor bands	£480	
		Set of 3 Cylinder Blocks	5.60	
		First Day Cover		1.40
		Presentation Pack 51	2.50	
		Souvenir Booklet	3.50	
		PHQ1 Card (3p) *	£55	£110

* Used price is for July 1973; the 16 May postmarks were cancelled by favour.
** These were discovered in 2007. 21 mint sets are known.

Set of 4		70	1.20
Set of 2 Cylinder Blocks		4.50	
First Day Cover			1.30
Presentation Pack 53		1.60	
PHQ2 Card (3p Type B)		£75	£75

1973 (4 July) British Paintings

No.	Val	Description	U/M	F/U
C342	3p	Sir Joshua Reynolds	10	10
C342a		Missing Gold (Queen's head)	£55	
C342b		Missing Gold and embossing	£60	
C342c		Perf. shift 6mm to right (3p at right)	£45	
C343	5p	Sir Henry Raeburn	15	20
C343a		Missing phosphor	£15	
C343b		Missing Gold (Queen's head)	£65	
C343c		Missing Yellow (Reddish faces)	£475	
C343d		Missing embossing	£20	
C344	7½p	Sir Joshua Reynolds	30	40
C344a		Missing phosphor	5.00	
C344b		Missing Gold (Queen's head)	£110	
C344c		Missing Cinnamon	£5250	
C344d		Missing embossing	£15	
C345	9p	Sir Henry Raeburn	30	40
C345a		Missing phosphor	£75	
C345b		Missing Brownish Rose (paler face) *	£55	
C345c		Missing embossing and phosphor	£100	
		Set of 4	65	70
		Set of 4 Cylinder Blocks	5.00	
		First Day Cover		1.25
		Presentation Pack 52	1.60	

* Difficult to identify without some of the selvedge showing the colours.

1973 (12 Sept.) 19th Commonwealth Parliamentary Conference

No.	Val	Description	U/M	F/U
C350	8p	View from Whitehall	25	25
C351	10p	View from Millbank	25	25
		Set of 2	35	45
		Set of 2 Cylinder Blocks	2.70	
		First Day Cover		1.25
		Presentation Pack 54	1.60	
		Souvenir Booklet 55	3.50	
		PHQ3 Card (8p)	£20	£25

A   B

C   D

1973 (15 Aug.) 400th Anniversary of Birth of Inigo Jones

No.	Val	Description	U/M	F/U
C346/7	3p	Pair se-tenant	38	50
C346/7a		Pair missing phosphor	£500	
C346/7b		Deep mauve printed double	£5000	
C346/7c		Shift 5mm to bottom of Gold (Queen's head)	£55	
C346/7d		24mm Black shift - missing value	£500	
C346/7e		24mm Black shift - shifted value	£125	
C346/7f		Extra 9mm band at left	£15	
C346	3p	Court Masque Costumes (A)	15	10
C347	3p	St. Pauls Church, Covent Garden (B)	15	10
C348	5p	Prince's Lodging, Newmarket (C)	30	40
C349	5p	Court Masque Stage Scene (D)	30	40
C348/9	5p	Pair se-tenant	70	1.05
C348/9a		Pair missing phosphor	£500	
C348/9b		Extra 9mm band at left	£30	

1973 (14 Nov.) Royal Wedding

No.	Val	Description	U/M	F/U
C352	3½p	Violet and silver	10	10
C352a		Missing phosphor	£80	
C352b		Imperforate pair	£1850	
C352c		Miscut gutter pair	£20	
C353	20p	Light brown and silver	40	50
C353a		Missing Silver (Queen's head) *	£1750	
		Set of 2	42	50
		Set of 2 Cylinder Blocks	3.10	
		Gutter Pairs	1.45	1.45
		Gutter Pairs (Traffic light)	£45	£45
		First Day Cover		1.25
		Presentation Pack 56	1.50	
		PHQ4 Card (3½p)	4.80	7.00

A   B

* Caution:Many stamps show trace of silver colour

C   D

E   F

1973 (28 Nov.) Christmas 1973 (Good Ming Wenceslas)

PVAD gum

No.		Description	U/M	F/U
C354/8	3p	**Strip of 5 se-tenant**	1.30	1.60
C354/8a		Missing Rosy-mauve (Page boy) (B, C, D & E)	£3500	
C354/8b		Missing Grey-black	£2500	
C354/8c		Imperforate	£1000	
C354/8d		Missing Salmon pink	£10	
C354		Multicoloured (centre band) (A)	25	10
C355		Multicoloured (centre band) (B)	25	10
C356		Multicoloured (centre band) (C)	25	10
C357		Multicoloured (centre band) (D)	25	10
C358		Multicoloured (centre band) (E)	25	10
C359	3½p	**Multicoloured**	10	10
C359a		Missing phosphor	6.00	
C359b		Missing Rosy mauve (Page boy's robes)	£50	
C359c		Imperforate pair	£350	
C359d		Missing Black (inscription and 3½p)	£60	
C359e		Missing Salmon (faces, etc.)	£50	
C359f		Missing Blue (Page boy's leg and robes)	£150	
C359g		Missing Blue & Rosy mauve (Page boy)	£350	
C359h		Missing Bright Red (King's robe)	£50	
C359i		Missing Red-brown (basket and logs)		£4500
C359j		Missing Gold		£750
C359k		Missing Turquoise-green	£2250	£1000
C359l		Missing phosphor	£10	
		Set of 6	1.30	1.60
		Set of 2 Cylinder Blocks	3.30	
		First Day Cover		1.40
		Presentation Pack 57 (may contain stamps with any of the different gums)	1.80	

Gum Arabic

C354/8g	3p	**Strip of 5 se-tenant**	2.00	
C354/8ga		Strip of 5 perf. through side margin	2.50	
C354/8gb		Missing Salmon (floor tiles only) (C)	£10	
C354g		Multicoloured (centre band) (A)	20	
C355g		Multicoloured (centre band) (B)	20	
C356g		Multicoloured (centre band) (C)	20	
C357g		Multicoloured (centre band) (D)	20	
C358g		Multicoloured (centre band) (E)	20	

PVA gum

C359p	3½p	Multicoloured	20	
C359pa		Missing phosphor	5.50	
C359pb		Imperforate pair	£350	
C359pc		Missing Black (inscription and 3½p)	£60	
C359pd		Missing Blue & Rosy mauve (Page boy)	£350	
C359pe		Missing Rosy mauve (Page boy's robes)	£50	
C359pf		Missing Bright Red (King's robe)	£50	
C359pg		Missing phosphor	£10	

1973 (28 Nov.) Collectors Year Pack 1973

| CP10 | Collectors Year Pack 58 | 13.50 | |

PVADextrin gum was used on all the following issues unless otherwise stated.

1974 (27 Feb.) British Trees. Horse Chestnut

C360	10p	**Horse Chestnut**	18	20
		Cylinder Block	1.30	
		Gutter pair	75	75
		Gutter pair (Traffic Light)	£25	£25
		First Day Cover		1.25
		Presentation Pack 58	1.10	
		PHQ5 Card	£85	

1974 (24 April) 200th Anniversary of The Fire Service

C361	3½p	Fire Engine 1904	10	10
C361a		PVA Gum	5.00	
C361b		Imperforate pair	£500	
C362	5½p	Fire Engine 1863	20	20
C362a		Missing phosphor	5.00	
C363	8p	Fire Engine 1860	20	35
C364	10p	Fire Engine 1766	27	27
		Set of 4	65	70
		Set of 4 Cylinder Blocks	5.00	
		Gutter Pairs	2.30	2.30
		Gutter Pairs (Traffic Light)	£24	£24
		First Day Cover		2.00
		Merryweather First Day Cover		5.00
		Presentation Pack 60	1.80	
		PHQ6 Card (3½p)	£69	£60

1974 (12 June) UPU Centenary

No.			U/M	F/U
C365	3½p	P & O Packet	10	10
C365a		Perf. shift 4mm to top	£45	
C366	5½p	Farman BiPlane	20	20
C367	8p	Airmail-blue Van	25	27
C368	10p	Imperial Airways	25	30
		Set of 4	50	55
		Set of 4 Cylinder Blocks	3.75	
		Gutter Pairs	1.50	1.50
		Gutter Pairs (Traffic Light)	£20	£20
		First Day Cover		1.25
		Presentation Pack 65	1.80	

1974 (10 July) Great Britons

No.			U/M	F/U
C369	4½p	Robert the Bruce	10	10
C370	5½p	Owain Glyndwr	20	30
C371	8p	Henry V	35	45
C372	10p	The Black Prince	35	30
C372a		Imperf. pair	£625	
		Set of 4	65	80
		Set of 4 Cylinder Blocks	4.90	
		Gutter Pairs	2.35	2.35
		Gutter Pairs (Traffic Light)	£28	£28
		First Day Cover		1.75
		Presentation Pack 65	1.80	
		PHQ7 Cards	£12	

1974 (9 Oct.) Centenary of Birth of Sir Winston Churchill

No.			U/M	F/U
C373	4½p	Royal Yacht Squadron	10	10
C374	5½p	Prime Minister 1940	30	30
C374a		Missing phosphor	5.00	
C375	8p	Secretary for War	40	30
C375a		PVA Gum	75	
C376	10p	War Correspondent	40	25
		Set of 4	1.00	80
		Set of 4 Cylinder Blocks	3.80	
		Gutter Pairs	1.70	1.70
		Gutter Pairs (Traffic Light)	£15	£15
		First Day Cover		1.20
		Presentation Pack 66	2.00	
		Souvenir Booklet	1.75	
		PHQ8 Card (5½p)	2.95	7.00
		PHQ Card missing Silver (Queen's head)	£350	

1974 (27 Nov.) Christmas 1974

No.			U/M	F/U
C377	3½p	Adoration of the Magi (1 right band)	10	10
C377a		Missing phosphor	£10	
C377b		Multicoloured (1 centre band)	11	11
C377c		Missing Light Stone (background)	£7500	
C377d		Missing Light brown		£3500
C378	4½p	The Nativity	9	10
C379	8p	Virgin and Child	20	25
C380	10p	Virgin and Child	20	25
		Set of 4	45	52
		Set of 4 Cylinder Blocks	3.40	
		Gutter Pairs	1.60	1.60
		Gutter Pairs (Traffic Light)	£15	£15
		First Day Cover		1.25
		Presentation Pack 67	1.80	
	3½p	Gutter pair (1 centre band)	50	50
	3½p	Gutter pair (1 centre band) (Traffic Light)	6.00	6.00

Nov.) Collectors Year Pack 1974

No.		U/M	F/U
CP11	Collectors Year Pack 68	6.00	

1975 (22 Jan.) Charity Issue

No.			U/M	F/U
C381	4½p +			
	1½p	Invalid in Wheelchair	10	
		Cylinder Block	70	
		Gutter Pairs	20	2
		Gutter Pairs (Traffic Light)	50	5
		First Day Cover		5

No.   U/M   F/U   No.

U/M   F/U

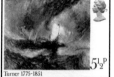

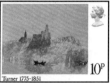

1975 (19 Feb.) 200th Birth Anniversary of J.W. Turner

No.			U/M	F/U
C382	4½p	'Peace - Burial at Sea'	10	10
C383	5½p	'Snowstorm'	12	12
C384	8p	'The Arsenal, Venice'	20	30
C385	10p	'St. Laurent'	25	25
		Set of 4	42	47
		Set of 4 Cylinder Blocks	3.10	
		Gutter Pairs	1.05	1.05
		Gutter Pairs (Traffic Light)	2.80	2.80
		First Day Cover		1.25
		Presentation Pack 69	1.80	
		PHQ9 Card (5½p)	£19	

1975 (11 June) Sailing. Black - Recess printed

No.			U/M	F/U
C391	7p	Dinghies	10	12
C391a		Miscut gutter pair	£28	
C391b		Shift 2mm to bottom of Gold		
		(Queen's head)	£15	
C392	8p	Racing Keel Boats	18	20
C392a		Missing Black (rigging)	£50	£125
C392b		Missing Gold (Queen's head, 'dry print')	£250	
C393	10p	Cruising Yachts	22	22
C394	12p	Multihulls	30	35
C394a		Dry print of Rose (white sails)	£10	
		Set of 4	55	70
		Set of 4 Cylinder Blocks	4.10	
		Gutter Pairs	1.25	1.25
		Gutter Pairs (Traffic Light)	7.50	7.50
		First Day Cover		1.20
		Presentation Pack 71	1.20	
		PHQ11 Card (8p)	3.00	

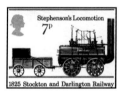

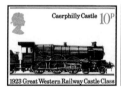

1975 (23 April) European Architectural Heritage Year

No.			U/M	F/U
C386/7	7p	Pair se-tenant	50	60
C386		Charlotte Square, Edinburgh	16	10
C387		The Rows, Chester	16	10
C388	8p	Greenwich	22	25
C389	10p	Windsor	23	25
C390	12p	National Theatre	30	25
		Set of 5	65	85
		Set of 4 Cylinder Blocks		
		Gutter Pairs	2.95	2.95
		Gutter Pairs (Traffic Light)	10.50	10.50
		First Day Cover		1.50
		Presentation Pack 70	1.80	
		PHQ10 Cards (7p's and 8p) (3)	4.95	

1975 (13 Aug.) 150th Anniversary of First Public Steam Railway

No.			U/M	F/U
C395	7p	Stephenson's Locomotion	15	10
C396	8p	Waverley Class	30	25
C397	10p	Caerphilly Castle	30	25
C398	12p	High-Speed Train	35	36
		Set of 4	70	70
		Set of 4 Cylinder Blocks	3.25	
		Gutter Pairs	1.65	1.65
		Gutter Pairs (Traffic Light)	4.50	4.50
		First Day Cover		1.80
		Presentation Pack 72	2.40	
		Souvenir Booklet	2.50	
		PHQ12 Cards	£30	

1975 (3 Sept.) 62nd Inter-Parliamentary Conference

No.			U/M	F/U
C399	12p	**Palace of Westminster**	20	20
		Cylinder Block	1.50	
		Gutter pair	35	35
		Gutter pair (Traffic Light)	1.20	1.20
		First Day Cover		1.25
		Presentation Pack 74	1.00	

1975 (22 Oct.) Bicentenary of the Birth of Jane Austen

			U/M	F/U
C400	8½p	**Emma and Mr Woodhouse**	15	10
C401	10p	**Catherine Moorland**	25	20
C402	11p	**Mr Darcy**	30	32
C403	13p	**Mary and Henry Crawford**	30	32
		Set of 4	70	65
		Set of 4 Cylinder Blocks	3.90	
		Gutter Pairs	1.25	1.25
		Gutter Pairs (Traffic Light)	2.95	2.95
		First Day Cover		1.25
		Presentation Pack 75	1.80	
		PHQ13 Cards	£10	

1975 (26 Nov.) Christmas 1975 (Angels)

			U/M	F/U
C404	6½p	**With Harp and Lute** (1 band)	11	10
C404a		PVA Gum	1.50	
C405	8½p	**With Mandolind** (phosphor ink)	13	8
C406	11p	**With Horn**	40	35
C407	13p	**With Trumpet**	40	35
		Set of 4	60	65
		Set of 4 Cylinder Blocks	4.50	
		Gutter Pairs	1.20	1.20
		Gutter Pairs (Traffic Light)	2.95	2.95
		First Day Cover		1.25
		Presentation Pack 76	2.20	
	6½p	Gutter pair (PVA)	1.00	
	6½p	Gutter pair (Traffic Light) (PVA Gum)	2.50	

1975 (26 Nov.) Collectors Year Pack 1975

			U/M	F/U
CP12		Collectors Year Pack 77	4.00	

1976 (10 March) Centenary of Alexander Graham Bell's First Telephone Transmission

			U/M	F/U
C408	8½p	**Housewife**	15	10
C408a		Missing Magenta (flowers, vase & picture)	£2000	
C408b		Shift 3mm to bottom of Magenta	£25	
C408c		Imperforate between stamps & bottom margin	£500	
C409	10p	**Policeman**	27	20
C410	11p	**Nurse**	35	36
C410a		Imperforate between stamps & bottom margin	£500	
C411	13p	**Industrialist**	40	35
		Set of 4	65	70
		Set of 4 Cylinder Blocks	4.90	
		Gutter Pairs	1.30	1.30
		Gutter Pairs (Traffic Light)	2.95	2.95
		First Day Cover		1.25
		Presentation Pack 78	2.80	

1976 (28 April) Social Reformers

			U/M	F/U
C412	8½p	Thomas Hepburn	15	10
C412a		Shift 2mm to bottom of Deep Grey		
		(moving hands)	£35	
C412b		Perf. shift 6mm to top (8½p at top)	£40	
C412c		Perf. shift 3mm to top (8½p bisected)	£25	
C413	10p	Robert Owen	27	20
C413a		Perf. shift 12mm to bottom		
		(10p above Queen's head)	£50	
C414	11p	Lord Shaftesbury	35	36
C415	13p	Eliazabeth Fry	40	27
		Set of 4	65	70
		Set of 4 Cylinder Blocks	4.90	
		Gutter Pairs	1.30	1.30
		Gutter Pairs (Traffic Light)	2.95	2.95
		First Day Cover		1.25
		Presentation Pack 79	1.90	
		PHQ14 Card	3.00	

1976 (30 June) Centenary of Royal National Rose Society

			U/M	F/U
C417	8½p	'Elizabeth of Glamis'	15	12
C418	10p	'Grandpa Dickson'	27	20
C419	11p	'Rosa Mundi'	30	35
C420	13p	'Sweet Briar'	40	30
C420a	13p	Missing Black (value only)	£25000	£20000
		Set of 4	65	70
		Set of 4 Cylinder Blocks	4.90	
		Gutter Pairs	1.35	1.35
		Gutter Pairs (Traffic Light)	4.00	4.00
		First Day Cover		1.25
		Presentation Pack 81	2.00	
		PHQ16 Cards	£15	

1976 (2 June) Bicentenary of American Independence

			U/M	F/U
C416	11p	Franklin	18	17
		Cylinder Block	1.30	
		Gutter pair	30	30
		Gutter pair (Traffic Light)	80	80
		First Day Cover		1.25
		Presentation Pack 80	1.00	
		PHQ15 Card	2.75	

1976 (4 Aug.) British Cultural Traditions

			U/M	F/U
C421	8½p	Archdruid	15	10
C422	10p	Morris Dancing	21	20
C422a		Missing phosphor	£250	
C423	11p	Scots Piper	40	45
C424	13p	Welsh Harpist	40	27
		Set of 4	70	70
		Set of 4 Cylinder Blocks	5.20	
		Gutter Pairs	1.35	1.35
		Gutter Pairs (Traffic Light)	3.50	3.50
		First Day Cover		1.25
		Presentation Pack 82	2.20	
		PHQ17 Cards	8.00	£11

1976 (29 Sept.) 500th Anniversary of the First Printing in Britain

			U/M	F/U
C425	8½p	Canterbury Tales	15	22
C426	10p	Trelyse of Love	21	21
C427	11p	Chesse	40	40
C427a		Imperf. at left (marginal)	£1500	
C427b		Shift 4mm to right of Gold (Queen's head)	£35	
C428	13p	Early Printing Press	40	30
		Set of 4	90	85
		Set of 4 Cylinder Blocks	6.70	
		Gutter Pairs	1.35	1.35
		Gutter Pairs (Traffic Light)	2.95	2.95
		First Day Cover		1.25
		Presentation Pack 83	2.00	
		PHQ18 Cards	6.00	

1976 (24 Nov.) Christmas 1976

			U/M	F/U
C429	6½p	Virgin and Child (1 band)	15	10
C429a		Imperforate pair	£350	
C430	8½p	Angel with Crown	15	10
C430a		Imperforate pair	£400	
C431	11p	Angel and Sheppherds	30	37
C431a		Uncoated paper	£70	£45
C432	13p	The Three Kings	40	30
		Set of 4	70	65
		Set of 4 Cylinder Blocks	5.30	
		Gutter Pairs	1.15	1.15
		Gutter Pairs (Traffic Light)	2.60	2.60
		First Day Cover		1.25
		Presentation Pack 87	2.20	
		PHQ19 Cards	2.00	

1976 (24 Nov.) Collectors Year Pack

		U/M	F/U
CP13	Collectors Year Pack 88	6.00	

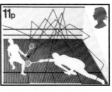

1977 (12 Jan.) Racket Sports

			U/M	F/U
C433	8½p	Lawn Tennis	15	12
C433a		Imperforate pair	£750	
C434	10p	Table Tennis	21	21
C435	11p	Squash	30	32
C435a		Imperforate pair	£2000	
C436	13p	Badminton	30	27
		Set of 4	65	65
		Set of 4 Cylinder Blocks	4.90	
		Gutter Pairs	1.25	1.25
		Gutter Pairs (Traffic Light)	2.95	2.95
		First Day Cover		1.25
		Presentation Pack 89	2.00	
		PHQ20 Cards	3.50	

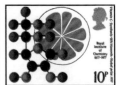
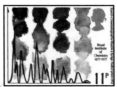
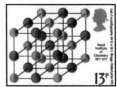

1977 (2 March) Chemistry

			U/M	F/U
C437	8½p	Steroids	15	10
C437a		Imperforate pair	£1200	
C438	10p	Vitamin C	21	21
C439	11p	Starch	30	33
C440	13p	Salt	30	27
		Set of 4	65	65
		Set of 4 Cylinder Blocks	4.90	
		Gutter Pairs	1.35	1.35
		Gutter Pairs (Traffic Light)	2.50	2.50
		First Day Cover		1.25
		Presentation Pack 92	2.00	
		PHQ21 Cards	3.50	

A

B   C

D   E

1977 (11 May) Silver Jubilee

No.			U/M	F/U
C441	8½p	**Multicoloured**	15	10
C441a		Imperforate pair	£750	
C442	**9p**	**Multicoloured**	15	10
C443	**10p**	**Multicoloured**	20	20
C443a		Imperforate pair	£1250	
C444	**11p**	**Multicoloured**	27	25
C444a		Imperforate pair	£1250	
C445	**13p**	**Multicoloured**	27	27
C445a		Imperforate pair	£950	
		Set of 5	72	55
		Set of 5 Cylinder Blocks	5.50	
		Gutter Pairs	1.85	1.85
		Gutter Pairs (Traffic Light)	2.15	2.15
		First Day Cover		1.30
		First Day Cover (9p only)		40
		Presentation Pack 94 (excludes 9p)	1.10	
		Souvenir Booklet (excludes 9p)	2.50	
		PHQ22 Cards	6.00	

1977 (5 Oct.) British Wildlife

No.			U/M	F/U
C447/51	**9p**	**Strip of 5 se-tenant**	85	1.10
C447		Hedgehog (A)	20	20
C448		Hare (B)	20	20
C449		Red Squirrel (C)	20	20
C450		Otter (D)	20	20
C451		Badger (E)	20	20
		Cylinder Block	2.10	
		Gutter strip of 10	2.00	2.00
		Gutter strip of 10 (Traffic Light)	3.00	3.00
		First Day Cover		1.40
		Presentation Pack 96	1.00	
		PHQ25 Cards	1.50	
C447/51	**9p**	Imperforate vertical pair (any)	£600	
C447/51	**9p**	Imperforate horizontal pair (any)	£1500	

1977 (8 June) Commonwealth Heads of Government

No.			U/M	F/U
C446	**13p**	**Gathering of Nations**	20	20
		Cylinder Block	1.40	
		Gutter pair	35	35
		Gutter pair (Traffic Light)	50	50
		First Day Cover		50
		Presentation Pack 95	60	
		PHQ23 Card	2.50	

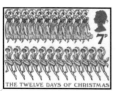

1977 (23 Nov.) Christmas 1977 (Twelve Days of Christmas)

No.		Description	U/M	F/U
C452/56	7p	Strip of 5 se-tenant	60	80
C452/56a		Imperforate se-tenant strip of 5	£1500	
C452		Three French Hens... (centre band) (A)	15	15
C453		Six Geese a Laying... (centre band) (B)	15	15
C454		Eight Maids a milking... (centre band) (C)	15	15
C455		Ten Pipers Piping,,, (centre band) (D)	15	15
C456		Twelve Lords a Leaping... (centre band) (E)	15	15
C457	9p	A Partridge in a Pear Tree	15	10
C457a		Imperforate pair	£1000	
		Set of 6	65	80
		Set of 2 Cylinder Blocks	2.60	
		Gutter Pairs	1.35	1.35
		Gutter Pairs (Traffic Light)	2.50	2.50
		First Day Cover		1.25
		Presentation Pack 97	1.70	
		PHQ26 Cards	1.75	

1977 (23 Nov.) Collectors Year Pack 1977

No.	Description	U/M	F/U
CP14	Collectors Year Pack 98	4.00	

1978 (25 Jan.) Energy Resources

No.		Description	U/M	F/U
C458	9p	Oil	15	10
C459	10½p	Coal	18	18
C460	11p	Natural Gas	19	25
C461	13p	Electricity	20	20
		Set of 4	60	65
		Set of 4 Cylinder Blocks	4.50	
		Gutter Pairs	1.25	1.25
		Gutter Pairs (Traffic Light)	1.80	1.80
		First Day Cover		1.25
		Presentation Pack 99	1.70	
		PHQ27 Cards	1.50	

1978 (1 March) British Architecture. Historic Buildings

No.		Description	U/M	F/U
C462	9p	Tower of London	15	10
C462a		Imperf. bottom margin	£200	
C463	10½p	Holyroodhouse	18	18
C464	11p	Caernarvon Castle	20	24
C465	13p	Hampton Court Palace	20	20
		Set of 4	62	70
		Set of 4 Cylinder Blocks	4.60	
		Gutter Pairs	1.25	1.25
		Gutter Pairs (Traffic Light)	1.80	1.80
		First Day Cover		1.25
		Presentation Pack 100	1.70	
		PHQ28 Cards	1.50	

No.		Description	U/M	F/U
MS1	53½p	Miniature Sheet (in original PO folder)	90	1.10
MS1a		Missing phosphor	£100	
MS1b		Missing Red (flag on 9p)	£3500	
MS1c		Missing Pale Orange (10p and 13p)	£3500	
MS1d		Missing Yellow-olive (Queen's head)	£4500	
MS1e		Missing Blue	£11000	
MS1f		Imperforate	£4500	
		First Day Cover		1.10

1978 (31 May) 25th Anniversary of the Coronation

No.		Description	U/M	F/U
C466	9p	State Coach	15	10
C467	10½p	St. Edwards Crown	18	18
C468	11p	The Sovereign's Orb	20	25
C469	13p	Imperial State Crown	20	20
C469a		Imperforate pair	£75	

			U/M	F/U
	Set of 4		62	65
	Set of 4 Cylinder Blocks		4.70	
	Gutter Pairs		1.15	1.15
	Gutter Pairs (Traffic Light)		1.80	1.80
	First Day Cover			1.25
	Presentation Pack 101		1.10	
	Souvenir Booklet		2.50	
	PHQ29 Cards		1.75	

1978 (5 July) Horses. Centenary of the Shire Horse Society.

			U/M	F/U
C470	9p	**Shire Horse**	15	10
C471	10½p	**Shetland Pony**	18	18
C471a		Imperforate between stamp & bottom margin	£400	
C472	11p	**Welsh Pony**	20	25
C473	13p	**Thoroughbred**	20	20
		Set of 4	62	65
		Set of 4 Cylinder Blocks	4.70	
		Gutter Pairs	1.20	1.20
		Gutter Pairs (Traffic Light)	1.80	1.80
		First Day Cover		1.25
		Presentation Pack 102	1.20	
		PHQ30 Cards	1.50	

1978 (2 Aug.) Cycling. Centenary of the Cyclists' Touring Club.

			U/M	F/U
C474	9p	**Penny-Farthing**	15	10
C474a		Imperforate pair	£350	
C475	10½p	**Touring Bicycles**	18	18
C475a		Imperforate between stamp & bottom margin	£700	
C476	11p	**Modern Bicycles**	20	25
C477	13p	**Road-racers**	20	20
C477a		Imperforate pair	£1000	

			U/M	F/U
	Set of 4		62	70
	Set of 4 Cylinder Blocks		4.70	
	Gutter Pairs		1.15	1.15
	Gutter Pairs (Traffic Light)		1.80	1.80
	First Day Cover			1.25
	Presentation Pack 103		1.00	
	PHQ31 Cards		1.20	

1978 (22 Nov.) Christmas 1978

			U/M	F/U
C478	7p	**Singing Carols**	13	10
C478a		Imperforate between stamp & bottom margin	£850	
C478b		Imperforate pair	£500	
C479	9p	**The Waits**	15	10
C479a		Imperforate pair	£850	
C480	11p	**18th Century Singers**	20	23
C480a		Imperforate pair	£950	
C481	13p	**'The Boars Head Carol'**	22	23
		Set of 4	55	65
		Set of 4 Cylinder Blocks	4.20	
		Gutter Pairs	1.10	1.10
		Gutter Pairs (Traffic Light)	1.80	1.80
		First Day Cover		1.25
		Presentation Pack 104	1.00	
		PHQ32 Cards	1.75	

1978 (21 Nov.) Collectors Year Pack 1976

			U/M	F/U
CP15		Collectors Year Pack 105	4.00	

1979 (7 Feb.) British Dogs

			U/M	F/U
C482	9p	**Old English Sheepdog**	15	10
C483	10½p	**Welsh Springer**	20	22
C483a		Shift 1½mm to top of Deep Grey (Queen's head) and Black (10½p)	£30	
C484	11p	**West Highland**	20	22
C484a		Imperforate pair	£1350	
C484a		Imperforate between stamp & bottom margin	£750	
C485	13p	**Irish Setter**	22	22

	U/M	F/U
Set of 4	60	65
Set of 4 Cylinder Blocks	4.50	
Gutter Pairs	1.15	1.15
Gutter Pairs (Traffic Light)	1.80	1.80
First Day Cover		1.25
Presentation Pack 106	1.30	
PHQ33 Cards	1.50	

1979 (21 March) British Wild Flowers

No.			U/M	F/U
C486	**9p**	**Primrose**	15	10
C486a		Imperforate pair	£400	
C487	**10½p**	**Daffodil**	20	20
C487a		Imperforate vertical pair	£1500	
C487b		Imperforate between stamp & left margin	£1000	
C488	**11p**	**Bluebell**	20	22
C488a		Imperforate pair	£1300	
C488b		Shift 2mm to left of Silver (Queen's head)	£35	
C489	**13p**	**Snowdrop**	22	21
C489a		Imperforate pair	£850	
		Set of 4	60	65
		Set of 4 Cylinder Blocks	4.50	
		Gutter Pairs	1.15	1.15
		Gutter Pairs (Traffic Light)	1.70	1.70
		First Day Cover		1.25
		Presentation Pack 107	1.00	
		PHQ34 Cards	1.20	

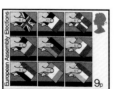 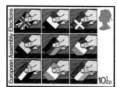

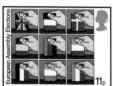 

1979 (9 May) Direct Elections to the European Assembly

No.			U/M	F/U
C490	**9p**	**Multicoloured**	15	10
C491	**10½p**	**Multicoloured**	20	20
C492	**11p**	**Multicoloured**	20	22
C493	**13p**	**Multicoloured**	22	21
		Set of 4	60	65
		Set of 4 Cylinder Blocks	4.50	
		Gutter Pairs	1.15	1.15
		Gutter Pairs (Traffic Light)	1.70	1.70
		First Day Cover		1.25
		Presentation Pack 108	1.00	
		PHQ35 Cards	1.20	

1979 (6 June) Horse Racing

No.			U/M	F/U
C494	**9p**	**'Mahmoud'**	15	10
C494a		Imperforate between stamp & left margin	£850	
C495	**10½p**	**'Liverpool National'**	20	20
C496	**11p**	**'Spring Meeting'**	20	22
C497	**13p**	**'Dorsett Ferry'**	22	20
C497a		Imperforate between stamp & bottom margin	£100	
		Set of 4	60	65
		Set of 4 Cylinder Blocks	4.50	
		Gutter Pairs	1.15	1.15
		Gutter Pairs (Traffic Light)	1.70	1.70
		First Day Cover		1.25
		Presentation Pack 109		
		(Pack includes a Cartoon insert)	1.00	
		PHQ36 Cards	1.20	

1979 (11 July) United Nations 'Year of the Child'

No.				U/M	F/U
C498	9p	Peter Rabbit		15	10
C499	10½p	Wind in the Willows		25	18
C500	11p	Winnie-the-Pooh		30	18
C501	13p	Alice in Wonderland		40	25
		Set of 4		90	70
		Set of 4 Cylinder Blocks		6.75	
		Gutter Pairs		1.50	1.50
		Gutter Pairs (Traffic Light)		2.00	2.00
		First Day Cover			1.25
		Presentation Pack 110		1.60	
		PHQ37 Cards		1.45	

1979 (22 Aug.) Sir Rowland Hill Centenary

No.			U/M	F/U
C502	10p	Sir Rowland Hill	15	10
C502a		Imperforate pair	£2250	
C503	11½p	General Post	19	20
C504	13p	London Post	20	20
C505	15p	Uniform Postage	22	20
		Set of 4	62	65
		Set of 4 Cylinder Blocks	4.70	
		Gutter Pairs	1.28	1.28
		Gutter Pairs (Traffic Light)	1.70	1.70
		First Day Cover		1.25
		Presentation Pack 111	1.00	
		PHQ38 Cards	1.20	

No.			U/M	F/U
MS2	59½p	Miniature sheet (24.10.79)	70	70
MS2a		Missing phosphor	£25	
MS2b		Imperforate	£2000	
MS2c		Missing Black and Yellow	£12500	
MS2d		Missing Yellow (10p windows, etc.)	£250	£225
MS2e		Missing Yellow and phosphor	£250	
MS2f		Missing Brown-ochre (15p sky, etc.)	£1750	
MS2g		Missing Brown-ochre, Green and Gold	£5000	
MS2h		Missing Rosine (11½p jacket, etc.)	£1000	
MS2i		Missing Rosine and phosphor	£750	
MS2j		Missing Blue (13p, jacket, sky, etc.)	£5500	
MS2k		Missing Green (10p sky & coat, 15p etc.)	£2500	
MS2l		Missing Brown (15p dress, 11½p, 13p etc.)	£750	
MS2m		Missing Gold (Queen's head)	£250	£225
MS2n		Missing Gold and phosphor	£250	
MS2o		Shift 6mm to top of Green	£175	
MS2p		Shift 2mm to right of Gold	£5	
MS2q		Offset on reverse of Gold (Queen's head)	£350	
		First Day Cover		75

There are numerous perforation shifts and colour shifts known of all the colours. This listing therefore is only representative.

1979 (26 Sept.) 150th Anniversary of Metropolitan Police

No.			U/M	F/U
C506	10p	Multicoloured	15	10
C507	11½p	Multicoloured	17	18
C508	13p	Multicoloured	20	20
C509	15p	Multicoloured	23	23
		Set of 4	65	67
		Set of 4 Cylinder Blocks	4.50	
		Gutter Pairs	1.35	1.35
		Gutter Pairs (Traffic Light)	1.70	1.70
		First Day Cover		1.25
		Presentation Pack 112	1.00	
		PHQ39 Cards	1.20	

1979 (21 Nov.) Christmas 1979

No.			U/M	F/U
C510	8p	The Three Kings	13	10
C510a		Imperforate pair	£400	
C510b		Perf. shift 6mm to top	£50	
C510c		Shift 6mm to bottom of Ochre (horse)	£20	
C510d		Shift 2.5mm to bottom of Ochre, 1mm to bottom of Blue and Violet.	£25	
C511	10p	Angel and Shepherds	15	10
C511a		Imperforate pair	£850	
C511b		Imperforate between, vertical pair	£450	
C511c		Imperforate between stamp & bottom margin	£800	
C512	11½p	The Nativity	17	18
C513	13p	Mary and Joseph	20	20
C513a		Perf. shift 3mm to top	£14	
C514	15p	The Annunciation	25	20

		U/M	F/U
Set of 5		80	75
Set of 5 Cylinder Blocks		5.20	
Gutter Pairs		1.55	1.55
Gutter Pairs (Traffic Light)		1.80	1.80
First Day Cover			1.25
Presentation Pack 113		1.00	
PHQ40 Cards		1.20	

✓ **1979 (21 Nov.) Collectors Year Pack 1979**

CP16	Collectors Year Pack 114	5.00

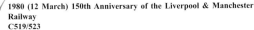

✓ **1980 (12 March) 150th Anniversary of the Liverpool & Manchester Railway**
C519/523

		U/M	F/U
12p	**Strip of 5 se-tenant**	85	90
C519/523a	Imperforate strip of 5	£1500	
C519/523b	Missing Lemon yellow	£15000	
C519	Stephenson's Rocket (A)	20	15
C520	First and Second Class Carriages (B)	20	15
C521	Third class Carriage (C)	20	15
C522	Horsebox and Carriage (D)	20	15
C523	Goods Truck and Mailcoach (E)	20	15
	Cylinder Block	2.80	
	Strip of 5 Gutter Pairs	2.20	2.20
	First Day Cover		1.25
	Presentation Pack 116	1.00	
	PHQ42 Cards	1.20	

✓ **1980 (16 Jan.) British Birds.** Perf 14 x 15

C515	**10p**	**Kingfisher**	15	10
C516	**11½p**	**Dipper**	16	17
C517	**13p**	**Moorhen**	20	20
C518	**15p**	**Wagtail**	25	25
		Set of 4	72	70
		Set of 4 Cylinder Blocks	5.50	
		Set of 4 Gutter Pairs	1.80	2.00
		First Day Cover		1.25
		Presentation Pack 115	1.00	
		PHQ41 Cards	1.20	

Type I
Shading lines above
and below Queen's head.
are broken

Type II
Shading lines above
and below Queen's head
are unbroken.

✓ **1980 (9 April) London 1980 International Stamp Exhibition.** Perf.14½ x 14

C524	**50p**	London 1980 (Type I)	75	6
		First Day Cover		1.0
C524a	50p	London 1980 (Type II)	75	8
		First Day Cover		1.2
		Presentation Pack 117	1.00	
		PHQ43 Card	40	

<u>Note</u>: Greenish shades of this stamp are due to problems met with the printi
and drying time, and can easily be faked.

1980 (7 May) London 1980 International Stamp Exhibition

No.			U/M	F/U
MS3	75p	Miniature sheet	80	1.00
MS3a		Imperforate sheet	£1250	£750
		First Day Cover		50

1980 (7 May) London Landmarks. Perf. 14 x 15

No.			U/M	F/U
C525	10½p	Buckingham Palace	20	20
C526	12p	Albert Memorial	18	10
C526a		Imperforate vertical pair	£950	
C527	13½p	Royal Opers House	20	20
C527a		Imperforate pair	£950	
C528	15p	Hampton Court	22	22
C528a		Perf. shift 3mm to right	£75	
C529	17½p	Kensington Palace	27	35
C529a		Missing Silver (Queen's head)	£450	
		Set of 5	95	95
		Set of 5 Cylinder Blocks	7.30	
		Set of 5 Gutter Pairs	2.40	2.40
		First Day Cover		1.25
		Presentation Pack 118	1.20	
		PHQ43 Cards	1.20	

1980 (9 July) Europa. Authoresses

No.			U/M	F/U
530	12p	Charlotte Bronte	18	10
530a		Missing 'P' in value (row 4, stamp 6)	£25	£10
531	13½p	George Eliot	20	30
531a		Missing Pale Blue	£3000	
532	15p	Emily Bronte	22	24
533	17½p	Mrs Gaskell	27	25
533a		Imperforate pair and missing Blue	£750	

		U/M	F/U
	Set of 4	82	80
	Set of 4 Cylinder Blocks	6.25	
	Set of 4 Gutter Pairs	2.00	2.00
	First Day Cover		1.25
	Presentation Pack 119	1.70	
	PHQ44 Cards	1.50	

1980 (4 Aug.) 80th Birthday of the Queen Mother

No.			U/M	F/U
C534	12p	The Queen Mother	30	20
C534a		Imperforate pair	£1250	
C534b		Perf. shift 3mm to the right	£65	
		Cylinder Block	1.65	
		Gutter pair	75	80
		First Day Cover		1.25
		PHQ45 Card	50	

1980 (10 Sept.) Music. British Conductors. Perf. 14 x 15

No.			U/M	F/U
C535	12p	Sir Henry Wood (PCP1)	18	10
C535a		Sir Henry Wood (PCP2)	35	
C536	13½p	Sir Thomas Beecham (PCP1)	20	22
C536a		Sir Thomas Beecham (PCP2)	30	
C537	15p	Sir Malcolm Sargent (PCP1)	20	22
C537a		Sir Malcolm Sargent (PCP2)	50	
C538	17½p	Sir John Barbirolli (PCP1)	27	25
C538a		Sir John Barbirolli (PCP2)	70	
C538b		Fluorescent Brightener Omitted	1.50	
		Set of 4	85	80
		Set of 4 Cylinder Blocks	6.50	
		Set of 4 Gutter Pairs	2.20	2.20
		First Day Cover		1.25
		FDC wuth 17½p FBO		8.50
		Presentation Pack 120	1.00	
		PHQ46 Cards	1.25	

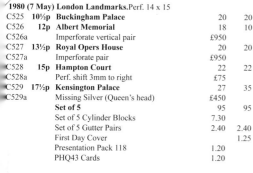

1980 (19 Nov.) Christmas 1980

No.			U/M	F/U
C543	10p	Tree	16	10
C543a		Imperforate between stamp & top margin	£650	
C544	12p	Candles	18	10
C544a		Imperforate between stamp & bottom margin	£450	
C545	13½p	Apples	20	22
C546	15p	Crown, Belal	22	22
C547	17½p	Holly	27	27
		Set of 5	95	90
		Set of 5 Cylinder Blocks	7.30	
		Set of 5 Gutter Pairs	2.40	2.60
		First Day Cover		1.25
		Presentation Pack 122	1.00	
		PHQ48 Cards	1.25	

1980 (19 Nov.) Collectors Year Pack 1980

CP17		Collectors Year Pack 123	7.00	

1980 (10 Oct.) Centenary of Sports Organisations. Perf. 14 x 14½

Printers: House of Questa in Lithography

No.			U/M	F/U
C539	12p	Running	18	10
C539a		Missing Gold (Queen's head)	£11500	
C540	13½p	Rugby	25	30
C541	15p	Boxing	25	30
C541a		Missing Gold (Queen's head)	£8000	
C541b		Imperforate between stamp & bottom margin	£150	
C541c		Shift 2½mm to right of Gold (Queen's head)	£40	
C542	17½p	Cricket	40	30
		Set of 4	80	90
		Set of 4 Cylinder Blocks	6.00	
		Set of 4 Gutter Pairs	2.00	2.00
		First Day Cover		1.25
		Presentation Pack 121	1.00	
		PHQ47 Cards	1.25	

1981 (6 Feb.) Europa. Folklore

No.			U/M	F/U
C548	14p	St. Valentine's Day	22	12
C548a		Missing Gold (Queen's head)	£7500	
C549	18p	Morris Dancers	27	28
C550	22p	Lamastide	35	32
C550a		Perf. shift 5mm to top and major shifts of several colours	£125	
C551	25p	Medieval Mummers	35	3
		Set of 4	1.15	1.1
		Set of 4 Cylinder Blocks	8.75	
		Set of 4 Gutter Pairs	2.90	2.9
		First Day Cover		1.2
		Presentation Pack 124	2.00	
		PHQ49 Cards	1.50	

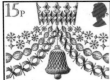

1981 (25 March) International Year of Disabled Persons

			U/M	F/U
C552	14p	Blind	22	12
C552a		Imperforate pair ('printers waste')	£500	
C553	18p	Deaf	27	28
C554	22p	Wheelchair	35	32
C555	25p	Painting	35	35
		Set of 4	1.15	1.15
		Set of 4 Cylinder Blocks	9.50	
		Set of 4 Gutter Pairs	2.90	2.90
		First Day Cover		1.25
		Presentation Pack 125	1.20	
		PHQ50 Cards	1.25	

1981 (13 May) Butterflies

			U/M	F/U
C556	14p	Tortoiseshell	22	12
C556a		Imperforate pair	£2000	
C557	18p	Large Blue	27	35
C557a		Shift 4mm to right of Gold (Queen's head)	£20	
C558	22p	Peacock	35	35
C559	25p	Chequered Skipper	35	40
		Set of 4	1.10	1.10
		Set of 4 Cylinder Blocks	8.40	
		Set of 4 Gutter Pairs	2.80	2.80
		First Day Cover		1.25
		Presentation Pack 126	1.20	
		PHQ51 Cards	1.25	

1981 (24 June) National Trust

			U/M	F/U
C560	14p	Glenfinnon	22	12
C561	18p	Derwentwater	27	35
C562	20p	Stackpole	30	30
C562a		Perf. shift 8mm to bottom and shift 13mm to bottom of Gold (Queen's head)	£200	
C563	22p	Giant's Causeway	35	33
C563a		Shift 1mm to bottom of Yellow brown (clouds at top left)	£10	
C564	25p	St. Kilda	35	32
		Set of 5	1.40	1.30
		Set of 5 Cylinder Blocks	10.50	
		Set of 5 Gutter Pairs	3.50	3.50
		First Day Cover		1.20
		Presentation Pack 127	1.40	
		PHQ52 Cards	1.20	

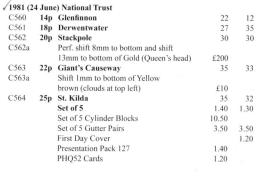

1981 (22 July) Royal Wedding

			U/M	F/U
C565	14p	Multicoloured	20	20
C565a		Shift 1¼mm to right of Silver (frame,date)	50	50
C566	25p	Multicoloured	50	50
		Set of 2	70	70
		Set of 2 Cylinder Blocks	5.50	
		Set of 2 Gutter Pairs	3.50	3.50
		First Day Cover		2.00
		Presentation Pack 127A	1.00	
		Souvenir Booklet	5.00	
		Japanese Pack	3.50	
		Japanese Pack Reprint	3.00	
		PHQ53 Cards	1.50	

1981 (12 Aug.) The Duke of Edinburgh Award Scheme. Perf. 14
Printers: John Waddington Ltd. in Lithography

			U/M	F/U
C567	14p	Expeditions	22	15
C568	18p	Skills	30	30
C569	22p	Service	35	35
C570	25p	Recreation	40	40
		Set of 4	1.15	1.20
		Set of 4 Cylinder Blocks	8.75	
		Set of 4 Gutter Pairs	2.90	2.90
		First Day Cover		1.20
		Presentation Pack 128	1.30	
		PHQ54 Cards	1.25	

1981 (18 Nov.) Christmas 1981

			U/M	F/U
C575	11½p	Father Christmas	18	10
C575a		Imperforate between stamp & bottom margin	£450	
C576	14p	Jesus Christ	21	10
C576a		Imperforate pair	£160	
C577	18p	Flying Angel	30	35
C578	22p	Joseph and Mary	33	35
C579	25p	The Kings	36	35
		Set of 5	1.30	1.25
		Set of 5 Cylinder Blocks	9.75	
		Set of 5 Gutter Pairs	3.25	3.25
		First Day Cover		1.35
		Presentation Pack 130	1.40	
		PHQ56 Cards	1.25	

1981 (18 Nov.) Collectors Year Pack

		U/M	F/U
CP18	Collectors Year Pack 131	8.00	

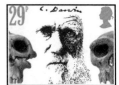

1981 (23 Sept.) Deep Sea Fishing

			U/M	F/U
C571	14p	Cockle Dredging	21	15
C572	18p	Trawl Net	30	30
C573	22p	Lobster Potting	35	35
C574	25p	Seine Net	45	40
		Set of 4	1.15	1.10
		Set of 4 Cylinder Blocks	8.75	
		Set of 4 Gutter Pairs	2.90	2.90
		First Day Cover		1.20
		Presentation Pack 129	1.30	
		PHQ55 Cards	1.25	

1982 (10 Feb.) Charles Darwin

			U/M	F/U
C580	15½p	Giant Tortoises	22	18
C581	19½p	Iguanas	29	32
C582	26p	Finches	38	38
C583	29p	Skulls	45	45
		Set of 4	1.30	1.25
		Set of 4 Cylinder Blocks	9.75	
		Set of 4 Gutter Pairs	3.25	3.25
		First Day Cover		1.35
		Presentation Pack 132	1.40	
		PHQ57 Cards	1.20	

✓ **1982 (24 March) Boy Scout and Youth Organisations**

No.			U/M	F/U
C584	15½p	Boys Brigade	22	18
C585	19½p	Girls Brigade	30	35
C585a		Perf. shift 7mm to left	£150	
C586	26p	Boy Scouts	40	40
C587	29p	Girl Guides	45	50
		Set of 4	1.30	1.35
		Set of 4 Cylinder Blocks	9.75	
		Set of 4 Gutter Pairs	3.25	3.50
		First Day Cover		1.50
		Presentation Pack 133	1.70	
		PHQ58 Cards	1.20	

1982 (28 April) Europa. British Theatre

No.			U/M	F/U
C588	15½p	Ballerina	22	19
C589	19½p	Harlequin	40	40
C590	26p	Hamlet	50	45
C591	29p	Opera Singer	50	50
		Set of 4	1.60	1.50
		Set of 4 Cylinder Blocks	11.90	
		Set of 4 Gutter Pairs	4.00	4.00
		First Day Cover		1.50
		Presentation Pack 134	2.20	
		PHQ59 Cards	1.50	

✓ **1982 (16 June) Maritime Heritage**

No.			U/M	F/U
C592	15½p	Mary Rose	25	20
C592a		Imperforate pair	£1000	
C592b		Missing black recess (Mary Rose) *	£2500	£750
C593	19½p	Triumph	30	35
C594	24p	HMS Victory	40	40
C594a		Imperforate between stamp & bottom margin	£400	
C595	26p	HMS Dreadnought	40	45
C596	29p	HMS Warspite	50	50
C596a		Imperforate pair	£1850	
		Set of 5	1.70	1.70
		Set of 5 Cylinder Blocks	12.80	
		Set of 5 Gutter Pairs	4.25	4.25
		First Day Cover		1.60
		Presentation Pack 136	2.20	
		PHQ60 Cards	1.50	

* A very small number of used examples have been discovered. Buy only with a competent certificate.

✓ **1982 (23 July) British Textiles**

No.			U/M	F/U
C597	15½p	'Strawberry Thief'	22	18
C597a		Imperforate pair	£1000	
C598	19½p	Untitled (Steiner & Co.)	30	40
C598a		Imperforate vertical pair	£1500	
C598b		Perf. shift 9mm to right ('19' at right)	£160	
C599	26p	'Cherry Orchard'	40	45
C600	29p	'Chevron'	50	50
C600a		Perf. shift 2½mm to right	£35	
		Set of 4	1.25	1.45
		Set of 4 Cylinder Blocks	9.50	
		Set of 4 Gutter Pairs	3.20	3.20
		First Day Cover		1.50
		Presentation Pack 137	1.40	
		PHQ61 Cards	1.50	

1982 (8 Sept.) Information Technology

No.			U/M	F/U
C601	**15½p**	**Communications**	20	20
C601a		PCP2	2.50	
C601b		Imperforate pair	£300	
C602	**26p**	**Technological Aids**	50	65
C602a		Imperforate pair	£1250	
		Set of 2	60	80
		Set of 2 Cylinder Blocks	4.50	
		Set of 2 Gutter Pairs	1.50	1.50
		First Day Cover		1.25
		Presentation Pack 138	90	
		PHQ62 Cards	75	

1982 (13 Oct.) British Motor Cars. Perf. 14½ x 14
Printers: House of Questa in Litho.

No.			U/M	F/U
C603	**15½p**	**Austin**	25	17
C604	**19½p**	**Ford**	40	50
C604a		Rose-red, grey & black printed double	£600	
C604b		Imperforate between stamp & right margin	£250	
C605	**26p**	**Jaguar**	40	40
C606	**29p**	**Rolls-Royce**	55	70
C606a		Black printed quadruple	£400	
C606b		Black, Bright orange & Carmine-red printed double	£750	
C606c		Shift 2mm to top of Slate	£55	
		Set of 4	1.40	1.50
		Set of 4 Cylinder Blocks	10.50	
		Set of 4 Gutter Pairs	3.50	4.00
		First Day Cover		1.80
		Presentation Pack 139	1.50	
		PHQ63 Cards	1.50	

1982 (17 Nov.) Christmas 1982 (Carols)

No.			U/M	F/U
C607	**12½p**	**While Shepperds...**	20	10
C608	**15½p**	**The Holly and the Ivy**	22	12
C608a		Fluorescent Brightener Omitted	1.00	
C608b		Imperforate pair	£1250	
C608c		Imperforate between stamp & bottom margin	£400	
C609	**19½p**	**I Saw Three Ships**	30	40
C609a		Imperforate pair	£1600	
C610	**26p**	**We Three Kings**	40	40
C611	**29p**	**Good King Wenceslas**	60	40
		Set of 5	1.40	1.40
		Set of 5 Cylinder Blocks	10.50	
		Set of 5 Gutter Pairs	3.50	3.50
		First Day Cover		1.80
		FDC with 15½p FBO		8.50
		Presentation Pack 140	1.50	
		PHQ64 Cards	1.50	

1982 (17 Nov.) Collectors Year Pack

No.		U/M	F/U
CP19	Collectors Year Pack 141	£11	

1983 (26 Jan.) British River Fishes

No.			U/M	F/U
C612	**15½p**	**Salmon**	22	12
C612a		Imperforate pair	£1450	
C613	**19½p**	**Pike**	30	45
C614	**26p**	**Trout**	40	45
C614a		Imperforate pair	£900	
C615	**29p**	**Perch**	60	65
		Set of 4	1.25	1.30
		Set of 4 Cylinder Blocks	9.50	
		Set of 4 Gutter Pairs	3.25	3.25
		First Day Cover		1.80
		Presentation Pack 142	1.60	
		PHQ65 Cards	1.50	

No.   U/M   F/U   No.   U/M   F/U

✓1983 (9 March) Commonwealth Day

No.	Value	Description	U/M	F/U
C616	15½p	Tropical Island	22	18
C617	19½p	Desert	40	40
C618	26p	Temperate Farmland	40	40
C619	29p	Mountain Range	60	60
		Set of 4	1.25	1.30
		Set of 4 Cylinder Blocks	9.50	
		Set of 4 Gutter Pairs	3.25	3.25
		First Day Cover		1.50
		Presentation Pack 143	1.60	
		PHQ66 Cards	1.50	

✓1983 (6 July) The British Army

No.	Value	Description	U/M	F/U
C623	16p	The Royal Scots	23	18
C624	20½p	Welsh Fuseliers	35	40
C625	26p	Green Jackets	50	50
C625a		Imperforate pair	£1500	
C625b		Perf. shift 6mm to right	£75	
C626	28p	The Irish Guards	50	50
C626a		Imperforate pair		£1750
C627	31p	Parachute Regiment	50	50
		Set of 5	1.80	1.85
		Set of 5 Cylinder Blocks	13.50	
		Set of 5 Gutter Pairs	4.50	4.80
		First Day Cover		2.40
		Presentation Pack 145	1.80	
		PHQ68 Cards	1.50	

✓1983 (25 May) Europa. British Engineering Achievements

No.	Value	Description	U/M	F/U
C620	16p	Humber Bridge	23	20
C621	20½p	Thames Flood Barrier	40	50
C622	28p	Iolair	60	70
		Set of 3	1.10	1.10
		Set of 3 Cylinder Blocks	8.20	
		Set of 3 Gutter Pairs	2.75	2.75
		First Day Cover		1.30
		Presentation Pack 144	2.20	
		PHQ67 Cards	1.50	

U/M   F/U

U/M   F/U

18TH CENTURY GARDEN
BLENHEIM

17TH CENTURY GARDEN
PITMEDDEN

1983 (24 Aug.) British Gardens. Perf. 14
Printers: John Waddington Ltd. in Lithography

			U/M	F/U
C628	16p	Sissinghurst	35	30
C629	20½p	Biddulph Grange	30	40
C630	28p	Blenheim	55	40
C631	31p	Pitmedden	60	40
		Set of 4	1.30	1.35
		Set of 4 Cylinder Blocks	9.50	
		Set of 4 Gutter Pairs	3.25	3.50
		First Day Cover		1.90
		Presentation Pack 146	1.50	
		PHQ69 Cards	1.50	

1983 (5 Oct.) British Fairs

			U/M	F/U
C632	16p	Merry-go-Round	23	20
C633	20½p	Big Wheel	35	32
C634	28p	Side Shows	40	50
C635	31p	Early Produce	50	50
		Set of 4	1.25	1.30
		Set of 4 Cylinder Blocks	9.50	
		Set of 4 Gutter Pairs	3.25	3.50
		First Day Cover		1.90
		Presentation Pack 147	1.50	
		PHQ70 Cards	1.50	

1983 (16 Nov.) Christmas 1983

			U/M	F/U
C636	12½p	Christmas Post	20	10
C636a		Imperforate pair	£950	
C636b		Shift 2mm to bottom of Red and of Blue, and 3mm to bottom of Yellow	£55	
C637	16p	The Three Kings	23	12
C637a		Imperforate pair	£950	
C637b		Imperforate between stamp & bottom margin	£450	
C638	20½p	World of Peace	35	35
C639	28p	Light of Christmas	48	50
C640	31p	Christmas Dove	45	45
		Set of 5	1.40	1.50
		Set of 5 Cylinder Blocks	10.50	
		Set of 5 Gutter Pairs	3.50	3.50
		First Day Cover		1.85
		Presentation Pack 148	1.50	
		PHQ71 Cards	1.50	

1983 (16 Nov.) Collectors Year Pack

			U/M	F/U
CP20		Collectors Year Pack 149	13.50	

1984 (17 Jan.) Heraldry. Perf. 14½

			U/M	F/U
C641	15p	College of Arms	23	18
C642	20½p	King Richard III	35	35
C643	28p	Earl Marshall	45	50
C644	31p	City of London	60	60
C644a		Imperforate pair	£1750	
		Set of 4	1.40	1.45
		Set of 4 Cylinder Blocks	10.50	
		Set of 4 Gutter Pairs	3.50	3.50
		First Day Cover		1.75
		Presentation Pack 150	1.50	
		PHQ72 Cards	1.50	

		U/M	F/U
Set of 4		1.45	1.40
Set of 4 Cylinder Blocks		10.80	
Set of 4 Gutter Pairs		3.70	3.70
26p Miscur gutter pair			£15
First Day Cover			1.75
Presentation Pack 152		1.50	
PHQ74 Cards		1.50	

A   B

A   B

1984 (6 March) British Cattle

			U/M	F/U
C645	16p	Highland Cow	23	18
C645a		Imperforate vertical pair	£3000	
C646	20½p	Chillingham Wild	35	35
C647	26p	Hereford Bull	45	45
C648	28p	Welsh Black Bull	45	50
C649	31p	Irish Moiled Cow	55	50
		Set of 5	1.60	1.70
		Set of 5 Cylinder Blocks	11.90	
		Set of 5 Gutter Pairs	4.00	4.00
		16p Miscur gutter pair	£15	
		First Day Cover		2.20
		Presentation Pack 151	1.80	
		PHQ73 Cards	1.50	

1984 (15 May) Europa

			U/M	F/U
C654/5	16p	Se-tenant pair	90	1.10
C654/5a		Imperforate pair	£1750	
C654		Multicoloured (A)	25	30
C655		Multicoloured (B)	25	30
C656/7	20½p	Se-tenant pair	1.50	1.55
C656/7a		Imperforate pair	£1750	
C656		Multicoloured (A)	38	70
C657		Multicoloured (B)	38	70
		Set of 4	2.20	2.30
		Set of 2 Cylinder Blocks	4.50	
		Set of 2 Gutter Blocks	5.50	5.50
		First Day Cover		2.10
		Presentation Pack 153	2.20	
		PHQ75 Cards	1.50	

1984 (5 June) London Economic Summit

			U/M	F/U
C658	31p	Lancaster House	60	55
		Cylinder Block	4.30	
		Gutter pair	1.50	1.50
		First Day Cover		85
		PHQ76 Cards	45	

1984 (10 April) Urban Renewal

			U/M	F/U
C650	16p	Festival Hall	23	18
C650a		Perf. shift 3mm to top	£30	
C651	20½p	Millburngate	35	35
C651a		Imperforate pair	£1750	
C652	28p	Bush House	50	50
C653	31p	Commercial Street	60	60
C653a		Imperforate pair	£1750	

1984 (26 June) Greenwich Meridian. Perf. 14 x 14½

Printers: House of Questa in Lithography

No.	Value	Description	U/M	F/U
C659	16p	**From Apollo 11**	23	20
C659a		Black printed double		£1750
C660	20½p	**Chart of Channel**	35	35
C661	28p	**Observatory**	45	50
C662	31p	**Transit Telescope**	60	60
		Set of 4	1.40	1.40
		Set of 4 Cylinder Blocks	10.50	
		Set of 4 Gutter Pairs	3.50	3.50
		First Day Cover		1.60
		Presentation Pack 154	1.50	
		PHQ77 Cards	1.50	

1984 (31 July) Royal Mail Coach Run Bicentenary

No.	Value	Description	U/M	F/U
C663/7	16p	**Strip of 5 se-tenant**	1.55	1.60
C663/7a		Perf shift 2mm down - Strip of 5 se-tenant	£100	
C663	16p	**Bath Mail Coach (A)**	30	35
C664	16p	**Attack on Exeter Mail (B)**	30	35
C665	16p	**Norwich Mail (C)**	30	35
C666	16p	**Holyhead and Liverpool Mail (D)**	30	35
C666/7		Imperforate pair	£2250	
C667	16p	**Edinburgh Mail (E)**	30	35
		Cylinder Block	4.20	
		Gutter Block of 10	3.90	4.00
		First Day Cover		1.75
		Presentation Pack 155	1.60	
		Souvenir Booklet	6.00	
		PHQ78 Cards	1.50	

1984 (25 Sept.) 50th Anniversary of the British Council

No.	Value	Description	U/M	F/U
C668	17p	**Nigerian Clinic**	24	24
C669	22p	**Violinist, Athens**	35	35
C669a		Perf. shift 2mm to left	£10	
C670	31p	**Building Project**	50	50
C671	34p	**Council Library**	60	70
		Set of 4	1.60	1.50
		Set of 4 Cylinder Blocks	12.00	
		Set of 4 Gutter Pairs	4.00	4.00
		Gutter Pairs with 'Ausipex' logo	8.50	8.50
		First Day Cover		1.70
		Presentation Pack 156	1.60	
		PHQ79 Cards	1.50	

1984 (20 Nov.) Christmas 1984

No.	Value	Description	U/M	F/U
C672	13p	**The Holy Family** (1 band)	20	20
C672a		Multiple Star underprint *	25	15
C672b		Imperforate between stamp & bottom margin	£450	
C673	17p	**Arrival**	25	15
C673a		Imperforate pair	£1750	
C674	22p	**Shepherd and Lamb**	35	35
C674a		Shift 6mm to bottom of Grey (Queen's head and 22p)	£30	
C675	31p	**Virgin and Child**	60	60
C676	34p	**Frankinsence**	80	80

* No. C672a originates from the 1984 Christmas Booklet

No.			U/M	F/U

			U/M	F/U
	Set of 5		1.70	1.80
	Set of 5 Cylinder Blocks		13.00	
	Set of 5 Gutter Pairs		4.25	4.25
	First Day Cover			2.00
	First Day Cover 13p (C672a)			3.00
	Presentation Pack 157		1.70	
	PHQ80 Cards		1.50	

1984 (20 Nov.) Collectors Year Pack

CP21	Collectors Year Pack 158	17.50	

1984 (20 Nov.) Royal Mail Year Book - 1

YB1	Royal Mail Year Book Book (C641/76)	£40	

1985 (22 Jan.) Famous Trains

C677	17p	Flying Scotsman	50	50
C677a		Imperforate pair	£1750	
C677b		Perf. shift 3mm to bottom	£75	
C678	22p	Golden Arrow	70	65
C679	29p	Cheltenham Flyer	50	50
C680	31p	Royal Scot	65	60
C681	34p	Cornish Riviera	65	60
		Set of 5	2.40	2.45
		Set of 5 Cylinder Blocks	18.00	
		Set of 5 Gutter Pairs	6.00	6.00
		First Day Cover		2.00
		Presentation Pack 159	3.60	
		PHQ81 Cards	2.50	

1985 (12 March) Insects

C682	17p	Bumble Bee	25	20
C683	22p	Ladybird	40	40
C683a		Imperforate between stamp & left margin	£750	
C684	29p	Cricket	50	50
C685	31p	Stag Beetle	60	55
C686	34p	Dragonfly	60	55
C686a		Imperforate vertical pair	£3500	
		Set of 5	2.05	2.00
		Set of 5 Cylinder Blocks	7.50	
		Gutter Pairs	4.50	4.50
		First Day Cover		2.00
		Presentation Pack 160	2.00	
		PHQ82 Cards	1.50	

1985 (14 May) Europa. Composers. Perf. 14 x 14½

C687	17p	Handel	30	20
C687a		Imperforate pair	£1500	
C688	22p	Holst	70	60
C688a		Imperforate pair	£1500	
C689	31p	Delius	75	70
C690	34p	Elgar	75	70
		Set of 4	2.25	2.40
		Set of 4 Cylinder Blocks	17.00	
		Set of 4 Gutter Pairs	5.75	5.75
		First Day Cover		2.00
		Presentation Pack 161	2.20	
		PHQ83 Cards	2.50	

1985 (18 June) Safety at Sea. Phosphor Coated Paper. Perf. 14
Printer: John Waddington Ltd. in Lithography

			U/M	F/U
C691	**17p**	**Lifeboat**	25	25
C691a		Imperforate between stamp & bottom margin	£500	
C692	**22p**	**Lighthouse**	40	40
C693	**31p**	**Satellite**	55	65
C694	**34p**	**Buoys**	60	60
		Set of 4	2.00	1.80
		Set of 4 Cylinder Blocks	15.00	
		Set of 4 Gutter Pairs	5.00	5.00
		First Day Cover		2.00
		Presentation Pack 162	1.70	
		PHQ84 Cards	1.50	

1985 (3 Sept.) Arthurian Legend

			U/M	F/U
C699	**17p**	**Arthur and Merlin**	25	25
C699a		Imperforate pair	£2250	
C700	**22p**	**Lady of the Lake**	35	35
C701	**31p**	**Queen Guinevere**	60	70
C702	**34p**	**Sir Galahad**	60	70
		Set of 4	1.70	1.80
		Set of 4 Cylinder Blocks	12.50	
		Set of 4 Gutter Pairs	4.25	4.25
		First Day Cover		2.00
		Presentation Pack 164	1.70	
		PHQ86 Cards	1.50	

1985 (30 July) 350th Anniversary of Post Office

			U/M	F/U
C695	**17p**	**Datapost**	25	25
C695a		Imperforate pair	£1500	
C695b		Multiple 'D' underprint *	35	45
C696	**22p**	**Rural Postbus**	35	35
C697	**31p**	**Parcel Delivery**	60	70
C697a		Imperforate pair	£1500	
C698	**34p**	**Letter Delivery**	60	70
C698a		Imperf. between (vertical pair)	£500	
		Set of 4	1.70	1.80
		Set of 4 Cylinder Blocks	12.70	
		Set of 4 Gutter Pairs	4.25	4.25
		First Day Cover		2.00
		Presentation Pack 163	1.70	
		PHQ85 Cards	1.50	

* No. C695b originates from the £1.53 Discount Booklet

1985 (10 Oct.) British Film Stars. Perf. 14½

			U/M	F/U
C703	**17p**	**Peter Sellers**	25	25
C704	**22p**	**David Niven**	35	45
C705	**29p**	**Charlie Chaplin**	60	70
C706	**31p**	**Vivien Leigh**	60	60
C707	**34p**	**Alfred Hitchcock**	60	60
C707a		Shift 15mm to bottom of Silver (Queen's head) £75		
		Set of 5	2.60	2.50
		Set of 5 Cylinder Blocks	19.50	
		Set of 5 Gutter Pairs	6.50	6.50
		First Day Cover		2.00
		Presentation Pack 165	2.50	
		Souvenir Booklet	7.50	
		PHQ87 Cards	1.50	

1985 (19 Nov.) Christmas 1985

No.			U/M	F/U
C708	12p	Principal Boy	20	20
C708a		Imperforate pair	£1250	
C708b		Perf. shift 5mm to top	£45	
C708c		Multiple star underprint	25	25
C709	17p	Genie	25	25
C709a		Imperforate pair	£1750	
C710	22p	Dame	35	45
C712	31p	Good Fairy	70	70
C713	34p	Panto Cat	70	70
		Set of 5	1.90	1.95
		Set of 5 Cylinder Blocks	14.50	
		Set of 5 Gutter Pairs	4.75	4.75
		First Day Cover		2.00
		Presentation Pack 166	1.80	
		PHQ88 Cards	1.50	
		Discount Folder (C708c x 50)	£15	

1985 (19 Nov.) Collectors Year Pack

CP22		Collectors Year Pack 167	17.50	

1985 (19 Nov.) Royal Mail Year Book - 2

YB2		Royal Mail Year Book C677/713	£37	

1986 (14 Jan.) Industry Year 1986. Phosphor Coated Paper. Perf. 14½ x 14
Printer: House of Questa in Lithography

No.			U/M	F/U
C714	17p	Light Bulb	25	20
C715	22p	Thermometer	50	50
C715a		Perf. shift 2.5mm to top	£50	
C715b		Perf. shift 3mm to right	£20	
C716	31p	Garden Hoe	70	70
C717	34p	Loaf of Bread	70	70
		Set of 4	1.90	2.10
		Set of 4 Cylinder Blocks	14.50	
		Set of 4 Gutter Pairs	4.75	4.75
		First Day Cover		2.00
		Presentation Pack 168	1.80	
		PHQ89 Cards	1.50	

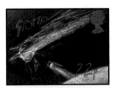

1986 (18 Feb.) Halley's Comet

No.			U/M	F/U
C718	17p	Dr. Edmund Haley	25	20
C718a		Imperforate between stamp & bottom margin	£1250	
C719	22p	Giotto Spacecraft	50	50
C720	31p	Twice in a Lifetime	70	70
C721	34p	Orbiting	70	70
		Set of 4	1.85	2.10
		Set of 4 Cylinder Blocks	14.00	
		Set of 4 Gutter Pairs	4.70	4.70
		First Day Cover		2.00
		Presentation Pack 169	1.80	
		PHQ90 Cards	1.95	

A  B

C  D

1986 (21 April) Sixtieth Birthday of Her Majesty The Queen

No.			U/M	F/U
C722/3	17p	Se-tenant pair	70	70
C722/3a		Perf. shift 3mm to top	£60	
C722		Multicoloured (A)	25	20
C723		Multicoloured (B)	25	20
C724/5	34p	Se-tenant pair	1.60	1.60
C724		Multicoloured (A)	70	70
C725		Multicoloured (B)	70	70

		U/M	F/U			U/M	F/U
	Set of 4	2.00	2.20				
	Set of 2 Cylinder Blocks	7.90					
	Set of 2 Gutter Blocks	5.00	5.00				
	First Day Cover		2.00				
	Presentation Pack 170	2.60					
	Souvenir Booklet	7.50					
	PHQ91 Cards	1.50					

1986 (20 May) Europa. Nature Conservation. Perf. 14½ x 14

No.			U/M	F/U
C726	**17p**	**Barn Owl**	25	25
C727	**22p**	**Pine Marten**	45	45
C728	**31p**	**Wild Cat**	70	70
C729	**34p**	**Toad**	70	70
		Set of 4	1.75	1.80
		Set of 4 Cylinder Blocks	13.00	
		Set of 4 Gutter Pairs	4.40	4.50
		First Day Cover		2.00
		Presentation Pack 171	2.20	
		PHQ92 Cards	1.50	

1986 (15 July) Commonwealth Games, Edinburgh and World Hockey Cup, London

No.			U/M	F/U
C734	**17p**	**Athletics**	25	25
C735	**22p**	**Rowing**	35	35
C735a		Imperforate pair		£750
C736	**29p**	**Weightlifting**	60	70
C737	**31p**	**Shooting**	60	60
C738	**34p**	**Hockey**	60	60
C738a		Imperforate pair	£1750	
		Set of 5	2.30	2.35
		Set of 5 Cylinder Blocks	17.50	
		Set of 5 Gutter Pairs	5.75	5.75
		First Day Cover		2.00
		Presentation Pack 173	2.30	
		PHQ94 Cards	1.95	

1986 (17 June) Domesday Book 1086

No.			U/M	F/U
C730	**17p**	**Peasants**	25	25
C731	**22p**	**Freemen**	45	50
C732	**31p**	**Knight and Retainers**	55	75
C733	**34p**	**Lord at Banquet**	55	70
		Set of 4	1.90	1.95
		Set of 4 Cylinder Blocks	14.50	
		Set of 4 Gutter Pairs	4.75	5.00
		First Day Cover		2.00
		Presentation Pack 172	2.00	
		PHQ93 Cards	1.50	

1986 (22 July) Royal Wedding

No.			U/M	F/U
C739	**12p**	**Multicoloured** (1 band)	35	25
C740	**17p**	**Multicoloured**	50	35
C740a		Imperforate pair	£500	
		Set of 2	80	55
		Set of 2 Cylinder Blocks	5.80	
		Set of 2 Gutter Pairs	2.00	2.00
		First Day Cover		1.25
		Presentation Pack 174	1.00	
		PHQ95 Cards	95	

1986 (19 Aug.) Commonwealth Parliamentary Association Conference. Perf. 14 x 14½

No.			U/M	F/U
C741	34p	Multicoloured	62	60
C741a		Imperforate between (vertical pair)	£300	
		Cylinder Block	4.50	
		Gutter pair	1.55	1.55
		First Day Cover		1.25
		PHQ96 Card	40	

1986 (16 Sept) Royal Air Force. Perf. 14½

			U/M	F/U
C742	17p	Hurricane	25	25
C742a		Imperforate pair	£1000	
C743	22p	Typhoon	42	40
C743a		Missing Pale Green (22p only)*	£450	
C743b		Missing Pale Green (Queen's head only)*	£450	
C744	29p	DH 9A	60	65
C745	31p	Lancaster	70	65
C746	34p	Mosquito	70	65
		Set of 5	2.45	2.50
		Set of 5 Cylinder Blocks	18.50	
		Set of 5 Gutter Pairs	6.25	5.25
		First Day Cover		2.00
		Presentation Pack 175	2.20	
		PHQ97 Cards	1.95	

Normally sold in se-tenant pairs. Caution is needed with C743a, as many examples show feint traces of pale green.

1986 (18 Nov. - 2 Dec.) Christmas 1986

			U/M	F/U
C747	12p	Glastonburt Thorn (centre band) (2 Dec.)	40	40
C747a		Imperforate pair	£1200	
C748	13p	Glastonburt Thorn (centre band)	20	20
C748b		Multiple star underprint (2 Dec.)	25	20
C749	18p	Tanad Valley Plygain	25	20
C750	22p	Hebrides Tribute	50	50
C751	31p	Dewsbury Church	80	60
C752	34p	Hereford Boy Bishop	70	60
		Set of 6	2.00	2.00
		Set of 6 Cylinder Blocks	15.00	
		Set of 6 Gutter Pairs	5.00	5.00
		Gutter pair 13p (C748b)	75	75
		First Day Cover (5 stamps)		2.00
		First Day Cover (12p)		75
		Presentation Pack 176 (5 stamps)	2.10	
		PHQ98 Cards (5)	1.50	
		Discount Folder (748b x 36)	8.50	

The 12p was issued on 2nd December and available until 24th December at Post Offices, however it was still available at the Philatelic Bureau long after that date. The 13p with underprint originated from the Discount Folder that included Gutter Pairs, but these are always folded.

1986 (18 Nov.) Collectors Year Pack

		U/M	F/U
CP23	Collectors Year Pack 177	17.50	

1986 (18 Nov.) Royal Mail Year Book - 3

		U/M	F/U
YB3	Royal Mail Year Book C714/752	£37	

Commemoratives
No.
U/M F/U
No.
U/M F/U

Queen Elizabeth II

1987 (20 Jan.) Flowers. Perf. 14½ x 14

No.			U/M	F/U
C753	18p	Blanket Flower	25	25
C754	22p	Glode Thistle	50	50
C755	31p	Echeveria	50	70
C755a		Imperforate pair	£1750	
C755b		Imperforate between stamp & left margin	£350	
C756	34p	Autumn Crocus	80	75
		Set of 4	1.90	2.00
		Set of 4 Cylinder Blocks	14.50	
		Set of 4 Gutter Pairs	4.75	4.75
		First Day Cover		2.00
		Presentation Pack 178	2.00	
		PHQ99 Cards	1.50	

1987 (24 March) Sir Isaac Newton

No.			U/M	F/U
C757	18p	Principia Mathmatica	25	25
C757a		Imperforate pair	£1500	
C758	22p	Motion of Bodies	50	60
C759	31p	Optick Treatise	70	65
C760	34p	System of the World	70	70
		Set of 4	1.90	2.00
		Set of 4 Cylinder Blocks	14.50	
		Set of 4 Gutter Pairs	4.75	4.75
		First Day Cover		2.00
		Presentation Pack 179	2.00	
		PHQ100 Cards	1.50	

1987 (12 May) Europa. British Architects in Europe

No.			U/M	F/U
C761	18p	Ipswich	25	25
C762	22p	Paris	50	60
C763	31p	Stuttgart	70	60
C763a		Imperforate pair	£1500	
C764	34p	Luxembourg	70	60
		Set of 4	1.90	1.90
		Set of 4 Cylinder Blocks	14.50	
		Set of 4 Gutter Pairs	4.75	4.75
		First Day Cover		2.00
		Presentation Pack 180	2.20	
		PHQ101 Cards	1.50	

1987 (16 June) St John Ambulance Centenary. Perf. 14 x 14½
Printer: House of Questa in Lithography

No.			U/M	F/U
C765	18p	Ashford Litter	25	25
C765a		Black printed double		£850
C765b		Black printed treble		£1500
C766	22p	Blitz Victim	50	60
C767	31p	Volunteer	70	60
C768	34p	Air Wing	70	65
		Set of 4	1.90	1.95
		Set of 4 Cylinder Blocks	14.50	
		Set of 4 Gutter Pairs	4.75	4.75
		First Day Cover		2.00
		Presentation Pack 181	2.00	
		PHQ102 Cards	1.50	

 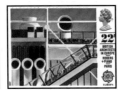

No. U/M F/U No. U/M F/U

1987 (21 July) Tercentenary of the Revival of the Order of the Thistle.
Perf. 14½

No.			U/M	F/U
C769	18p	Lord of Lyon	25	20
C769a		Imperforate between stamp & bottom margin	£450	
C769b		Imperforate between stamp & bottom		
		and right margin	£750	
C770	22p	Heraldic Banner	50	60
C771	31p	Scottish Academy	70	65
C772	34p	Society of Edinburgh	70	65
		Set of 4	1.90	1.90
		Set of 4 Cylinder Blocks	14.50	
		Set of 4 Gutter Pairs	4.75	4.75
		First Day Cover		2.00
		Presentation Pack 182	2.00	
		PHQ103 Cards	1.50	

1987 (13 Oct.) Studio Pottery. Perf. 14½ x 14

No.			U/M	F/U
C777	18p	Bernard Leach	25	25
C778	26p	Elizabeth Fritsch	50	50
C779	31p	Lucie Rie	70	65
C780	34p	Hans Coper	70	65
C780a		Imperforate vertical strip of three	£2500	
		Set of 4	1.90	1.90
		Set of 4 Cylinder Blocks	14.50	
		Set of 4 Gutter Pairs	4.75	4.75
		First Day Cover		2.00
		Presentation Pack 184	2.00	
		PHQ105 Cards	1.50	

1987 (8 Sept.) 150th Anniversary of Queen Victoria's Accession
Printer: Harrison & Sons in photogravure & recess

No.			U/M	F/U
C773	18p	Crystal Palace	25	25
C774	22p	Great Eastern	50	50
C775	31p	Albert Memorial	70	65
C776	34p	Diamond Jubilee	70	65
		Set of 4	1.90	1.90
		Set of 4 Cylinder Blocks	14.50	
		Set of 4 Gutter Pairs	4.75	4.75
		First Day Cover		2.00
		Presentation Pack 183	2.00	
		PHQ104 Cards	1.50	

1987 (17 Nov.) Christmas 1987

No.			U/M	F/U
C781	13p	Decorating the Tree	25	20
C781a		Multiple star underprint *	30	35
C781b		Imperforate between stamp & left margin	£650	
C782	18p	Waiting	25	20
C783	26p	Sleeping Child	70	70
C784	31p	Child Reading	70	70
C784a		Fluorescent Brightener omitted		
C785	34p	Child and Snowman	70	70

* C781a originates from the Discount Folder, the gutter pair only exists folded.

No.   U/M   F/U   No.   U/M   F/U

		U/M	F/U
	Set of 5	1.85	2.00
	Set of 5 Cylinder Blocks	13.90	
	Set of 5 Gutter Pairs	4.70	4.70
	Gutter pair 13p (C781a) *	60	1.20
	First Day Cover		2.00
	Presentation Pack 185	2.00	
	PHQ106 Cards	1.50	
	Discount Folder (C781a x 36)	8.50	

1987 (17 Nov.) Collectors Year Pack

CP24	Collectors Year Pack 186	£20	

1987 (17 Nov.) Royal Mail Year Book - 4

YB4	Royal Mail Year Book C753/785	£18	

1988 (19 Jan.) The Linnean Society Bicentenary

C786	18p	Short Spined Seascorpion	25	25
C787	26p	Yellow Waterlily	60	50
C788	31p	Bewick's Swan	60	55
C788a		Imperforate pair	£1250	
C789	34p	Marchella Esculenta	60	55
		Set of 4	1.80	1.80
		Set of 4 Cylinder Blocks	13.60	
		Set of 4 Gutter Pairs	4.50	4.50
		First Day Cover		2.00
		Presentation Pack 187	2.00	
		PHQ107 Cards	1.50	

1988 (1 March) The Welsh Bible. Perf. 14½ x 14

C790	18p	Revd. W. Morgan	25	25
C790a		Imperforate pair	£1250	
C791	26p	William Salesbury	60	65
C791a		Perf. shift 3.5mm to right	£25	
C792	31p	Bishop R. Davies	60	65
C793	34p	Bishop R. Parry	60	65
		Set of 4	1.80	1.90
		Set of 4 Cylinder Blocks	13.50	
		Set of 4 Gutter Pairs	4.50	4.50
		First Day Cover		2.00
		Presentation Pack 188	2.00	
		PHQ108 Cards	1.50	

1988 (22 March) Sports. Perf. 14½

C794	18p	Gymnastics	25	25
C795	26p	Downhill Skiing	60	70
C796	31p	Tennis	60	70
C797	34p	Football	70	70
		Set of 4	1.90	1.90
		Set of 4 Cylinder Blocks	14.50	
		Set of 4 Gutter Pairs	4.75	4.75
		First Day Cover		2.00
		Presentation Pack 189	2.00	
		PHQ109 Cards	1.20	

No.   U/M   F/U   No.   U/M   F/U

1988 (10 May) Europa. Transport

No.			U/M	F/U
C798	**18p**	**Mallard**	25	25
C799	**26p**	**QEII**	65	70
C800	**31p**	**Glasgow Tram**	65	70
C801	**34p**	**'HP24'**	65	70
		Set of 4	1.80	1.90
		Set of 4 Cylinder Blocks	13.50	
		Set of 4 Gutter Pairs	4.50	4.50
		First Day Cover		2.00
		Presentation Pack 190	2.20	
		PHQ110 Cards	1.50	

1988 (21 June) Australian Bicentenary. Perf. 14½

Printer: House of Questa in Lithography

C802/3	**18p**	**Se-tenant pair**	70	70
C802		Early Settler	30	25
C803		Queen Elizabeth II	30	25
C804/5	**34p**	**Se-tenant pair**	1.50	1.70
C804		W. G. Grace	70	60
C805		Shakespeare	70	60
		Set of 4	2.00	2.10
		Set of 2 Cylinder Blocks	7.50	
		Set of 2 Gutter Blocks	5.00	5.20
		First Day Cover		2.00
		Presentation Pack 191*	2.00	
		Souvenir Booklet	5.00	
		PHQ111 Cards	1.00	

* Presentation Pack issued by both countries

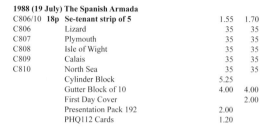

1988 (19 July) The Spanish Armada

			U/M	F/U
C806/10	**18p**	**Se-tenant strip of 5**	1.55	1.70
C806		Lizard	35	35
C807		Plymouth	35	35
C808		Isle of Wight	35	35
C809		Calais	35	35
C810		North Sea	35	35
		Cylinder Block	5.25	
		Gutter Block of 10	4.00	4.00
		First Day Cover		2.00
		Presentation Pack 192	2.00	
		PHQ112 Cards	1.20	

1988 (6 Sept.) Edward Lear

			U/M	F/U
C811	**19p**	**'Owl and the Pusseycat'**	27	22
C812	**27p**	**'Lear as a Bird'**	50	50
C813	**32p**	**'Cat'**	70	75
C814	**35p**	**'There was a Young..'**	70	75
		Set of 4	2.10	2.10
		Set of 4 Cylinder Blocks	15.50	
		Set of 4 Gutter Pairs	5.25	5.25
		First Day Cover		2.00
		Presentation Pack 193	2.00	
		PHQ113 Cards	1.00	

1988 (27 Sept.) Edward Lear

			U/M	F/U
MS4	**£1.35**	**Miniature Sheet**	2.40	2.50
		First Day Cover		5.00

1988 (15 Nov.) Christmas Cards. Perf. 15 x 14

No.			U/M	F/U
C815	**14p**	**Journey to Bethlehem** (centre band to right)	25	20
C815a	**13p**	Error of value	£5000	
		First Day Cover		£1750
		Used		£1000
C815b		Imperforate pair (14p)	£450	
C816	**19p**	**Shepherd and Star**	27	20
C816a		Imperforate pair	£750	
C816b		Imperforate bewteen stamp & bottom margin	£100	
C817	**27p**	**Three Wise Men**	45	45
C818	**32p**	**Nativity**	75	75
C819	**35p**	**The Annunciation**	75	75
		Set of 5	2.10	2.10
		Set of 5 Cylinder Blocks	15.90	
		Set of 5 Gutter Pairs	5.25	5.25
		First Day Cover		1.50
		Presentation Pack 194	2.00	
		PHQ114 Cards	1.20	

1988 (15 Nov.) Collectors Year Pack

CP24	Collectors Year Pack 195	£20	

1988 (15 Nov.) Royal Mail Year Book - 5

YB5	Royal Mail Year Book C786/819	£18	

1989 (17 Jan.) Birds. RSPB Centenary. Perf. 14 x 15

No.			U/M	F/U
C820	**19p**	**Puffin**	27	27
C821	**27p**	**Avocet**	45	50
C822	**32p**	**Oystercatcher**	70	75
C823	**35p**	**Gannet**	70	75
		Set of 4	2.00	2.10
		Set of 4 Cylinder Blocks	15.25	
		Set of 4 Gutter Pairs	5.00	5.00
		First Day Cover		1.50
		Presentation Pack 196	2.00	
		PHQ115 Cards	1.20	

A

B   C

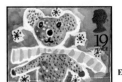

D   E

1989 (31 Jan.) Advanced Coated Paper. Perf. 15 x 14

No.			U/M	F/U
C824/28	**19p**	**Se-tenant strip of 5**	11.50	11.50
C824	**19p**	Rose (A)	3.00	1.50
C825	**19p**	Cupid (B)	3.00	1.50
C826	**19p**	Yachts (C)	3.00	1.50
C827	**19p**	Fruit Bowl (D)	3.00	1.50
C828	**19p**	Teddy Bear (E)	3.00	1.50
		Booklet pane of 10	£30	
		First Day Cover (5v)		12.50

The above are from the first Greetings Book listed on Page 414

No.   U/M   F/U   No.   U/M   F/U

1989 (7 March) Food and Farming Year. Perf. 14 x 14½

No.			U/M	F/U
C829	19p	Fruit and Veg	28	25
C830	27p	Meat	60	50
C831	32p	Dairy	70	70
C832	35p	Cereal	70	70
		Set of 4	2.00	2.00
		Set of 4 Cylinder Blocks	14.25	
		Set of 4 Gutter Pairs	5.00	5.00
		First Day Cover		1.40
		Presentation Pack 197	2.00	
		PHQ116 Cards	1.00	

A   PUBLIC EDUCATION IN ENGLAND 1839 TO 1989   EUROPEAN PARLIAMENT THIRD DIRECT ELECTIONS   B

C   POSTAL TELEGRAPH & TELEPHONE INTERNATIONAL WORLD CONGRESS   INTER-PARLIAMENTARY UNION CENTENARY CONFERENCE   D

1989 (11 April) Anniversaries. Perf. 14 x 14½
Printer: House of Questa in Lithography

No.			U/M	F/U
C833/34	19p	Se-tenant pair	1.00	1.00
C833	19p	Mortar Board (A)	35	25
C834	19p	Cross on Ballot Paper (B)	35	25
C835/36	35p	Se-tenant pair	2.25	2.30
C835	35p	Posthorn (C)	50	50
C836	35p	Globe (D)	50	50
C836a		Error. Inscribed 'One Hundreth Conference....'	£4500	
		Set of 4	3.20	3.20
		Set of 2 Cylinder Blocks	7.50	
		Set of 2 Gutter Strips	8.00	8.00
		First Day Cover		1.70
		Presentation Pack 198	2.50	
		PHQ117 Cards	1.00	

1989 (16 May) Europa. Games and Toys. Perf. 14 x 15

No.			U/M	F/U
C837	19p	Train and Plane	30	25
C838	27p	Bricks	50	45
C839	32p	Dice and Ladder	75	80
C840	35p	Robot/Boat	75	80
		Set of 4	1.85	1.90
		Set of 4 Cylinder Blocks	13.90	
		Set of 4 Gutter Pairs	7.40	7.40
		First Day Cover		1.70
		Presentation Pack 199	2.50	
		PHQ118 Cards	2.00	

Ironbridge, Shropshire   Tin mine, St Agnes, Cornwall

Mills, New Lanark, Strathclyde   Pontcysyllte Aqueduct, Clwyd

1989 (4 July) Industrial Archaeology. Perf. 14 x 15

No.			U/M	F/U
C841	19p	Ironbridge	28	25
C842	27p	Tin Mine	60	50
C843	32p	Cotton Mills	70	70
C844	35p	Aqueduct	70	70
		Set of 4	1.90	1.90
		Set of 4 Cylinder Blocks	14.50	
		Set of 4 Gutter Pairs	4.75	4.75
		First Day Cover		1.70
		Presentation Pack 200	2.10	
		PHQ119 Cards	1.00	

1989 (25 July) Industrial Archaeology. Perf. 15 x14

No.			U/M	F/U
MS5	£1.40	Miniature Sheet	2.90	3.20
		First Day Cover		3.50

The stamp designs in the miniature sheet are in horizontal format.

1989 (5 Sept.) Microscopes. Perf 14½ x 14

No.			U/M	F/U
C845	19p	Multicoloured	28	25
C846	27p	Multicoloured	60	50
C847	32p	Multicoloured	70	75
C848	35p	Multicoloured	70	70
		Set of 4	1.90	1.90
		Set of 4 Cylinder Blocks	14.50	
		Set of 4 Gutter Pairs	4.75	4.75
		First Day Cover		1.50
		Presentation Pack 201	2.10	
		PHQ120 Cards	1.00	

A

B   C

D   E

1989 (17 Oct.) Lord Mayor's Show. Perf. 14 x 15

No.			U/M	F/U
C849/853	20p	**Strip of 5 se-tenant**	1.80	1.80
C849/853a		Imperforate strip of 5 but with C853 having several blind peforations on the right	£7500	
C849	20p	Royal Mail Coach (A)	35	30
C850	20p	Escort (B)	35	30
C851	20p	Lord Mayor's Coach (C)	35	30
C852	20p	Passing St. Pauls (D)	35	30
C853	20p	Blues and Royals (E)	35	30
		Cylinder Block	4.20	
		Gutter Strip of 10	4.50	4.80
		First Day Cover		1.50
		Presentation Pack 202	2.10	
		PHQ121 Cards	1.20	

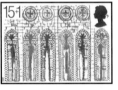

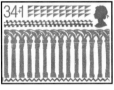

1989 (14 Nov.) Christmas. Charity Issue.

No.			U/M	F/U
C854	**15p**	14th Century Peasants (centre band)	25	2!
C855	**15p+1p**	Arches and Roundels (centre band)	30	2.
C855a		Imperforate pair	£1250	
C856	**20p+1p**	Octagen Towers	35	3!
C856a		Imperforate pair	£1250	
C857	**34p+1p**	Arcade	70	8!
C858	**37p+1p**	Triple Arch	70	8!
		Set of 5	2.10	2.2
		Set of 5 Cylinder Blocks	15.90	
		Set of 5 Gutter Pairs	5.25	5.2
		First Day Cover		1.5!
		Presentation Pack 203	1.90	
		PHQ122 Cards	1.20	

1989 (14 Nov.) Collectors Year Pack

CP26		Collectors Year Pack 204	£21	

1989 (14 Nov.) Royal Mail Year Book - 6

YB6		Royal Mail Year Book C820/858	£18	

 A    B

 C    D

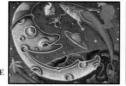 E    F

 G    H

 I    J

1990 (10 Jan.) 150th Anniversary of the Penny Black

No.			U/M	F/U
C859	15p	**Blue** (centre band)	35	30
C859a		Imperforate pair	£1250	
C860	20p	**Black and pale buff**	35	35
C861	29p	**Mauve**	70	70
C862	34p	**Slate**	90	90
C863	37p	**Red**	90	90
		Set of 5 *	3.00	3.00
		Set of 5 Cylinder Blocks		
		First Day Cover		3.50
		Presentation Pack 204	4.20	

* The set of five stamps were issued as commemoratives. This issue is detailed more fully in the definitives section.

1990 (23 Jan.) RSPCA 150th Anniversary. Perf. 14 x 14½
Printer: House of Questa in Lithography

No.			U/M	F/U
C864	20p	**Kitten**	30	30
C864a		Missing Silver (Queen's head & 20p)	£200	£45
C865	29p	**Rabbit**	55	60
C865a		Imperforate pair	£1800	
C866	34p	**Duckling**	70	75
C866a		Missing Silver (Queen's head & 34p)	£450	
C867	37p	**Puppy**	70	75
		Set of 4	1.90	2.00
		Set of 4 Cylinder Blocks	14.50	
		Set of 4 Gutter Pairs	4.75	4.75
		First Day Cover		1.50
		Presentation Pack 205	2.30	
		PHQ123 Cards	2.00	

1990 (6 Feb.) 'Smiles'. Fluorescent Coated Paper. Perf. 15 x 14

No.			U/M	F/U
C868	20p	**Teddy Bear** (2 bands) (A)	1.60	1.70
C869	20p	**Dennis the Menace** (2 bands) (B)	1.60	1.70
C870	20p	**Punch** (2 bands) (C)	1.60	1.70
C871	20p	**Cheshire Cat** (2 bands) (D)	1.60	1.70
C872	20p	**Man in the Moon** (2 bands) (E)	1.60	1.70
C873	20p	**Laughing Policeman** (2 bands) (F)	1.60	1.70
C874	20p	**Clown** (2 bands) (G)	1.60	1.70
C875	20p	**Mona Lisa** (2 bands) (H)	1.60	1.70
C876	20p	**Queen of Hearts** (2 bands) (I)	1.60	1.70
C877	20p	**Stan Laurel** (2 bands) (J)	1.60	1.70
	20p	**Booklet pane of 10**	13.50	£14
		First Day Cover		£14

The above are from the second Greetings Book listed on Page 414

1990 (6 March) Europa 1990

No.		Description	U/M	F/U
C878	20p	**London 90** (A) *	30	30
C879	20p	**Glasgow School of Art** (B)	45	40
C880	29p	**Philatelic Bureau**	70	50
C881	37p	**Templeton Carpet**	70	60
		Set of 4	2.00	2.00
		Set of 4 Cylinder Blocks	15.00	
		Set of 4 Gutter Pairs	5.00	5.00
		First Day Cover		1.50
		Presentation Pack 206	3.00	
		PHQ124 Cards	2.00	

* C879 also occurs as a booklet pane of 4 in the £5 London Life booklet.

1990 (10 April) Queen's Awards. Perf. 14 x 14½
Printer: House of Questa in Lithography

No.		Description	U/M	F/U
C882/883	20p	**Se-tenant pair**	70	70
C882	20p	Export	35	35
C883	20p	Technology	35	35
C884/885	37p	**Se-tenant pair**	1.70	1.70
C884	37p	Export	85	85
C885	37p	Technology	85	85
		Set of 4	2.25	2.15
		Set of 2 Cylinder Blocks	5.90	
		Set of 2 Gutter Strips	5.60	5.60
		First Day Cover		1.50
		Presentation Pack 207	2.20	
		PHQ125 Cards	1.20	

1990 (3 May) 'Stamp World 90', London
Printed in Photogravure and recess by Harrison

No.		Description	U/M	F/U
MS6	£1	**Miniature sheet** containing 20p stamp	2.70	2.85
MS6a		Missing Black (Recess printing)	£7500	
MS6b		Missing Cream (Recess printing)	£4000	
MS6c		Imperforate	£3500	
MS6d		Imperforate. First Day Cover		£3500
MS6e		Recess printing inverted (background)	£7500	
		First Day Cover		3.00
		Souvenir Book. *Contents:* C854/8 and MS6	£15	

1990 (5 June) Kew Gardens, 150th Anniversary

No.		Description	U/M	F/U
C886	20p	**Cycad**	30	30
C887	29p	**Stone Pine**	60	60
C888	34p	**Willow Tree**	85	80
C889	37p	**Cedar Tree**	85	80
		Set of 4	2.40	2.25
		Set of 4 Cylinder Blocks	14.50	
		Set of 4 Gutter Pairs	6.00	6.00
		First Day Cover		1.50
		Presentation Pack 208	2.20	
		PHQ126 Cards	1.20	

1990 (10 July) Thomas Hardy, 150th Birth Anniversary

No.			U/M	F/U
C890	20p	Thomas Hardy	40	35
C890a		Imperforate pair	£1350	
		Cylinder Block	2.90	
		Gutter pair	1.00	1.00
		First Day Cover		1.00
		Presentation Pack 209	90	
		PHQ127 Card	40	

1990 (2 Aug.) Queen Mother's 90th Birthday

No.			U/M	F/U
C891	20p	Queen Mother	30	30
C892	29p	Queen	55	60
C893	34p	Duchess of York	70	70
C894	37p	Lady Bowes-Lyon	70	70
		Set of 4	2.20	1.50
		Set of 4 Cylinder Blocks	16.50	
		Set of 4 Gutter Pairs	5.50	5.50
		First Day Cover		2.30
		Presentation Pack 210	3.50	
		PHQ128 Cards	2.50	

1990 (11 Sept.) Awards for Gallantry. Multicoloured designs.

No.			U/M	F/U
C895	20p	Victoria Cross	45	50
C895a		Imperforate pair	£1250	
C896	20p	George Cross	45	50
C897	20p	Service	45	50
C898	20p	Military	45	50
C899	20p	Flying	45	50
		Set of 5	1.90	1.90
		Set of 4 Cylinder Blocks	14.50	
		Set of 4 Gutter Pairs	4.80	4.80
		First Day Cover		2.00
		Presentation Pack 211	2.30	
		PHQ129 Cards	1.50	

1990 (16 Oct.) Astronomy. Perf. 14 x 14½
Printer: House of Questa in Lithography

No.			U/M	F/U
C900	22p	Armagh	30	30
C900a		Missing Gold (Queen's head)	£350	
C901	26p	Newton	60	45
C902	31p	Greenwich	65	70
C903	37p	Stonehenge	70	70
		Set of 4	2.00	2.00
		Set of 4 Cylinder Blocks	14.50	
		Set of 4 Gutter Pairs	5.00	5.00
		First Day Cover		2.00
		Presentation Pack 212	2.30	
		PHQ130 Cards	1.20	

1991 (8 Jan.) Dogs. George Stubbs. Perf. 14 x 14½

C909	22p	'King Charles Spaniel'	30	30
C909a		Imperforate pair	£800	
C909b		Imperforate between stamp/bottom margin	£400	
C910	26p	'A Pointer'	45	30
C911	31p	'Two Hounds'	60	70
C911a		Imperforate pair	£800	
C912	33p	'A Rough Dog'	65	70
C913	37p	'Fino and Tiny'	65	70
		Set of 5	2.50	1.85
		Set of 5 Cylinder Blocks	18.50	
		Set of 5 Gutter Pairs	6.25	6.25
		First Day Cover		2.20
		Presentation Pack 215	2.40	
		PHQ132 Cards	1.80	

1990 (13 Nov.) Christmas. Snow scenes

C904	17p	Building a Snowman	25	25
C904a		Imperforate pair	£1350	
C904b		Imperforate top or bottom edge		
		ex Christmas book (pair)	3.00	
C905	22p	Fetching the Tree	30	30
C905a		Imperforate pair	£450	
C906	26p	Carol Singing	45	45
C907	31p	Tobogganing	65	70
C908	37p	Ice-Skating	65	70
		Set of 5	2.20	2.20
		Set of 5 Cylinder Blocks	16.50	
		Set of 5 Gutter Pairs	5.50	5.50
		First Day Cover		2.00
		Presentation Pack 213	2.20	
		PHQ131 Cards	1.50	
		Booklet (10 x 17p)	3.50	

1990 (13 Nov.) Collectors Year Pack

CP27	Collectors Year Pack 214	22.50

1990 (13 Nov.) Royal Mail Year Book - 7

YB7	Royal Mail Year Book	£19

A   B

C   D

E   F

G   H

I   J

No.   U/M   F/U   No.   U/M   F/U

1991 (5 Feb.) 'Good Luck'. Fluorescent Coated Paper. Perf. 15 x 14.

No.				U/M	F/U
C914	1st	**Bird's Nest**	(2 bands) (A)	65	65
C915	1st	**Rainbow**	(2 bands) (B)	65	65
C916	1st	**Magpie**	(2 bands) (C)	65	65
C917	1st	**Black Cat**	(2 bands) (D)	65	65
C918	1st	**Kingfisher**	(2 bands) (E)	65	65
C919	1st	**Mallard**	(2 bands) (F)	65	65
C920	1st	**Boot**	(2 bands) (G)	65	65
C921	1st	**Pot of Gold**	(2 bands) (H)	65	65
C922	1st	**Butterflies**	(2 bands) (I)	65	65
C923	1st	**Wishing Well**	(2 bands) (J)	65	65
	1st	**Booklet pane of 10**		6.50	5.90
		First Day Cover			5.70

The above are from the third Greetings Book losted on Page 414

 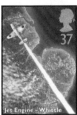

1991 (5 March) Scientific Achievements. Perf. 14 x 15

			U/M	F/U
C924	22p	**Faraday**	32	32
C924a		Imperforate pair.	£400	
C925	22p	**Babbage**	50	60
C926	31p	**Radar**	60	65
C927	37p	**Gloster Whittle E28/39**	60	65
		Set of 4	1.90	1.95
		Set of 4 Cylinder Blocks	14.50	
		Set of 4 Gutter Pairs	4.75	4.75
		First Day Cover		2.00
		Presentation Pack 216	2.20	
		PHQ133 Cards	1.50	

1991 (26 March.) 'Smiles'. Fluorescent Coated Paper. Perf. 15 x 14.
As numbers GS6/15 but inscribed 1st

No.				U/M	F/U
C928	1st	**Multicoloured**	(2 bands) (A)	60	60
C929	1st	**Multicoloured**	(2 bands) (B)	60	60
C930	1st	**Multicoloured**	(2 bands) (C)	60	60
C931	1st	**Multicoloured**	(2 bands) (D)	60	60
C932	1st	**Multicoloured**	(2 bands) (E)	60	60
C933	1st	**Multicoloured**	(2 bands) (F)	60	60
C934	1st	**Multicoloured**	(2 bands) (G)	60	60
C935	1st	**Multicoloured**	(2 bands) (H)	60	60
C936	1st	**Multicoloured**	(2 bands) (I)	60	60
C937	1st	**Multicoloured**	(2 bands) (J)	60	60
	1st	**Booklet pane of 10**		6.00	5.95
		First Day Cover			7.00

2000 (22 May) The Stamp Show 2000 Smilers sheet

SSP1	C928 to C937 1st (any) with The Stamp Show 2000 label - Set of 10		£20

2001 (3 July) 'Smiles' Smilers sheet

SSP5	C928 to C937 1st (any) with Smiles greeing label		
	Set of 10		£85

2002 (1 Oct.) 1st Smiles from Smilers sheet

| SSP9 | Horizontal strip of two stamps (Teddy and Dennis) and label | 4.00 | |

1991 (8 April) Europa. Space

C938/939	22p	Se-tenant pair	70	70
C938		Multicoloured	35	35
C939		Multicoloured	35	35
C940/941	37p	Se-tenant pair	1.30	1.40
C940		Multicoloured	85	90
C941		Multicoloured	85	90
		Set of 4	1.90	2.00
		Set of 2 Cylinder Blocks	4.90	
		Set of 2 Gutter Strips	4.75	4.75
		First Day Cover		2.00
		Presentation Pack 217	2.40	
		PHQ134 Cards	1.50	

1991 (11 June) Sport

C942	22p	Fencing	30	30
C943	26p	Hurdling	60	70
C944	31p	Diving	60	70
C945	37p	Rugby	60	70
		Set of 4	2.00	1.85
		Set of 4 Cylinder Blocks	14.90	
		Set of 4 Gutter Pairs	5.00	5.00
		First Day Cover		2.00
		Presentation Pack 218	2.20	
		PHQ135 Cards	1.20	

1991 (16 July) Roses

C946	22p	'Silver Jubilee'	30	30
C946a		Missing Silver (Queen's head)	£1000	
C946b		Black printed double		£2500
C947	26p	'Mme A. Carriere'	45	45
C948	31p	'Rosa Mayesii'	52	52
C949	33p	'Harvest Fayre'	55	60
C950	37p	'Mutabilis'	60	65
		Set of 5	2.30	2.00
		Set of 5 Cylinder Blocks	17.50	
		Set of 4 Gutter Pairs	5.75	5.75
		First Day Cover		2.00
		Presentation Pack 219	2.20	
		PHQ136 Cards	1.50	

1991 (20 Aug.) Dinosaurs. Perf. 14½ x 14

No.			U/M	F/U
C951	22p	Iguanadon	35	30
C951a		Imperforate pair	£1350	
C951b		Imperforate between stamp & bottom margin	£650	
C952	26p	Stegossaurus	50	50
C953	31p	Tyrannosaurus	60	60
C954	33p	Protocerstops	60	65
C955	37p	Triceratops	65	70
		Set of 5	2.60	2.30
		Set of 5 Cylinder Blocks	19.50	
		Set of 5 Gutter Pairs	6.50	6.50
		First Day Cover		2.00
		Presentation Pack 220	2.80	
		PHQ137 Cards	1.50	

1991 (12 Nov.) Christmas

No.			U/M	F/U
C960	18p	Adoration of the Magi (1 band)	27	27
C960a		Imperforate pair	£1750	
C961	24p	Mary and Jesus	33	33
C961a		Black (litho) treble & carmine double	£900	
C961b		Black (litho) and carmine double	£1250	
C961c		Black (litho) double	£1250	
C962	28p	The Holy Family	48	60
C963	33p	The Annunciation	55	60
C964	39p	The Flight to Egypt	58	60
		Set of 5	2.30	2.15
		Set of 5 Cylinder Blocks	17.50	
		Set of 5 Gutter Pairs	5.75	5.75
		First Day Cover		2.00
		Presentation Pack 222	2.30	
		PHQ139 Cards	1.50	
		Booklet pane (20 x 18p)	6.50	

1991 (12 Nov.) Collectors Pack

		U/M	F/U
CP28	Collectors Year Pack 223	22.50	

1991 (12 Nov.) Royal Mail Year Book - 8

		U/M	F/U
YB8	Royal Mail Year Book	£19	

1991 (17 Sept.) Ordnance Survey. Perf. 14½ x 14
Printers: Harrison & Sons (24p, 28p) in Lithography and Recess (24p) and
House of Questa in Lithography (33p, 39p)

No.			U/M	F/U
C956	24p	Map of 1816	33	33
C956a		Black printed double	£1750	
C956b	26p	Error of value	£3750	
C957	28p	Map of 1906	50	60
C958	33p	Map of 1959	65	65
C959	39p	Map of 1991	65	65
		Set of 4	2.00	1.90
		Set of 4 Cylinder Blocks	14.90	
		Set of 4 Gutter Pairs	5.00	5.00
		First Day Cover		2.00
		Presentation Pack 221	2.30	
		PHQ138 Cards	1.50	

1992 (14 Jan.) The Four Seasons. Winter

No.			U/M	F/U
C965	18p	Stag (1 band)	27	27
C966	24p	Hare	33	33
C966a		Imperforate pair	£400	
C967	28p	Fox	48	48
C968	33p	Thrush	65	65
C969	39p	Sheep	65	65
		Set of 5	2.25	2.20
		Set of 5 Cylinder Blocks	16.90	
		Set of 5 Gutter Pairs	5.65	5.65
		First Day Cover		2.00
		Presentation Pack 224	2.30	
		PHQ140 Cards	2.50	
		Booklet pane (4 x 39p)	3.00	

1992 (28 Jan.) 'Memories'. Fluorescent Coated Paper. Perf. 15 x 14.

No.			U/M	F/U
C970	1st	Multicoloured (2 bands) (A)	60	60
C971	1st	Multicoloured (2 bands) (B)	60	60
C972	1st	Multicoloured (2 bands) (C)	60	60
C973	1st	Multicoloured (2 bands) (D)	60	60
C974	1st	Multicoloured (2 bands) (E)	60	60
C975	1st	Multicoloured (2 bands) (F)	60	60
C976	1st	Multicoloured (2 bands) (G)	60	60
C977	1st	Multicoloured (2 bands) (H)	60	60
C978	1st	Multicoloured (2 bands) (I)	60	60
C979	1st	Multicoloured (2 bands) (J)	60	60
	1st	Booklet pane of 10	6.00	7.00
		First Day Cover		7.50
		Presentation Pack	7.00	

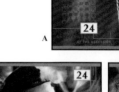

A

A

B

B

C

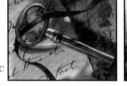

C

D

D

E

E

F

1992 (6 Feb.) 40th Anniversary of Accession. Perf. 14½ x 14

No.			U/M	F/U
C980/84	24p	Strip of 5 se-tenant	3.00	3.00
C980		Multicoloured (2 bands) (A)	75	50
C981		Multicoloured (2 bands) (B)	75	50
C982		Multicoloured (2 bands) (C)	75	50
C983		Multicoloured (2 bands) (D)	75	50
C984		Multicoloured (2 bands) (E)	75	50
		Strip of 5 Missing phosphor	£200	
		Any single stamp Missing phosphor	£32	
		Cylinder Block	6.90	
		Gutter Block of 10	7.50	7.50
		First Day Cover		2.20
		Presentation Pack 225	3.30	
		PHQ141 Cards	2.50	

G

I

H

J

1992 (10 March) Lord Tennyson. Perf. 14½ x 14

C985	24p	Marlin and Vivien	36	38
C986	28p	The Millers Daughter	48	50
C987	33p	Lady of Shalott	55	58
C988	39p	Mariana	60	65
		Set of 4	1.95	2.05
		Set of 4 Cylinder Blocks	14.60	
		Set of 4 Gutter Pairs	4.90	4.90
		First Day Cover		2.00
		Presentation Pack 226	2.40	
		PHQ142 Cards	2.20	

A

B

C

D

E

1992 (7 April) Europa. International Events
Printers: Harrison & Sons in Lithography and Recess (C and D) and House
of Questa in Lithography (A, B and E)

C989/990	24p	Se-tenant Pair	85	90
C989		Olympics '92 (A)	40	35
C990		Olympics '92 (B)	40	35
C991	24p	Columbus (C)	36	40
C991a		Missing Cream	£4750	
C992	39p	Operation Raleigh (D)	60	65
C993	39p	Expo '92 Seville (E)	60	65
		Set of 5	2.00	2.30
		Set of 4 Cylinder Blocks	14.50	
		Set of 3 Gutter Pairs & Gutter Strip of 4	7.50	7.50
		First Day Cover		2.00
		Presentation Pack 227	3.00	
		PHQ143 Cards	2.20	

1992 (16 June) The Civil War 1642 - 51

C994	24p	Pikeman	36	36
C994a		Imperforate pair *	£250	
C995	28p	Drummer	48	50
C996	33p	Musketeer	60	65
C997	39p	Standard Bearer	60	65
		Set of 4	2.10	2.15
		Set of 4 Cylinder Blocks	15.50	
		Set of 4 Gutter Pairs	5.25	5.25
		First Day Cover		2.00
		Presentation Pack 228	2.30	
		PHQ144 Cards	2.20	

* Caution, as some are damaged (waste)

1992 (21 July) Gilbert and Sullivan

			U/M	F/U
C998	18p	Yeoman of the Guard (1 band)	28	28
C999	24p	Gondoliers	36	40
C999a		Imperforate pair	£250	
C1000	28p	Mikado	48	50
C1001	33p	Pirates of Penzance	55	60
C1002	39p	Iolanthe	65	65
		Set of 5	2.10	2.20
		Set of 5 Cylinder Blocks	15.75	
		Set of 5 Gutter Pairs	5.25	5.25
		First Day Cover		2.00
		Presentation Pack 229	2.40	
		PHQ145 Cards	2.50	

1992 (15 Sept.) The Environment. Perf. 14 x 14½

			U/M	F/U
C1003	24p	Acid Rain	36	36
C1004	28p	Ozone Layer	48	50
C1005	33p	Greenhouse Effect	55	60
C1006	39p	Bird of Hope	65	65
		Set of 4	2.00	2.10
		Set of 4 Cylinder Blocks	15.20	
		Set of 4 Gutter Pairs	5.00	5.00
		First Day Cover		2.00
		Presentation Pack 230	2.20	
		PHQ146 Cards	2.50	

1992 (10 Nov.) Christmas. Stained Glass Windows

			U/M	F/U
C1008	18p	Angel Gabriel (centre band)	28	28
C1009	24p	Mary and Jesus	36	38
C1010	28p	King in Crown	40	45
C1011	33p	Three Shepherds	50	55
C1012	39p	Two Kings with Gifts	70	75
		Set of 5	2.20	2.15
		Set of 5 Cylinder Blocks	16.50	
		Set of 5 Gutter Pairs	5.50	5.50
		First Day Cover		2.00
		Presentation Pack 232	2.20	
		PHQ148 Cards	2.50	
		Booklet pane (20 x 18p)		

1992 (10 Nov.) Collectors Pack

CP29		Collectors Year Pack 233	22.50

1992 (11 Nov.) Royal Mail Year Book - 9

YB9		Royal Mail Year Book	£23

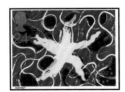

1992 (13 Oct.) Single European Market.

			U/M	F/U
C1007	24p	Multicoloured	40	35
		Cylinder Block	2.90	
		Gutter pair	1.00	1.00
		First Day Cover		1.00
		Presentation Pack 231	1.00	
		PHQ147 Card	40	

1993 (19 Jan.) Swans

No.			U/M	F/U
C1013	**18p**	**Swans Head** (1 band)	35	28
C1014	**24p**	**Cygnet**	70	70
C1015	**28p**	**Nesting Pair**	80	80
C1016	**33p**	**Eggs**	1.00	1.00
C1017	**39p**	**Mute Swan**	1.00	1.00
		Set of 5	3.40	2.50
		Set of 5 Cylinder Blocks	24.90	
		Set of 5 Gutter Pairs	8.50	8.50
		First Day Cover		2.10
		Presentation Pack 234	3.80	
		PHQ149 Cards	3.75	

A

B

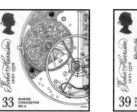

C

D

1993 (16 Feb.) Marine Chronometers. Perf. 14½ x 14

No.			U/M	F/U
C1028	**24p**	**Front View**	36	36
C1029	**28p**	**Escapement**	50	50
C1030	**33p**	**Balance and Spring**	60	65
C1031	**39p**	**Engraved Back**	65	65
		Set of 4	2.00	2.10
		Set of 4 Cylinder Blocks	14.90	
		Set of 4 Gutter Pairs	5.00	5.00
		First Day Cover		2.00
		Presentation Pack 235	2.80	
		PHQ150 Cards	2.95	

E

F

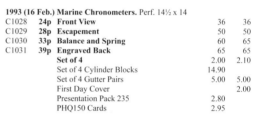

G

H

I

J

1993 (2 Feb.) 'Gifts'. Perf. 15 x 14 elliptical

No.			U/M	F/U
C1018	**1st**	**Multicoloured** (2 bands) (A)	60	60
C1019	**1st**	**Multicoloured** (2 bands) (B)	60	60
C1020	**1st**	**Multicoloured** (2 bands) (C)	60	60
C1021	**1st**	**Multicoloured** (2 bands) (D)	60	60
C1022	**1st**	**Multicoloured** (2 bands) (E)	60	60
C1023	**1st**	**Multicoloured** (2 bands) (F)	60	60
C1024	**1st**	**Multicoloured** (2 bands) (G)	60	60
C1025	**1st**	**Multicoloured** (2 bands) (H)	60	60
C1026	**1st**	**Multicoloured** (2 bands) (I)	60	60
C1027	**1st**	**Multicoloured** (2 bands) (J)	60	60
	1st	**Booklet pane of 10**	5.50	6.00
		First Day Cover		7.50
		Presentation Pack	8.50	
		PHQ Cards	4.00	5.50

1993 (16 March) Orchids

No.			U/M	F/U
C1032	**18p**	Dendrobium (1 band)	28	28
C1032a		Imperforate pair	£1750	
C1032b		Imperforate between stamp & bottom margin	£450	
C1033	**24p**	Paphiopedilum	36	38
C1034	**28p**	Cymbidium	50	50
C1035	**33p**	Vanda Rothschildiana	65	65
C1035a		Year omitted	7.50	7.50
C1035a		Coyypright & logo missing	£15	£10
C1036	**39p**	Dendrobium Vexillarius	65	65

No. C1023 also occurs as a pane of 4 in the £6 Beatrix Potter booklet.

	U/M	F/U
Set of 5	2.40	2.40
Set of 5 Cylinder Blocks	17.90	
Set of 5 Gutter Pairs	6.00	6.00
First Day Cover		2.00
Presentation Pack 236	2.40	
PHQ151 Cards	3.00	

1993 (11 May) Europa. Contemporary Art

			U/M	F/U
C1037	24p	Henry Moore	35	38
C1038	28p	Edward Bawden	50	50
C1039	33p	Stanley Spencer	60	65
C1040	39p	Ben Nicolson	65	65
		Set of 4	2.00	2.10
		Set of 4 Cylinder Blocks	14.90	
		Set of 4 Gutter Pairs	5.00	5.00
		First Day Cover		2.00
		Presentation Pack 237	3.00	
		PHQ152 Cards	3.00	

1993 (15 June) Roman Britain

			U/M	F/U
C1041	24p	Claudius (2 bands)	36	38
C1042	28p	Hadrian (2 bands)	50	55
C1043	33p	Roman (2 bands)	60	65
C1044	39p	'Christ' (2 bands)	65	65
		Set of 4	2.00	2.10
		Set of 4 Cylinder Blocks	14.90	
		Set of 4 Gutter Pairs	5.00	5.00
		First Day Cover		2.00
		Presentation Pack238	2.20	
		PHQ153 Cards	3.00	

1993 (20 July) Inland Waterways. Perf. 14½ x 14

			U/M	F/U
C1045	24p	Grand Junction (2 bands)	36	38
C1046	28p	Stainforth and Keadby (2 bands)	50	50
C1047	33p	Brecknock and Abergavenny (2 bands)	60	65
C1048	39p	Crinan (2 bands)	65	65
		Set of 4	2.00	2.10
		Set of 4 Cylinder Blocks	14.90	
		Set of 4 Gutter Pairs	5.00	5.00
		First Day Cover		2.00
		Presentation Pack 239	2.20	
		PHQ154 Cards	3.00	

1993 (11 Sept.) The Four Seasons. Autumn

			U/M	F/U
C1049	18p	Horse Chestnut (1 band)	30	3
C1050	24p	Blackberry	36	3
C1051	28p	Hazel	40	4
C1052	33p	Rowan	50	5
C1053	39p	Pear	65	6
		Set of 5	2.30	2.4
		Set of 5 Cylinder Blocks	17.30	
		Set of 5 Gutter Pairs	5.75	5.7
		First Day Cover		2.0
		Presentation Pack 240	2.20	
		PHQ155 Cards	3.75	

A SHERLOCK HOLMES & DR. WATSON
   "THE REIGATE SQUIRE"

B SHERLOCK HOLMES & SIR HENRY
   "THE HOUND OF THE BASKERVILLES"

SHERLOCK HOLMES & LESTRADE
"THE SIX NAPOLEONS" C

D SHERLOCK HOLMES & MYCROFT
   "THE GREEK INTERPRETER"

SHERLOCK HOLMES & MORIARTY
"THE FINAL PROBLEM" E

1993 (11 Oct.) Sherlock Holmes. Perf. 14 x 14½

No.			U/M	F/U
C1054	**24p**	**Dr. Watson** (A)	50	50
C1055	**24p**	**Sir Henry** (B)	50	50
C1056	**24p**	**Lestrade** (C)	50	50
C1057	**24p**	**Mycroft** (D)	50	50
C1058	**24p**	**Moriarty** (E)	50	50
		Strip of 5 se-tenant	2.50	2.50
		Cylinder Block	5.90	
		Gutter Strip of 10	6.25	6.25
		First Day Cover		2.50
		Presentation Pack 241	2.40	
		PHQ156 Cards	3.75	

1993 (9 Nov.) Christmas. Dickens' Christmas Carol

No.			U/M	F/U
C1059	**19p**	**Bob Cratchit** (1 band)	29	34
C1059a		Imperforate pair	£1500	
C1059b		Imperforate at lower margin	£350	
C1060	**25p**	**Mr and Mrs Fezziwig**	38	42
C1061	**30p**	**Scrooge**	50	55
C1062	**35p**	**The Prize Turkey**	60	65
C1063	**41p**	**Scrooge's Nephew**	65	70
		Set of 5	2.15	2.25
		Set of 5 Cylinder Blocks	16.00	
		Set of 5 Gutter Pairs	5.40	5.40
		First Day Cover		2.00
		Presentation Pack 242	2.80	
		PHQ157 Cards	3.75	

1993 (9 Nov.) Collectors Year Pack

			U/M
CP30		Collectors Year Pack 243	£30

1993 (9 Nov.) Royal Mail Year Book - 10

			U/M
YB10		Royal Mail Year Book	£28

1994 (18 Jan.) Age of Steam. Railway photographs. Perf. 14½

No.			U/M	F/U
C1064	19p	**West Highland Line** (1 band)	29	34
C1065	25p	**Kings Cross** (2 bands)	38	45
C1066	30p	**Blyth North** (2 bands)	50	55
C1067	35p	**Wigan Central** (2 bands)	60	65
C1068	41p	**Worc. and Birmingham Canal** (2 bands)	65	70
		Set of 5	2.15	2.25
		Set of 5 Cylinder Blocks	16.25	
		Set of 5 Gutter Pairs	5.40	5.40
		First Day Cover		2.50
		Presentation Pack 244	3.10	
		PHQ158 Cards	3.75	

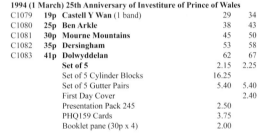

1994 (1 March) 25th Anniversary of Investiture of Prince of Wales

No.			U/M	F/U
C1079	19p	**Castell Y Wan** (1 band)	29	34
C1080	25p	**Ben Arkle**	38	43
C1081	30p	**Mourne Mountains**	45	50
C1082	35p	**Dersingham**	53	58
C1083	41p	**Dolwyddelan**	62	67
		Set of 5	2.15	2.25
		Set of 5 Cylinder Blocks	16.25	
		Set of 5 Gutter Pairs	5.40	5.40
		First Day Cover		2.40
		Presentation Pack 245	2.50	
		PHQ159 Cards	3.75	
		Booklet pane (30p x 4)	2.00	

A

B

C

D

E

F

G

H

I

J

1994 (1 Feb.) 'Messages'. Perf. 15 x 14 elliptical

No.			U/M	F/U
C1069	1st	**Multicoloured** (2 bands) (A)	55	60
C1070	1st	**Multicoloured** (2 bands) (B)	55	60
C1071	1st	**Multicoloured** (2 bands) (C)	55	60
C1072	1st	**Multicoloured** (2 bands) (D)	55	60
C1073	1st	**Multicoloured** (2 bands) (E)	55	60
C1074	1st	**Multicoloured** (2 bands) (F)	55	60
C1075	1st	**Multicoloured** (2 bands) (G)	55	60
C1076	1st	**Multicoloured** (2 bands) (H)	55	60
C1077	1st	**Multicoloured** (2 bands) (I)	55	60
C1078	1st	**Multicoloured** (2 bands) (J)	55	60
	1st	**Booklet pane of 10**	8.50	8.50
		First Day Cover		5.50
		Presentation Pack G4	8.50	
		PHQ Cards	4.00	7.50

1994 (12 April) Centenary of the Picture Postcard. Perf. 14 x 14½

			U/M	F/U
C1084	**19p**	**Blackpool Tower** (1 band)	29	34
C1085	**25p**	**'Where's my Litle Lad'** (2 bands)	38	43
C1086	**30p**	**'Wish you were Here'** (2 bands)	45	50
C1087	**35p**	**Punch and Judy** (2 bands)	53	58
C1088	**41p**	**Tower Bridge** (2 bands)	62	67
		Set of 5	2.15	2.25
		Set of 5 Cylinder Blocks	16.25	
		Set of 5 Gutter Pairs	5.40	5.40
		First Day Cover		2.40
		Presentation Pack 246	2.50	
		PHQ160 Cards	3.75	4.00

A

B

C

D

1994 (3 May) Channel Tunnel. Perf. 14 x 14½

			U/M	F/U
C1089/90	**25p**	**Se-tenant pair**	80	80
C1089		Lion and Cockerel (A)	38	43
C1090		Hands Across the Channel (B)	38	43
C1091/92	**41p**	**Se-tenant pair**	1.50	1.50
C1091/2a		Multiple colour shifts to left	£95	
C1091/2b		Imperforate pair	£1250	
C1091		Lion and Cockerel (C)	70	75
C1092		Hands Across the Channel (D)	70	75
		Set of 4	2.20	2.20
		Set of 2 Cylinder Blocks	5.50	
		First Day Cover		2.00
		Presentation Pack 247	2.50	
		PHQ161 Cards	3.00	

A

B   C

D   E

1994 (6 June) D - Day. War photographs. Perf. 14½ x 14

C1093/97

			U/M	F/U
	25p	**Strip of 5 se-tenant**	2.50	1.95
C1093		RAF Bostons (2 bands) (A)	60	65
C1094		HMS Warspite (2 bands) (B)	60	65
C1095		Gold Beach (2 bands) (C	60	65
C1096		**Sword Beach** (2 bands) (D)	60	65
C1097		Ouistreham (2 bands) (E)	60	65
		Cylinder Block	5.90	
		Gutter Block of 10	6.25	6.25
		First Day Cover		2.40
		Presentation Pack 248	3.60	
		PHQ162 Cards	3.75	

No.			U/M	F/U

1994 (5 July) Golf

C1098	19p	St. Andrews (1 band)	29	34
C1099	25p	Muirfield (2 bands)	38	43
C1100	30p	Carnoustie (2 bands)	45	50
C1101	35p	Royal Troon (2 bands)	53	58
C1102	41p	Turnberry (2 bands)	70	85
		Set of 5	2.40	2.40
		Set of 5 Cylinder Blocks	18.25	
		Set of 5 Gutter Pairs	6.00	6.00
		First Day Cover		2.00
		Presentation Pack 249	2.60	
		PHQ163 Cards	3.75	

1994 (2 Aug.) The Four Seasons. Summertime

C1103	19p	Lanelwedd (1 band)	29	34
C1104	25p	Wimbledon	38	43
C1105	30p	Cowes	50	55
C1106	35p	Lords	53	58
C1107	41p	Braemar	60	75
		Set of 5	2.10	2.40
		Set of 5 Cylinder Blocks	15.50	
		Set of 5 Gutter Pairs	5.25	5.25
		First Day Cover		2.00
		Presentation Pack 250	2.50	
		PHQ164 Cards	3.75	

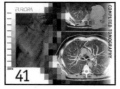

No.			U/M	F/U

1994 (27 Sept.) Europa. Medical Discoveries. Perf. 14 x 14½
Printer: Enschedé in Photogravure

C1108	25p	Ultrasonic	38	43
C1108a		Imperforate pair	£1750	
C1109	30p	Scanning	50	55
C1110	35p	Resonance	60	65
C1111	41p	Tanography	70	75
		Set of 4	1.90	1.90
		Set of 4 Cylinder Blocks	14.50	
		Set of 4 Gutter Pairs	4.75	4.75
		First Day Cover		2.00
		Presentation Pack 251	2.80	
		PHQ165 Cards	3.00	

1994 (1 Nov.) Christmas. Children

C1112	19p	Virgin Mary (1 band)	29	34
C1112a		Imperforate pair	£150	
C1112b		Multiple colour shift	£175	
C1113	25p	Three Wise Men	38	43
C1114	30p	Virgin and Child	50	55
C1114a		Imperforate pair	£2000	
C1115	35p	Shepherds	60	65
C1116	41p	Angels	70	75
		Set of 5	2.20	2.35
		Set of 5 Cylinder Blocks	16.25	
		Set of 5 Gutter Pairs	5.50	5.50
		First Day Cover		2.00
		Presentation Pack 252	2.50	
		PHQ166 Cards	3.75	

1994 (14 Nov.) Collectors Year Pack

CP31	Collectors Year Pack 253	22.50

1994 (14 Nov.) Royal Mail Year Book - 11

YB11	Royal Mail Year Book	£23

1995 (17 Jan.) Cats. Perf. 14½ x 14

No.	Value	Description	U/M	F/U
C1117	19p	**Black Sophie** (1 band)	29	34
C1118	25p	**Siamese and Tabby** (2 bands)	38	43
C1119	30p	**Ginger Chloe** (2 bands)	50	55
C1120	35p	**Tortoiseshell** (2 bands)	60	65
C1121	41p	**Fred** (2 bands)	70	75
		Set of 5	2.50	2.45
		Set of 5 Cylinder Blocks	18.50	
		Set of 5 Gutter Pairs	6.25	6.25
		First Day Cover		2.20
		Presentation Pack 254	3.30	
		PHQ167 Cards	4.00	

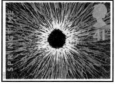

1995 (14 March) The Four Seasons. Springtime

No.	Value	Description	U/M	F/U
C1122	19p	**Dandelion** (1 band)	29	34
C1123	25p	**Sweet Chestnut Leaves** (2 bands)	38	43
C1124	30p	**Garlic Leaves** (2 bands)	50	55
C1125	35p	**Hazel Leaves** (2 bands)	60	65
C1126	41p	**Spring Grass** (2 bands)	70	75
		Set of 5	2.20	2.35
		Set of 5 Cylinder Blocks	16.50	
		Set of 5 Gutter Pairs	5.50	5.50
		First Day Cover		2.20
		Presentation Pack 255	2.50	
		PHQ168 Cards	4.00	

1995 (21 March) "Works of Art". Perf. 15 x 14 elliptical

No.	Value	Description	U/M	F/U
C1127	1st	**Multicoloured** (2 bands) (A)	60	60
C1128	1st	**Multicoloured** (2 bands) (B)	60	60
C1129	1st	**Multicoloured** (2 bands) (C)	60	60
C1130	1st	**Multicoloured** (2 bands) (D)	60	60
C1131	1st	**Multicoloured** (2 bands) (E)	60	60
C1132	1st	**Multicoloured** (2 bands) (F)	60	60
C1133	1st	**Multicoloured** (2 bands) (G)	60	60
C1134	1st	**Multicoloured** (2 bands) (H)	60	60
C1135	1st	**Multicoloured** (2 bands) (I)	60	60
C1136	1st	**Multicoloured** (2 bands) (J)	60	60
		Booklet pane of 10	6.00	6.00
		First Day Cover		4.75
		Presentation Pack G4	8.50	
		PHQ Cards	3.75	7.50
		Missing phosphor (Complete booklet)	£8000	
		Missing phosphor (FDC)		£3500
		Missing phosphor (Used single)		£400
		Missing phosphor (unfolded pres. pack)	£5500	

1995 (11 April) National Trust

No.			U/M	F/U
C1137	19p	Fireplace (1 band)	29	34
C1138	25p	Oak Seedling (2 bands)	38	43
C1139	30p	Carved Table Leg (2 bands)	50	55
C1140	35p	St. Davids (2 bands)	60	70
C1141	41p	Elizabethan Window (2 bands)	70	75
		Set of 5	2.20	2.15
		Set of 5 Cylinder Blocks	16.50	
		Set of 5 Gutter Pairs	5.50	5.50
		First Day Cover		2.20
		Presentation Pack 256	2.50	
		PHQ169 Cards	4.00	

1995 (2 May) Peace

No.			U/M	F/U
C1142	19p	Troops (1 band) (A)	35	38
C1143	19p	Hand and Red Cross (1 band) (B)	35	38
C1144	25p	St. Paul's Cathedral (2 bands) (C)	45	48
C1145	25p	Hand and Dove (2 bands) (D)	45	48
C1145a		Imperforate vertical pair	£2750	
C1146	30p	UN Hands (2 bands)	60	70
		Set of 5	2.20	2.50
		Set of 5 Cylinder Blocks	16.50	
		Set of 5 Gutter Pairs	5.50	5.50
		First Day Cover		2.20
		Presentation Pack 257	2.90	
		PHQ170 Cards	4.00	

2005 (5 July) End of the War 1945 - 2005

No.			U/M	F/U
C1144a	1st	St. Paul's Cathedral	1.75	1.85
MS32		Miniature Sheet	3.50	
		First Day Cover		3.50

1995 (6 June) Science Fiction

No.			U/M	F/U
C1147	25p	The Time Machine (2 bands)	38	43
C1147a		Imperforate between stamp & top margin	£150	
C1148	30p	First Men on the Moon (2 bands)	45	50
C1149	35p	War of the Worlds (2 bands)	53	58
C1150	41p	Shape of Things (2 bands)	70	75
		Set of 4	2.10	2.25
		Set of 4 Cylinder Blocks	15.60	
		Set of 4 Gutter Pairs	5.25	5.25
		First Day Cover		2.20
		Presentation Pack 258	2.60	
		PHQ171 Cards	3.00	

A   B

C   D

A

1995 (8 Aug.) Shakespeare's Globe Theatre (2 bands) Perf 14½

Printer: Walsall in Lithography

No.			U/M	F/U
C1151	**25p**	The Swan (A)	55	55
C1152	**25p**	The Rose (B)	55	55
C1153	**25p**	The Globe 1599 (C)	55	55
C1154	**25p**	The Hope (D)	55	55
C1155	**25p**	The Glose 1614 (E)	55	55
		Set of 5	2.50	2.65
		Cylinder Block	6.25	
		Gutter Strip of 10	6.25	6.25
		First Day Cover		2.20
		Presentation Pack 259	2.60	
		PHQ172 Cards	4.00	

1995 (3 Oct.) Centenary of Rugby League Perf 14½ x 14

No.			U/M	F/U
C1160	**19p**	Harold Wagstaff (1 band)	35	38
C1161	**25p**	Gus Risman (2 bands)	45	48
C1162	**30p**	Jim Sullivan (2 bands)	50	55
C1163	**35p**	Billy Battem (2 bands)	55	60
C1164	**41p**	Brian Bevan (2 bands)	60	80
		Set of 5	2.30	2.45
		Set of 5 Cylinder Blocks	17.25	
		Set of 5 Gutter Pairs	5.75	5.75
		First Day Cover		2.50
		Presentation Pack 261	3.00	
		PHQ174 Cards	4.00	

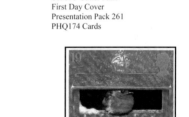

1995 (5 Sept.) Pioneers of Communications Perf 14½ x 14

No.			U/M	F/U
C1156	**19p**	Rowland Hill - Penny Post (1 band)	35	38
C1157	**25p**	Rowland Hill - Penny Black	45	48
C1157a		Missing silver	£350	
C1158	**41p**	Marconi - Wireless	65	70
C1159	**60p**	Marconi - SOS	1.00	1.10
		Set of 4	2.20	2.25
		Set of 4 Cylinder Blocks	16.50	
		Set of 4 Gutter Pairs	5.50	5.50
		First Day Cover		2.20
		Presentation Pack 260	2.60	
		PHQ173 Cards	3.00	

1995 (30 Oct.) Christmas. Robins Perf 15 x 14

No.			U/M	F/U
C1165	19p	Letter Box (1 band)	35	38
C1166	25p	Holly (2 bands)	45	48
C1167	30p	Milk Bottles (2 bands)	50	55
C1168	41p	Road Sign (2 bands)	70	67
C1169	60p	Door Handle (2 bands)	1.00	95
		Set of 5	2.40	2.35
		Set of 5 Cylinder Blocks	17.90	
		Set of 5 Gutter Pairs	6.00	6.00
		First Day Cover		2.50
		Presentation Pack 262	3.00	
		PHQ175 Cards	4.00	

2000 (3 Oct.) 19p Christmas Robin from Smilers sheet

SSP2	Strip of two stamps *plus* label	£10	

1995 (30 Oct.) Collectors Year Pack

CP32	Presentation Pack 263	22.50

1995 (30 Oct.) Royal Mail Year Book -12

YB12	Royal Mail Year Book	£23

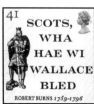

1996 (25 Jan.) Bi-centenary of death of Robert Burns Perf 14½

C1170	19p	'To a Mouse' (1 band)	35	38
C1171	25p	'My Luves Like' (2 bands)	50	48
C1172	41p	'Scots who Hae' (2 bands)	70	67
C1173	60p	'Auld Lang Syne' (2 bands)	1.00	95
		Set of 4	2.50	2.25
		Set of 4 Cylinder Blocks	18.50	
		Set of 4 Gutter Pairs	6.25	6.25
		First Day Cover		2.50
		Presentation Pack 264	2.50	
		PHQ1765 Cards	3.00	

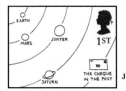

1996 (26 Feb.) "Cartoons". All over phosphor. Perf. 14½ x 14 elliptical

C1174	1st	Multicoloured (A)	55	60
C1175	1st	Multicoloured (B)	55	60
C1176	1st	Multicoloured (C)	55	60
C1177	1st	Multicoloured (D)	55	60
C1178	1st	Multicoloured (E)	55	60
C1179	1st	Multicoloured (F)	55	60
C1180	1st	Multicoloured (G)	55	60
C1181	1st	Multicoloured (H)	55	60
C1182	1st	Multicoloured (I)	55	60
C1183	1st	Multicoloured (J)	55	60
		Booklet pane of 10	6.00	6.00
		First Day Cover		6.00
		Presentation Pack G5	8.50	
		PHQ Cards	4.00	

1996 (11 Nov.) "Cartoons". Two blue phosphor bands.
Perf. 14½ x 14 elliptical.
Designs as No's:C1174 - C1183

C1184	1st	Multicoloured (2 bands) (A)	2.60	2.00
C1185	1st	Multicoloured (2 bands) (B)	2.60	2.00
C1186	1st	Multicoloured (2 bands) (C)	2.60	2.00
C1187	1st	Multicoloured (2 bands) (D)	2.60	2.00
C1188	1st	Multicoloured (2 bands) (E)	2.60	2.00
C1189	1st	Multicoloured (2 bands) (F)	2.60	2.00
C1190	1st	Multicoloured (2 bands) (G)	2.60	2.00
C1191	1st	Multicoloured (2 bands) (H)	2.60	2.00
C1192	1st	Multicoloured (2 bands) (I)	2.60	2.00
C1193	1st	Multicoloured (2 bands) (J)	2.60	2.00
		Booklet pane of 10	£26	£20
		First Day Cover		6.00

2001 (18 Dec.) 1st Cartoons from Smilers sheet

SSP6	Stamp *plus* label (any)		4.00

2003 (29 July) Crossword Cartoons from Smilers sheet

SSP13	1st Cartoons *plus* label (any)		1.00
SSP13a	Missing phosphor, set of 10		£500

1996 (12 March) 50th Anniversary of Wildfowl and Wetlands Perf 14 x 14½

No.			U/M	F/U
C1194	**19p**	**Muscovy Duck** (1 band)	35	38
C1195	**25p**	**Lapwing**	45	48
C1196	**30p**	**White-fronted Goose**	50	55
C1197	**35p**	**Bittern**	62	67
C1198	**41p**	**Whooper Swan**	60	70
		Set of 5	2.20	2.35
		Set of 5 Cylinder Blocks	16.50	
		Set of 5 Gutter Pairs	5.50	5.50
		First Day Cover		2.50
		Presentation Pack 265	2.50	
		PHQ177 Cards	4.00	

1996 (16 April) Centenary of Cinema Perf 14 x 14½

No.			U/M	F/U
C1199	**19p**	**Cinema** (1 band)	38	38
C1200	**25p**	**Screen Kiss** (2 bands)	45	48
C1201	**30p**	**Ticket** (2 bands)	50	55
C1202	**35p**	**Pathe News** (2 bands)	65	70
C1203	**41p**	**Big Screen Showing** (2 bands)	70	80
		Set of 5	2.30	2.50
		Set of 5 Cylinder Blocks	17.50	
		Set of 5 Gutter Pairs	5.75	5.75
		First Day Cover		2.50
		Presentation Pack 266	2.50	
		PHQ178 Cards	4.00	

U/M   F/U   No.

1996 (14 May) European Football Championship Perf 14½ x 14

No.			U/M	F/U
C1204	**19p**	**Dixie Dean** (1 band)	38	38
C1205	**25p**	**Bobby Moore** (2 bands)	45	48
C1206	**35p**	**Duncan Edwards** (2 bands)	50	55
C1207	**41p**	**Billy Wright** (2 bands)	65	75
C1208	**60p**	**Danny Blanchflower** (2 bands)	70	75
		Set of 5	2.30	2.50
		Set of 5 Cylinder Blocks	17.25	
		Set of 5 Gutter Pairs	5.75	5.75
		First Day Cover		2.50
		Presentation Pack 267	3.30	
		PHQ179 Cards	4.00	

1996 (9 July) Olympics and Paralympics - Atlanta Perf. 14½ x 14

No.			U/M	F/U
C1209/1213				
	26p	**Strip of 5 se-tenant**	2.00	2.00
C1209/1213a				
		Imperforate between stamp and left margin only (strip of five)	£750	
C1209	**26p**	Sprint Start (2 bands) (A)	40	45
C1210	**26p**	Javelin (2 bands) (B)	40	45
C1211	**26p**	Basketball (2 bands) (C)	40	45
C1212	**26p**	Swimming (2 bands) (D)	40	45
C1213	**26p**	Victory (2 bands) (E)	40	45
		Cylinder Block		
		Gutter Block of 10	5.00	5.00
		First Day Cover		2.50
		Presentation Pack 268	2.20	
		PHQ180 Cards	3.50	

2005 (5 Aug.) London 2012 Host City

No.			U/M	F/U
C1209a	**1st**	**Sprint Start** (2 bands) (D)	40	45
C1210b	**1st**	**Javelin** (2 bands) (B)	40	45
C1211c	**1st**	**Basketball** (2 bands) (E)	40	45
C1212d	**1st**	**Swimming** (2 bands) (C)	40	45
C1213e	**1st**	**Victory** (2 bands) (A)	40	45
MS33		Complete Miniature Sheet	2.70	2.75
		First Day Cover		3.95
		Presentation Pack		
		PHQ Cards		

1996 (6 Aug.) Europa - Famous Women Perf 14

No.			U/M	F/U
C1214	**20p**	**Dorothy Hodgkin** (1 band)	30	30
C1215	**26p**	**Margot Fonteyn** (2 bands)	40	40
C1215a		Imperforate pair	£300	
C1216	**31p**	**Elisabeth Frink** (2 bands)	45	50
C1217	**37p**	**Daphne Du Maurier** (2 bands)	60	70
C1218	**43p**	**Marea Hartman** (2 bands)	70	80
		Set of 5	2.45	2.55
		Set of 5 Cylinder Blocks	18.25	
		Set of 5 Gutter Pairs	6.20	6.20
		First Day Cover		2.50
		Presentation Pack 269	2.50	
		PHQ181 Cards	2.50	

1996 (3 Sept.) 50th Anniversary of Children's Television Perf 14½ x 14

No.			U/M	F/U
C1219	20p	**Muffin the Mule** (1 band)	30	30
C1219a		Perf 15 x 14 ex Prestige book	2.50	
C1220	26p	**Sooty** (2 bands)	75	80
C1221	31p	**Stingray** (2 bands)	40	40
C1222	37p	**Clangers** (2 bands)	45	50
C1223	43p	**Dangermouse** (2 bands)	70	70
		Set of 5	2.65	2.65
		Set of 5 Cylinder Blocks	19.75	
		Set of 5 Gutter Pairs	6.75	6.75
		First Day Cover		2.50
		Presentation Pack 270	2.70	
		PHQ182 Cards	4.00	

1996 (1 Oct.) Classic Sports Cars Perf 14½

No.			U/M	F/U
C1224	20p	**Triumph** (1 band)	30	30
C1225	26p	**M. G.** (2 bands)	40	40
C1225a		Imperforate pair	£600	
C1226	37p	**Austin Healey** (2 bands)	45	50
C1226a		Imperforate pair	£750	
C1227	43p	**Jaguar** (2 bands)	70	70
C1227a		Imperforate pair	£1100	
C1228	63p	**Morgan** (2 bands)	90	95
		Set of 5	2.55	2.65
		Set of 5 Cylinder Blocks	19.90	
		Set of 5 Gutter Pairs	6.40	6.40
		First Day Cover		2.50
		Presentation Pack 271	3.50	
		PHQ183 Cards	2.50	

1996 (28 Oct.) Christmas Perf 15 x 14

No.			U/M	F/U
C1229	2nd	**Lo, The Star** (1 band)	30	30
C1230	1st	**Blessed are Thou..** (2 bands)	40	40
C1231	31p	**Every one to his own City** (2 bands)	45	50
C1232	43p	**and shall be called the Son ...**(2 bands)	70	70
C1233	63p	**I bring you tidings of great joy** (2 bands)	1.00	1.05
		Set of 5	2.55	2.65
		Set of 5 Cylinder Blocks	19.25	
		Set of 5 Gutter Pairs	6.40	6.40
		First Day Cover		2.50
		Presentation Pack 272	2.90	
		PHQ184 Cards	4.00	

1996 (28 Oct.) Collectors Year Pack

		U/M	F/U
CP33	Collectors Year Pack 273	22.50	

1996 (28 Oct.) Royal Mail Year Book - 13

		U/M	F/U
YB13	Royal Mail Year Book	£23	

2003 (21 Jan.) 1st Flowers from Smilers sheet

		U/M	F/U
SSP11	1st Flowers *plus* label (any)	2.50	
SSP11a	Broad centre band	£50	

1997 (6 Jan.) "19th Century Flower Paintings". Perf. 14½ x 14 elliptical

			U/M	F/U
C1234	**1st**	**Multicoloured** (2 bands) (A)	55	60
C1235	**1st**	**Multicoloured** (2 bands) (B)	55	60
C1236	**1st**	**Multicoloured** (2 bands) (C)	55	60
C1237	**1st**	**Multicoloured** (2 bands) (D)	55	60
C1238	**1st**	**Multicoloured** (2 bands) (E)	55	60
C1239	**1st**	**Multicoloured** (2 bands) (F)	55	60
C1240	**1st**	**Multicoloured** (2 bands) (G)	55	60
C1241	**1st**	**Multicoloured** (2 bands) (H)	55	60
C1242	**1st**	**Multicoloured** (2 bands) (I)	55	60
C1243	**1st**	**Multicoloured** (2 bands) (J)	55	60
	1st	**Booklet pane of 10**	5.00	5.20
		Set of 10 singles		2.20
		First Day Cover		7.00
		Presentation Pack G6	9.50	
		PHQ Cards	4.50	6.50
		Gold & Phosphor missing (complete book)	£15000	
		Gold & Phosphor missing (pane only)	£8000	

1997 (21 Jan.) 450th Death Anniversary of Henry VIII Perf. 15 (No. C1244)
Perf 14 x 15 (Others)

			U/M	F/U
C1244	**26p**	**King Henry VIII** (A)	70	70
C1244a		Imperforate pair	£750	
C1245	**26p**	**Catherine of Aragon** (B)	50	55
C1246	**26p**	**Anne Boleyn** (C)	50	55
C1247	**26p**	**Jane Seymour** (D)	50	55
C1248	**26p**	**Anne of Cleaves** (E)	50	55
C1249	**26p**	**Catherine Howard** (F)	50	55
C1250	**26p**	**Catherine Parr** (G)	50	55
		Set of 7	3.20	3.20
		Se-tenant Strip of 6 C1245-C1250)	3.75	
		Set of 2 Cylinder Blocks	12.50	

		U/M	F/U
Gutter Pair & Gutter Strip of 12		8.00	8.00
First Day Cover			3.00
Presentation Pack 274		5.00	
PHQ185 Cards		4.00	

1997 (11 March) Religious Anniversaries Perf 14½

			U/M	F/U
C1251	26p	St. Columbia in Boat	45	48
C1252	37p	St. Columbia on Iona	50	55
C1253	43p	St. Augustine with King Ethelbert	70	75
C1254	63p	St. Augustines with Model of Cathedral	1.00	1.05
		Set of 4	2.30	2.45
		Set of 4 Cylinder Blocks	17.25	
		Set of 4 Gutter Pairs	5.75	5.75
		First Day Cover		2.00
		Presentation Pack 275	2.60	
		PHQ186 Cards	3.00	

1997 (10 June) British Aircraft Designers Perf 15 x 14

			U/M	F/U
C1259	20p	Mitchell - Supermarine (1 band)	35	40
C1260	26p	Chadwick - Avro (2 bands)	45	48
C1261	37p	Bishop - De Havilland (2 bands)	50	55
C1262	43p	Carter - Gloster (2 bands)	80	85
C1263	63p	Camm - Hawker (2 bands)	1.10	1.15
		Set of 5	2.90	2.95
		Set of 5 Cylinder Blocks	21.50	
		Set of 5 Gutter Pairs	7.25	7.25
		First Day Cover		2.60
		Presentation Pack 277	4.40	
		PHQ188 Cards	2.50	

Dracula · Frankenstein · Dr Jekyll and Mr Hyde · The Hound of the Baskervilles

1997 (13 May) Tales and Legends Perf 14 x 15 - 16mm bands

			U/M	F/U
C1255	26p	Dracula	1.50	48
C1255a		9mm bands	2.50	
C1256	31p	Frankenstein	60	65
C1257	37p	Dr Jekyll and Mr Hyde	60	75
C1258	43p	Hound of the Baskevilles	2.00	95
C1258a		9mm bands	2.50	
		Set of 4	2.40	2.40
		Set of 4 Cylinder Blocks	17.95	
		Set of 4 Gutter Pairs	6.00	6.00
		First Day Cover		2.50
		Presentation Pack 276	2.50	
		PHQ187 Cards	3.00	

1997 (8 July) 50th Anniversary of the British Horse Society Perf 14½

			U/M	F/U
C1264	20p	St. Patrick (1 band)	35	40
C1265	26p	River Star (2 bands)	45	48
C1266	43p	Thompson (2 bands)	70	75
C1267	63p	Janus (2 bands)	1.00	1.05
		Set of 4	2.20	2.35
		Set of 4 Cylinder Blocks	16.50	
		Set of 4 Gutter Pairs	5.50	5.50
		First Day Cover		2.60
		Presentation Pack 278	2.90	
		PHQ189 Cards	3.00	

1997 (12 Aug.) Sub-Post Offices Perf 14½

No.			U/M	F/U
C1268	20p	Haroldswick (1 band)	35	40
C1269	26p	Painswick (2 bands)	45	48
C1270	43p	Beddgelert (2 bands)	70	75
C1271	63p	Ballyroney (2 bands)	1.00	1.15
		Set of 4	2.20	2.35
		Set of 4 Cylinder Blocks	16.50	
		Set of 4 Gutter Pairs	5.50	5.50
		First Day Cover		2.60
		Presentation Pack 279	2.90	
		PHQ190 Cards	3.00	

Enid Blyton's *Noddy*

Enid Blyton's *Famous Five*

Enid Blyton's *Secret Seven*

Enid Blyton's *Faraway Tree*

Enid Blyton's *Malory Towers*

1997 (9 Sept.) Birth Centenary of Enid Blyton Perf 14 x 14½

No.			U/M	F/U
C1272	20p	Noddy (1 band)	35	40
C1273	26p	Famous Five (2 bands)	45	48
C1274	37p	Secret Seven (2 bands)	50	55
C1275	43p	Faraway Tree (2 bands)	80	85
C1276	63p	Malory Towers (2 bands)	1.00	1.25
		Set of 5	2.60	2.60
		Set of 5 Cylinder Blocks	19.50	
		Set of 5 Gutter Pairs	6.50	6.50
		First Day Cover		2.80
		Presentation Pack 280	2.90	
		PHQ191 Cards	4.00	

1997 (27 Oct.) Christmas, 150ᵗʰ Anniversary of the Cracker Perf 15 x 14

No.			U/M	F/U
C1277	2nd	Santa 'in the Moon' (1 band)	35	40
C1277a		Imperforate pair	£1250	
C1278	1st	Santa 'Bursting out' (2 bands)	45	48
C1279	31p	Santa 'Riding a Cracker' (2 bands)	48	50
C1279a		Imperforate pair	£1250	
C1280	43p	Santa 'Riding a Snowball' (2 bands)	70	75
C1281	63p	Santa ' Down the Chimney' (2 bands)	1.10	1.05
		Set of 5	2.60	2.90
		Set of 5 Cylinder Blocks	19.50	
		Set of 5 Gutter Pairs	6.50	6.50
		First Day Cover		2.80
		Presentation Pack 281	2.90	
		PHQ193 Cards	3.95	4.40

2000 (3 Oct.) 1st Father Christmas from Smilers sheet

SSP3		Stamp *plus* label		£10

2002 (1 Oct.) 1st Father Christmas from Smilers sheet

No.			U/M	F/U
SSP10	Se-tenant pair *plus* label (any)		2.50	

1997 (13 Nov.) Royal Golden Wedding Perf 15

No.			U/M	F/U
C1282	20p	**"Driver"** - Sepia (1 band)	35	40
C1282a		Imperforate pair	£2000	
C1283	26p	**"Snowdon"** - Blue (2 bands)	45	48
C1283a		Imperforate pair	£2500	
C1284	43p	**"Driver"** - Grey (2 bands)	70	75
C1285	63p	**"Snowdon"** - Grey (2 bands)	1.00	1.15
		Set of 4	2.30	2.30
		Set of 4 Cylinder Blocks	17.25	
		Set of 4 Gutter Pairs	5.75	5.75
		First Day Cover		2.75
		Presentation Pack 282	3.30	
		PHQ192 Cards	3.95	

1997 (13 Nov.) Collectors Pack

No.			U/M	F/U
CP34	Collectors Year Pack 283		£30	

1997 (13 Nov.) Royal Mail Year Book - 14

No.			U/M	F/U
CB14	Royal Mail Year Book		£30	

1998 (20 Jan.) Endangered Species Perf 14 x 14½

No.			U/M	F/U
C1286	20p	**Dormouse** (1 band)	35	40
C1286a		Imperforate pair	£100	
C1287	26p	**Lady Slipper Orchid** (2 bands)	45	48
C1288	31p	**Song Thrush** (2 bands)	48	50
C1289	37p	**Ram's-horn Snail** (2 bands)	50	55
C1290	43p	**Mole Cricket** (2 bands)	80	75
C1291	63p	**Devil'sBolete** (2 bands)	1.10	1.05
		Set of 6	3.30	3.45
		Set of 6 Cylinder Blocks	24.50	
		Set of 6 Gutter Pairs	8.25	8.25
		First Day Cover		2.95
		Presentation Pack 284	3.30	
		PHQ194 Cards	5.00	

A

B   C

Commemoratives
No.   U/M F/U No.

Queen Elizabeth II
U/M F/U

D   **E**

1998 (3 Feb.) Diana, Princess of Wales Perf 14 x 15
C1292/96

26p	**Se-tenant strip of 5**	2.20	2.10
C1292/96a			
	Imperforate strip of five	£15000	
C1292	Photo by Snowden (1 band) (A)	55	48
C1293	Photo by John Stilwell (2 bands) (B)	55	48
C1294	Photo by Snowden (2 bands) (C)	55	48
C1295	Photo by Tim Graham (2 bands) (D)	55	48
C1296	Photo by T. Donovan (2 bands) (E)	55	48
	Cylinder Block	5.50	
	Gutter strip of 10	5.50	5.50
	First Day Cover		2.50
	Presentation Pack	4.50	
	Presentation Pack (Welsh version)	£57	

A

B   **C**

D   **E**

1998 (24 Feb.) The Queen's Beasts (2 bands) Perf 15 x 14
C1297/C1301

	Se-tenant strip of 5	2.30	2.40
C1297/1301a			
	Missing green (Se-tenant strip of five)	£8500	
C1297/1301b	Missing phosphor (Se-tenant strip of five)	£25	
C1297	Lion of England (A)	40	48
C1298	Falcon of Plantagenet (B)	40	48
C1299	Lion of Mortimer (C)	40	48
C1300	Greyhound of Richmond (D)	40	48
C1301	Unicorn of Scotland (E)	40	48
	Cylinder Block	7.70	
	Gutter strip of 10	5.75	5.75
	First Day Cover		2.45
	Presentation Pack 285	2.50	
	PHQ195 Cards	4.00	

1998 (24 Mar.) Lighthouses Perf 15 x 14
Printer: House of Questa in Lithography

C1302	**20p**	**St. John's Point** (1 band)	35	40
C1303	**26p**	**The Smalls** (2 bands)	45	48
C1304	**37p**	**Needles Rock** (2 bands)	50	55
C1305	**43p**	**Bell Rock** (2 bands)	70	75
C1306	**63p**	**Eddystone** (2 bands)	1.00	1.20
		Set of 5	2.55	2.55
		Set of 5 Cylinder Blocks	19.25	
		Set of 5 Gutter Pairs	6.40	6.80
		First Day Cover		2.70
		Presentation Pack 286	3.00	
		PHQ196 Cards	4.00	

Commemoratives
No.
U/M   F/U

Queen Elizabeth II
No.
U/M   F/U

1998 (23 Apr.) Comedians Perf 15 x 14
Printer: Walsall in Lithography

			U/M	F/U
C1307	20p	**Tommy Cooper** (1 band)	35	40
C1307a		Vermillion printed double	£1500	
C1308	26p	**Eric Morcombe** (2 bands)	45	48
C1308a		Vermillion printed double	£250	
C1309	37p	**Joyce Grenfell** (2 bands)	50	55
C1309a	30p	Value error (mint & FDC)	£1450	£1800
C1310	43p	**Les Dawson** (2 bands)	80	75
C1311	63p	**Peter Cook** (2 bands)	1.00	1.05
		Set of 5	2.65	2.70
		Set of 5 Cylinder Blocks	19.80	
		Set of 5 Gutter Pairs	6.70	6.70
		First Day Cover		2.70
		Presentation Pack 287	3.00	
		PHQ197 Cards	4.00	

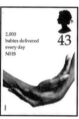

1998 (23 June) 50 Years of NHS Perf 15 x 14
Printer: House of Questa in Lithography

			U/M	F/U
C1312	20p	**10,000 Donors** (1 band)	35	40
C1313	26p	**1,700,000 Prescriptions** (2 bands)	45	48
C1314	43p	**2,000 Babies** (2 bands)	70	75
C1315	63p	**130,000 Outpatients** (2 bands)	1.20	1.35
		Set of 4	2.40	2.40
		Set of 4 Cylinder Blocks	17.80	
		Set of 4 Gutter Pairs	6.00	6.00
		First Day Cover		3.00
		Presentation Pack 288	2.70	
		PHQ198 Cards	3.00	

1998 (21 July) Magical Worlds Perf 15 x 14
Printer: De La Rue in Photogravure

			U/M	F/U
C1316	20p	**The Hobbit** (1 band)	35	40
C1317	26p	**Lion, Witch and Wardrobe** (2 bands)	45	48
C1317a		Imperforate pair	£750	
C1318	37p	**The Phoenix and the Carpet** (2 bands)	50	55
C1319	43p	**The Borrowers** (2 bands)	70	85
C1320	63p	**Through the Looking Glass** (2 bands)	1.20	1.35
		Set of 5	2.80	2.60
		Set of 5 Cylinder Blocks	21.50	
		Set of 5 Gutter Pairs	7.00	7.00
		First Day Cover		3.40
		Presentation Pack 289	3.00	
		PHQ199 Cards	4.50	

1998 (25 Aug.) Europa Carnival Perf 15 x 14
Printer: Walsall in Photogravure

			U/M	F/U
C1321	20p	**Woman in Yellow** (1 band)	35	40
C1321a		Imperforate pair		
C1322	26p	**Woman in Blue** (2 bands)	45	48
C1323	43p	**Children** (2 bands)	70	75
C1323A	63p	**Child in Green** (2 bands)	1.00	1.25
		Set of 4	2.30	2.25
		Set of 4 Cylinder Blocks	16.95	
		Set of 4 Gutter Pairs	5.75	5.75
		First Day Cover		3.00
		Presentation Pack 290	2.70	
		PHQ200 Cards	3.00	

1998 (29 Sep.) Speed Perf 15 x 14
Printer: De La Rue in Photogravure

No.			U/M	F/U
C1324	**20p**	**Sir Malcolm Campbell** (1 centre band)	35	40
C1324a		Left band	1.25	1.25
C1324b		Right band	1.25	1.25
C1325	**26p**	**Sir Henry Seagrave** (2 bands)	45	48
C1325a		Missing Rosine	£2250	
C1326	**30p**	**John G. Parry Thomas** (2 bands)	50	55
C1327	**43p**	**John R. Cobb** (2 bands)	80	75
C1328	**63p**	**Donald Campbell** (2 bands)	1.10	1.05
		Set of 5	2.75	2.90
		Set of 5 Cylinder Blocks	21.25	
		Set of 5 Gutter Pairs	6.90	6.90
		First Day Cover		3.00
		Presentation Pack 291	3.30	
		PHQ201 Cards	4.00	

C1324a and C1324b are Perf 14 x 13 and are from 'Breaking Barriers'
Prestige Book issued 13th Oct. 1998

1998 (2 Nov.) Christmas Perf 15 x 14
Printer: De La Rue in Photogravure

No.			U/M	F/U
C1329	**20p**	**Adoring Angel** (1 band)	35	40
C1329a		Imperforate pair	£400	
C1330	**26p**	**Praying Angel** (2 bands)	45	48
C1330a	26p	Imperforate pair	£1300	
C1331	**30p**	**Angel Playing Pipe** (2 bands)	50	55
C1332	**43p**	**Angel Playing Lute** (2 bands)	80	75
C1332a	43p	Imperforate pair	£1300	
C1333	**63p**	**Angel in Prayer** (2 bands)	1.00	1.05

No.		U/M	F/U
	Set of 5	2.75	2.90
	Set of 5 Cylinder Blocks	20.50	
	Set of 5 Gutter Pairs	6.90	6.90
	First Day Cover		3.00
	Presentation Pack 292	3.10	
	PHQ202 Cards	4.00	

1998 (2 Nov.) Collectors Year Pack

CP35	Collectors Year Pack 293	32.50	

1998 (2 Nov.) Royal Mail Year Book - 15

CB15	Royal Mail Year Book	£42	

 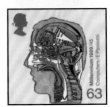

1999 (12 Jan.) Inventors Tale Perf 15 x 14

No.			U/M	F/U
C1334	**20p**	**Timekeeping** (1 band)	35	40
C1334a		Imperforate pair	£1350	
C1335	**26p**	**Steam Power** (2 bands)	45	48
C1336	**43p**	**Photography** (2 bands)	80	80
C1337	**63p**	**Computers** (2 bands)	1.30	1.30
		Set of 4	2.70	2.70
		Set of 4 Cylinder Blocks	20.00	
		Set of 4 Gutter Pairs	6.75	6.75
		First Day Cover		3.50
		Presentation Pack 294	3.00	
		PHQ203 Cards	3.00	

Perf 13 x 14 - From The World Changers Prestige Book - 21 Sep 1999

C1337a	**63p**	Perf 13 x 14	2.00	2.10

Commemoratives

No.   U/M   F/U

Queen Elizabeth II

No.   U/M   F/U

1999 (2 Feb.) Travellers Tale Perf 14 x 15
Printer: De La Rue in Photogravure (26p), Enschedé in Photogravure (20p & 63p) and Enschedé in Lithography (43p)

No.			U/M	F/U
C1338	20p	**Jet Travel** (1 band)	35	40
C1339	26p	**Liberation by Bike** (2 bands)	45	48
C1340	43p	**Linking the Nation** (2 bands)	80	80
C1341	63p	**Cook's Endeavour** (2 bands)	1.30	1.50
		Set of 4	2.70	2.70
		Set of 4 Cylinder Blocks	20.00	
		Set of 4 Gutter Pairs	6.75	6.75
		First Day Cover		3.50
		Presentation Pack 295	3.00	
		PHQ204 Cards	3.00	

1999 (6 April) Settler's Tale Perf 14 x 15
Printer: Walsall in Lithography (20p), Photogravure others

No.			U/M	F/U
C1346	20p	**Migration to Scotland** (1 band)	35	40
C1347	26p	**Pilgrim Fathers** (2 bands)	45	48
C1347a		Imperforate pair	£750	
C1348	43p	**Destination Australia** (2 bands)	80	80
C1349	63p	**Migration to U.K.** (2 bands)	1.30	1.30
		Set of 4	2.70	2.60
		Set of 4 Cylinder Blocks	20.00	
		Set of 4 Gutter Pairs	6.75	6.75
		First Day Cover		3.50
		Presentation Pack 297	3.00	
		PHQ206 Cards	3.00	

  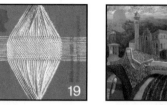

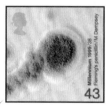  

1999 (2 Mar.) Patients Tale Perf 13 x 14
Printer: Questa in Photogravure

No.			U/M	F/U
C1342	20p	**Jenner's Vacination** (1 band)	35	40
C1343	26p	**Nursing Care** (2 bands)	45	48
C1343a		Imperforate pair	£1450	
C1344	43p	**Fleming's Penicillin** (2 bands)	80	75
C1345	63p	**Test Tube Baby** (2 bands)	1.30	1.30
		Set of 4	2.70	2.70
		Set of 4 Cylinder Blocks	20.00	
		Set of 4 Gutter Pairs	6.75	6.75
		First Day Cover		3.50
		Presentation Pack 296	3.00	
		PHQ205 Cards	3.00	

1999 (4 May) Worker's Tale Perf 14 x 15
Printer: De La Rue in Lithography (19p) and Photogravure (others)

No.			U/M	F/U
C1350	19p	**Weaverscraft** (1 band)	35	40
C1350a		Missing Bronze	£300	
C1350b		Missing Bronze & Phosphor	£300	
C1351	26p	**Mill Towns** (2 bands)	45	48
C1352	44p	**Ship Building** (2 bands)	80	80
C1353	64p	**City Finance** (2 bands)	1.30	1.30
		Set of 4	2.70	2.60
		Set of 4 Cylinder Blocks	20.00	
		Set of 4 Gutter Pairs	6.75	6.75
		First Day Cover		3.50
		Presentation Pack 298	3.00	
		PHQ207 Cards	3.00	

No.   U/M   F/U   No.   U/M   F/U

1999 (1 June) Entertainers's Tale Perf 14 x 15
Printer: Enschedé in Photogravure

			U/M	F/U
C1354	19p	**Mercury's Magic** (1 band)	35	40
C1355	26p	**World Cup** (2 bands)	45	48
C1356	44p	**Dr. Who** (2 bands)	80	80
C1357	64p	**Chaplin's Genius** (2 bands)	1.30	1.30
		Set of 4	2.70	2.60
		Set of 4 Cylinder Blocks	20.00	
		Set of 4 Gutter Pairs	6.75	6.75
		First Day Cover		3.50
		Presentation Pack 299	3.00	
		PHQ208 Cards	3..00	

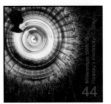

1999 (15 June) Royal Wedding Perf 14 x 15
Printer: De La Rue in Photogravure

			U/M	F/U
C1358	26p	**Portrait** (2 bands)	50	55
C1358a		Imperforate pair	£750	
C1359	64p	**Profile** (2 bands)	1.30	1.30
		Set of 2	1.60	1.70
		Set of 2 Cylinder Blocks	11.25	
		Set of 2 Gutter Pairs	4.00	4.00
		First Day Cover		2.50
		Presentation Pack MO1	1.90	
		PHQ PSM01 Cards	2.00	

1999 (3 Aug.) Scientist's Tale Perf 13 x 14
Printer: Questa in Lithography (26p & 44p) or Photogravure (19p & 64p)

			U/M	F/U
C1364	19p	**Decoding DNA** (1 band)	35	40
C1365	26p	**Darwin's Theory** (2 bands)	45	48
C1365a		Imperforate pair	£750	
C1366	44p	**Faraday's Electricity** (2 bands)	80	80
C1367	64p	**Newton/Hubble** (2 bands)	1.30	1.30
		Set of 4	2.70	2.60
		Set of 4 Cylinder Blocks	20.00	
		Set of 4 Gutter Pairs	6.75	6.75
		First Day Cover		3.50
		Presentation Pack 301	3.00	
		PHQ210 Cards	3.00	

Perf 15 x 14 - From The World Changers Prestige Book

			U/M	F/U
C1365b	26p	**Darwin's Theory** (2 bands)	1.30	1.40
C1366a	44p	**Faraday's Electricity** (2 bands)	1.60	1.70
C1367a	63p	**Computers**	2.00	2.10

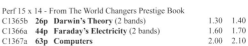

1999 (6 July) Citizens's Tale Perf 14 x 15
Printer: De La Rue in Photogravure

			U/M	F/U
C1360	19p	**Equal Rights** (1 band)	35	40
C1361	26p	**Right to Health** (2 bands)	45	48
C1362	44p	**Right to Learn** (2 bands)	80	80
C1363	64p	**First Rights** (2 bands)	1.30	1.40
		Set of 4	2.70	2.60
		Set of 4 Cylinder Blocks	20.00	
		Set of 4 Gutter Pairs	6.75	6.75
		First Day Cover		3.50
		Presentation Pack 300	3.00	
		PHQ209 Cards	3.00	

1999 (11 Aug.) Solar Eclipse Miniature sheet Perf 14 x 15

			U/M	F/U
MS7	**4 x 64p**	Multicoloured (2 bands)	12.50	12.5
MS7a		Imperforate sheet (Mint & FDC)	£3250	£175
		First Day Cover		12.5

No.			U/M	F/U

1999 (7 Sep.) Farmers's Tale Perf 14 x 15
Printer: De La Rue in Photogravure

No.			U/M	F/U
C1368	**19p**	**Upland Landscapes** (1 band)	35	40
C1369	**26p**	**Horse Plough** (2 bands)	45	48
C1370	**44p**	**Man Peeling Potato** (2 bands)	80	80
C1371	**64p**	**Harvester** (2 bands)	1.30	1.30
		Set of 4	2.60	2.20
		Set of 4 Cylinder Blocks	19.50	
		Set of 4 Gutter Pairs	6.50	6.50
		First Day Cover		3.50
		Presentation Pack 302	3.00	
		PHQ211 Cards	3.00	

1999 (2 Nov.) Christians Tale Perf 14 x 15
Printer: De La Rue in Photogravure

No.			U/M	F/U
C1376	**19p**	**Hark the Herald** (1 band)	35	40
C1376a		Imperforate pair	£400	
C1377	**26p**	**King James's Bible** (2 bands)	45	48
C1378	**44p**	**St. Andrews** (2 bands)	80	80
C1379	**64p**	**Nativity** (2 bands)	1.30	1.30
		Set of 4	2.60	2.70
		Set of 4 Cylinder Blocks	19.50	
		Set of 4 Gutter Pairs	6.50	6.50
		First Day Cover		3.50
		Presentation Pack 304	3.00	
		PHQ213 Cards	3.00	

1999 (5 Oct.) Soldiers's Tale Perf 14 x 15
Printer: Walsall in Lithography (19p) or Photogravure (others)

No.			U/M	F/U
C1372	**19p**	**Robert the Bruce** (1 band)	35	40
C1373	**26p**	**Cavalier and Horse** (2 bands)	45	48
C1374	**44p**	**War Graves** (2 bands)	80	80
C1375	**64p**	**Peacekeeping** (2 bands)	1.30	1.30
		Set of 4	2.60	2.70
		Set of 4 Cylinder Blocks	19.50	
		Set of 4 Gutter Pairs	6.50	6.50
		First Day Cover		3.50
		Presentation Pack 303	3.00	
		PHQ212 Cards	3.00	

1999 (7 Dec.) Artists Tale Perf 14 x 15
Printer: Walsall in Photogravure

No.			U/M	F/U
C1380	**19p**	**World of Stage** (1 band)	35	40
C1381	**26p**	**World of Music** (2 bands)	45	48
C1382	**44p**	**World of Literature** (2 bands)	80	80
C1383	**64p**	**New Worlds** (2 bands)	1.30	1.30
		Set of 4	2.60	2.70
		Set of 4 Cylinder Blocks	19.50	
		Set of 4 Gutter Pairs	6.50	6.50
		First Day Cover		3.50
		Presentation Pack 305	3.00	
		PHQ214 Cards	3.00	

1999 (7 Dec.) Collectors Year Pack

No.		U/M	F/U
CP36	Collectors Year Pack 306	42.50	

1999 (7 Dec.) Royal Mail Year Book - 16

No.		U/M	F/U
YB16	Royal Mail Year Book	£53	

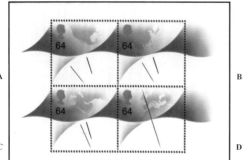
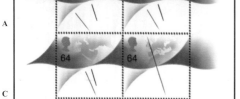

1999 (14 Dec.) Millennium Timekeeper Perf 14 x 15
Printer: De La Rue in Photogravure

No.				U/M	F/U
C1384	64p	Clockface (2 bands) A		1.30	1.30
C1385	64p	Clockface (2 bands) B		1.30	1.30
C1386	64p	Clockface (2 bands) C		1.30	1.30
C1387	64p	Clockface (2 bands) D		1.30	1.30
		First Day Cover			11.50
		Presentation Pack MO2		13.50	
		PHQ PSM02 Cards		11.00	
MS8	4 x 64p	Miniature sheet		11.50	11.50
MS8a	4 x 64p	Stamp Show 2000 overprint (22.5.00)		15.00	

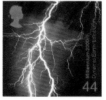
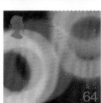

2000 (1 Feb.) Millennium 2000 - Fire and Light Perf 14 x 15
Printer: De La Rue in Photogravure

				U/M	F/U
C1393	19p	Beacons (1 band)		35	40
C1394	26p	Phelyffordd Eryri (2 bands)		45	48
C1395	44p	Dynamic Earth (2 bands)		80	80
C1396	64p	Lighting Croydons Skyline (2 bands)		1.30	1.10
		Set of 4		2.50	2.50
		Set of 4 Cylinder Blocks		18.75	
		Set of 4 Gutter Pairs		6.25	6.25
		First Day Cover			3.50
		Presentation Pack 308		3.00	
		PHQ216 Cards		3.00	

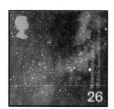

2000 (18 Jan.) Millennium 2000 - Above and Beyond Perf 14 x 15

				U/M	F/U
C1388	19p	Barn Owl (1 band)		35	40
C1389	26p	Night Sky (2 bands)		45	48
C1390	1st	Night Sky (2 bands) From 'Across the Universe' Prestige Book		2.50	2.50
C1391	44p	River Gayte and Mills (2 bands)		80	80
C1392	64p	Cape Gannets (2 bands)		1.30	1.30
		Set of 4		2.60	2.50
		Set of 4 Cylinder Blocks		19.50	
		Set of 4 Gutter Pairs		6.50	6.50
		First Day Cover			3.50
		Presentation Pack 307		3.00	
		PHQ215 Cards		3.00	

C1390 and C1402					
		Se-Tenant pair with margins but from 10 x 1st Millennium book		3.50	

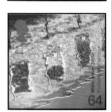

2000 (1 Feb.) Millennium 2000 - Water and Coast Perf 14 x 15
Printer: Walsall in Lithography (44p), Photogravure (others)

				U/M	F/U
C1397	19p	Turning the Tide (1 band)		35	40
C1398	26p	National Pondlife (2 bands)		45	48
C1399	44p	Parc Arfordirol (2 bands)		80	80
C1400	64p	Portsmouth Harbour (2 bands)		1.30	1.30
C1400a		Missing Phosphor		£125	
		Set of 4		2.50	2.50
		Set of 4 Cylinder Blocks		18.75	
		Set of 4 Gutter Pairs		6.25	6.25
		First Day Cover			3.50
		Presentation Pack 309		3.00	
		PHQ217 Cards		3.00	

2000 (4 Apr.) Millennium 2000 - Life and Earth Perf 14 x 15
Printer: De La Rue in Photogravure

C1401	2nd	ECOS (1 band)	35	40
C1402	1st	Web of Life (2 bands)	45	48
C1403	44p	Earth Centre (2 bands)	80	80
C1404	64p	Project SUZY (2 bands)	1.30	1.30
		Set of 4	2.50	2.60
		Set of 4 Cylinder Blocks	18.75	
		Set of 4 Gutter Pairs	6.25	6.25
		First Day Cover		3.60
		Presentation Pack 310	3.00	
		PHQ218 Cards	3.00	

C1390 and C1402

	Se-Tenant pair with margins but from 10 x 1st		
	Millennium book	3.50	

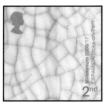

2000 (2 May) Millennium 2000 - Arts and Craft Perf 14 x 15
Printer: Enschedé in Photogravure

C1405	2nd	Cermaica (1 band)	35	40
C1406	1st	Tate Modern (2 bands)	45	48
C1407	45p	Cycle Network (2 bands)	80	80
C1408	65p	The Lowry (2 bands)	1.10	1.10
		Set of 4	2.60	2.70
		Set of 4 Cylinder Blocks	19.50	
		Set of 4 Gutter Pairs	6.50	6.50
		First Day Cover		3.60
		Presentation Pack 311	3.00	
		PHQ219 Cards	3.00	

2000 (22 May) Stamp Show 2000 Jeffrey Matthews Pallette - Perf 15 x 14

MS9	Complete miniature sheet	19.50	19.50
MS9a	Souvenir Wallet	£25	

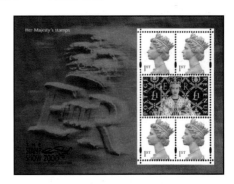

2000 (23 May) Stamp Show 2000 Her Majesty's Stamps - Perf 15 x 14
Printer: De La Rue in Photogravure

MS10	Complete miniature sheet	£13	£13
	Presentation Pack MO3	£36	
	PHQ Cards PSM03	11.50	

2000 (6 June) Millennium 2000 - People and Places Perf 14 x 15
Printer: Walsall in Lithography (1st, 65p), Photogravure (2nd, 45p)

C1409	2nd	Millennium Greens (1 band)	35	40
C1410	1st	Millennium Bridge, Gateshead (2 bands)	48	53
C1411	45p	Mile End Park, London (2 bands)	80	80
C1412	65p	On the Meridian Line (2 bands)	1.10	1.10
		Set of 4	2.60	2.70
		Set of 4 Cylinder Blocks	19.50	
		Set of 4 Gutter Pairs	6.50	6.50
		First Day Cover		3.60
		Presentation Pack 312	3.00	
		PHQ220 Cards	3.00	

No.   U/M   F/U   No.   U/M   F/U

2000 (4 July) Millennium 2000 - Stone and Soil Perf 14 x 15
Printer: Enschedé in Photogravure

No.			U/M	F/U
C1413	2nd	Strangford Stone (1 band)	35	40
C1414	1st	Trans Penine Trail (2 bands)	48	53
C1415	45p	Cyclist (2 bands)	80	80
C1416	65p	Bluebell Wood (2 bands)	1.20	1.10
		Set of 4	2.50	2.60
		Set of 4 Cylinder Blocks	18.75	
		Set of 4 Gutter Pairs	6.25	6.25
		First Day Cover		3.60
		Presentation Pack 313	3.00	
		PHQ221 Cards	3.00	

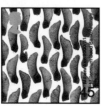

2000 (1 Aug.) Millennium 2000 - Tree and Leaf Perf 14 x 15
Printer: De La Rue in Photogravure

No.			U/M	F/U
C1417	2nd	Yews (1 band)	35	40
C1418	1st	Eden Project (2 bands)	48	53
C1419	45p	Seed Bank (2 bands)	80	80
C1420	65p	Forest for Scotland (2 bands)	1.10	1.10
		Set of 4	2.60	2.70
		Set of 4 Cylinder Blocks	19.50	
		Set of 4 Gutter Pairs	6.50	6.50
		First Day Cover		3.60
		Presentation Pack 314	3.00	
		PHQ222 Cards	3.00	

2000 (4 Aug.) Queen Mother's Birthday Perf 15
Printer: De La Rue in Photogravure (Miniature sheet) or Questa in Photogravure (Prestige panes)

No.			U/M	F/U
C1421	27p	Queen Mother	3.50	3.50
C1422	27p	Queen Elizabeth II	1.20	1.30
C1423	27p	Prince Charles	1.20	1.30
C1424	27p	Prince William	1.20	1.30
MS11		Complete Miniature sheet	6.50	7.00
MS11a		Imperforate miniature sheet	£3750	
		Pane from Prestige Book (4 x C1421)	4.60	5.00
		Pane from Prestige Book (C1421-C1424)	5.00	6.00
		First Day Cover		8.50
		Presentation Pack MO4	9.00	
		PHQ PSM04 Cards	8.00	

All of the above are from 'The Life of the Century' Prestige book and miniature sheet only.

2000 (1 Aug.) Millennium 2000 - Mind and Matter Perf 14 x 15
Printer: Walsall in Lithography

No.			U/M	F/U
C1425	2nd	Wildscreen of Bristol (1 band)	35	40
C1426	1st	Norfolk & Norwich Project (2 bands)	48	53
C1427	45p	Millennium Point (2 bands)	80	80
C1428	65p	SCRAN (2 bands)	1.10	1.10
		Set of 4	2.60	2.70
		Set of 4 Cylinder Blocks	19.50	
		Set of 4 Gutter Pairs	6.50	6.50
		First Day Cover		3.60
		Presentation Pack 315	3.00	
		PHQ223 Cards	3.00	

2000 (3 Oct.) Millennium 2000 - Body and Bone
Perf 14 x 15 (C1305) or 13 x 14
Printer: Questa in Lithography (2nd) or Photogravure (others)

			U/M	F/U
C1429	**2nd**	**Body/The Dome** (1 band)	35	40
C1430	**1st**	**Hampden Park/Glasgow** (2 bands)	48	53
C1431	**45p**	**Bath Spa** (2 bands)	80	80
C1432	**65p**	**Centre for Life** (2 bands)	1.10	1.10
		Set of 4	2.60	2.70
		Set of 4 Cylinder Blocks	19.50	
		Set of 4 Gutter Pairs	6.50	6.50
		First Day Cover		3.60
		Presentation Pack 316	3.00	
		PHQ224 Cards	3.00	

2000 (5 Dec.) Millennium 2000 - Sound and Vision Perf 14 x 15
Printer: De La Rue in Photogravure

			U/M	F/U
C1437	**2nd**	**Ringing in Millennium** (1 band)	35	40
C1438	**1st**	**Year of the Artist** (2 bands)	48	53
C1439	**45p**	**Canolff Mileniwn/Cardiff** (2 bands)	80	80
C1440	**65p**	**TS2K Talent and Skill** (2 bands)	1.10	1.10
		Set of 4	2.60	2.70
		Set of 4 Cylinder Blocks	19.50	
		Set of 4 Gutter Pairs	6.50	6.50
		First Day Cover		3.60
		Presentation Pack 318	3.00	
		PHQ226 Cards	3.00	

2000 (5 Dec.) Collectors Year Pack

		U/M	F/U
CP37	Collectors Year Pack 319	42.50	

2000 (5 Dec.) Royal Mail Year Book - 17

		U/M	F/U
YB17	Royal Mail Year Book	£53	

2000 (7 Nov.) Millennium 2000 - Spirit and Faith Perf 14 x 15
Printer: De La Rue in Photogravure

			U/M	F/U
C1433	**2nd**	**St. Edmundsbury** (1 band)	35	40
C1433a		Imperforate pair	£525	
C1434	**1st**	**Church Floodlighting** (2 bands)	48	53
C1434a		Imperforate pair	£500	
C1435	**45p**	**St. Pattrick Centre** (2 bands)	80	80
C1436	**65p**	**Mystery Plays/York** (2 bands)	1.10	1.10
		Set of 4	2.60	2.70
		Set of 4 Cylinder Blocks	19.50	
		Set of 4 Gutter Pairs	6.50	6.50
		First Day Cover		3.60
		Presentation Pack 317	3.00	
		PHQ225 Cards	3.00	

2001 (16 Jan.) New Millennium 2001 - Rights of the Child Perf 14 x 15
Printer: De La Rue in Photogravure

			U/M	F/U
C1441	**2nd**	**Nurture Children** (1 band)	35	40
C1442	**1st**	**Listen to Children** (2 bands)	48	53
C1443	**45p**	**Teach Children** (2 bands)	80	80
C1444	**65p**	**Ensure Children's Freedom** (2 bands)	1.10	1.10
		Set of 4	2.50	2.60
		Set of 4 Cylinder Blocks	18.75	
		Set of 4 Gutter Pairs	6.25	6.25
		First Day Cover		3.25
		Presentation Pack 319	3.00	
		PHQ227 Cards	3.50	

A

B

C

D

E

2001 (5 Feb.) Occasions Stamps Printed in gravure Perf 15 x 14
Printer: Enschedé in Photogravure

C1445	**1st**	**Love** (A)	65	60
C1446	**1st**	**Thanks** (B)	65	60
C1447	**1st**	**ABC** (C)	65	60
C1448	**1st**	**Welcome** (D)	65	60
C1449	**1st**	**Cheers** (E)	65	60
		Set of 5	2.70	2.80
		Set of 5 Cylinder Blocks	20.00	
		Set of 5 Gutter Pairs	6.75	6.75
		First Day Cover		3.50
		Presentation Pack MO5	4.50	
		PHQ PSM05Cards	6.50	

2001 (5 June) 1st Occasions Printed in Litho from Smilers sheet

SSP4	Vertical strip of five stamps & five labels	£25
	First Day Cover (Customised sheets) (1.5.01)	£25

2001 (13 Feb.) Cats and Dogs - Self Adhesive Die cut Perf 15 x 14
Printer: Walsall in Photogravure

C1450	**1st**	**Dog & Man on Bench**	80	80
C1451	**1st**	**Dog in Bath**	80	80
C1452	**1st**	**Dog in Pen**	80	80
C1453	**1st**	**Cat in Bag**	80	80
C1454	**1st**	**Cat on Gate**	80	80
C1455	**1st**	**Dog in Car**	80	80
C1456	**1st**	**Cat at Window**	80	80
C1457	**1st**	**Dog Behind Fence**	80	80
C1458	**1st**	**Cat Watching Bird**	80	80
C1459	**1st**	**Cat in Sink**	80	80
		Set of 10	7.50	7.50
		First Day Cover		7.5
		Presentation Pack 320	9.25	
		PHQ228 Cards	8.50	
		Imperforate pane of 10	£3500	

2001 (13 Mar.) The Weather Perf 15
Printer: De La Rue in Photogravure

C1461	**19p**	**Rain** (1 band)	35	40
C1462	**27p**	**Fair** (2 bands)	45	53
C1463	**45p**	**Much Rain/Stormy** (2 bands)	80	80
C1464	**65p**	**Very Dry/Set Fair** (2 bands)	1.10	1.10
		Set of 4	2.55	2.60
		Set of 4 Cylinder Blocks	18.90	
		Set of 4 Gutter Pairs	6.40	6.40
		First Day Cover		3.25
		Presentation Pack 321	5.95	
		PHQ229 Cards	4.00	

No.		U/M	F/U
MS12	Miniature Sheet	7.50	7.50
	First Day Cover		7.50

2001 (22 Oct.) Miniature Sheet Perf 15½ x 15

C1469	**1st**	**White Ensign**	1.70	1.80
C1470	**1st**	**Union Flag**	1.70	1.80
C1471	**1st**	**Jolly Roger**	1.70	1.80
C1472	**1st**	**Chief of Defence Flag**	1.70	1.80
MS13		Miniature Sheet	3.50	3.70
		First Day Cover		4.00
		Presentatiom Pack MO6	8.25	
		PHQ PSM07 Cards	9.00	

Self Adhesive Perf 15½ x 14 Die Cut

C1466c	**1st**	**Swiftsure Class**	32.00	27.00
C1469a	**1st**	**White Ensign**	9.00	9.00
C1471a	**1st**	**Jolly Roger**	9.00	9.00

2004 (27 July) 1st Union flag from 'Rule Britannia' Smilers sheet

SSP20	1st Union flag *plus* label (any)	2.00

2001 (10 Apr.) Centenary of Royal Navy Submarine Service Perf 15 x 14
Printer: Questa in Photogravure

C1465	**2nd**	**Vanguard Class**	35	40
C1466	**1st**	**Swiftsure Class**	45	53
C1467	**45p**	**Unity Class**	80	80
C1468	**65p**	**Holland Class**	1.10	1.10
		Set of 4	2.35	2.40
		Set of 4 Cylinder Blocks	17.50	
		Set of 4 Gutter Pairs	5.90	5.90
		First Day Cover		3.25
		Presentation Pack 322	3.90	
		PHQ230 Cards	3.50	

2005 (21 June) 1st White Ensign from 'White Ensign' Smilers sheet

SSP24	Stamp *plus* label (any)	75
SSP24a	Solid all over phosphor	£9

2001 (22 Oct.) Perf 15½ x 15 From 'Unseen & Unheard' Prestige Book

C1465a	**2nd**	**Vanguard Class**	2.00	2.00
C1466b	**1st**	**Swiftsure Class**	2.00	2.00
C1467c	**45p**	**Unity Class**	2.50	2.50
C1468d	**65p**	**Holland Class**	2.50	2.50

U/M F/U   No.   U/M   F/U

2001 (15 May.) 150th Anniversary of First Double Decker Bus
Perf 15 x 14
Printer: Questa in Lithography
C1473/1477

		U/M	F/U
	1st Se-tenant strip of five	2.30	2.40
C1473/1477a			
	Missing grey	£5000	
C1473	Leyland (A)	48	53
C1474	AEC/Daimler (B)	48	53
C1475	AEC/Bristol (C)	48	53
C1476	Bristol/Leyland (D)	48	53
C1477	Daimler/MCW (E)	48	53
	Set of 5	2.30	2.40
	Cylinder Block	7.90	
	Gutter Strip of 10	5.75	5.75
	First Day Cover		3.00
	Presentation Pack 323	4.60	
	PHQ231 Cards	9.00	
	Imperforate strip of 5	£2000	
MS14	Miniature Sheet	4.50	4.50
	First Day Cover		5.00

2001 (19 Jun.) Hats Perf 15
Printer: Enschedé in Lithography

			U/M	F/U
C1478	**1st**	**Toque Hat**	45	80
C1479	**E**	**Butterfly Hat**	55	60
C1480	**45p**	**Top Hat**	80	75
C1481	**65p**	**Spiral Hat**	1.20	1.30
		Set of 4	2.75	2.80
		Set of 4 Cylinder Blocks	20.50	
		Set of 4 Gutter Pairs	6.90	6.90
		First Day Cover		3.75
		Presentation Pack 324	3.60	
		PHQ232 Cards	3.50	

2001 (10 Jul.) Europa - Pond Life Perf 15
Printer: De La Rue in Photogravure

			U/M	F/U
C1482	**1st**	**Common Frog**	40	45
C1483	**E**	**Great Diving Beetle**	60	65
C1484	**45p**	**Stickleback**	75	80
C1485	**65p**	**Hawker Dragonfly**	1.10	1.15
		Set of 4	2.80	2.80
		Set of 4 Cylinder Blocks	20.50	
		Set of 4 Gutter Pairs	7.00	7.00
		First Day Cover		3.75
		Presentation Pack 325	3.60	
		PHQ233 Cards	3.50	

2001 (4 Sep.) Punch and Judy Show Puppets Perf 14 x 15
Printer: Walsall in Photogravure

			U/M	F/U
C1486	1st	Policeman	50	55
C1487	1st	Clown	50	55
C1488	1st	Mr Punch	50	55
C1489	1st	Judy	50	55
C1490	1st	Beadle	50	55
C1491	1st	Crocodile	50	55
		Set of 6	2.80	2.90
		Cylinder Block	7.00	
		Gutter Block of 12	7.00	7.00
		First Day Cover		3.50
		Presentation Pack 326	3.30	
		PHQ234 Cards	5.00	

Self Adhesive Perf 14 x 15½ Die Cut
Printer: Questa in Photogravure

C1488a	1st	Mr Punch	8.50	8.50
C1489a	1st	Judy	8.50	8.50

2001 (2 Oct.) Nobel Prizes Perf 15

			U/M	F/U
C1492	2nd	Carbon 60 Molecule	40	45
C1493	1st	Globe Economic Sciences	45	50
C1494	E	Peace	1.00	1.00
C1495	40p	Physiology and Medicine	1.00	1.00
C1496	45p	Literature	1.50	1.50
C1497	65p	Physics	1.50	1.50
C1497a		Missing hologram	£4500	
		Set of 6	5.50	5.50
		Set of 6 Cylinder Blocks	29.50	

		U/M	F/U
Set of 6 Gutter Pairs		10.00	10.00
First Day Cover			4.75
Presentation Pack 327		£10	
PHQ235 Cards		5.00	

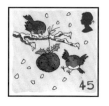
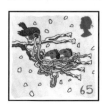

2001 (6 Nov.) Christmas Self Adhesive Perf 15 Die Cut
Printer: De La Rue in Photogravure

			U/M	F/U
C1498	2nd	Robins with Snowman	40	35
C1498a		Imperforate pair	£500	
C1499	1st	Robins on Bird Table	45	50
C1500	E	Robins Skating	50	55
C1501	45p	Robins with Pudding	65	70
C1502	65p	Robins in Paper Chain	1.00	1.10
C1502a		Imperforate pair (stamps & roulleting)	£750	
C1502b		Imperforate pair (stamps only)	£275	
		Set of 5	3.00	3.20
		Set of 5 Gutter Pairs	7.50	7.50
		First Day Cover		3.75
		Presentation Pack 328	3.60	
		PHQ236 Cards	4.00	

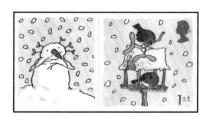

2003 (30 Sep.) Christmas from Smilers sheet

SSP14	1st Christmas plus label (any)	2.00	

2001 (6 Nov.) Collectors Year Pack

CP38	Collectors Year Pack 329	42.50

2001 (6 Nov.) Royal Mail Year Book - 18

YB18	Royal Mail Year Book	£53

No.   U/M F/U No.   U/M F/U

A

B

E

C

D

45   65

E

F

2002 (6 Feb.) Golden Jubilee Perf 15 x 14 Watermark Sideways
Printer: De La Rue in Photogravure

No.			U/M	F/U
C1513	2nd	Queen Elizabeth II	40	45
C1514	1st	Queen Elizabeth II	45	50
C1515	E	Queen Elizabeth II	50	55
C1516	45p	Queen Elizabeth II	70	75
C1517	65p	Queen Elizabeth II	1.15	1.20
		Set of 5	3.00	3.10
		Set of 5 Cylinder Blocks	22.50	
		Set of 5 Gutter Pairs	7.50	7.50
		First Day Cover		3.70
		Presentation Pack 331	3.50	
		PHQ238 Cards	3.50	

Perf 15 x 14 Watermark Upright
From 'A Gracious Accession' Prestige Book

No.			U/M	F/U
C1513a	2nd	Queen Elizabeth II	75	75
C1514a	1st	Queen Elizabeth II	75	75
C1515a	E	Queen Elizabeth II	2.00	2.00
C1516a	45p	Queen Elizabeth II	4.50	4.00
C1517a	65p	Queen Elizabeth II	4.50	4.00
		Set of 5	10.50	10.50

G

H

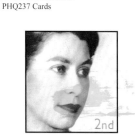

I

J

2002 (15 Jan.) Kipling's Just So Stories Self Adhesive
Perf 15 x 14 Die Cut
Printer: Walsall in Photogravure

No.			U/M	F/U
C1503	1st	Whale (A)	60	65
C1504	1st	Camel (B)	60	65
C1505	1st	Rhino (C)	60	65
C1506	1st	Leopard (D)	60	65
C1507	1st	Elephant (E)	60	65
C1508	1st	Kangaroo (F)	60	65
C1509	1st	Armadillos (G)	60	65
C1510	1st	Crab (H)	60	65
C1511	1st	Cat (I)	60	65
C1512	1st	Butterfly (J)	60	65
		Set of 10	5.00	5.20
		First Day Cover		5.15
		Presentation Pack 330	7.75	
		PHQ237 Cards	6.50	

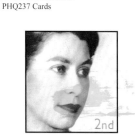

2002 (5 Mar.) Occasions 16mm phosphor bands Perf 15 x 14
Printer: Questa in Lithography

No.			U/M	F/U
C1518	1st	A New Baby	55	60
C1519	1st	Love	55	60
C1520	1st	Hello	55	60
C1521	1st	Moving Home	55	60
C1522	1st	Best Wishes	55	60
		Set of 5	2.25	2.35
		Set of 5 Cylinder Blocks	16.90	
		Set of 5 Gutter Pairs	5.65	5.65
		First Day Cover		3.15
		Presentation Pack MO7	2.50	
		PHQ PSM08 Cards	3.50	

Varieties
18mm phosphor bands Perf 15 x 14 from Smilers sheet

C1518a	1st	A New Baby	5.00	5.00
C1519a	1st	Love	5.00	5.00
C1520a	1st	Hello	5.00	5.00
C1521a	1st	Moving Home	5.00	5.00
C1522a	1st	Best Wishes	5.00	5.00

Self Adhesive Gravure printed Perf 15 x 14 Die Cut
Printer: Questa in Photogravure

C1520b	1st	Hello	3.50	3.50

2001 (23 Apr.) 1st Occasions from Smilers sheet Litho printed

SSP7	Vertical strip of five stamps & five labels	£10

2004 (30 Jan.) 1st Hello from Hong Kong Smilers sheet

SSP17	1st *plus* label (any)	2.00

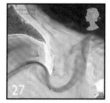

A   B   C   D

E   27    F

G   27   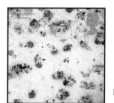 H

I   27    J

2002 (19 Mar.) British Coastlines Perf 15
Printer: Walsall in Lithography
C1523/32

No.			U/M	F/U
	1st	Block of ten (5 x 2)	4.50	4.50
C1523/32		Missing silver (block of ten)	£4000	
C1523	1st	Studland (A)	50	60
C1524	1st	Luskentyre (B)	50	60
C1525	1st	Dover (C)	50	60
C1526	1st	Padstow (D)	50	60
C1527	1st	Broadstairs (E)	50	60
C1528	1st	St. Abb's Head (F)	50	60
C1529	1st	Dunster Beach (G)	50	60
C1530	1st	Newquay (H)	50	60
C1531	1st	Portrush (I)	50	60
C1532	1st	Conwy (J)	50	60
		Set of 10	4.20	4.25
		Cylinder Block	9.75	
		Gutter Block of 20	10.50	10.50
		First Day Cover		5.15
		Presentation Pack 332	4.70	
		PHQ239 Cards	5.50	

2002 (10 Apr.) Europa Circus Perf 15
Printer: Questa in Photogravure

No.			U/M	F/U
C1533	**2nd**	**Slack Wire**	40	45
C1534	**1st**	**Lion Tamer**	45	50
C1535	**E**	**Trick Cycle**	55	60
C1535a		Imperforate pair	£850	
C1536	**45p**	**Krazy Kar**	65	70
C1537	**65p**	**Equestrienne**	1.00	1.05
		Set of 5	3.00	3.20
		Set of 5 Cylinder Blocks	22.50	
		Set of 5 Gutter Pairs	7.50	7.50
		First Day Cover		4.20
		Presentation Pack 333	3.50	
		PHQ240 Cards	3.50	

2002 (2 May) Airliners Perf 15
Printer: De La Rue in Photogravure

No.			U/M	F/U
C1542	**2nd**	**Airbus**	40	45
C1543	**1st**	**Concorde**	45	50
C1544	**E**	**Trident**	55	60
C1545	**45p**	**VC10**	65	70
C1546	**65p**	**Comet**	1.00	1.05
		Set of 5	3.00	3.20
		Set of 5 Cylinder Blocks	22.50	
		Set of 5 Gutter Pairs	7.50	7.50
		First Day Cover		4.20
		Presentation Pack 334	3.50	
		PHQ241 Cards	3.50	
MS15		Miniature Sheet	5.00	5.00
		First Day Cover		5.00

Self Adhesive Perf 15 x 14 Die Cut
Printer: Questa in Photogravure

C1543a	**1st**	**Concorde**	2.50	2.50

2002 (25 Apr.) The Queen Mother Perf 14 x 15
Printer: De La Rue in Photogravure

No.			U/M	F/U
C1538	**1st**	**The Queen Mother**	45	50
C1539	**E**	**The Queen Mother**	55	60
C1540	**45p**	**The Queen Mother**	65	70
C1541	**65p**	**The Queen Mother**	1.00	1.05
		Set of 4	2.80	3.00
		Set of 4 Cylinder Blocks	20.50	
		Set of 4 Gutter Pairs	7.00	7.00
		First Day Cover		4.00
		Presentation Pack MO8	3.20	
		PHQ Cards	3.00	5.00

A

C   D

2002 (21 May) World Cup Perf 15
Printer: Walsall in Photogravure

No.		Description	U/M	F/U
C1547	1st	Lion and St. George Shield	1.50	1.75
C1548	1st	English Flag & Football (A)	75	80
C1549	1st	English Flag & Football (B)	75	80
C1550	1st	English Flag & Football (C)	75	80
C1551	1st	English Flag & Football (D)	75	80
		First Day Cover		3.20
		Presentation Pack 335	4.40	
		PHQ242 Cards	3.50	

2002 (16 July) The Friendly Games Perf 15
Printer: Enschedé in Photogravure

No.		Description	U/M	F/U
C1552	2nd	Swimming	40	45
C1553	1st	Track	45	50
C1554	E	Cycling	55	60
C1555	47p	Long Jump	70	75
C1556	68p	Disabled	1.30	1.40
		Set of 5	3.40	3.50
		Set of 5 Cylinder Blocks	24.50	
		Set of 5 Gutter Pairs	8.50	8.50
		First Day Cover		4.30
		Presentation Pack 336	3.60	
		PHQ243 Cards	3.50	

2002 (21 May) World Cup, Printed in Litho from Smilers sheet

No.		Description	U/M	F/U
SSP8		1st *plus* label (any)	2.50	

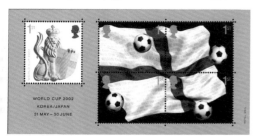

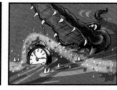

No.		Description	U/M	F/U
MS16		Miniature Sheet	3.00	3.00

Self Adhesive Perf 15 x 14 Die Cut

No.		Description	U/M	F/U
C1548a	1st	English Flag & Football (A)	2.25	2.35
C1549a	1st	English Flag & Football (B)	2.25	2.35

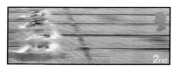

2002 (20 Aug.) Peter Pan Perf 15 x 14
Printer: De La Rue in Photogravure

No.		Description	U/M	F/U
C1557	2nd	Tinkerbell	40	45
C1558	1st	Group	45	50
C1559	E	Crocodile	65	70
C1560	47p	Hook	90	1.00
C1561	68p	Peter	1.30	1.40
		Set of 5	3.50	3.60
		Set of 5 Cylinder Blocks	25.50	
		Set of 5 Gutter Pairs	8.75	8.75
		First Day Cover		4.30
		Presentation Pack 337	3.60	
		PHQ244 Cards	4.50	

MS17	Miniature Sheet	2.60	2.70
	First Day Cover		3.50
	Prestige Book pane	2.25	2.50

2002 (10 Sep.) London Bridges Perf 15 x 14
Printer: Questa in Lithography

C1562	2nd	Millennium	40	45
C1563	1st	Tower	45	50
C1564	E	Westminster	65	70
C1565	47p	Blackfriar's	80	85
C1566	68p	London	1.60	1.60
		Set of 5	3.80	3.00
		Set of 5 Cylinder Blocks	25.50	
		Set of 5 Gutter Pairs	8.75	8.75
		First Day Cover		4.30
		Presentation Pack 338	3.50	
		PHQ245 Cards	3.50	

Self Adhesive Perf 14½ x 14 Die Cut
Printer: Questa in Photogravure

C1563a	1st	Tower	2.25	2.35

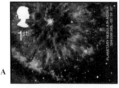

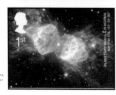

2002 (24 Sep.) Astronomy Perf 14½ x 14

C1567	1st	Aquilla (A)	60	65
C1568	1st	Pegasus (B)	60	65
C1569	1st	Norma (C)	60	65
C1570	1st	Circinus (D)	60	65
		Presentation Pack 339	3.00	
		PHQ246 Cards	3.50	

2002 (8 Oct.) Pillar to Post Perf 15 x 14
Printer: Enschedé in Lithography and Recess

C1571	2nd	1857 Box	40	45
C1572	1st	1874 Box	45	50
C1573	E	1934 Box	60	65
C1574	47p	1939 Box	80	85
C1575	68p	1980 Box	1.20	1.30
		Set of 5	3.40	3.50
		Set of 5 Cylinder Blocks	25.50	
		Set of 5 Gutter Pairs	8.50	8.50
		First Day Cover		4.50
		Presentation Pack 340	4.40	
		PHQ247 Cards	3.00	

All the above were from a miniature sheet and Prestige Book pane.

2002 (5 Nov.) Christmas Self Adhesive Perf 15 x 14 Die Cut
Printer: De La Rue in Photogravure

No.			U/M	F/U
C1576	**2nd**	**Spruce**	40	45
C1576a		Imperforate pair	£25	
C1577	**1st**	**Holly**	45	50
C1577a		Imperforate pair	£100	
C1578	**E**	**Ivy**	60	65
C1579	**47p**	**Mistletoe**	80	85
C1580	**68p**	**Cone**	1.20	1.30
		Set of 5	3.40	3.50
		Set of 5 Gutter Pairs	6.75	6.75
		First Day Cover		4.50
		Presentation Pack 341	3.60	
		PHQ248 Cards	3.00	

The Wilding definitives collection 1 ~ 1952 - 1953

2002 (5 Dec.) Anniversary of Wilding Definitives (1st) Perf 15 x 14

		U/M	F/U
MS18	Complete Miniature Sheet	3.50	3.80
	First Day Cover		3.80
	Presentation Pack	3.80	

Individual stamps from this miniature sheet will be found in the definitives section.

2002 (5 Nov.) Collectors Year Pack

CP39	Collectors Year Pack 342	42.50

2002 (5 Nov.) Royal Mail Year Book - 19

YB19	Royal Mail Year Book	£53

A

B

C

D

E

F

G

H

I

J

2003 (14 Jan.) Birds of Prey Perf 14½
Printer: Walsall in Lithography

No.		U/M	F/U
C1581/90	**1st Block of ten** (5 x 2)	4.90	4.90
C1581/90a	Missing Brownish grey & Phosphor		
	(Blocks of ten - mint & FDC)	£1750	£1100
C1581/90b	Upward shift of all colours except		
	brownish-grey	£1250	
C1581	Barn Owl in Flight (A)	55	65
C1582	Barn Owl in Flight (B)	55	65
C1583	Barn Owl in Flight (C)	55	65
C1584	Barn Owl in Flight (D)	55	65
C1585	Barn Owl in Flight (E)	55	65
C1586	Kestrel in Flight (F)	55	65
C1587	Kestrel in Flight (G)	55	65
C1588	Kestrel in Flight (H)	55	65
C1589	Kestrel in Flight (I)	55	65
C1590	Kestrel in Flight (J)	55	65
	Set of 10	5.50	5.70
	Cylinder Block	11.25	
	Gutter Block of 20	12.25	12.25
	First Day Cover		5.50
	Presentation Pack 343	4.70	
	PHQ249 Cards	4.50	

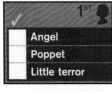 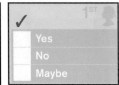

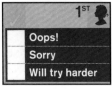 

2003 (4 Feb.) Occasions Perf 14½ x 14
Printer: Questa in Lithography

No.			U/M	F/U
C1591/96	**1st**	**Block of six**	2.60	2.70
C1591/96		Imperforate block of six £1550		
C1591		Gold Star... (A)	55	60
C1592		I Love You... (B)	55	60
C1593		Angel... (C)	55	60
C1594		Yes... (D)	55	60
C1595		Oops!... (E)	55	60
C1596		I Did it!... (F)	55	60
		Set of 6	2.60	2.70
		Gutter Block of 12	6.50	6.50
		First Day Cover		3.55
		Presentation Pack MO9	3.10	
		PHQ PSM09 Cards	3.00	

2003 (4 Feb.) Occasions from Smilers sheet

		U/M
SSP12	1st Occasions *plus* label (any)	2.00

Genome Genetic Engineering   Genome Medical Futures

2003 (25 Feb.) Discovery of DNA Perf 14½
Printer: Enschedé in Lithography

No.			U/M	F/U
C1597	**2nd**	**Genome Jigsaw**	40	45
C1598	**1st**	**Ape and Scientist**	45	50
C1598a		Missing phosphor		
C1599	**E**	**Snakes and Ladders**	60	60
C1600	**47p**	**Animal Scientist**	80	75
C1601	**68p**	**Crystal Ball**	1.20	1.30
		Set of 5	3.20	3.40
		Set of 5 Cylinder Blocks	24.50	
		Set of 5 Gutter Pairs	8.00	8.00
		First Day Cover		5.00
		Presentation Pack 344	3.80	
		PHQ250 Cards	2.50	

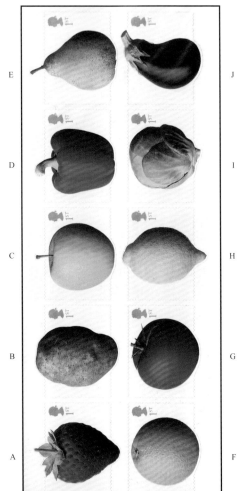

2003 (25 Mar.) Fruit and Vegetables Self Adhesive Perf 14 Die Cut

Printer: Walsall in Photogravure

No.			U/M	F/U
C1602/11	**1st**	**Complete sheetlet**	5.50	5.75
C1602/11a		Imperforate sheetlet	£1750	
C1602		Strawberry (A)	65	70
C1603		Potato (B)	65	70
C1604		Apple (C)	65	70
C1605		Red Pepper (D)	65	70
C1606		Pear (E)	65	70
C1607		Orange (F)	65	70
C1608		Tomato (G)	65	70
C1609		Lemon (H)	65	70
C1610		Brussels Sprout (I)	65	70
C1611		Aubergine (J)	65	70
		Set of 10	5.75	5.85
		First Day Cover		7.00
		Presentation Pack 345	£25	
		PHQ251 Cards	7.50	

Self Adhesive Perf 14½ Die Cut

No.			U/M	F/U
C1613a	**1st**	**Everest Team**	3.00	3.00

The Wilding definitives collection II ~ 1953 - 1959

2003 (20 May) Anniversary of Wilding Definitives (2nd) Perf 15 x 14

No.		U/M	F/U
MS19	Complete miniature sheet	3.50	3.50
	First Day Cover		3.80
	Presentation Pack	3.80	

Individual stamps from this miniature sheet will be found in the definitives section.

2003 (29 Apr.) Extreme Endeavours Perf 15 x 14

Printer: Questa in Photogravure

No.			U/M	F/U
C1612	**2nd**	**Amy Johnson**	40	45
C1613	**1st**	**Everest Team**	45	50
C1614	**E**	**Freya Stark**	55	60
C1615	**42p**	**Ernest Shackleton**	75	80
C1616	**47p**	**Francis Chichester**	80	85
C1617	**68p**	**Robert F Scott**	1.20	1.25
		Set of 6	3.80	4.00
		Set of 6 Cylinder Blocks	27.50	
		Set of 6 Gutter Pairs	9.50	9.50
		First Day Cover		4.80
		Presentation Pack 346	4.20	
		PHQ252 Cards	3.50	

2003 (2 June) Anniversary of the Coronation Perf 14½ x 14
Printer: De La Rue in Photogravure

C1618/27	**1st**	**Block of ten**	5.50	5.75
C1618		Coronation Procession	50	55
C1619		Street Party Poster	50	55
C1620		The Coronation	50	55
C1621		Royal Wall Mosaic	50	55
C1622		Cecil Beaton Portrait	50	55
C1623		Children's Race	50	55
C1624		Marble Arch Procession	50	55
C1625		Children at Street Party	50	55
C1626		Royal Carriage	50	55
C1627		Children and Cakes	50	55
C1627a		Image printed double	£1250	
		Set of 10	4.40	4.60
		Cylinder Block	11.00	
		Gutter Block of 20	11.00	11.00
		First Day Cover		5.30
		Presentation Pack 347	12.50	
		PHQ253 Cards	6.50	

2003 (2 June) Anniversary of the Coronation from Prestige Book
Perf 15 x 14

C1628	**£1**	**Coronation**	21.50	21.50

The 47p and 68p individual stamps from this miniature sheet will be found in the definitives section.

2003 (17 June) Birthday of Prince William Perf 14½
Printer: Walsall in Photogravure

C1629	**28p**	**Prince William**	45	50
C1630	**E**	**Prince William**	1.50	1.50
C1631	**47p**	**Prince William**	2.50	2.50
C1632	**68p**	**Prince William**	3.50	3.50
		Set of 4	7.50	7.50
		Set of 4 Cylinder Blocks	£58	
		Set of 4 Gutter Pairs	£30	£30
		First Day Cover		4.00
		Presentation Pack 348	14.50	
		PHQ254 Cards	4.50	

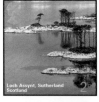 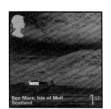

2003 (15 July) A British Journey - Scotland Perf 14½
Printer: De La Rue in Photogravure

C1633	**2nd**	**Loch Assynt**	40	45
C1634	**1st**	**Ben More**	45	50
C1635	**E**	**Rothiemurchus**	55	60
C1636	**42p**	**Dalveen Pass**	65	70
C1637	**47p**	**Glenfinnan Viaduct**	70	75
C1638	**68p**	**Papa Little**	1.10	1.15
		Set of 6	3.65	3.80
		Set of 6 Cylinder Blocks	27.50	
		Set of 6 Gutter Pairs	9.00	9.50
		First Day Cover		4.75
		Presentation Pack 349	4.20	
		PHQ255 Cards	3.00	

Self Adhesive Perf 14½ Die Cut

C1634a	**1st**	Ben More	2.00	2.00

				U/M	F/U
		Set of 5		3.50	3.60
		Set of 5 Cylinder Blocks		25.50	
		Set of 5 Gutter Pairs		8.75	9.00
		First Day Cover			4.50
		Presentation Pack 351		3.90	
		PHQ257 Cards		3.00	

Self Adhesive Perf 14½ x 14 Die Cut

C1644a	1st	Biplane	3.60	3.60

MS20		Miniature Sheet	3.75	4.00
		First Day Cover		6.25

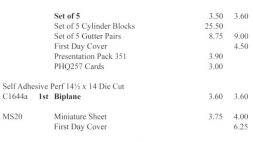

2003 (12 Aug.) British Pub Signs Perf 14 x 14½

Printer: De La Rue in Photogravure

No.	Value	Name	U/M	F/U
C1639	1st	The Station	45	50
C1640	E	Black Swan	55	60
C1641	42p	The Cross Keys	70	75
C1642	47p	The Mayflower	85	90
C1643	68p	The Barleysheaf	1.70	1.70
		Set of 5	4.00	4.00
		Set of 5 Cylinder Blocks	26.50	
		Set of 5 Gutter Pairs	9.00	9.25
		First Day Cover		4.65
		Presentation Pack 350	6.50	
		PHQ256 Cards	2.50	

2003 (7 Oct.) The British Museum Perf 14 x 14½

Printer: Walsall in Photogravure

No.	Value	Name	U/M	F/U
C1649	2nd	Denytenamun	40	45
C1650	1st	Alexander the Great	45	50
C1651	E	Sutton Hoo Helmet	65	70
C1652	42p	Pavati	75	80
C1653	47p	Mask of Xiuhtecuhtli	85	90
C1654	68p	Hoa Hakananai	1.30	1.40
		Set of 6	4.00	4.20
		Set of 6 Cylinder Blocks	28.50	
		Set of 6 Gutter Pairs	10.00	10.50
		First Day Cover		4.75
		Presentation Pack 352	6.50	
		PHQ258 Cards	3.00	

2003 (18 Sep.) Transports of Delight Perf 14 x 14½

Printer: Enschedé in Photogravure

No.	Value	Name	U/M	F/U
C1644	1st	Biplane	45	50
C1645	E	Omnibus	55	60
C1646	42p	Locomotive	75	80
C1647	47p	Ford Zephyr	80	90
C1648	68p	Space Ship	1.30	1.40

2003 (4 Nov.) Christmas Self Adhesive Perf 14½ x 14 Die cut
Printer: De La Rue in Photogravure

			U/M	F/U
C1655	**2nd**	**Ice Spiral**	40	45
C1656	**1st**	Icicle Star	45	50
C1656a		**Icicle Star** (Matrix intact -		
		Post Office Staff Issue)	2.50	
C1657	**E**	**Wall of Frozen Snow**	65	70
C1658	**53p**	**Ice Ball**	95	1.00
C1659	**68p**	**Ice Hole**	1.20	1.30
C1660	**£1.12**	**Snow Pyramids**	2.00	2.10
		Set of 6	5.20	5.40
		Set of 6 Gutter Pairs	13.00	13.50
		First Day Cover		6.00
		Presentation Pack 353	5.50	
		PHQ259 Cards	3.00	

2003 (19 Dec.) Rugby World Cup Winners Perf 14 x 14½
Printer: Walsall in Lithography

			U/M	F/U
C1661	**1st**	**St. George's Flag**	65	75
C1662	**1st**	**Australia Team**	65	75
C1663	**68p**	**Rugby World Cup**	1.75	1.95
C1664	**68p**	**England Team**	1.75	1.95
		First Day Cover		7.50
		Presentation Pack M9B	£40	
MS21		Miniature Sheet	11.00	11.50

2003 (4 Nov) Christmas Ice Sculptures from Smilers sheet

SSP15	2nd Ice spiral *plus* label (any)	1.75
SSP16	1st Icicle star *plus* label (any)	1.75

2003 (4 Nov.) Collectors Year Pack

CP40	Collectors Year Pack 353	£45

2003 (4 Nov.) Royal Mail Year Book - 20

YB20	Royal Mail Year Book	£53

2004 (13 Jan.) Classic Locomotives Perf 14 x 14½
Printer: De La Rue in Lithography

No.			U/M	F/U
C1665	20p	Gwynedd	30	35
C1666	28p	West Lothian	45	50
C1667	E	Leicstershire	65	70
C1668	42p	Worcestershire	70	75
C1669	47p	East Sussex	85	90
C1669a		Imperforate pair	£1000	
C1669b		Missing yellow		
C1670	68p	Yorkshire	1.30	1.40
		Set of 6	4.00	4.20
		Set of 6 Cylinder Blocks	28.50	
		Set of 6 Gutter Pairs	10.00	10.75
		First Day Cover		6.00
		Presentation Pack 355	£20	
		PHQ260 Cards	5.50	
MS22		Miniature Sheet	13.00	13.50
		First Day Cover		£16

2004 (3 Feb.) Occassions Perf 14 x 14½
Printer: De La Rue in Lithography

No.			U/M	F/U
C1671	1st	Postman	60	65
C1672	1st	Face	60	65
C1673	1st	Duck	60	65
C1674	1st	Baby	60	65
C1675	1st	Aircraft	60	65
		Set of 5	2.75	2.80
		Set of 5 Cylinder Blocks	18.50	
		Set of 5 Gutter Pairs	6.25	6.50
		First Day Cover		4.00
		Presentation Pack M10	3.20	
		PHQ PSM10 Cards	2.00	

2004 (3 Feb) Occasions from Smilers sheet

No.		U/M
SSP18	Vertical strip of five stamps & five labels	7.50

 A
 B

 C
 D

 E
 F

 G
 H

 I
 J

2004 (26 Feb.) J R Tolkien 50th Anniversary Perf 14 x 14½
Printer: Walsall in Lithography

No.			U/M	F/U
C1676	1st	Middle Earth	55	55
C1677	1st	Lothlorien Forest	55	55
C1678	1st	Dust Jacket	55	55
C1679	1st	1st Rivendell	55	55
C1680	1st	Hall at Bag End	55	55
C1681	1st	Orthanc	55	55
C1682	1st	Doors of Durin	55	55
C1683	1st	Barad-dur	55	55
C1684	1st	Minas Tirith	55	55
C1685	1st	Fangorn Forest	55	55
		Set of 10	5.50	5.60
		Cylinder Block	12.50	
		Gutter Block of 20	13.00	13.00
		First Day Cover		6.00
		Presentation Pack 356	9.50	
		PHQ261 Cards	6.00	

2004 (16 Mar.) Northern Ireland Perf 14 x 14½
Printer: Enschedé in Photogravure

			U/M	F/U
C1686	2nd	Ely Island	30	35
C1687	1st	Giant's Causeway	45	50
C1688	E	Antrim Mountains	60	65
C1689	42p	Mourne Mountains	65	70
C1690	47p	Glenelly Valley	75	80
C1691	68p	Strangford Lough	1.10	1.20
		Set of 6	3.65	3.85
		Set of 6 Cylinder Blocks	26.50	
		Set of 6 Gutter Pairs	9.25	9.50
		First Day Cover		6.00
		Presentation Pack 357	4.40	
		PHQ262 Cards	2.50	

Self Adhesive Perf 14½ x 14 Die Cut

			U/M	F/U
C1687a	1st	Giant's Causeway	2.00	2.00

2004 (6 Apr.) Entente Cordiale Perf 14 x 14½
Printer: Walsall in Photogravure

			U/M	F/U
C1692	28p	Lace 1 1968	60	60
C1693	57p	Coccinelle	1.10	1.10
		Set of 2	1.60	1.65
		Set of 2 Cylinder Blocks	11.50	
		Set of 2 Gutter Pairs	4.00	4.25
		First Day Cover		3.20
		Presentation Pack 358	£15	
		Presentation Pack (Anglo French)	12.50	
		PHQ263 Cards	3.50	

2004 (13 Apr.) Ocean Liners Perf 14 x 14½
Printer: De La Rue in Photogravure

			U/M	F/U
C1694	1st	RMS Queen Mary 2	45	50
C1695	E	SS Canberra	60	65
C1696	42p	RMS Queen Mary	65	70
C1697	47p	RMS Mauretania	75	80
C1698	57p	SS City of New York	1.00	1.10
C1699	68p	PS Great Western	1.20	1.30
		Set of 6	4.40	4.60
		Set of 6 Cylinder Blocks	33.50	
		Set of 6 Gutter Pairs	11.00	11.60
		First Day Cover		5.00
		Presentation Pack 359	4.90	
		PHQ264 Cards	3.50	
MS23		Miniature Sheet	6.00	6.00
		First Day Cover		10.00
C1700		Error of value - 57p printed 53p		

This is from the Ocean Liners Miniature sheet printed before a price rise was granted. These sheets were recalled but a few were found in a dealers stock in the USA.Unlikely to be available as a single!

Self Adhesive Perf 14½ x 14 Die Cut

			U/M	F/U
C1692a	1st	RMS Queen Mary 2	2.00	2.10

2004 (25 May) Bicentenary of the RHS Perf 14 x 14½
Printer: Enschedé in Photogravure

No.			U/M	F/U
C1701	2nd	Dianthus	35	40
C1702	1st	Dahlia	45	50
C1703	E	Clematis	60	65
C1704	42p	Miltonia	70	80
C1705	47p	Lilium	80	90
C1706	68p	Delphinium	1.20	1.30
		Set of 6	3.80	3.90
		Set of 6 Cylinder Blocks	27.50	
		Set of 6 Gutter Pairs	9.50	10.00
		First Day Cover		5.50
		Presentation Pack 360	4.70	
		PHQ265 Cards	3.50	
MS24		Miniature Sheet	5.50	5.50

Perf 15 x 14 From 'The Glory of the Garden' Prestige Book. These were originally issued in the Flowers Greetings books but perf 14 x 14½

C1707	1st	Camellia Japonica	1.80	1.90
C1708	1st	Tulipa	1.80	1.90
C1709	1st	Iris Latifolia	1.80	1.90

2004 (25 May) RHS Smilers sheet

SSP19	Stamp with label (any)	2.00	

2004 (15 June) Wales Perf 14 x 14½
Printer: De La Rue in Photogravure

			U/M	F/U
C1710	2nd	Barmouth Bridge	35	40
C1711	1st	Hydden	45	50
C1712	40p	Brecon Beacons	60	65
C1713	43p	Rhondda Valley	65	70
C1714	47p	Dee Valley	75	80
C1715	68p	Marloes Sands	1.10	4.25
		Set of 6	3.70	3.85
		Set of 6 Cylinder Blocks	26.50	
		Set of 6 Gutter Pairs	9.25	9.75
		First Day Cover		5.50
		Presentation Pack 361	4.70	
		PHQ266 Cards	2.50	

Self Adhesive Perf 14½ x 14 Die Cut

C1711a	1st	Hydden	2.00	2.10

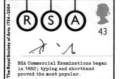 

2004 (10 Aug.) 50th Anniversary of the RSA Perf 14 x 14½
Printer: Walsall in Lithography

			U/M	F/U
C1716	1st	Sir Rowland Hill	45	50
C1717	40p	William Shipley	60	65
C1718	43p	Typewriter/Shorthand	70	75
C1719	47p	Chimney Sweep	85	90
C1720	57p	Gill Typeface	1.00	1.05
C1721	68p	Zero Waste	1.30	1.35
		Set of 6	4.40	4.40
		Set of 6 Cylinder Blocks	31.50	
		Set of 6 Gutter Pairs	11.00	11.00
		First Day Cover		6.00
		Presentation Pack 362	5.00	
		PHQ267 Cards	2.50	

 A
 B

 C
 D

 E
 F

 G
 H

 I
 J

2004 (12 Oct.) 150th Anniversary of the Crimean War Perf 14 x 14½
Printer: Walsall in Lithography

No.				U/M	F/U
C1732	2nd	Pt. McNamara		35	40
C1732a		Missing Silver-grey & phosphor		£750	
C1732b		Missing phosphor		£100	
C1733	1st	Piper Muir		50	60
C1734	40p	Sgt. Major Edwards		65	70
C1735	57p	Sgt. Powell		1.00	1.10
C1735a		Imperforate pair		£350	
C1736	68p	Sgt. Major Poole		1.20	1.30
C1736a		Imperforate pair		£1000	
C1737	£1.12	Sgt. Glasgow		1.80	1.90
		Set of 6		5.30	5.40
		Set of 6 Cylinder Blocks		38.50	
		Set of 6 Gutter Pairs		13.25	13.75
		First Day Cover			7.50
		Presentation Pack 364		5.80	
		PHQ269 Cards		2.50	

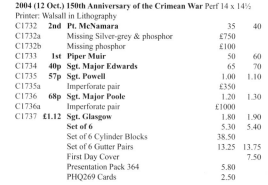

2004 (16 Sep.) Woodland Animals Perf 14 x 14½
Printer: Enschedé in Photogravure

No.				U/M	F/U
C1722	1st	Pine Martin (A)		50	60
C1723	1st	Roe Deer (B)		50	60
C1724	1st	Badger (C)		50	60
C1725	1st	Mouse (D)		50	60
C1726	1st	Wild Cat (E)		50	60
C1727	1st	Red Squirrel (F)		50	60
C1728	1st	Stoat (G)		50	60
C1729	1st	Natters Bat (H)		50	60
C1730	1st	Mole (I)		50	60
C1731	1st	Fox (J)		50	60
		Set of 10		5.50	5.60
		Cylinder Block		11.50	
		Gutter Block of 20		12.25	13.00
		First Day Cover			6.00
		Presentation Pack 363		5.00	
		PHQ268 Cards		4.00	

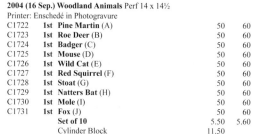

2004 (2 Nov.) Christmas Perf 14 x 14½
Printer: De La Rue in Photogravure

No.			U/M	F/U
C1738	**2nd**	**On Snowy Roof**	35	40
C1739	**1st**	**Sunrise**	50	60
C1739a		Matrix intact -		
		(Post Office Staff Issue)	2.50	
C1740	**40p**	**On Roof in Gale**	65	70
C1741	**57p**	**Umbrella in Rain**	1.00	1.10
C1742	**68p**	**In Fog on Roof**	1.20	1.30
C1743	**£1.12**	**Sheltering from Hailstorm**	1.70	1.80
		Set of 6	5.25	5.40
		Set of 6 Gutter Pairs	13.25	13.75
		First Day Cover		7.50
		Presentation Pack 365	5.80	
		PHQ270 Cards	3.20	5.00
MS26		Miniature sheet	5.00	5.10
		First Day Cover		8.00

2004 (2 Nov.) from 'Christmas' Smilers sheet

		U/M	F/U
SSP21	2nd and label	1.50	
SSP21a	1st and label	1.50	

2004 (2 Nov.) Collectors Year Pack

CP41	Collectors Year Pack 366	£48

2004 (2 Nov.) Royal Mail Year Book - 21

YB21	Royal Mail Year Book	£53

2005 (11 Jan.) Farm Animals Printed in gravure Perf 14½ x 14½
Printer: Enschedé in Photogravure

No.			U/M	F/U
C1744	**1st**	**Saddle Back Pig**	50	60
C1745	**1st**	**Khaki Campbell Duck**	50	60
C1746	**1st**	**Clydesdale Horse**	50	60
C1747	**1st**	**Shorthorn Cow**	50	60
C1748	**1st**	**Border Collie Puppy**	50	60
C1749	**1st**	**Chicks**	50	60
C1750	**1st**	**Suffolk Sheep**	50	60
C1751	**1st**	**Bagot Goat**	50	60
C1752	**1st**	**Norfolk Black Turkey**	50	60
C1753	**1st**	**Embden Geese**	50	60
		Set of 10	4.70	4.90
		Cylinder Block of 20	11.75	
		Gutter Block of 20	11.75	12.00
		First Day Cover		6.00
		Presentation Pack 367	5.00	
		PHQ271 Cards	4.50	

2005 (11 Jan.) from 'Farm Animals' Printed in Litho from Smilers sheet

		U/M	F/U
SSP23	1st plus *label* (any)	1.50	
SSP23a	Set of 10 stamps and labels	£12	

2005 (8 Feb.) South West England
Printer: De La Rue in Photogravure

			U/M	F/U
C1754	2nd	Old Harry Rocks	35	40
C1755	1st	Wheal Coates, St. Agnes	45	50
C1756	40p	Start Point, Start Bay	65	70
C1757	43p	Horton Down, Wiltshire	70	75
C1758	57p	Chiselcombe, Exmoor	1.10	1.15
C1759	68p	St James's Stone, Lundy	1.20	1.25
		Set of 6	3.80	3.90
		Set of 6 Cylinder Blocks	28.50	
		Set of 6 Gutter Pairs	9.50	9.50
		First Day Cover		5.50
		Presentation Pack 368	4.70	
		PHQ272 Cards	2.50	

2005 (24 Feb.) Jane Eyre Perf 14 x 14½
Printer: Walsall in Lithography

			U/M	F/U
C1760	2nd	Mr Rochester	35	40
C1761	1st	Jane as Thornfield Hall Burns	45	50
C1762	40p	Jane Eyre	65	70
C1763	57p	Jane with Adele	1.05	1.10
C1764	68p	Jane as a child at Lowood School	1.20	1.25
C1765	£1.12	Rev. Brocklehurst	1.65	1.70
		Set of 6	4.90	5.10
		Set of 6 Cylinder Blocks	36.50	
		Set of 6 Gutter Pairs	12.25	12.50
		First Day Cover		5.50
		Presentation Pack 369	5.80	
		PHQ273 Cards	3.00	
MS27		Miniature Sheet	5.20	5.30
		First Day Cover		5.50

2005 (15 Mar.) Magic Perf 14½ x 14½
Printer: Walsall in Photogravure

			U/M	F/U
C1766	1st	Heads	50	60
C1766a		Tails	50	60
C1767	40p	Hat and Rabbit	60	70
C1768	47p	Scarves and Tube	80	90
C1769	68p	Ace of Hearts	95	1.00
C1770	£1.12	Fez and Pyramid	1.65	1.70
		Set of 5	4.90	5.10
		Set of 5 Cylinder Blocks	36.50	
		Set of 5 Gutter Pairs	12.25	12.50
		First Day Cover		5.00
		Presentation Pack 370	5.30	
		PHQ274 Cards	2.00	

2005 (15 Mar.) from 'Magic' Smilers sheet

SSP23	1st Heads *plus* label (any)	2.00	
SSP23a	1st Tails *plus* label (any)	2.00	

2005 (8 Apr.) Royal Wedding 14½ x 14½

C1771	30p	**Prince Charles and Camilla Parker-Bowles**	60	60
C1772	68p	**Prince Charles and Camilla Parker-Bowles**	1.40	1.40
MS29		Miniature Sheet	3.00	3.00
		First Day Cover		3.90
		Presentation Pack M10	4.20	

2005 (21 Apr.) World Heritage Sites Perf 14½ x 14½

Printer: Enschedé in Lithography

C1773	**2nd**	**Hadrian's Wall**	40	40
C1774	**2nd**	**Uluru-Kata, Tjuta National Park**	40	40
C1775	**1st**	**Stonehenge**	45	45
C1776	**1st**	**Wet Tropics of Queensland**	45	45
C1777	**47p**	**Blenheim Palace**	80	80
C1778	**47p**	**Greater Blue Mountains**	80	80
C1779	**68p**	**Heart of Neolithic Orkney**	95	95
C1780	**68p**	**Purnululu National Park**	95	95
		Set of 8	4.60	4.70
		Set of 4 Cylinder Blocks	13.50	
		Set of 4 Se-Tenant Pairs	5.75	5.80
		Set of 4 Gutter Pairs	6.00	6.00
		First Day Cover		6.00
		Presentation Pack 371	6.00	
		PHQ275 Cards	3.20	

Each of the values were printed se-tenant within the sheet

2005 (7 June) Trooping the Colour Perf 14½ x 14½
Printer: Walsall in Lithography

C1781	2nd	Ensign of the Scots Guards with Colour	35	40
C1782	1st	HM The Queen	45	50
C1783	42p	Trumpeter from Household Cavalry	65	70
C1784	60p	Welsh Guards Sgt.	90	95
C1785	68p	HM the Queen	1.15	1.20
C1786	£1.12	HM the Queen and The Duke of Edinburgh	1.60	1.65
		Set of 6	4.80	4.90
		Set of 6 Cylinder Blocks	35.50	
		Set of 6 Gutter Pairs	12.00	12.00
		First Day Cover		6.00
		Presentation Pack 372	6.00	
		PHQ276 Cards	2.80	
MS30		Miniature Sheet	5.20	5.30

2005 (5 July) End of the War

Printer: Enschedé in Gravure

C1144a	1st	St. Paul's Cathedral (also listed on page 218)	1.75	1.85
MS31		Miniature sheet	2.60	2.60
		First day cover		3.50

1930 **Brough Superior** bespoke luxury motorcycle

1914 **Royal Enfield** small engined motor bicycle

2005 (19 July) Motorcycles Perf 14½ x 14½
Printer: Walsall in Lithography

C1787	1st	1991 Norton F.1	45	50
C1788	40p	1969 BSA Rocket 3	65	70
C1789	42p	1949 Vincent Black Shadow	70	80
C1790	47p	1938 Triumph Speed Twin	80	90
C1791	60p	1030 Brough Superior	90	95
C1792	68p	1914 Royal Enfield	95	1.00
		Set of 6	4.40	4.50
		Set of 6 Cylinder Blocks	29.50	
		Set of 6 Gutter Pairs	10.50	
		First Day Cover		5.00
		Presentation Pack 373	5.30	
		PHQ277 Cards	2.60	

2005 (5 Aug.) London 2012 Perf 14½ x 14½
Printer: Walsall in Lithography

C1793	1st	Shot Putt (A)	65	65
C1794	1st	Javelin (B)	65	65
C1795	1st	Diving (C)	65	65
C1796	1st	Sprinting (D)	65	65
C1797	1st	Netball (E)	65	65
MS32		Miniature sheet	3.00	3.00
		First Day Cover		3.50
		Presentation Pack M11	3.70	

No.			U/M	F/U	No.			U/M	F/U

	Set of 6	3.80	4.00
	Set of 6 Cylinder Blocks	27.50	
	Set of 6 Gutter Pairs	9.50	9.50
	First Day Cover		5.00
	Presentation Pack 375	5.00	
	PHQ279 Cards	2.50	

2005 (15 Sep.) from 'Classic ITV' Smilers sheet

SSP25	1st Emmerdale *plus* label (any)	1.50

2005(23 Aug.) Changing Tastes of Britain Perf 14½ x 14½
Printer: Enschedé in Gravure

1798	2nd	Woman eating Rice	30	35
1799	1st	Woman drinking tea	45	50
1800	42p	Boy eating Suchi	65	70
1801	47p	Woman eating Pasta	75	80
1802	60p	Woman eating Chips	90	95
1803	68p	Man eating Apple	1.00	1.10
		Set of 6	3.80	4.00
		Set of 6 Cylinder Blocks	27.50	
		Set of 6 Gutter Pairs	9.50	9.50
		First Day Cover		5.00
		Presentation Pack 374	5.00	
		PHQ278 Cards	2.60	

2005 (6 Oct.) The Ashes
Printer: Cartor in Lithography

C1810	1st		65	70
C1811	1st		65	70
C1812	68p		1.35	1.40
C1813	68p		1.35	1.40
MS33		Miniature Sheet	3.00	3.25
		First Day Cover		4.00
		Presentation Pack M12	3.90	
		PHQ Cards	2.80	4.50

This was the first issue to show recognisable living persons, apart from Royalty, on GB stamps.

2005 (15 Sep.) Classic ITV Perf
Printer: De La Rue in Lithography

1804	2nd	Inspector Morse	30	35
1805	1st	Emmerdale	45	50
1806	42p	Rising Damp	65	70
1807	47p	The Avengers	70	75
1808	60p	The South Bank Show	90	95
1809	68p	Who Wants to be a Millionaire	1.00	1.10

A

B

C

D

E

F

2005 (18 Oct.) Battle of Trafalgar

Printer: Cartor in Lithography

			U/M	F/U
C1814	1st	Entrepreante/Belle Isle (A)	45	50
C1815	1st	HMS Victory (B)	45	50
C1816	42p	Entrepreante/Achille (C)	65	70
C1817	42p	H M S Pickle (D)	65	70
C1818	68p	British Fleet Attacking (E)	1.00	1.10
C1819	68p	Franco/Spanish Fleet (F)	1.00	1.10
		Set of 6	4.00	4.50
		Set of 3 Cylinder Blocks	29.50	
		Set of Gutter Blocks	10.00	10.00
		First Day Cover		5.00
		Presentation Pack 376	5.00	
		PHQ280 Cards	3.00	

These were issued as se-tenant pairs of each individual value

MS34	Miniature Sheet	4.00	4.50
	First day cover		5.50

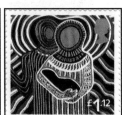

2005 (1 Nov.) Christmas Self Adhesive Perf 14 x 14.5

Printer: De La Rue in Gravure

			U/M	F/
C1820	2nd	Madonna and child Haiti	30	3
C1821	1st	Madonna and child	45	5
C1821a	1st	Madonna and child (Matrix intact - Post Office Staff Issue)	2.50	
C1822	42p	Virgin Mary/Infant Christ	65	7
C1823	60p	Virgin Mother/Child (Choctaw)	90	9
C1824	68p	Madonna and Infant Jesus	1.00	1.
C1825	£1.12	Come Let Us Adore Him	1.70	1.8
		Set of 6	5.00	5.2
		Set of 6 Gutter Blocks	11.75	12.0
		First Day Cover		6.
		Presentation Pack 377	5.20	
		PHQ281 Cards	3.00	

MS35	Miniature Sheet	5.00	5.2
	First Day Cover		6.0

2005 (1 Nov.) Collectors Year Pack

CP42	Collectors Year Pack 378	£40

2005 (1 Nov.) Royal Mail Year Book - 22

YB22	Royal Mail Year Book	£53

A

C

E

G

No.			U/M	F/U

2006 (10 Jan.) Animal Tales

Printer: De La Rue in Lithography

No.	Value	Description	U/M	F/U
C1826	2nd	Mr Jeremy Fisher (A)	35	40
C1827	2nd	Kipper (B)	35	40
C1828	1st	The Enormous Crocodile (C)	50	55
C1829	1st	More about Paddington (D)	65	55
C1830	42p	Comic Adventures about Boots (E)	65	70
C1831	42p	Alice's Adventures in Wonderland (F)	1.05	70
C1832	68p	The Very Hungry Caterpillar (G)	1.05	1.10
C1833	68p	Maisy's ABC (H)	1.05	1.10
		Set of 8	5.00	5.30
		Set of 4 Cylinder Blocks	15.00	
		Set of 4 Gutter Blocks	10.00	
		First Day Cover		5.75
		Presentation Pack 379	5.80	
		PHQ 282 Cards	3.50	

Each value was issued as a se-tenant pair

2006 (7 Feb) England

Printer: De La Rue in Gravure

No.	Value	Description	U/M	F/U
C1834	1st	Carding Mill Valley	50	55
C1835	1st	Beachy Head	50	55
C1836	1st	St. Paul's Cathedral	50	55
C1837	1st	Brancaster	50	55
C1838	1st	Derwent Edge	50	55
C1839	1st	Robin Hood's Bay	50	55
C1840	1st	Buttermere	50	55
C1841	1st	Chipping Campden	50	55
C1842	1st	St Boniface Down	50	55
C1843	1st	Chamberlain Square	50	55
		Set of 10	4.75	5.00
		Cylinder Block of 20	10.00	
		Gutter Block of 20	10.00	
		First Day Cover		5.75
		Presentation Pack 380	5.50	
		PHQ 283 Cards	4.20	

2006 (23 Feb.) Brunel

Printer: Enschedé in Lithography

No.	Value	Description	U/M	F/U
C1844	1st	Royal Albert Bridge	50	55
C1845	40p	Box Tunnel	60	65
C1846	42p	Paddington Station	65	70
C1847	47p	PSS Great Britain	70	75
C1848	60p	Clifton Suspension Bridge	90	95
C1849	68p	Maidenhead Bridge	1.05	1.10
		Set of 6	4.10	4 40
		Set of 6 Cylinder Blocks	£26	
		Set of 6 Gutter Blocks	8.20	
		First Day Cover		5.40
		Presentation Pack 381	5.40	
		PHQ284 Cards	4.00	
MS36		Miniature Sheet	4.10	4.40
		First day cover		5.40

2006 (21 Mar.) Ice Age Animals

Printer: Enschedé in Lithography

			U/M	F/U
C1850	1st	Sabre-tooth Cat	50	55
C1851	42p	Giant Deer	65	70
C1852	47p	Wooly Rhino	70	75
C1853	68p	Wooly Mammoth	1.05	1.10
C1854	£1.12	Cave Bear	1.70	1.75
		Set of 5	4.40	4.65
		Set of 5 Cylinder Blocks	£28	
		Set of 5 Gutter Blocks	8.80	
		First Day Cover		5.75
		Presentation Pack 382	5.50	
		PHQ 285 Cards	2.20	

2006 (18 April) Queen's 80th Birthday

Printer: Enschedé in Gravure

			U/M	F/U
C1855	2nd	Aboard Brittania 1972	35	40
C1856	2nd	Royal Windsor Horse Show May 1985	35	40
C1857	1st	Meeting dignitaries at Heathrow Airport 2001	50	55
C1858	1st	With her Mother the Duchess of York 1931	50	55
C1859	44p	State Banquet Ottawa, Canada, October 1951	65	70
C1860	44p	HM The Queen 1960	65	70
C1861	72p	Age 14, 1940	1.10	1.15
C1862	72p	With the Duke of Edinburgh c.1950	1.10	1.15
		Set of 8	5.00	5.40
		Set of 4 Cylinder Blocks	£15	
		Set of 4 Gutter Blocks	£10	
		First Day Cover		
		Presentation Pack 383	6.10	
		PHQ 286 Cards	3.50	

2006 (6 June) World Cup Winners

Printer: Walsall in Lithography

			U/M	F/U
C1863	1st	England	50	5
C1864	42p	Italy	65	7
C1865	44p	Argentina	65	7
C1866	50p	Germany	75	8
C1867	64p	France	1.00	1.0
C1868	72p	Brazil	1.10	1.1
		Set of 6	4.50	4.7
		Set of 6 Cylinder Blocks	£29	
		Set of 6 Gutter Blocks	9.00	
		First Day Cover		6.0
		Presentation Pack 384	5.50	
		PHQ 287 Cards	2.60	

2006 (18 July) National Portrait Gallery
Printer: De La Rue in Gravure

C1875	1st	Sir Winston Churchill	50	55
C1876	1st	Sir Joshua Reynolds	50	55
C1877	1st	T.S. Eliott	50	55
C1878	1st	Emmeline Pankhurst	50	55
C1879	1st	Virginia Woolf	50	55
C1880	1st	Sir Walter Scott	50	55
C1881	1st	Mary Seacole	50	55
C1882	1st	William Shakespear	50	55
C1883	1st	Dame Cicely Saunders	50	55
C1884	1st	Charles Darwin	50	55
		Set of 10	4.80	5.10
		Cylinder Block	£10	
		Gutter Blocks	£10	
		First Day Cover		6.50
		Presentation Pack 386	5.80	
		PHQ 289 Cards	4.30	

2006 (20 June) Modern Architecture
Printer: Walsall in Gravure

C1969	1st	30 St Mary Axe, London	50	55
C1870	42p	Maggie's Centre, Dundee	65	70
C1871	44p	Selfridges, Birmingham	65	70
C1872	50p	Downland Gridshell, Chichester	75	80
C1873	64p	An Turas, Tiree	1.00	1.05
C1874	72p	The Deep, Hull	1.10	1.15
		Set of 6	4.50	4.75
		Set of 6 Cylinder Blocks	£29	
		Set of 6 Gutter Blocks	9.00	
		First Day Cover		6.00
		Presentation Pack 385	5.50	
		PHQ 288 Cards	2.60	

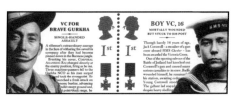

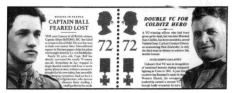

No.			U/M	F/U

2006 (21 September) Victoria Cross
Printer: Enschedé in Lithography

C1885	1st	Agansing Rai	50	55
C1886	1st	Jack Cornwall	50	55
C1887	64p	Charles Lucas	1.00	1.00
C1888	64p	Noel Chavasse	1.00	1.05
C1889	72p	Albert Ball	1.10	1.15
C1890	72p	Charles Upham	1.10	1.15
		Set of 6	5.00	5.20
		Set of 3 Cylinder Blocks	£16	
		Set of 3 Gutter Blocks	£10	
		First Day Cover		7.00
		Presentation Pack 387	6.00	
		PHQ290 Cards	3.00	

These were issued as se-tenant pairs of each individual value

MS39	Miniature Sheet	5.50	5.75
	First day cover		7.25

2006 (3 October) Sounds of Britain
Printer: Cartor in Lithography

C1891	1st	Bhangrs and Bollywood	50	55
C1892	42p	Africa and the Caribean	65	70
C1893	50p	Celtic	75	80
C1894	72p	Blues and Jazz	1.10	1.15
C1895	£1.19	Latin American	1.80	1.85
		Set of 5	4.60	4.90
		Set of 5 Cylinder Blocks	£25	
		Set of 5 Gutter Blocks	9.20	
		First Day Cover		5.75
		Presentation Pack 388	5.80	
		PHQ291 Cards	3.00	

2006 (7 November) Christmas Self Adhesive Perf 14 x 14.5
Printer: De La Rue in Gravure

C1896	2nd	Snowman	35	40
C1897	2nd	Large Snowman	55	55
C1898	1st	Father Christmas	50	60
C1898a	1st	Father Christmas (Matrix intact - Post Office Staff Issue)	2.50	
C1899	1st	Large Father Christmas	65	70
C1900	72p	Reindeer	1.10	1.20
C1901	£1.19	Christmas Tree	1.80	1.90
		Set of 6	4.80	5.10
		Set of 6 Cylinder Blocks	£30	
		First Day Cover		6.00
		Presentation Pack 389	5.90	
		PHQ292 Cards	3.00	

MS40	Miniature Sheet	4.80	5.10
	First day cover		6.00

2006 (9 November) Lest we Forget
Printer: De La Rue in Gravure

C1902	1st	Poppy		

MS41	Miniature Sheet	4.80	5.10
	Presentation Pack 390	5.80	
	First day cover		5.75

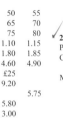

2006 (30 November) Celebrating Scotland

No.			U/M	F/U
C1903	72p	Saint Andrew		
C1904	72p	Edinburgh Castle		
		First Day Cover		5.50
		Presentation Pack M14	4.00	
		PHQ CGB1 Cards	2.20	
MS42		Miniature Sheet	2.95	3.50

2006 (2 Nov.) Collectors Year Pack

CP43		Collectors Year Pack 391	£55	

2006 (2 Nov.) Royal Mail Year Book - 23

YB23		Royal Mail Year Book	£58	

2007 (9 January) The Beatles Miniature sheet
Printer: Walsall in Lithography

No.			U/M	F/U
C1911	1st	Beatles memorabilia guitar	75	80
C1912	1st	Beatles memorabilia lunchbox	75	80
C1913	1st	45rpm single	75	80
C1914	1st	Beatles memorabilia tea tray	75	80
MS43		Miniature Sheet	2.00	2.20
		First day cover		3.00

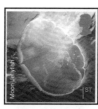

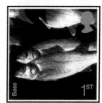
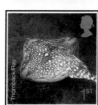

2007 (9 January) The Beatles Self Adhesive Perf 14 x 14.5
Printer: Walsall in Gravure

No.			U/M	F/U
C1905	1st	With the Beatles	70	75
C1906	1st	Sgt. Pepper's Lonely Hearts Club Band	70	75
C1907	64p	Help!	1.50	1.60
C1908	64p	Abbey Road	1.50	1.60
C1909	72p	Revolver	1.60	1.70
C1910	72p	Let it Be	1.60	1.70
		Set of 6	6.00	6.40
		Set of 3 Cylinder Blocks	£20	
		First Day Cover		6.50
		Presentation Pack 392	7.50	
		PHQ 293 Cards	4.50	

✓ **2007 (1 February) Sea Life**
Printer: Cartor in Lithography

No.			U/M	F/U
C1915	1st	Moon Jellyfish	75	80
C1916	1st	Common Starfish	75	80
C1917	1st	Beadlet Anemone	75	80
C1918	1st	Bass	75	80
C1919	1st	Thornback Ray	75	80
C1920	1st	Lesser Octopus	75	80
C1921	1st	Common Mussels	75	80
C1922	1st	Grey Seal	75	80
C1923	1st	Shore Crab	75	80
C1924	1st	Common Sun Star	75	80
		Set of 10	5.80	6.00
		Cylinder Block	£30	
		Gutter Blocks	11.60	
		First Day Cover		6.50
		Presentation Pack 393	5.90	
		PHQ294 Cards	4.20	

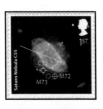
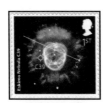

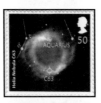

✓ **2007 (13 February) Sky at Night** Self Adhesive Perf 14 x 14.5
Printer: Walsall in Gravure

No.			U/M	F/U
C1925	1st	Saturn Nebula C55	75	80
C1926	1st	Eskimo Nebula C39	75	80
C1927	50p	Cat's Eye Nebula C6	1.20	1.25
C1928	50p	Helix Nebula C63	1.20	1.25
C1929	72p	Flaming Star Nebula C31	1.70	1.75
C1930	72p	The Spindle C53	1.70	1.75
		Set of 6	5.60	5.80
		Set of 3 Cylinder Blocks	£18	
		Set of 3 Gutter Blocks	£12	
		First Day Cover		6.50
		Presentation Pack 394	5.50	
		PHQ295 Cards	2.50	

✓ **2007 (1 March) World of Invention** Self Adhesive Perf 14 x 14.5
Printer: De La Rue in Gravure

No.			U/M	F/U
C1931	1st	Thomas Telford and Bridge Building	50	55
C1932	1st	George Stephenson and Railways	50	55
C1933	64p	Alexander Graham Bell and the Telephone	1.25	1.30
C1934	64p	John Logie Baird and Television	1.25	1.30
C1935	72p	Sir Tim-Berners Lee and the World Wide Web	2.00	2.20
C1936	72p	Space Tourism	2.00	2.50
		Set of 6	6.00	6.40
		Set of 3 Cylinder Blocks	£20	
		Set of 3 Gutter Blocks	£12	
		First Day Cover		7.50
		Presentation Pack 395	5.90	
		PHQ296 Cards	3.00	

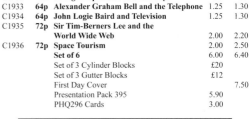

2007 (1 March) World of Invention Miniature sheet

No.			U/M	F/U
C1931a	1st	Thomas Telford and Bridge Building	55	60
C1932a	1st	George Stephenson and Railways	55	60
C1933a	64p	Alexander Graham Bell and the Telephone	75	80
C1934a	64p	John Logie Baird and Television	75	80
C1935a	72p	Sir Tim-Berners Lee and the World Wide Web	2.10	2.20
C1936a	72p	Space Tourism	2.10	2.20
		Set of 6	6.20	6.30

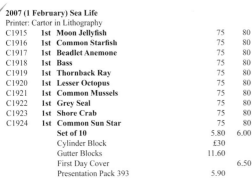

No.			U/M	F/U
MS44	Miniature Sheet		6.40	6.80
	First day cover			7.95

2007 (22 March) Abolition of Slavery
Printer: Cartor in Lithography

C1937	1st	William Wilberforce	50	55
C1938	1st	Claudah Equiano	50	55
C1939	50p	Granville Sharp	75	80
C1940	50p	Thomas Clarkson	75	80
C1941	72p	Hannah More	1.10	1.20
C1942	72p	Ignatius Sancho	1.10	1.20
		Set of 6	4.60	4.80
		Set of 3 Cylinder Blocks	£15	
		Set of 3 Gutter Blocks	9.20	
		First Day Cover		6.00
		Presentation Pack 396	5.40	
		PHQ297 Cards	2.50	

These were issued as se-tenant pairs of each individual value

2007 (23 April) Celebrating England
Printer: De La Rue in Gravure

C1943	78p	St. George and the Dragon	1.50	1.70
C1944	78p	Houses of Parliament	1.50	1.70
		First Day Cover		3.90
		Presentation Pack M15	4.30	
		PHQ CGB2 Cards	2.10	
MS45		Miniature Sheet	3.20	3.30

2007 (15 May) Beside the Seaside
Printer: De La Rue in Gravure

C1945	1st	Ice Cream Cone	50	55
C1946	46p	Sandcastle	75	80
C1947	48p	Merry-go-round	80	85
C1948	54p	Beach Huts	1.00	1.10
C1949	69p	Deckchairs	1.10	1.20
C1950	78p	Donkeys	1.25	1.35
		Set of 6	5.00	5.25
		Set of 6 Cylinder Blocks	£32	
		Set of 6 Gutter Blocks	£10	
		First Day Cover		6.50
		Presentation Pack 397	5.90	
		PHQ298 Cards	2.50	

2007 (16 May) Field of Dreams
Printer: De La Rue in Gravure

C1547a	1st	Lion and St. George Shield		
MS45		Miniature Sheet	3.60	3.85
		First day cover		5.50

Also listed on Page 245

2007 (5 June) Machin Definitive 40th Anniversary
Printer: De La Rue in Gravure

No.			U/M	F/U
C1951	1st	Portrait of Arnold Machin	60	65
C1952	1st	First Machin Stamp	60	65
		Presentation Pack 398	4.90	
MS47		Miniature Sheet	4.10	4.20
		PHQ 299 Cards	1.30	
		First day cover		5.50

2007 (3 July) Grand Prix
Printer: Cartor in Lithography

No.			U/M	F/U
C1953	1st	1957 Vanwall 2.5L driven by Stirling Moss	50	55
C1954	1st	1962 BRM P57 driven by Graham Hill	50	55
C1955	54p	1963 Lotus 25 Climax driven by Jim Clark	1.00	1.05
C1956	54p	1973 Tyrrell 006/2 driven by Jackie Stewart	1.00	1.05
C1957	78p	1976 McLaren M23 driven by James Hunt	1.25	1.30
C1958	78p	1986 Williams FW11 driven by Nigel Mansell	1.25	1.30
		Set of 6	5.00	5.25
		Set of 6 Cylinder Blocks	£32	
		Set of 6 Gutter Blocks	£10	
		First Day Cover		6.50
		Presentation Pack 399	4.90	
		PHQ300 Cards	2.50	

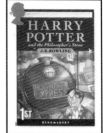
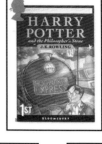
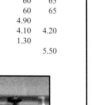

2007 (17 July) Harry Potter
Printer: Walsall in Lithography

No.			U/M	F/U
C1959	1st	Harry Potter and the Philosopher's Stone	50	55
C1960	1st	Harry Potter and the Chamber of Secrets	50	55
C1961	1st	Harry Potter and the Prisonaer of Azkaban	50	55
C1962	1st	Harry Potter and the Goblet of Fire	50	55
C1963	1st	Harry Potter and the Order of the Phoenix	50	55
C1964	1st	Harry Potter and the Half-Blood Prince	50	55
C1965	1st	Harry Potter and the Deathly Hallows	50	55
		Set of 7	3.20	3.60
		Cylinder Block	£11	
		Gutter Block	6.50	
		First Day Cover		5.75
		Presentation Pack M16	7.30	
		PHQ HP Cards	5.50	

These were issued as a se-tenant strip of 7.

2007 (17 July) Harry Potter Miniature sheet

Printer: Walsall in Lithography

No.			U/M	F/U
C1966	1st	Gryffindor	55	60
C1967	1st	Hufflepuff	55	60
C1968	1st	Hogwarts	55	60
C1969	1st	Ravenclaw	55	60
C1970	1st	Slytherin	55	60
MS48		Miniature sheet	2.55	2.75
		First day cover		4.75

2007 (17 July) Harry Potter Generic Sheet Self adhesive

C1966a	1st	Gryffindor	55	60
C1967a	1st	Hufflepuff	55	60
C1968a	1st	Hogwarts	55	60
C1969a	1st	Ravenclaw	55	60
C1970a	1st	Slytherin	55	60

2007 (26 July) Scouting

Printer: Enschedé in Lithography

C1971	1st	11 of the 12 Astronauts...	50	55
C1972	46p	The Youngest Climber...	75	80
C1973	48p	450,000 UK Scouts...	80	85
C1974	54p	Adult Scout Volunteers...	1.00	1.10
C1975	69p	The First Non-stop Solo...	1.10	1.20
C1976	78p	Scouting is the Largest...	1.25	1.35
		Set of 6	4.95	5.70
		Set of 6 Cylinder Block	£32	
		Set of 6 Gutter Blocks	£10	
		First Day Cover		6.95
		Presentation Pack 400	5.40	
		PHQ301 Cards	2.50	

2007 (4 September) Birds

Printer: De La Rue in Lithography

C1977	1st	White-tailed Eagle	50	55
C1978	1st	Bearded Tit	50	55
C1979	1st	Red Kite	50	55
C1980	1st	Cirl Bunting	50	55
C1981	1st	Marsh Harrier	50	55
C1982	1st	Avocet	50	55
C1983	1st	Bitern	50	55
C1984	1st	Dartford Warbler	50	55
C1985	1st	Corncrake	50	55
C1986	1st	Peregrin	50	55
		Set of 10	4.90	5.30
		Cylinder Block of 10	£11	
		Gutter Block of 10	£11	
		First Day Cover		6.75
		Presentation Pack 401	6.00	
		PHQ302 Cards	4.20	

2007 (20 September) British Army Uniforms
Printer: Enschedé in Lithography

No.			U/M	F/U
C1987	1st	NCO Royal Military Police 1999	50	55
C1988	1st	Tank Commander 5th Royal Tank Regiment 1944	50	55
C1989	1st	Observer Royal Field Artillery	50	55
C1990	78p	Rifleman 95th Rifles 1813	1.25	1.35
C1991	78p	Grenadier Royal Regiment of Foot of Ireland 1704	1.25	1.35
C1992	78p	Trooper Earl of Oxford's Horse 1661	1.25	1.35
		Set of 2 Se-tenant strips	5.05	5.50
		Set of 2 Cylinder Blocks	£17	
		Set of 2 Gutter Blocks	10.50	
		First Day Cover		6.75
		Presentation Pack 402	6.00	
		PHQ303 Cards	2.50	

These were issued as se-tenant strips of 3 of each value

2007 (16 October) Diamond Wedding Anniversary
Printer: Cartor in Lithography

No.			U/M	F/U
C1993	1st	The Queen and Prince Philip leave St. Pauls Cathedral after a thanksgiving service for her 80th and his 85th birthdays in 2006	50	55
C1994	1st	The Queen and Prince Philip inspect the King's Troop Royal Horse Artillery in Regents Park, 30 April 1997	50	55
C1995	54p	The Queen and Prince Philip at the Garter Ceremony, Windsor, 16 June 1980	1.00	1.10
C1993	54p	The Queen and Prince Philip at Royal Ascot, 1969	1.00	1.10
C1994	78p	The Queen and Prince Philip at the premier of The Guns of Navarone, 27 April 1961	1.25	1.35
C1995	78p	Princess Elizabeth and Lieutenant Philip Mountbatten RN at Clydebank, 1947	1.25	1.35
		Set of 3 Se-tenant strips	5.20	5.60
		Set of 3 Cylinder Blocks	£17	
		Set of 3 Gutter Blocks	£11	
		First Day Cover		6.95
		Presentation Pack 403	8.70	
		PHQ 304 Cards Set of 11 including one of miniature sheet	4.50	
MS49		Miniature sheet	3.30	6.00

These were issued as se-tenant pairs of each value

2007 (16 October) Diamond Wedding Anniversary
Self adhesive miniature sheet
Printer: Walsall in Gravure

No.			U/M	F/U
C1996	1st	The Royal Family at Balmoral 1972	50	55
C1997	1st	The Queen and Prince Philip photographed at Buckingham Palace by Lord Snowdon, 2007	50	55
C1998	69p	The Royal Family at Windsor Castle, 1965	1.10	1.15
C1999	78p	Princess Elizabeth and Prince Philip with Prince Charles and Princess Anne at Clarence House, 1951	1.25	1.35
		Set of 4	3.20	3.50
		First Day Cover		6.00

U/M   F/U   No.   U/M   F/U

2007 (6 November) Christmas Self adhesive
Printer: De La Rue in Gravure

No.			U/M	F/U
C2000	**2nd**	**Peace**	35	40
C2001	**2nd**	**Large Peace**	65	70
C2002	**2nd**	**Madonna and Child by William Dyce**		
C2003	**1st**	**Goodwill**	50	55
C2003a	**1st**	**Goodwill** (Matrix intact - Post Office Staff Issue)	2.50	
C2004	**1st**	**Large Goodwill**	80	85
C2004	**1st**	**The Madonna of Humility by Lippo di Dalmasio**		
C2005	**78p**	**Joy**	1.25	1.35
C2007	**£1.24**	**Glory**	1.90	2.00
		Set of 8	5.50	
		Set of 6 Cylinder Blocks	£35	
		Set of 3 Gutter Blocks	£11	
		First Day Cover		6.95
		Presentation Pack 404	6.60	
		PHQ305 Cards Set of 9 including one of miniature sheet (next column)	3.75	

2007 (6 November) Christmas Conventionally gummed
Printer: De La Rue in Gravure

No.			U/M	F/U
C2008	**2nd**	**Peace**		
C2009	**2nd**	**Large Peace**		
C2010	**1st**	**Goodwill**		
C2011	**1st**	**Large Goodwill**		
C2012	**78p**	**Joy**		
C2013	**£1.24**	**Glory**		
MS50		Miniature Sheet	5.00	5.20
		First day cover		6.95

2007 (8 November) Lest We Forget Miniature Sheet
Printer: De La Rue in Lithography

No.			U/M	F/U
C2014	**1st**	**Poppy**		
MS51		Miniature Sheet	5.00	5.40
		Presentation Pack 405	5.70	
		First day cover		6.50

2007 (8 Nov.) Collectors Year Pack
| CP43 | Collectors Year Pack | |

2006 (8 Nov.) Royal Mail Year Book - 24
| YB24 | Royal Mail Year Book | £85 |

Post Office Machine Labels (Framas)

Post Office machine labels have now commonly become known as 'Frama' labels, this being the machine manufacturer's name. From 1 May 1984 machines were installed on an experimental basis at five offices: Cambridge, Edinburgh, London, Southampton (Shirley Avenue) and Windsor.

The labels were dispensed from automatic machines that imprinted on command any denomination from ½p to 16p in ½p increments. On 18 August, two further values were made available, 16½p and 17p.

The Post Office supplied labels from Philatelic Bureaux in 'Packs' of either all 32 denominations or in sets of 3½p, 12½p and 16p values. The latter combination was the only type to be serviced to subscribers by the Philatelic Bureau. In early 1985 after abandonment of the ½p coin the machines were withdrawn.

Used labels with legible postmarks from any of the 5 experimental areas are worth a premium of 50%.

			U/M	F/U
Set of 34			£13	£16
First Day Covers (½p to 16p)				£25
First Day Cover (3½p, 12½p and 16p)				4.00
Philatelic "Pack" (½p to 16p)			£25	
Philatelic "Pack" (3½p, 12½p and 16p)			3.50	
Philatelic "Pack" (16½p and 17p)			4.50	
NPM 'PHQ' Card (16p)*			4.50	6.00
First Day Cover (16½p and 17p)				5.00

* The National Postal Museum produced a 16p value 'PHQ' style card for this issue.

Varieties

			U/M
FR1a	½p	Missing "½" (label reads "0.00")	£50
FR1b	½p	Printed on white paper	£100
FR2a	1p	Printed on white paper	£100
FR2b	1p	Dry print of Red (blank label)	£20
FR4a	2p	Printed on white paper	£100
FR6a	3p	Printed on the gummed side	£225
FR25a	12½p	Printed on white paper	£100
FR25b	12½p	Printed on the gummed side	£130
FR26a	13p	Printed on the gummed side	£225
FR32a	16p	Printed on white paper	£100
FR32b	16p	Printed on the gummed side	£130
FR33a	16½p	Printed on the gummed side	£225
FR34a	17p	Printed on the gummed side	£225
		Set of 17 NPM 'Specimen' labels in red on white paper. *	£18
		Set of 17 NPM 'Specimen' labels in black on white paper. *	£14

* These were only available from a machine at The National Postal Museum London.

1984 (1 May) Phosphor Coated Paper. No watermark. Imperforate.

No.			U/M	F/U
FR1	½p	Red on grey	15	20
FR2	1p	Red on grey	15	20
FR3	1½p	Red on grey	15	20
FR4	2p	Red on grey	15	20
FR5	2½p	Red on grey	20	25
FR6	3p	Red on grey	20	25
FR7	3½p	Red on grey	25	30
FR8	4p	Red on grey	25	30
FR9	4½p	Red on grey	30	35
FR10	5p	Red on grey	30	35
FR11	5½p	Red on grey	35	40
FR12	6p	Red on grey	35	40
FR13	6½p	Red on grey	40	45
FR14	7p	Red on grey	40	45
FR15	7½p	Red on grey	45	50
FR16	8p	Red on grey	45	50
FR17	8½p	Red on grey	50	55
FR18	9p	Red on grey	50	55
FR19	9½p	Red on grey	55	60
FR20	10p	Red on grey	55	60
FR21	10½p	Red on grey	65	70
FR22	11p	Red on grey	65	70
FR23	11½p	Red on grey	70	75
FR24	12p	Red on grey	70	75
FR25	12½p	Red on grey	75	85
FR26	13p	Red on grey	75	85
FR27	13½p	Red on grey	80	85
FR28	14p	Red on grey	80	85
FR29	14½p	Red on grey	85	90
FR30	15p	Red on grey	85	90
FR31	15½p	Red on grey	90	95
FR32	16p	Red on grey	90	95
FR33	16½p	Red on grey	1.40	1.60
FR34	17p	Red on grey	1.40	1.60

Miniature Sheets

Britains first miniature sheet was issued on 1 March 1978. The following year the second in the series was released to commemorate the death of Sir Rowland Hill; it was sold 10p above face value to help fund the London 1980 Stamp Exhibition the following year. It was another eight years (1988) before the next appeared. From 1978 to 1999 (21 years) only eight miniature sheets were issued; since then - from 2000 to 2005 there have been another 28 sheets issued in only 6 years. We predict this section will expand much more for the next edition of this catalogue!

			U/M	F/U
1978 (1 March) British Architecture. Historic Buildings				
MS1	**53½p**	**Complete Miniature Sheet**		
		(in original PO folder)	90	1.10
MS1a		Missing phosphor	£100	
		First Day Cover		1.00
Varieties				
MS1b	MS	Missing Red (flag on 9p)	£3500	
MS1c	MS	Missing Pale Orange (10p and 13p)	£3500	
MS1d	MS	Missing Yellow-olive (Queen's head)	£4500	
MS1e	MS	Missing Blue	£11000	
MS1f	MS	Imperforate	£4500	

1979 (22 Aug.) Sir Rowland Hill Centenary				
MS2	**59½p**	**Miniature sheet** (24.10.79)	70	70
MS2a		Missing phosphor	£25	
		First Day Cover		75

Varieties				
MS2b	MS	Imperforate	£2000	
MS2c	MS	Missing Black and Yellow	£12500	
MS2d	MS	Missing Yellow (10p windows, etc.)	£250	£225
MS2e	MS	Missing Yellow and phosphor	£250	
MS2f	MS	Missing Brown-ochre (15p sky, etc.)	£1750	
MS2g	MS	Missing Brown-ochre, Green and Gold	£5000	
MS2h	MS	Missing Rosine (11½p jacket, etc.)	£1000	
MS2i	MS	Missing Rosine and phosphor	£750	
MS2j	MS	Missing Blue (13p, jacket, sky, etc.)	£5500	
MS2k	MS	Missing Green (10p sky & coat, 15p etc.)	£2500	
MS2l	MS	Missing Brown (15p dress, 11½p, 13p etc.)	£750	
MS2m	MS	Missing Gold (Queen's head)	£250	£225
MS2n	MS	Missing Gold and phosphor	£250	
MS2o	MS	Shift 6mm to top of Green	£175	
MS2p	MS	Shift 2mm to right of Gold	£5	
MS2q	MS	Offset on reverse of Gold (Queen's head)	£350	

1980 (7 May) London 1980 International Stamp Exhibition				
MS3	**75p**	**Complete Miniature sheet**	80	1.00
MS3a		Imperforate sheet	£1250	£750
		First Day Cover		75

1988 (27 Sept.) Edward Lear				
MS4	**£1.35**	**Complete Miniature Sheet**	2.40	2.50
		First Day Cover		3.50

1989 (25 July) Industrial Archaeology

			U/M	F/U
MS5	**£1.40**	**Complete Miniature Sheet**	2.90	
		First Day Cover		3.00

1990 (3 May) 'Stamp World 90', London

			U/M	F/U
MS6	**£1**	**Miniature sheet** containing 20p stamp	2.70	2.85
		First Day Cover		3.00
Varieties				
MS6a	£1	Missing Black (Recess printing)	£33,000	
MS6b	£1	Missing Cream (Recess printing)	£4000	
MS6c	£1	Imperforate	£3500	
MS6d	£1	Imperforate. First Day Cover		£3500
MS6e	£1	Recess printing inverted (background)	£7500	

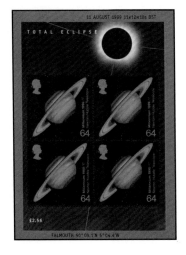

1999 (11 Aug.) Solar Eclipse

			U/M	F/U
MS7	**4 x 64p**	Complete Miniature Sheet	12.50	12.50
MS7a		Impeforate sheet (Mint & FDC)	£3250	£1750
		First Day Cover		£16

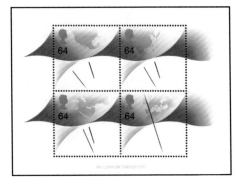

1999 (14 Dec.) Millennium Timekeeper

			U/M	F/U
MS8	**4 x 64p**	Complete Miniature sheeet	11.50	11.50
		First Day Cover		£15

2000 (22 May) Millennium Timekeeper Stamp Show Overprint

			U/M	F/U
MS8a	**4 x 64p**	Stamp Show 2000 overprint	£15	£15
		First Day Cover		£65

2000 (22 May) Stamp Show 2000 Jeffrey Matthews Colour Pallette

			U/M	F/U
MS9		Complete miniature sheet	£13	
		First Day Cover		£2:
MS9a		Souvenir Wallet	£50	

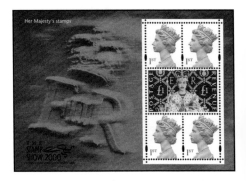

2000 (23 May) Stamp Show 2000 Her Majesty's Stamps

			U/M	F/U
MS10		Complete miniature sheet	7.00	
		First Day Cover		£:
		Presentation Pack MO3	47.50	

2000 (4 Aug.) Queen Mother's Birthday

		U/M	F/U
MS11	Complete Miniature sheet	2.90	
	Presentation Pack MO4	11.95	
	First Day Cover		4.50
Variety			
MS11a	Imperforate miniature sheet	£3750	

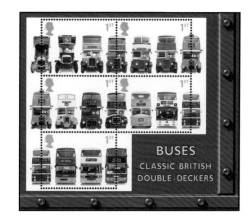

2001 (15 May.) 150th Anniversary of First Double Decker Bus

		U/M	F/U
MS14	Complete Miniature Sheet	4.50	4.50
	First Day Cover		4.50

2001 (13 Mar.) The Weather

		U/M	F/U
MS12	Complete Miniature Sheet	7.50	7.50
	First Day Cover		8.00

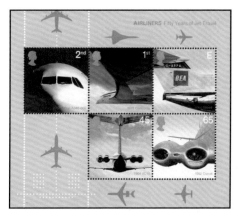

2002 (2 May) Airliners

		U/M	F/U
MS15	Complete Miniature Sheet	5.00	5.00
	First Day Cover		6.00

2002 (21 May) World Cup

		U/M	F/U
MS16	Complete Miniature Sheet	2.70	2.80
	First Day Cover		4.00

2001 (10 Apr.) Centenary of Royal Navy Submarine Service (Flags)

		U/M	F/U
MS13	Complete Miniature Sheet	3.50	3.00
	First Day Cover		3.50

2002 (24 Sep.) Astronomy

		U/M	F/U
MS17	Complete Miniature Sheet	2.60	2.70
	First Day Cover		3.50

2002 (5 Dec.) Anniversary of Wilding Definitives (1st)

		U/M	F/U
MS18	Complete Miniature Sheet	3.50	
	First Day Cover		5.00
	Presentation Pack	£45	

2003 (20 May) Anniversary of Wilding Definitives (2nd)

		U/M	F/U
MS19	Complete Miniature Sheet	3.50	
	First Day Cover		5.00
	Presentation Pack	£10	

2003 (18 Sep.) Transports of Delight

		U/M	F/U
MS20	Complete Miniature Sheet	3.75	4.00
	First Day Cover		6.25

2003 (19 Dec.) Rugby World Cup Winners

		U/M	F/U
MS21	Complete Miniature Sheet	£11	
	First Day Cover		4.00
	Presentation Pack	£20	

2004 (13 Jan.) Classic Locomotives

		U/M	F/U
MS22	Complete Miniature Sheet	£13	
	First Day Cover		20.00

2004 (13 Apr.) Ocean Liners

		U/M	F/U
MS23	Complete Miniature Sheet	6.00	6.00
	First Day Cover		10.00
MS23a	Error of value - The 57p printed as 53p (C1700)	£6000	

2004 (25 May) Bicentenary of the RHS

		U/M	F/U
MS24	Complete Miniature Sheet	5.50	5.50
	First Day Cover		4.95

2004 Scottish Parliament

		U/M	F/U
MS25	Complete Miniature sheet	3.00	
	First Day Cover		4.00

2004 (2 Nov.) Christmas

		U/M	F/U
MS26	Complete Miniature sheet	4.50	
	First Day Cover		8.00

2005 (24 Feb.) Jane Eyre

		U/M	F/U
MS27	Complete Miniature Sheet	5.20	5.30
	First Day Cover		5.50

2005 (22 Mar.) Castles

		U/M	F/U
MS28	Complete Miniature Sheet	4.40	4.50
	First Day Cover		6.50

2005 (5 July) End of the War 1945 - 2005

No.		U/M	F/U
MS31	Complete Miniature Sheet	2.60	2.60
	First Day Cover		3.95

2005 (8 Apr.) Royal Wedding

No.		U/M	F/U
MS29	Complete Miniature Sheet	3.20	3.30
	First Day Cover		3.90
	Presentation Pack M10	3.60	

2005 (5 Aug.) London 2012 Host City

No.		U/M	F/U
MS32	Complete Miniature Sheet	2.75	
	First Day Cover		4.00

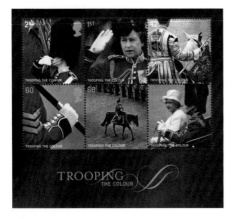

2005 (7 June) Trooping the Colour

No.		U/M	F/U
MS30	Complete Miniature Sheet	5.20	5.30
	First Day Cover		6.50

2005 (6 Oct.) The Ashes

No.		U/M	F/U
MS33	Complete Miniature Sheet	4.00	4.50
	First Day Cover		4.00

2005 (18 Oct.) The Battle of Trafalgar

No.		U/M	F/U
MS34	Complete Miniature Sheet	4.30	
	First Day Cover		5.50

2005 (1 Nov.) Christmas

		U/M	F/U
MS35	Complete Miniature Sheet	5.00	5.25
	First Day Cover		6.50

2006 (23 Feb.) Brunel

MS36	Complete Miniature Sheet	4.10	4.40
	First Day Cover		

2006 (1 March) Welsh Assembly

MS37	Complete Miniature Sheet	3.40	
	First Day Cover		

2006 (31 Aug.) Three Kings

MS38	Complete Miniature Sheet	4.50	4.70
	First Day Cover		

2006 (21 Sep.) Victoria Cross

MS39	Complete Miniature Sheet	5.35	5.65
	First Day Cover		

2006 (7 Nov.) Christmas

MS40	Complete Miniature Sheet	4.80	5.10
	First Day Cover		

2006 (9 Nov.) Lest we Forget

MS41	Complete Miniature Sheet	4.80	5.10
	First Day Cover		

2006 (30 Nov.) Celebrating Scotland
MS42   Complete Miniature Sheet   3.30   3.50
            First Day Cover

2007 (23 April) Celebrating England
MS45   Complete Miniature Sheet   3.20   3.30
            First Day Cover

2007 (9 Jan.) The Beatles
MS43   Complete Miniature Sheet   2.00   2.20
            First Day Cover

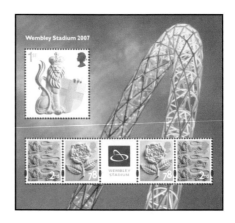

2007 (16 May) Field of Dreams
MS46   Complete Miniature Sheet   3.60   3.85
            First Day Cover

2007 (1 March) World of Invention
MS44   Complete Miniature Sheet   6.40   6.80
            First Day Cover

2007 (5 June) Machin Definitives 40th Anniversary
MS47   Complete Miniature Sheet   4.10   4.20
            First Day Cover

2007 (17 July) Harry Potter

MS48   Complete Miniature Sheet   2.55   2.75
          First Day Cover

2007 (16 Oct.) Diamond Wedding Anniversary

MS49   Complete Miniature Sheet   3.30   6.00
          First Day Cover

2007 (6 Nov.) Christmas

MS50   Complete Miniature Sheet   5.25   5.50
          First Day Cover

2007 (8 Nov.) Lest we forget

MS51   Complete Miniature Sheet   5.20   5.40
          First Day Cover

Royal Mail Presentation Packs

Presentation packs were first introduced in 1964 and were intially not numbered. These packs are listed in the Commemorative issues section under their respective issue details, but are repeated here in a Chronological order for the convenience of readers. We have included all presentation packs, including definitive and regional issues.

Issue date	No.	Description	Pack		Issue date	No.	Description	Pack
23 April 1964		Shakespeare	£13		28 July 1971	32	Literary	2.90
					25 August 1971	32A	Anniversaries	2.90
					22 September 1971	33	Universities	3.70
					13 October 1971	35	Christmas	2.20
					16 February 1972	39	Explorers	2.50
					26 April 1972	40	Anniversaries	2.20
					21 June 1972	41	Churches	4.00
					13 September 1972	43	BBC	2.20
					18 October 1972	44	Christmas	2.20

Issue date	No.	Description	Pack		Issue date	No.	Description	Pack
1 July 1964		Geographical	£85		20 November 1972	45	Silver Wedding	2.00
5 August 1964		Botanical	£85		3 January 1973	48	EEC	1.60
4 September 1964		F.R. Bridge	£375		28 February 1973	49	Oak Tree	1.30
8 July 1965		Churchill	£35		18 April 1973	50	Explorers	1.80
19 July 1965		Parliament	£58		16 May 1973	51	Cricket	3.20
13 September 1965		Battle of Britain	£42		4 July 1973	52	Paintings	1.60
8 October 1965		Post Office Tower	3.00		15 August 1973	53	Inigo Jones	1.60
25 January 1966		Burns	£36		12 September 1973	54	Parliament	1.60
28 February 1966		Westminster Abbey	£36		14 November 1973	56	Royal Wedding	1.50
1 June 1966		Football World Cup	9.00		28 November 1973	57	Christmas	1.80
15 August 1966		Birds	7.00		27 February 1974	58	Chestnut Tree	1.30
19 September 1966		Technology	8.00		24 April 1974	60	Fire Service	1.80
14 October 1966		Hastings	3.50		12 June 1974	64	UPU	1.80
1 December 1966		Christmas	4.00		10 July 1974	65	Great Britons	1.80
10 February 1967		EFTA	1.75		9 October 1974	66	Churchill	2.00
24 April 1967		Flowers	3.50					
10 July 1967		Paintings	2.70					
19 September 1967		Discoveries	1.80					
29 April 1968		Bridges	1.80					
29 May 1968		Anniversaries	1.70					
12 August 1968	1	Paintings	1.70					
25 November 1968	4	Christmas	1.70					
15 January 1969	5	Ships	2.30					

Issue date	No.	Description	Pack		Issue date	No.	Description	Pack
3 March 1969	6	Concorde	6.50		27 November 1974	67	Christmas	1.80
2 April 1969	9	Anniversaries	2.50		19 February 1975	69	Turner	1.80
28 May 1969	10	Cathedrals	2.50		23 April 1975	70	Architecture	1.80
1 July 1969	11	Investiture	1.75		11 June 1975	71	Sailing	1.20
1 October 1969	13	PO Technology	1.60		13 August 1975	72	Railway	2.40
26 November 1969	14	Christmas	1.60		3 September 1975	74	Parliament	1.00
11 February 1970	15	Cottages	2.50		22 October 1975	75	Jane Austen	1.80
1 April 1970	16	Anniversaries	1.60		26 November 1975	76	Christmas	2.20
3 June 1970	17	Dickens	1.80		10 March 1976	78	Telephones	2.80
15 July 1970	19	Commonwealth	1.60		28 April 1976	79	Pioneers	1.90
					2 June 1976	80	USA Bicentenary	1.00
					30 June 1976	81	Roses	2.00
					4 August 1976	82	Culture	2.20
					20 September 1976	83	Caxton	2.00
					24 November 1976	87	Christmas	2.20
					12 January 1977	89	Racket Sports	2.00
					2 March 1977	92	Chemistry	2.00
					11 May 1977	94	Silver Jubilee	1.10

Issue date	No.	Description	Pack
18 September 1970	21	Philympia	1.60
25 November 1970	22	Christmas	1.50
16 June 1971	26A	Ulster Paintings	2.90

Issue date	No.	Description	Pack
8 June 1977	95	Heads of Govt	0.60

Issue date	No.	Description	Pack		Issue date	No.	Description	Pack
5 October 1977	96	Wildlife	1.00		15 May 1984	153	1984 Europa	2.20
23 November 1977	97	Christmas	1.70		26 June 1984	154	1984 Greenwich	1.50
25 January 1978	99	Energy	1.70		31 July 1984	155	1984 Mail Coach	1.60
1 March 1978	100	Buildings	1.70		25 September 1984	156	1984 Council	1.60
31 May 1978	101	Coronation Jubilee	1.10		20 November 1984	157	1984 Christmas	1.70
5 July 1978	102	Horses	1.20		22 January 1985	159	1985 Trains	3.60
2 August 1978	103	Cycling	1.00		12 March 1985	160	1985 Insects	2.00
22 November 1978	104	Christmas	1.00		14 May 1985	161	1985 Composers / Europa	2.20
7 February 1979	106	Dogs	1.30		18 June 1985	162	1985 Safety at Sea	1.70
21 March 1979	107	Flowers	1.00		30 July 1985	163	1985 Royal Mail	1.70
19 May 1979	108	Elections	1.00		3 September 1985	164	1985 Arthurian	1.70
6 June 1979	109	Derby	1.00		8 October 1985	165	1985 Films	2.50
11 July 1979	110	Year of the Child	1.60		19 November 1985	166	1985 Christmas	1.80
22 August 1979	111	Rowland Hill	1.00		14 January 1986	168	1986 Industry	1.80
26 September 1979	112	Police	1.00		18 February 1986	168	1986 Comet	1.80
21 November 1979	113	Christmas	1.00		21 April 1986	170	1986 60th Birthday	2.60
16 January 1980	115	Birds	1.00		20 May 1986	171	1986 Conservation / Europa	2.20
12 March 1980	116	Railways	1.00		17 June 1986	172	1986 Medieval	2.00
9 April 1980	117	50p London	1.00		15 July 1986	173	1986 Sport	2.30
7 May 1980	118	Landmark	1.20		22 July 1986	174	1986 Royal Wedding	1.00
9 July 1980	119	Authors	1.70		16 September 1986	175	1986 RAF	2.20
10 September 1980	120	Conductors	1.00		18 November 1986	176	1986 Christmas	2.10
10 October 1980	121	1980 Sport	1.00		20 January 1987	178	1987 Flowers	2.00
19 November 1980	122	1980 Christmas	1.00					
6 February 1981	124	1981 Folklore / Europa	2.00					
25 March 1981	125	1981 Disabled	1.20					
13 May 1981	126	1981 Butterflies	1.20					
24 June 1981	127	1981 National Trust	1.40					
22 July 1981	127A	1981 Royal Wedding	1.00					
12 August 1981	128	1981 D of E Award	1.30					
23 September 1981	129	1981 Fishing	1.30					
18 November 1981	130	1981 Christmas	1.40		24 March 1987	179	1987 Newton	2.00
10 February 1982	132	1982 Darwin	1.40		12 May 1987	180	1987 Architects / Europa	2.20
24 March 1982	133	1982 Youth Groups	1.70		16 June 1987	181	1987 St Johns	2.00
28 April 1982	134	1982 Theatre / Europa	2.20		21 July 1987	182	1987 Heraldry	2.00
16 June 1982	136	1982 Maritime	2.20		8 September 1987	183	1987 Victoria	2.00
23 July 1982	137	1982 Textiles	1.40		13 October 1987	184	1987 Pottery	2.00
8 September 1982	138	1982 Information	0.90		17 November 1987	185	1987 Christmas	2.00
13 October 1982	139	1982 Cars	1.50		19 January 1988	187	1988 Linnean	2.00
17 November 1982	140	1982 Christmas	1.50		1 March 1988	188	1988 Welsh Bible	2.00
					22 March 1988	189	1988 Sport	2.00
					10 May 1988	190	1988 Transport / Europa	2.20
					21 June 1988	191	1988 Australia	2.00
					19 July 1988	192	1988 Armada	2.00
					6 September 1988	193	1988 Lear	2.00
					15 November 1988	194	1988 Christmas	2.00
					17 January 1989	196	1989 Birds	2.00
					7 March 1989	197	1989 Food	2.00
					11 April 1989	198	1989 Anniversaries	2.50
26 January 1983	142	1983 Fish	1.60		16 May 1989	199	1989 Toys / Europa	2.50
9 March 1983	143	1983 Commonwealth	1.60		4 July 1989	200	1989 Industry	2.10
25 May 1983	144	1983 Engineering / Europa	2.20		5 September 1989	201	1989 Microscopes	2.10
6 July 1983	145	1983 Army	1.80		17 October 1989	202	1989 Lord Mayor	2.10
24 August 1983	146	1983 Gardens	1.30		14 November 1989	203	1989 Christmas	1.90
5 October 1983	147	1983 Fairs	1.50		10 January 1990	21	1990 Penny Black	4.20
16 November 1983	148	1983 Christmas	1.50		23 January 1990	205	1990 RSPCA	2.30
17 January 1984	150	1984 Heraldry	1.50		6 March 1990	206	1990 Buildings/Europa	3.00
6 March 1984	151	1984 Cattle	1.80		10 April 1990	207	1990 Queens Awards	2.20
10 April 1984	152	1984 Urban Renewal	1.50		5 June 1990	208	1990 Kew Gardens	2.20

Issue date	No.	Description	Pack
10 July 1990	209	1990 Thomas Hardy	0.90
2 August 1990	210	1990 Queen Mother	3.50
11 September 1990	211	1990 Gallantry	2.30
16 October 1990	212	1990 Astronomy	2.30
13 November 1990	213	1990 Christmas	2.20
8 January 1991	215	1991 Dogs	2.40
5 March 1991	216	1991 Science	2.20
23 April 1991	217	1991 Space/Europa	2.40
11 June 1991	218	1991 Sport	2.20
16 July 1991	219	1991 Roses	2.20
20 August 1991	220	1991 Dinosaurs	2.80
17 September 1991	221	1991 Ordnance	2.30
12 November 1991	222	1991 Christmas	2.30
14 January 1992	224	1992 Wintertime	2.30
6 February 1992	225	1992 Happy & Glorious	3.30
10 March 1992	226	1992 Tennyson	2.40
7 April 1992	227	1992 International/Europa	3.00
16 June 1992	228	1992 Civil War	2.30
21 July 1992	229	1992 Gilbert & Sull	2.40
15 September 1992	230	1992 Green	2.20
13 October 1992	231	1992 Europe	1.00
10 November 1992	232	1992 Christmas	2.20
19 January 1993	234	1993 Swans	3.80
16 February 1993	235	1993 Harrison / Timekeepers	2.80
16 March 1993	236	1993 Orchids	2.40
11 May 1993	237	1993 Art/Europa	3.00
15 June 1993	238	1993 Roman	2.20
20 July 1993	239	1993 Canals	2.20
14 September 1993	240	1993 Autumn	2.20
12 October 1993	241	1993 Holmes	2.40
9 November 1993	242	1993 Christmas	2.80

Issue date	No.	Description	Pack
18 January 1994	244	1994 Steam Trains	3.10
1 March 1994	245	1994 HRH Paintings	2.50
12 April 1994	246	1994 Postcards	2.50
3 May 1994	247	1994 Tunnel	2.50
6 June 1994	248	1994 D-Day	3.60
5 July 1994	249	1994 Golf	2.60
2 August 1994	250	1994 Summertime	2.50
27 September 1994	251	1994 Medical	2.80
1 November 1994	252	1994 Christmas	2.50
17 January 1995	254	1995 Cats	3.30
14 March 1995	255	1995 Spring	2.50
11 April 1995	256	1995 National Trust	2.50
2 May 1995	257	1995 Peace/Europa	2.90
6 June 1995	258	1995 Sci-Fi	2.60
8 August 1995	259	1995 Shakespeare	2.60
5 September 1995	260	1995 Communication	2.60
3 October 1995	261	1995 Rugby	3.00
30 October 1995	262	1995 Christmas	3.00
25 January 1996	264	1996 Burns	2.50
12 March 1996	265	1996 Wildfowl	2.50
16 April 1996	266	1996 Cinema	2.50

Issue date	No.	Description	Pack
14 May 1996	267	1996 Football	3.30
9 July 1996	268	1996 Olympics	2.20
6 August 1996	269	1996 Women	2.50
3 September 1996	270	1996 Kids TV	2.70
1 October 1996	271	1996 Classic Cars	3.50
28 October 1996	272	1996 Christmas	2.90
21 January 1997	274	1997 Henry VIII	5.00
11 March 1997	275	1997 Missions of Faith	2.60
13 May 1997	276	1997 Legends	2.50
10 June 1997	277	1997 Air Architects	4.40
8 July 1997	278	1997 Horses	2.90
12 August 1997	279	1997 Sub PO	2.90

Issue date	No.	Description	Pack
9 September 1997	280	1997 Enid Blyton	2.90
27 October 1997	282	1997 Christmas	2.90
13 November 1997	281	1997 Golden Wedding	3.30
20 January 1998	284	1998 Endangered Species	3.30
3 February 1998		1998 Diana	4.50
24 February 1998	285	1998 Queens Beasts	2.50
24 March 1998	286	1998 Lighthouses	3.00
23 April 1998	287	1998 Comedians	3.00
23 June 1998	288	1998 NHS	2.70
21 July 1998	289	1998 Fantasy Novels	3.00
25 August 1998	290	1998 Carnival	2.70
29 September 1998	291	1998 Speed	3.30
2 November 1998	292	1998 Christmas	3.10
12 January 1999	294	1999 Inventors' Tale	3.00
2 February 1999	295	1999 Travellers' Tale	3.00
2 March 1999	296	1999 Patients' Tale	3.00
6 April 1999	297	1999 Settlers' Tale	3.00
4 May 1999	298	1999 Workers' Tale	3.00
1 June 1999	299	1999 Entertainers' Tale	3.00

Issue date	No.	Description	Pack
15 June 1999	M01	1999 Royal Wedding	1.90
6 July 1999	300	1999 Citizens' Tale	3.00
3 August 1999	301	1999 Scientists' Tale	3.00
7 September 1999	302	1999 Farmers' Tale	3.00
5 October 1999	303	1999 Soldiers' Tale	3.00
2 November 1999	304	1999 Christians' Tale	3.00
7 December 1999	305	1999 Artists' Tale	3.00
14 December 1999	M02	1999 Millennium Timekeeper M/S	13.50
18 January 2000	307	2000 Above and Beyond	3.00
1 February 2000	308	2000 Fire and Light	3.00
7 March 2000	309	2000 Water and Coast	3.00
4 April 2000	310	2000 Life and Earth	3.00
2 May 2000	311	2000 Art and Craft	3.00

Issue date	No.	Description	Pack
23 May 2000	M03	2000 Her Majesty's Stamps M/S	£36
6 June 2000	312	2000 People and Place	3.00
4 July 2000	313	2000 Stone and Soil	3.00
1 August 2000	314	2000 Tree and Leaf	3.00
4 August 2000	M04	2000 Queen Mothers Birthday M/S	9.00
5 September 2000	315	2000 Mind and Matter	3.00
3 October 2000	316	2000 Body and Bone	3.00
7 November 2000	317	2000 Spirit and Faith	3.00
5 December 2000	318	2000 Sound and Vision	3.00
16 January 2001	319	2001 Hopes for the Future	3.30
6 February 2001	M05	2001 Occasions	4.50
13 February 2001	320	2001 Cats and Dogs	9.25
31 March 2001	321	2001 Weather	5.00
10 April 2001	322	2001 Royal Navy Submarines	3.90
15 May 2001	323	2001 British Double-Decker's	4.60
19 June 2001	324	2001 Fabulous Hats	3.60
10 July 2001	325	2001 Pond Life/Europa	3.60
4 September 2001	326	2001 Punch & Judy	3.30
2 October 2001	327	2001 Nobel Prizes	£10
22 October 2001	M06	2001 Royal Navy Flags M/S	8.25
6 November 2001	328	2001 Christmas	3.60
15 January 2002	330	2002 Kipling Stories	7.75
6 February 2002	331	2002 Golden Jubilee	3.50
5 March 2002	M07	2002 Occasions	2.50
19 March 2002	332	2002 Coastlines	4.70
9 April 2002	333	2002 Circus	3.20
25 April 2002	M08	2002 Queen Mother	3.50

Issue date	No.	Description	Pack
2 May 2002	334	2002 Airliners	3.50
21 May 2002	335	2002 World Cup M/S	4.80
16 July 2002	336	2002 Commonwealth Games	3.60
20 August 2002	337	2002 Peter Pan	3.60
10 September 2002	338	2002 London Bridges	3.80
24 September 2002	339	2002 Astronomy M/S	3.00
8 October 2002	340	2002 Pillar Boxes	4.40
5 November 2002	341	2002 Christmas	3.60
14 January 2003	343	2003 Birds of Prey	4.70
4 February 2003	M09	2003 Occasions	3.10
25 February 2003	344	2003 The Secret of Life	3.50
25 March 2003	345	2003 Fun Fruit & Veg	£25
29 April 2003	346	2003 Extreme Endeavours	4.20
2 June 2003	347	2003 The Coronation	12.50
17 June 2003	348	2003 HRH Prince William	14.50
15 July 2003	349	2003 Scotland	4.20
12 August 2003	350	2003 Pub Signs	6.50
18 September 2003	351	2003 Transport Toys	3 90
7 October 2003	352	2003 British Museum	6.50
4 November 2003	353	2003 Christmas	5.50
19 December 2003	M9B	2003 England Winners M/S	£40
13 January 2004	355	2004 Classic Locomotives	£20
3 February 2004	M10	2004 Occasions	3.20
26 February 2004	356	2004 Lord of the Rings	9.50
16 March 2004	357	2004 Northern Ireland	4.40

Issue date	No.	Description	Pack
6 April 2004	358	2004 Entente Cordiale	£15
13 April 2004	359	2004 Ocean Liners	4.90
25 May 2004	360	2004 Royal Horticultural Society	4.70
15 June 2004	361	2004 Wales	4.70
10 August 2004	362	2004 Royal Society of Arts	5.00
16 September 2004	363	2004 Woodland Animals	5.00
12 October 2004	364	2004 The Crimean War	5.80

Issue date	No.	Description	Pack
2 November 2004	365	2004 Christmas	5.80
11 January 2005	367	2005 Farm Animals	5.00
8 February 2005	368	2005 South West England	4.70
24 February 2005	369	2005 Jane Eyre	5.80
15 March 2005	370	2005 Magic	5.30
8 April 2005	M10	2005 Royal Wedding M/S	4.20
21 April 2005	371	2005 World Heritage Sites	6.00
7 June 2005	372	2005 Trooping The Colour	6.00
19 July 2005	373	2005 Motorcycles	5.30
5 August 2005	M11	2005 London 2012	3.70
23 August 2005	374	2005 Changing Tastes in Britain	5.00
15 September 2005	375	2005 Classic ITV	5.00
6 October 2005	M12	2005 The Ashes M/S	3.90
18 October 2005	376	2005 The Battle of Trafalgar	5.00
1 November 2005	377	2005 Christmas	5.20
10 January 2006	379	2006 Animal Tales	5.80
7 February 2006	380	2006 England	5.50
23 February 2006	381	2006 Brunel	5.40
21 March 2006	382	2006 Ice Age Animals	5.50
18 April 2006	383	2006 The Queen's Birthday	6.10
6 June 2006	384	2006 World Cup Winners	5.50
20 June 2006	385	2006 Modern Architecture	5.50
18 July 2006	386	2006 National Portrait Gallery	5.80
21 September 2006	387	2006 Victoria Cross	6.00
3 october 2006	388	2006 Sounds of Britain	5.80
17 October 2006	M13	2006 Smilers	3.60
7 November 2006	389	2006 Christmas	5.90
9 November 2006	390	2006 Lest We Forget	5.80
30 November 2006	391	2006 Celebrating Scotland	4.00
9 January 2007	392	2006 The Beatles	7.50
1 Februaty 2007	393	2007 Sea Life	5.90
13 February 2007	394	2007 Sky at Night	5.50
1 March 2007	395	2007 World of Invention	5.90
22 March 2007	396	2007 Abolition of Slavery	5.40
23 April 2007	M15	2007 Celebrating England	4.30
15 May 2007	397	2007 Beside the Seaside	5.90
5 June 2007	398	2007 Machin 40th Anniversary	4.90
3 July 2007	399	2007 Grand Prix	4.90
17 July 2007	M16	2007 Harry Potter	7.30
25 July 2007	400	2007 Scouting	5.40
4 September 2007	401	2007 Birds	6.00
20 September 2007	402	2007 British Army Uniforms	6.00
16 October 2007	403	2007 Diamond Wedding Anniversary	8.70
6 November 2007	404	2007 Christmas	6.60
8 November 2007	405	2007 Lest We Forget	5.70

Presentation Packs

Issue date	No.	Description	Pack

Low Values Definitive Packs

Issue date	No.	Description	Pack
5 June 1967	8	1967 Definitives ½d to 1/9	2.10
15 February 1971	26	1971 Machin ½ to 9p	2.10
25 November 1971	37	1971 Machin ½ to 10p	8.00
2 February 1977	90	1977 Machin to 50p	2.50
28 October 1981	129a	1981 Machin to 75p	11.50
3 August 1983	1	1983 Machin to 75p	24.50
23 October 1984	5	1984 Machin ½ to 75p	£20
3 March 1987	9	1987 Machin 1p to 75p	£25
23 August 1988	15	1988 Machin 14p to 35p	5.90
26 September 1989	19	1989 Machin 15p to 37p	4.70
10 January 1990	21	1990 Penny Black Anniversary	3.60
4 September 1990	22	1990 Machin 10p to 33p	4.80
14 May 1991	24	1991 Machin 1p to 75p	£25
10 September 1991	25	1991 Machin 6p to 39p	4.75
19 October 1993	29	1993 Machin 1st Booklet	8.00
26 October 1993	30	1993 Machin 19p to 41p	3.95
21 November 1995	34	1995 Machin 1p to £1	19.50
25 June 1996	35	1996 Machin 20p to 63p	5.75
18 March 1997	37	1997 Machin 2nd & 1st	3.75
21 April 1997	38	1997 Machin 26p & 1st	3.75
20 October 1998	41	1998 Machin 1p to £1, 2nd & 1st	£10
20 April 1999	44	1999 Machin 7p - 64p	4.90
6 January 2000	48	2000 Machin 1st	2.70
25 April 2000	49	2000 Machin 8p to 65p	5.20
12 March 2002	57	2002 Machin 1p to £1, 2nd & 1st	7.30
4 July 2002	58	2002 Machin 37p to 68p	3.20
5 December 2002	59	2002 Wildings Collection I M/S	£30
27 March 2003	60	2003 Universal European	2.80
20 May 2003	61	2003 Wildings Collection II M/S	7.00
1 April 2004	67	2004 World, 1st, 7p to 43p	3.80
6 September 2005	71	2005 World, Europe, 1st, 2nd, 1p to £1.00	£11
28 March 2006	72	2006 Machin 37p to 72p	3.50
1 August 2006	74	2006 Machin Pricing in Proportion	3.20
27 March 2007	75	2007 Machin 16p to 78p	4.50
5 June 2007	77	2007 Machin 40th Anniversary	

High Values Definitive Packs

Issue date	No.	Description	Pack
5 March 1969	7	1969 Machin 2/6 to £1	5.00
17 July 1970	18	1970 Machin 10p - 50p	3.95
25 November 1971	38	1971 Machin 20p - £1	6.50
2 February 1977	91	1977 Machin £1 to £5	10.50
3 March 1987	13	1987 Machin £1 to £5	£123
15 September 1987	14	1987 Machin £1.60	£15

Queen Elizabeth II

Issue date	No.	Description	Pack
18 October 1988	18	1988 Castles £1 to £5	£14
24 March 1992	27	1992 Castles £1 to £5	£17
2 March 1993	28	1993 Britannia £10	£27
22 August 1995	33	1995 Castle £3	£10
29 July 1997	40	1997 Castles £1.50 to £5	£65
9 March 1999	43	1999 Machin £1.50 to £5	£35
12 March 2002	43a	2002 Machin £1.50 to £5	£27
1 July 2003	62	2003 Machin £1.50 to £5	£17
22 March 2005	69	2005 Castles 50p to £1	4.50

Greetings Packs

Issue date	No.	Description	Pack
28 January 1992	G1	1992 Memories Greeting pack	7.00
2 February 1993	G2	1993 Greetings Giving	8.50
1 February 1994	G3	1994 Greetings. Messages	8.50

Issue date	No.	Description	Pack
21 March 1995	G4	1995 Greetings. Art	8.50
26 February 1996	G5	1996 Greetings. Cartoons	8.50
6 January 1997	G6	1997 Greetings. Flowers	9.50

Regional Definitive Packs

Issue date	No.	Description	Pack
9 December 1970	25	1970 Northern Ireland	1.10
9 December 1970	23	1970 Scotland	3.50
9 December 1970	24	1970 Wales	1.40
7 July 1971	30	1971 Isle of Man	1.00
7 July 1971	29	1971 Northern Ireland	1.40
7 July 1971	27	1971 Scotland	1.40
7 July 1971	28	1971 Wales	1.40
29 May 1974	61	1974 Northern Ireland	1.00
29 May 1974	62	1974 Scotland	1.00
29 May 1974	63	1974 Wales	1.00
20 October 1976	84	1976 Northern Ireland	1.00
20 October 1976	85	1976 Scotland	1.00
20 October 1976	86	1976 Wales	1.00
28 October 1981	129d	1981 Northern Ireland	4.00
28 October 1981	129b	1981 Scotland	4.00
28 October 1981	129c	1981 Wales	4.00
3 August 1983	4	1983 Northern Ireland	£11
3 August 1983	2	1983 Scotland	£11
3 August 1983	3	1983 Wales	£11

Presentation/Year Packs

Issue date	No.	Description	Pack
23 October 1984	8	1984 Northern Ireland	9.00
23 October 1984	6	1984 Scotland	9.00
23 October 1984	7	1984 Wales	9.00
3 March 1987	12	1987 Northern Ireland	£13
3 March 1987	10	1987 Scotland	£13
3 March 1987	11	1987 Wales	£13
8 November 1988	17	1988 3 Regions	9.00
28 November 1989	20	1989 3 Regions	9.00
4 December 1990	23	1990 3 Regions	9.00
3 December 1991	26	1991 3 Regions	9.00
7 December 1993	31	1993 3 Regions	9.00
23 July 1996	36	1996 3 Regions	£15
1 July 1997	39	1997 Wales	£10

Issue date	No.	Description	Pack
20 October 1998	42	1998 3 Regions	£13
8 June 1999	47	1999 Northern Ireland	7.50
8 June 1999	45	1999 Scotland	7.50
8 June 1999	46	1999 Wales	7.50
25 April 2000	50	2000 Scotland	£8
25 April 2000	51	2000 Wales	£8
25 April 2000	52	2000 Northern Ireland	£13
6 March 2001	53	2001 Northern Ireland	4.00
23 April 2001	54	2001 England	4.00
12 March 2002	55	2002 Scotland	5.00
12 March 2002	56	2002 Wales	6.00
4 July 2002	59	2002 4 Regions	5.00
14 October 2003	63	2003 England	4.00
14 October 2003	66	2003 Northern Ireland	4.00
14 October 2003	64	2003 Scotland	4.00
14 October 2003	65	2003 Wales	4.00
11 May 2004	68	2004 4 Regions	3.00
5 April 2005	70	2005 4 Regions	3.50
28 March 2006	73	2006 4 Regions	8.00
27 March 2007	76	2007 4 Regions	8.75

Postage Due Packs

Issue date	No.	Description	Pack
3 November 1971	36	1971 Postage Dues	£13
30 March 1977	93	1977 Postage Dues	7.50

June 1982	135	1982 Postage Dues	£22
5 February 1994	32	1994 Postage Dues	£30

Queen Elizabeth II

Issue date	No.	Description	Pack

Japanese Packs

Issue date	No.	Description	Pack
20 November 1972		1972 Silver Wedding	4.50
22 July 1981		1981 Royal Wedding	3.50

Welsh Packs

Issue date	No.	Description	Pack
July 1969		1969 Investiture	£18

3 February 1998		1998 Princess Diana	£50

German Packs

Issue date	No.	Description	Pack
12 August 1968		1968 Paintings	6.50
16 September 1968		1968 Gift Pack	£21
25 November 1968		1968 Christmas	5.00
15 January 1969		1969 Ships	£19
3 March 1969		1969 Concorde	£24
5 March 1969		1967 Machin - Low values	£80
5 March 1969		1969 Machin - High Values	£44
2 April 1969		1969 Anniversaries	£39
28 May 1969		1969 Cathedrals	£14
1 July 1969		1969 Investiture	£14

Souvenir Packs

Issue date	No.	Description	Pack
20 November 1972		1972 Silver Wedding	1.00
16 May 1973		1973 Cricket	3.30
12 September 1973		1973 Parliament	4.40
9 October 1974		1974 Churchill	2.00
13 August 1975		1975 Railways	2.20
11 May 1977		1977 Silver Jubilee	1.20
31 May 1978		1978 Coronation	1.40
22 July 1981		1981 Royal Wedding	1.80
31 July 1984		1984 Mail History	3.80
8 October 1985		1985 British Films	5.75
21 April 1986		1986 Queen's Birthday	4.00
21 June 1988		1988 Australian Bicentenary	7.00
10 January 1990		1990 Penny Black	£11
13 November 1997		1997 Golden Wedding	£27

Year Books/Souvenir Packs

Queen Elizabeth II

Royal Mail Year Packs

27 November 1967		1967 Year Pack	0.95
16 September 1968		1968 Year Pack - Blue	2.85
16 September 1968		1968 Year Pack - Red	1.85
15 September 1969		1969 Year Pack	8.25
14 September 1970	20	1970 Year Pack	12.50
29 September 1971	34	1971 Year Pack	24.50
20 November 1972	47	1972 Year Pack	16.00
28 November 1973	58	1973 Year Pack	11.50
27 November 1974	68	1974 Year Pack	4.00
26 November 1975	77	1975 Year Pack	3.95
24 November 1976	88	1976 Year Pack	4.95
23 November 1977	98	1977 Year Pack	3.50
22 November 1978	105	1978 Year Pack	3.50
21 November 1979	114	1979 Year Pack	4.50
19 November 1980	123	1980 Year Pack	4.95
18 November 1981	131	1981 Year Pack	6.95
17 November 1982	141	1982 Year Pack	11.50
16 November 1983	149	1983 Year Pack	11.50
20 November 1984	158	1984 Year Pack	13.50
19 November 1985	167	1985 Year Pack	13.50
18 November 1986	177	1986 Year Pack	13.50
17 November 1987	186	1987 Year Pack	13.50
15 November 1988	195	1988 Year Pack	13.50
14 November 1989	204	1989 Year Pack	13.50
13 November 1990	214	1990 Year Pack	15.95
12 November 1991		1991 Year Pack	15.95
10 November 1992	233	1992 Year Pack	15.95
9 November 1993	243	1993 Year Pack	15.95
14 November 1994	253	1994 Year Pack	£21
30 October 1995	263	1995 Year Pack	£21
28 October 1996	273	1996 Year Pack	£24
13 November 1997	283	1997 Year Pack	27.50
2 November 1998	293	1998 Year Pack	39.95
7 December 1999	306	1999 Year Pack	49.50
5 December 2000	319	2000 Year Pack	49.50
6 November 2001	329	2001 Year Pack	49.50
5 November 2002	342	2002 Year Pack	51.50
4 November 2003	354	2003 Year Pack	£41
2 November 2004	366	2004 Year Pack	£41
2 November 2005	378	2005 Year Pack	39.95

Royal Mail Year Books

20 November 1984	1	1984 Year Book	£40
19 November 1985	2	1985 Year Book	£37
18 November 1986	3	1986 Year Book	£37
17 November 1987	4	1987 Year Book	£18
15 November 1988	5	1988 Year Book	£18
14 November 1989	6	1989 Year Book	£18
13 November 1990	7	1990 Year Book	£19
12 November 1991	8	1991 Year Book	£19
11 November 1992	9	1992 Year Book	£23
9 November 1993	10	1993 Year Book	£28
1 November 1994	11	1994 Year Book	£23
30 October 1995	12	1995 Year Book	£23
28 October 1996	13	1996 Year Book	£23
13 November 1997	14	1997 Year Book	£30
2 November 1998	15	1998 Year Book	£42
7 December 1999	16	1999 Year Book	£53
7 November 2000	17	2000 Year Book	£53
6 November 2001	18	2001 Year Book	£53
5 November 2002	19	2002 Year Book	£53
4 November 2003	20	2003 Year Book	£53
2 November 2004	21	2004 Year Book	£53
2 November 2005	22	2005 Year Book	£53
2 November 2006	23	2006 Year Book	£58
8 November 2007	24	2007 Year Book	£85

'Generic' Smilers Sheets

'Smilers' sheets were first issued during the Stamp Show 2000. The designs used were from the 'Smilers' greetings book and were available with either a photograph, taken at the show, or with a Stamp Show label from Philatelic outlets or the Bureau at Edinburgh.

Generic Smilers sheets have standard images in the lable position, as shown in the following listing. In conjunction with these, customers could supply their own photo or image in the label position - These are known as Personalised Smilers Sheets.

2000 (2 May) The Stamp Show 2000 10 x 1st
Printer: House of Questa in Gravure

SS1	Complete sheet	£27
SSP1	Se-tenant pair - stamp with label (any)	3.00

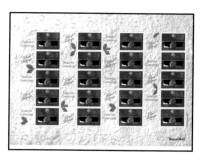

2000 (3 Oct.) Christmas 20 x 19p
Printer: House of Questa in Gravure

SS2	Complete sheet	£200
SSP2	Strip of two stamps and two labels	£25

2000 (3 Oct.) Christmas 10 x 1st
Printer: House of Questa in Gravure

SS3	Complete sheet	£110
SSP3	Strip of two stamps and two labels	£30

2001 (9 Oct.) Christmas 20 x 19p
As SS2 but inscribed 'Consignia 2001'
Printer: House of Questa in Gravure

SS4	Complete sheet	£400
SSP2	Strip of two stamps and two labels	£25

2001 (9 Oct.) Christmas 10 x 1st
As SS2 but inscribed 'Consignia 2001'
Printer: House of Questa in Gravure

SS5	Complete sheet	£450
SSP3	Strip of two stamps and two labels	£30

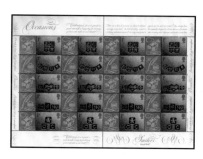

2001 (5 June) Occasions 20 x 1st
Printer: House of Questa in Lithography

SS6	Complete sheet	£150
SSP4	Vertical strip of five stamps & five labels	£40

2001 (3 July) Smiles 10 x 1st
Printer: House of Questa in Lithography

SS7	Complete sheet	£200
SSP5	Se-tenant pair - stamp with label (any)	£25

2001 (18 Dec.) Cartoons 10 x 1st
Printer: House of Questa in Lithography

| SS8 | Complete sheet | £35 |
| SSP6 | Se-tenant pair - stamp with label (any) | 4.00 |

2001 (23 Apr.) Occasions 20 x 1st
Printer: House of Questa in Lithography

| SS9 | Complete sheet | £48 |
| SSP7 | Vertical strip of five stamps & five labels | £10 |

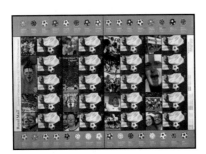

2002 (21 May) World Cup 20 x 1st
Printer: House of Questa in Lithography

| SS10 | Complete sheet | £22 |
| SSP8 | Se-tenant pair - stamp with label (any) | 2.50 |

2002 (1 Oct.) Smiles 10 x 1st
Printer: House of Questa in Lithography

| SS11 | Complete sheet | £22 |
| SSP9 | Horizontal strip of two stamps (Teddy & Dennis) and two labels | 2.00 |

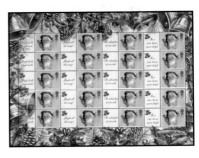

2002 (1 Oct.) Christmas 20 x 1st
Printer: House of Questa in Lithography

| SS12 | Complete sheet | £25 |
| SSP10 | Se-tenant pair - stamp with label (any) | 1.00 |

2003 (21 Jan.) Flowers 20 x 1st
Printer: House of Questa in Lithography

SS13	Complete sheet	£2
SS13a	Broad Centre Band	£75
SSP11	Se-tenant pair - stamp with label (any)	1.0
SSP11a	Broad Centre Band	£5

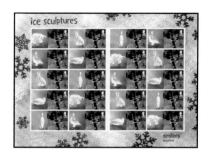

2003 (4 Feb.) Occasions 20 x 1st
Printer: House of Questa in Lithography

| SS14 | Complete sheet | £20 |
| SSP12 | Se-tenant pair - stamp with label (any) | 1.00 |

2003 (4 Nov.) Christmas 20 x 2nd
Printer: De La Rue in Lithography

| SS17 | Complete sheet | £14 |
| SSP15 | Se-tenant pair - stamp with label (any) | 1.25 |

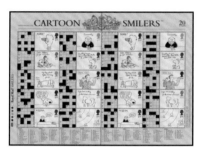

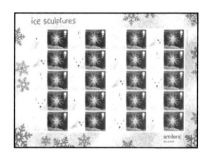

2003 (29 July) Crossword Cartoons 20 x 1st
Printer: House of Questa in Lithography

SS15	Complete sheet	£19
SS15a	Missing phosphor	£1000
SSP13	Se-tenant pair - stamp with label (any)	1.00
SSP13a	Missing phosphor	£75

2003 (4 Nov.) Christmas 20 x 1st
Printer: De La Rue in Lithography

| SS18 | Complete sheet | £32 |
| SSP16 | Se-tenant pair - stamp with label (any) | 1.25 |

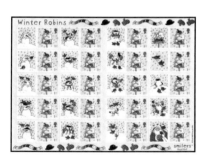

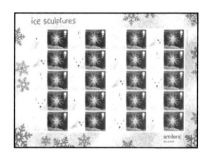

2003 (30 Sep.) Christmas 20 x 1st
Printer: De La Rue in Lithography

| SS16 | Complete sheet | £19 |
| SSP14 | Se-tenant pair - stamp with label (any) | 1.00 |

2004 (30 Jan.) Hong Kong 20 x 1st
Printer: Walsall in Lithography

| SS19 | Complete sheet | £15 |
| SSP17 | Se-tenant pair - stamp with label (any) | 1.00 |

No.   U/M   No.   U/M

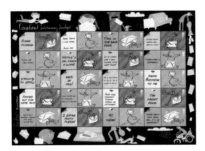

2004 (3 Feb.) Occasions 20 x 1st
Printer: De La Rue in Lithography

SS20	Complete sheet	£17
SSP18	Vertical strip of five stamps & five labels	4.00

2004 (25 May) RHS 20 x 1st
Printer: Walsall in Lithography

SS21	Complete sheet	£17
SSP19	Se-tenant pair - stamp with label (any)	1.00

2004 (27 July) Rule Britannia 20 x 1st
Printer: Walsall in Lithography

SS22	Complete sheet	£15
SSP20	Se-tenant pair - stamp with label (any)	1.00

2004 (2 Nov.) Christmas 10 x 2nd *and* 10 x 1st
Printer: De La Rue in Lithography

SS23	Complete sheet	£15
SSP21	Vertical strip of two stamps (1st and 2nd class) and two labels	7.00

2005 (11 Jan.) Farm Animals 20 x 1st
Printer: Walsall in Lithography

SS24	Complete sheet	£16
SSP22	Se-tenant pair - stamp with label (any)	1.00

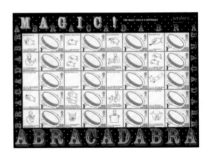

2005 (15 Mar.) Magic 20 x 1st

SS25	Complete sheet	£20
SSP23	Se-tenant pair - stamp with label (any)	1.0

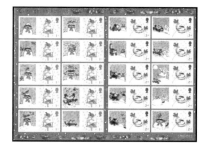

2005 (21 Apr.) Australia Expo 20 x 1st

| SS26 | Complete sheet | £20 |
| SSP24 | Se-tenant pair - stamp with label (any) | 1.00 |

2005 (1 Nov.) Christmas Robins 10 x 1st *plus* 10 x 2nd

| SS29 | Complete sheet | £12 |
| SSP27 | Se-tenant pair - stamp with label (any) | |

2005 (21 June) White Ensign 20 x 1st

SS27	Complete sheet	£14
SS27a	Solid all over phosphor (left 3 columns)	£150
SSP25	Se-tenant pair - stamp with label (any)	.75
SSP25a	Solid all over phosphor (strip of 5)	£45

2006 (10 Jan.) Paddington Bear 20 x 1st

| SS30 | Complete sheet | £14 |
| SSP28 | Se-tenant pair - stamp with label (any) | 90 |

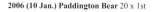

2006 (7 Mar.) Fun Fruit & Veg. 20 x 1st

| SS31 | Complete sheet | £18 |
| SSP29 | Se-tenant pair - stamp with label (any) | 1.00 |

2005 (15 Sep.) Classic ITV 20 x 1st

| S28 | Complete sheet | £14 |
| SP26 | Se-tenant pair - stamp with label (any) | .75 |

2006 (25 May) Hello Washington 20 x 1st

SS32	Complete sheet	£14
SSP30	Se-tenant pair - stamp with label (any)	90

2006 (6 June) World Cup 20 x 1st

SS33	Complete sheet	£17
SSP31	Se-tenant pair - stamp with label (any)	90

2006 (4 Jul.) Lifes Special Moments 20 x 1st

SS34	Complete sheet	£12
SSP32	Se-tenant pair - stamp with label (any)	80

2006 (17 Oct.) Extra Special Moments 20 x 1st

SS35	Complete sheet	£12
SSP33	Se-tenant pair - stamp with label (any)	80

2006 (7 Nov.) Christmas 10 x 1st and 10 x 2nd

SS36	Complete sheet	£12
SSP34	Se-tenant pair - stamp with label (any)	80

2006 (9 Nov.) We Will Remember Them 20 x 1st

SS37	Complete sheet	£1
SSP35	Se-tenant pair - stamp with label (any)	8

2006 (14 Nov.) Belgica 20 x 1st

SS38	Complete sheet	£12
SSP36	Se-tenant pair - stamp with label (any)	80

2007 (16 May) Wembley 20 x 1st

SS41	Complete sheet	£13
SSP39	Se-tenant pair - stamp with label	80

2007 (1 Mar.) Glorious Wales 20 x 1st

SS39	Complete sheet	£12
SSP37	Se-tenant pair - stamp with label (any)	80

2007 (5 June) Machin Anniversary 20 x 1st

SS42	Complete sheet	£13
SSP40	Se-tenant pair - stamp with label	80

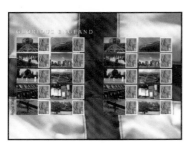

2007 (23 April) Glorious England 20 x 1st

SS40	Complete sheet Error 1st printing Wight spelt White	£475
SS40a	2nd printing spelling corrected (Wight)	£12
SSP38	Se-tenant pair - stamp with label (any with corrected spelling)	80

Stampex Smilers Sheets

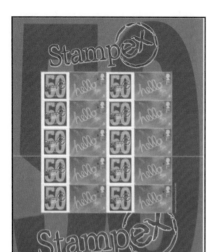

2004 (25 Feb.) Spring 2004

SSS3	Complete sheet	£18

2003 (28 Feb.) Spring 2003

SSS1	Complete sheet	£17

2004 (15 Sep.) Autumn 2004

SSS4	Complete sheet	£15

2003 (17 Sep.) Autumn 2003

SSS2	Complete sheet	£17

2005 (23 Feb.) Spring 2005

SSS5   Complete sheet   £15

2005 (23 Feb.) Spring 2006

SSS7   Complete sheet   £12

2005 (14 Sep.) Autumn 2005

SSS6   Complete sheet   £12

2005 (23 Feb.) Autumn 2006

SSS8   Complete sheet   £12

2005 (23 Feb.) Spring 2007

SSS7   Complete sheet   £12

2005 (23 Feb.) Autumn 2007

SSS8   Complete sheet   £12

Guernsey

On the 27 December 1940, authority was given to bisect British stamps as the stocks of 1d stamps were almost exhausted. The locally printed 1d stamps were not issued until the 18th February 1941. Almost all examples of the bisects found are of a philatelic nature and genuine commercially used covers are of the utmost rarity and worth considerably more than the prices quoted.

1940 (27 Dec.) - 1941 (24 Feb.) Stamps of Great Britain bisected on cover or piece.

King George V

				Cover	Piece
GyB1	1d	(2d) Orange	(1912 Wmk. Royal Cypher)	£260	£50
GyB2	1d	(2d) Orange	(1924 Wmk. Block Cypher)	£225	£45
GyB3	1d	(2d) Orange	(1934 Photogravure issue)	£200	£40

King George VI

				Cover	Piece
GyB4	½d	(1d) Scarlet	(1937 Definitive)	£450	
GyB5	1d	(2d) Orange	(1938 Definitive)	£20	4.00
GyB6	½d	(1d)	(1940 Centenary)	£400	
GyB7	1d	(2d)	(1940 Centenary)	£17	4.00
GyB8	1d	(2½d)	(1940 Centenary)	£650	
GyB9	1½d	(3d)	(1940 Centenary)	£450	

1941 (18 Feb.) - 44 Arms of Guernsey. Roulette perf.
Printer: Guernsey Press Co. Ltd in Typography
A. White Paper. No watermark.

			U/M	M/M	F/U	✉
Gy1	½d	**Pale yellow green** (1.44)	3.50	1.25	1.20	3.00
Gy1a		Emerald green (6.4.41)	4.50	2.00	1.50	2.00
Gy1b		Light green (7.4.41)	3.50	2.20	1.50	2.00
Gy1c		Dull green (9.42)	3.50	2.00	2.00	3.00
Gy1d		Bright green (2.42)	£18	8.00	7.50	£10
Gy1e		Bluish green (11.41)	£29	£16	£18	£22
Gy1f		Olive green (2.43)	£18	£10	9.00	£20
Gy2	1d	**Scarlet** (18.2.41)	1.70	1.00	1.00	2.00
Gy2a		Pale vermilion (7.4.37)	1.90	1.00	1.50	3.00
Gy2b		Carmine (12.43)	2.70	1.50	2.25	4.50
Gy3	2½d	**Ultramarine** (12.4.44)	4.50	3.00	4.50	5.00
Gy3a		Pale ultramarine	4.50	3.00	4.50	5.00
		Set of 3	8.50	6.50	6.00	
		First Day Cover (½d)				5.00
		First Day Cover (1d)				5.00
		First Day Cover (2½d)				7.00

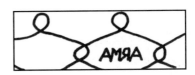

B. Blue French Bank Note Paper. Wmk. Loops (sideways)

			U/M	M/M	F/U	✉
Gy4	½d	**Bright green** (11.3.42)	£15	£10	£15	£27
Gy5	1d	**Scarlet** (9.4.42)	8.00	6.00	£15	£25
		Set of 2	20.50	£15	£28	
		First Day Cover (½d)				£70
		First Day Cover (1d)				£50

Jersey

1941 (4 April). Arms of Jersey. No watermark. Perf. 11.

White paper.

			U/M	M/M	F/U	✉
J1	½d	Bright green (29.1.42)	3.50	2.10	2.00	2.50
J2	1d	Scarlet (1.4.41)	3.00	1.80	2.50	3.50
		First Day Cover (½d)				3.50
		First Day Cover (1d)				2.50

Chalky Paper

			U/M	M/M	F/U	✉
J3	1d	Scarlet (10.41)	£27	£15	£25	£35

Greyish paper

			U/M	M/M	F/U	✉
J4	½d	Bright green	4.00	2.75	6.00	6.50
J5	1d	Scarlet (1.43)	4.00	2.75	6.00	6.50

1943 (1 June) - 44. Views of Jersey. No watermark. Perf 13½.
Printer: French Government Printing Works, Paris in Typography.

White Paper

			U/M	M/M	F/U	✉
J6	½d	Green (1.6.43)	5.00	2.00	2.50	5.00
J7	1d	Scarlet (1.6.43)	1.75	50	30	1.00
J8	1½d	Brown (8.6.43)	2.00	75	2.00	2.50
J9	2d	Orange yellow (8.6.43)	2.50	1.00	1.50	2.00
J10	2½d	Blue (29.6.43)	1.50	60	1.50	2.50
J11	3d	Violet (29.6.43)	75	30	3.00	3.50
		First Day Cover (½d, 1d)				3.50
		First Day Cover (1½d, 2d)				5.50
		First Day Cover (2½d, 3d)				3.50
		First Day Cover (½d, 3d)				£12

Grey Paper

			U/M	M/M	F/U	✉
J12	½d	Green (6.10.41)	6.00	3.00	6.00	£10

Newsprint

			U/M	M/M	F/U	✉
J13	1d	Scarlet (28.2.44)	6.00	3.50	6.00	3.00
J14	2½d	Blue (25.2.44)	2.90	1.75	3.30	3.50
		Set of 6	8.50	5.00	9.00	

Regional Stamps

The first Elizabethan regional stamps were originally issued for Guernsey, Jersey, Isle of Man, Northern Ireland, Scotland and Wales in 1958. The three small islands, Jersey, Guernsey and the Isle of Man were granted independent postal status during the 1970's. It was not until 2001 that the largest country in the UK, England, had its own country stamps.

Prices listed here are for either unmounted mint or fine used with good CDS cancels. Prices for First Day Covers are for Philatelic Bureau handstamps. Illustrated covers with regional postmarks are worth approximately double the price shown.
All stamps are from sheets unless stated otherwise.

Guernsey

Printer: Harrison & Sons in Photogravure

2½d   3d, 4d, 5d   Multiple Crown
                               Watermark

Isle of Man

Printer: Harrison & Sons in Photogravure

2½d   3d, 4d, 5d   Multiple Crown
                               Watermark

1958 (18 Aug.) Wmk. Multiple Crowns. Perf. 15 x 14

1958 (18 Aug.) Wmk. Multiple Crowns. Perf. 15 x 14

Cream paper/GA

			U/M	F/U
GY6	**3d**	**Lilac**	75	50
		First Day Cover		£12

Cream paper/GA

			U/M	F/U
MX1	**3d**	**Lilac**	60	25
		First Day Cover		£17

White paper/GA

			U/M	F/U
GY7	**2½d**	**Carmine** (8.6.64)	20	30
GY7a		Pale carmine	30	40
GY8	**3d**	**Lilac** (5.7.62)	15	20
GY9	**4d**	**Ultramarine** (7.2.66)	15	20
		Set of 3	50	55
		First Day Cover (2½d)		£15

White paper/GA

			U/M	F/U
MX2	**2½d**	**Carmine** (8.6.64)	20	35
MX3	**3d**	**Lilac** (1963)	20	20
MX3a		Chalky paper (17.5.63)	4.95	4.75
MX4	**4d**	**Ultramarine** (7.2.66)	75	1.00
		Set of 3	1.10	1.50
		First Day Cover (2½d)		£18

1967 (24 May) Phosphor issue. Wmk. Multiple Crowns. Perf. 15 x 14

1967 (5 July) Phosphor issue. Wmk. Multiple Crowns. Perf. 15 x 14

White paper/GA

			U/M	F/U
GY10	**3d**	**CB Lilac** (24.5.67)	10	20
GY10a		Reddish lilac	15	20
GY11	**4d**	**2B Ultramarine** (24.10.67)	10	20

White paper/GA

			U/M	F/U
MX5	**3d**	**CB Lilac** (27.6.68)	10	15
MX6	**4d**	**2B Ultramarine**	10	20
		First Day Cover (4d)		50

1968 (16 April) Phosphor issue. No watermark. Perf. 15 x 14

1968 (24 June) Phosphor issue. No watermark. Perf. 15 x 14

Chalky paper/PVA

			U/M	F/U
GY12	**4d**	**2B Ultramarine**	10	20
GY12a		Missing phosphor	£40	
GY13	**4d**	**CB Sepia** (4.9.68)	10	20
GY13a		Missing phosphor	£40	
GY13b		Horizontal phosphor band	£400	
GY14	**4d**	**CB Vermilion** (26.2.69)	10	20
GY15	**5d**	**2B Deep blue** (4.9.68)	10	20
		Set of 4	35	70
		First Day Cover (4d sepia, 5d)		1.00

Chalky paper/PVA

			U/M	F/U
MX7	**4d**	**2B Ultramarine**	10	20
MX8	**4d**	**CB Sepia** (4.9.68)	10	20
MX8a		Missing phosphor	£20	
MX9	**4d**	**CB Vermilion** (26.2.69)	20	30
MX10	**5d**	**2B Deep blue** (4.9.68)	20	30
MX10a		Missing phosphor	£175	
		Set of 4	50	90
		First Day Cover (4d sepia, 5d)		1.00

The above stamps were no longer valid on Guernsey from 30 September 1969. However, the current issues remained on sale and in use in the United Kingdom for one year until 30th September 1970.

Jersey

Printer: Harrison & Sons in Photogravure

2½d   3d, 4d, 5d   Multiple Crown
Watermark

1971 (7 July) Decimal. Phosphor issue. No watermark. Perf. 15 x 14. Two 9.5mm phosphor bands or one 4mm centre band, unless stated otherwise

1958 (18 Aug.) Wmk. Multiple Crowns. Perf. 15 x 14

OCP/PVA

			U/M	F/U
MX11	2½p	**CB Magenta**	10	10
MX11a		Missing phosphor	£1500	
MX12	3p	**2B Ultramarine**	10	10
MX13	5p	**2B Bright violet**	40	70
MX13a		Missing phosphor	£275	
MX14	7½p	**2B Chestnut**	40	70
		Set of 4	1.00	1.40
		First Day Cover		2.50
		Presentation Pack No. 30	1.10	

Cream paper/GA

			U/M	F/U
J15	3d	**Lilac**	75	50
		First Day Cover		4.50

White paper/GA

			U/M	F/U
J16	2½d	**Carmine** (8.6.64)	30	45
J17	3d	**Lilac** (23.9.62)	25	10
J18	4d	**Ultramarine** (7.2.66)	12	20
		Set of 3	60	65
		First Day Cover (2½d)		£15

FCP/PVA

			U/M	F/U
MX15	2½p	**CB Magenta** (3.73)	25	15
MX16	3p	**2B Ultramarine** (7.73)	1.00	1.00

In 1973 the Isle of Man was granted Postal Independence and became responsible for their own stamp issues. The post 1973 issues of Isle of Man are outside the scope of this catalogue.

1967 (9 June - Sept.) Phosphor issue. Wmk. Multiple Crowns. Perf. 15 x 14

White paper/GA

			U/M	F/U
J19	3d	**CB Lilac** (9.6.67)	15	20
J19a		Reddish lilac	50	55
J20	4d	**2B Ultramarine** (5.9.67)	10	15

1968 (4 Sept.) - 69 Phosphor issue. No watermark. Perf. 15 x 14

Chalky paper/PVA

			U/M	F/U
J21	4d	**CB Sepia** (4.9.68)	10	20
J21a		Missing phosphor	£1000	
J22	4d	**CB Vermilion** (26.2.69)	10	20
J23	5d	**2B Deep blue** (4.9.68)	10	20
		Set of 3	28	55
		First Day Cover (4d sepia, 5d)		1.00

The above stamps were no longer valid on Jersey from 30 September 1969. However, the current issues remained on sale and in use in the United Kingdom for one year until 30th September 1970.

Regionals Non Elliptical
No.   U/M   F/U

Northern Ireland
No.   U/M   F/U

Queen Elizabeth II
          U/M   F/U

Northern Ireland

Printer: Harrison & Sons in Photogravure

3d, 4d, 5d	6d, 9d	1s3d, 1s6d

1958 (18 Aug.) Wmk. Multiple Crowns. Perf. 15 x 14

Cream paper/GA

U1	3d	Lilac	75	25
U2	6d	Claret (29.9.58)	1.00	40
U3	1s3d	Green (29.9.58)	2.25	70
		First Day Cover (3d)	£16	

White paper/GA

U4	3d	Lilac (21.5.62)	20	15
U5	4d	Ultramarine (7.2.66)	10	15
U6	6d	Claret (4.6.62)	10	15
U7	1s3d	Green (9.11.62)	20	25
		Set of 4	50	60

1967 (1 Mar.) Phosphor issue. Wmk. Multiple Crowns. Perf. 15 x 14

White paper/GA

U8	3d	CB Lilac (9.6.67)	10	15
U9	4d	2B Ultramarine (2.10.67)	10	15
U10	9d	2B Deep green	20	25
U11	1s6d	2B Grey blue	20	25
U11a		Missing phosphor	£200	
		Set of 4	45	60
		First Day Cover (9d, 1s6d)		4.50

1968 (27 June) Phosphor issue. No watermark. Perf. 15 x 14

Chalky paper/GA

U12	4d	2B Ultramarine (27.6.68)	10	15

Chalky paper/PVA

U13	4d	2B Ultramarine (23.10.68)	9.50	
U14	4d	CB Sepia (4.9.68)	10	15
U14a		Missing phosphor	£200	
U15	4d	CB Vermilion (26.2.69)	15	15
U15a		Missing phosphor	5.00	
U16	5d	2B Deep blue (4.9.68)	10	10
U16a		Missing phosphor	£35	
U17	1s6d	2B Grey blue (20.5.69)	1.30	1.40
U17a		Missing phosphor	£650	
		Set of 5	1.50	1.65
		First Day Cover (4d sepia, 5d)		1.00
		Presentation Pack 25 (9.12.70)		
		Contents: U7, 8, 10, 11, 14/16 (7v)	1.10	

Printer: Harrison & Sons in Photogravure

1971 (7 July). Decimal. Phosphor issue. No watermark. Perf. 15 x 14. Two 9.5mm phosphor bands or one 4mm centre band, unless stated otherwise.

OCP/PVA

U18	2½p	CB Magenta	50	20
U19	3p	2B Ultramarine	20	20
U19a		Missing phosphor	£50	
U20	5p	2B Bright violet	80	85
U21	7½p	2B Chestnut	1.20	1.20
U21a		Missing phosphor	£95	
		First Day Cover		2.00
		Presentation Pack 29	1.50	

FCP/PVA

U22	2½p	CB Magenta (6.73)	5.00	1.25
U23	3p	2B Ultramarine (4.73)	£22	1.50
U23a		'JET' yellow phosphor (7.73)	7.50	
U24	3p	CB Ultramarine (7.73)	10	15

FCP/PVAD

U25	3p	CB Ultramarine (23.1.74)	1.00	
U26	3½p	2B Bronze green (23.1.74)	15	15
U27	3½p	CB Bronze green (6.11.74)	15	15
U28	4½p	2B Steel blue (6.11.74)	15	15
U29	5½p	2B Violet (23.1.74)	15	15
U29a		Missing phosphor	£300	
U29b		Missing right band	£700	
U30	5½p	CB Violet (21.5.75)	15	15

U31	6½p	CB Greenish blue (14.1.76)	15	15
U32	7p	CB Red brown (18.1.78)	20	20
U33	8p	2B Rose red (23.1.74)	20	20
U33a		Missing phosphor	£85	

Regionals Non Elliptical
No.   U/M F/U

Northern Ireland
No.

Queen Elizabeth II
U/M F/U

No.			U/M	F/U
U34	8½p	**2B Yellow green** (14.1.76)	20	20
U35	9p	**2B Violet** (18.1.78)	20	20
U35a		Missing phosphor	£25	
U35b		Right band (left band omitted)	£100	
U35c		Left band (right band omitted)	£100	
U36	10p	**2B Orange brown** (20.10.76)	25	25
U37	10p	**CB Orange brown** (23.7.80)	30	30
U38	10½p	**2B Steel blue** (18.1.78)	30	30
U39	11p	**2B Scarlet** (20.10.76)	30	30
U39a		Missing phosphor	7.00	
U39b		Right band (left band omitted)	£75	
U39c		Left band (right band omitted)	£20	
		First Day Cover (3p, 3½p, 5½p, 8p)		3.00
		Presentation Pack 61 (29.5.74)		
		Contents: U25, 26, 29, 33 (4v)	1.10	
		First Day Cover (3½p, 4½p)		3.00
		Presentation Pack 61 (6.11.74)		
		Contents: U24, 27/29, 33 (5v)	1.10	
		First Day Cover (6½p, 8½p)		3.00
		First Day Cover (10p, 11p)		3.00
		Presentation Pack 84 (20.10.76)		
		Contents: U31, 34, 36, 38 (4v)	1.10	
		First Day Cover (7p, 9p, 10½p)		3.00

PCP/PVAD

No.			U/M	F/U
U40	12p	**Yellow green** (23.7.80)	30	30
U41	13½p	**Red brown** (23.7.80)	40	40
U42	15p	**Bright blue** (23.7.80)	35	40
		First Day Cover (12p, 13½p, 15p)		3.00

Printer: House of Questa in Litho

1981 (8 April) **Decimal.** Phosphor issue. No watermark. Perf. 13½ x 14. One 4mm side band on 11½p and 12½p.

OCP/PVA

No.			U/M	F/U
U43	11½p	**LB Drab** (8.4.81)	50	55

PCP/PVA

No.			U/M	F/U
U44	14p	**Grey blue** (8.4.81)	40	40
U45	18p	**Violet blue** (8.4.81)	60	65
U46	22p	**Blue** (8.4.81)	75	80
		First Day Cover (11½p, 14p, 18p, 22p)		3.00
		Presentation Pack 129d (28.10.81)		
		Contents: U32, 35, 38, 40/46 (10v)	3.90	

FCP/PVAD

No.			U/M	F/U
U47	12½p	**LB Light emerald** (24.2.82)	30	3

PCP/PVAD

No.			U/M	F/U
U48	15½p	**Pale violet** (24.2.82)	50	5
U49	16p	**Drab** (27.4.83)	60	6
U50	19½p	**Olive grey** (24.2.82)	1.10	1.5

No.			U/M	F/U
U51	20½p	**Ultramarine** (27.4.83)	2.00	2.00
U52	26p	**Rosine**. Type I (24.2.82)	65	65
U53	28p	**Violet blue**. Type I (27.4.83)	75	75
		First Day Cover (12½p, 15½p, 19½p, 26p)		3.00
		First Day Cover (16p, 20½p, 28p)		3.00
		Presentation Pack 4 (3.8.83)		
		Contents: U37, 47, 50/53 (6v)	8.50	

1984 (28 Feb.) Decimal. Phosphor issue. No watermark. Perf. 15 x 14.
One 4mm phosphor band or 'bar' on 12p, 12½p, 13p, 14p and 15p.

Printer: House of Questa in Litho

Type I	Type II
Line on the hand weak or absent	Line on the hand much bolder

OCP/PVA

U54	12½p	**LB Light emerald** (28.2.84)	3.50	3.25

FCP/PVAD

J55	12p	**LB Emerald** (7.1.86)	50	55
J55a		Left bar (7.86)	70	75
J56	12½p	**LB Light emerald** (28.2.84)	2.90	2.50
J57	13p	**LB Pale chestnut** Type I (23.10.84)	50	55
J57a		Missing phosphor	£275	
J57b		Left bar. Type II (11.12.86)	50	55
		First Day Cover (12p)		2.00

FCP/PVA

58	13p	**LBar Pale chestnut** Type II (14.4.87)	80	40
58a		Short band at top	£20	
58b		Short band at bottom	6.00	
59	14p	**CBar Dark blue** (8.11.88)	40	40
59a		Short band at bottom	6.00	

U60	15p	**CBar Bright blue** (28.11.89)	45	45
U60a		Short band at top	1.50	
U60b		Short band at bottom	1.50	
U61	17p	**CBar Dark blue** (4.12.90)	40	40
U61a		Short band at top	4.00	
U61b		Short band at bottom	2.00	
U62	18p	**CBar Bright green** (3.12.91)	40	45
U62a		Short band at top	2.00	
U82b		Short band at bottom	2.00	
U62c		Perf error, (13½ x 14)	1.00	1.00
U62d		Short band at top	2.50	
U62e		Short band at bottom	2.50	

U63	39p	**Mauve** (paper error, non-phosphor) (.91)	£30	

PCP/PVAD

U64	16p	**Drab** (28.2.84)	5.00	4.00
U65	17p	**Grey blue** Type I (23.10.84)	55	50
U66	31p	**Bright purple** Type I (23.10.84)	90	90

ACP/PVA

U67	19p	**Orange red** (8.11.88)	50	50
U68	20p	**Black** (28.11.89)	50	50
U68a		Low OBA	1.25	
U69	23p	**Bright green** (8.11.88)	65	65

U70	24p	**Indian red** (28.11.89)	65	65
U71	24p	**Chestnut** (3.12.91)	60	65
U72	28p	**Blue grey** (3.12.91)	80	80

No.			U/M	F/U
U73	**32p**	**Deep greenish blue** (8.11.88)	80	80
U74	**34p**	**Slate** (28.11.89)	90	90
U75	**39p**	**Mauve** (3.12.91)	1.20	1.30

ACP/PVAD

No.			U/M	F/U
U76	**17p**	**Grey blue** Type I (25.2.86)	75	35
U76a		Type II (10.9.86)	£80	£65
U77	**18p**	**Olive grey** (6.1.87)	50	55
U78	**22p**	**Yellow green** (23.10.84)	55	55
U79	**22p**	**Orange red** (4.12.90)	60	65
U80	**26p**	**Rosine** Type II (27.1.87)	2.50	2.50

No.			U/M	F/U
U81	**26p**	**Stone** (4.12.90)	65	65
U82	**28p**	**Violet blue** Type II (27.1.87)	75	75
U83	**31p**	**Bright purple** Type II (14.4.87)	2.50	2.50
U84	**37p**	**Red** (4.12.90)	95	95
		First Day Cover (13p, 17p, 22p, 31p) (23.10.84)		3.00
		Presentation Pack 8 (23.10.84)		
		Contents: U37, 58, 65/7, 70, 79, 81, 83 (8v)	8.50	
		First Day Cover (18p) (6.1.87)		1.50
		Presentation Pack 12 (3.3.87)		
		Contents: U56a, 58b, 66, 77, 78, 80, 81,		
		83 (8v)	8.75	
		First Day Cover (12p)		1.50
		First Day Cover (14p, 19p, 23p, 32p)		3.00
		First Day Cover (15p, 20p, 24p, 34p)		3.00
		First Day Cover (17p, 22p, 26p, 37p)		3.00
		First Day Cover (18p, 24p, 28p, 39p)		3.00

OFNP/PVA - C (Yellow) fluor

No.			U/M	F/U
U85	**18p**	**LB Bright green** - SP62 (B. Potter book)		
		(10.8.93)	1.70	1.80
U86	**24p**	**2B Chestnut** - - SP62 (B. Potter book)		
		(10.8.93)	2.00	2.00
U86a		Inset left band	4.50	4.00

For issues previously listed as U88 to U91 please see 'ellipticals' section

Scotland

Printer: Harrison & Sons in Photogravure

3d, 4d, 5d   6d, 9d   1s3d, 1s6d

1958 (18 Aug.) Wmk. Multiple Crowns. Perf. 15 x 14

Cream paper/GA

No.			U/M	F/U
S1	**3d**	**Lilac**	40	15
S2	**6d**	**Claret** (29.9.58)	75	30
S3	**1s3d**	**Green** (29.9.58)	2.25	75
		First Day Cover (3d)		£10

White paper/GA

No.			U/M	F/U
S4	**3d**	**Lilac** (9.7.62)	10	15
S5	**4d**	**Ultramarine** (7.2.66)	10	15
S6	**6d**	**Claret** (14.6.62)	10	15
S7	**1s3d**	**Green** (9.11.62)	25	20
		Set of 4	40	35

1963 (29 Jan.) Phosphor issue. Wmk. Multiple Crowns. Perf. 15 x 14

White paper/GA

No.			U/M	F/U
S8	**3d**	**2B Lilac** (29.1.63)	7.00	1.50
S9	**3d**	**LB Lilac** blue phosphor (30.4.65)	3.75	1.20
S9a		violet phosphor (16.12.65)	20	20
S10	**3d**	**RB Lilac** blue phosphor (30.4.65)	3.50	1.00
S10a		violet phosphor (16.12.65)	20	20
S11	**3d**	**CB Lilac** (6.11.67)	10	15
S12	**4d**	**2B Ultramarine** (7.2.66)	10	15
S13	**6d**	**2B Claret** (blue phosphor) (29.1.63)	15	15
S13a	**6d**	**2B Claret** (violet phosphor) (7.2.66)	75	50
S14	**9d**	**2B Deep green** (1.3.67)	25	20
S15	**1s3d**	**2B Green** (blue phosphor) (29.1.63)	1.25	60
S15a		violet phosphor (26.11.65)	25	20
S16	**1s6d**	**2B Grey blue** (1.3.67)	25	25
		Set of 6	85	90
		First Day Cover (9d, 1s6d)		4.50

1967 (28 Nov.) Phosphor issue. No watermark. Perf. 15 x 14

Chalky paper/GA

No.			U/M	F/U
S17	**3d**	**CB Lilac** (16.5.68)	10	1
S17a		Missing phosphor	7.00	
S18	**4d**	**2B Ultramarine** (28.11.67)	10	1
S18a		Missing phosphor	£10	

Chalky paper/PVA

No.			U/M	F/U
S19	**3d**	**CB Lilac** (11.7.68)	10	1
S19a		Missing phosphor	4.00	
S20	**4d**	**2B Ultramarine** (25.7.68)	10	1
S21	**4d**	**CB Sepia** (4.9.68)	10	1
S21a		Missing phosphor	3.00	
S22	**4d**	**CB Vermilion** (26.2.69)	15	1
S22a		Missing phosphor	3.00	
S23	**5d**	**2B Deep blue** (4.9.68)	15	1
S23a		Missing phosphor	£55	

Regionals Non Elliptical
No. U/M F/U
Scotland
No.
Queen Elizabeth II
U/M F/U

S24	9d	**2B Deep green** (28.9.70)	2.60	2.70
S24a		Missing phosphor	£250	
S25	1s6d	**2B Grey blue** (12.12.68)	90	60
S25a		Missing phosphor	£125	
		Set of 7	3.80	3.75
		First Day Cover (4d sepia, 5d)		1.00
		Presentation Pack 23 (9.12.70)		
		Contents: S12, 15, 19, 21/25 (8v)	3.65	

Printer: Harrison & Sons in Photogravure

1971 (7 July) Decimal. Phosphor issue. No watermark. Perf. 15 x 14. Two 9.5mm phosphor bands or one 4mm centre band, unless stated otherwise.

OCP/PVA

S26	2½p	**CB Magenta**	20	20
S26a		Missing phosphor	8.00	
S27	3p	**2B Ultramarine**	20	25
S27a		Missing phosphor	£50	
S28	5p	**2B Bright violet**	60	70
S29	7½p	**2B Chestnut**	85	90
S29a		Broad band (right)	£25	
S29b		Missing phosphor	5.00	
		First Day Cover		2.00
		Presentation Pack 27	1.50	

FCP/GA

S30	2½p	**CB Magenta** (22.9.72)	20	10
S31	3p	**2B Ultramarine** (14.12.72)	45	45
S31a		'JET' (yellow) phosphor	1.75	
S31b		Imperforate pair	£300	
S31c		Imperf. top margin	£200	

FCP/PVA

S32	2½p	**CB Magenta** (6./3)	5.00	
S32a		Missing phosphor	£20	
S33	3p	**2B Ultramarine** (1973)	7.50	
S33a		Missing phosphor	£15	
S33b		Broad centre band	£350	
S34	3p	**CB Ultramarine** (23.1.74)	25	25
S35	3½p	**2B Bronze green** (23.1.74)	8.50	
S36	5p	**2B Bright violet** (6.73)	£20	£20
S36a		Broad left band	£1000	
S36b		'JET' (yellow) phosphor	6.00	
S37	7½p	**2B Chestnut** (11.73)	£70	

FCP/PVAD

S38	3p	**CB Ultramarine** (9.74)	60	
S39	3½p	**2B Bronze green** (23.1.74)	15	15
S39a		Missing phosphor	£50	
S40	3½p	**CB Bronze green** (6.11.74)	15	15
S41	4½p	**2B Steel blue** (6.11.74)	20	15
S41a		Full stop after 'P' of value	3.50	
S42	5½p	**2B Violet** (23.1.74)	15	15
S43	5½p	**CB Violet** (21.5.75)	15	15
S44	6½p	**CB Greenish blue** (14.1.76)	15	15
S44a		Dull greenish blue	4.00	

S45	7p	**CB Red brown** (18.1.78)	15	15
S46	8p	**2B Rose red** (23.1.74)	20	20
S47	8½p	**2B Yellow** green (14.1.76)	20	20

S48	9p	**2B Violet** (18.1.78)	20	20
S49	10p	**2B Orange brown** (20.10.76)	25	20
S50	10p	**CB Orange brown** (23.7.80)	25	25
S51	10½p	**2B Steel blue** (18.1.78)	30	30
S52	11p	**2B Scarlet** (20.10.76)	30	30
S52a		Missing phosphor	2.00	
S52b		Right band (left band omitted)	£100	
S52c		Left band (right band omitted)	£75	
		First Day Cover (3p, 3½p, 5½p, 8p)		3.00
		Presentation Pack 62 (29.5.74)		
		Contents: S34, 39, 42, 46 (4v)	1.10	
		First Day Cover (4½p)		3.00
		First Day Cover (3½p, 4½p)		3.00
		Presentation Pack 62 (6 11.74)		
		Contents: S34, 40/42, 46 (5v)	1.10	
		First Day Cover (6½p, 8½p)		3.00
		First Day Cover (10p, 11p)		3.00
		Presentation Pack 85 (20.10.76)		
		Contents: S44, 47, 49, 52 (4v)	1.10	
		First Day Cover (7p, 9p, 10½p)		3.00

Regionals Non Elliptical

No.   U/M   F/U

Scotland

No.

Queen Elizabeth II

U/M   F/U

PCP/PVAD

No.			U/M	F/U
S53	12p	Yellow green (23.7.80)	30	30
S54	13½p	Red brown (23.7.80)	40	40
S55	15p	Bright blue (23.7.80)	40	45
		First Day Cover (12p, 13½p, 15p)		3.00
		First Day Cover (10p, 12p, 13½p, 15p)		3.00

Printer: Waddington in Litho

1981 (8 April) Decimal. Phosphor issue. No watermark. Perf. 13½ x 14 One 4mm side band on 11½p, 12p, 12½p and 13p.

FCP/PVA

No.			U/M	F/U
S56	11½p	LB Drab (8.4.81)	50	50
S56a		Missing phosphor	£700	
S56b		Imperf. at right (marginal)	£60	
S57	12p	LB Emerald (7.1.86)	1.20	1.10
S58	12½p	LB Light emerald (24.2.82)	35	35
S58a		Varnished paper	22.50	
S59	13p	LB Pale chestnut Type I (23.10.84)	40	40
S59a		Missing phosphor	£700	
S59b		Type II (1.85)	4.00	3.50
S59c		Missing phosphor	£750	
		First Day Cover (12p)		2.00

PCP/PVAD

No.			U/M	F/U
S60	14p	Grey blue (8.4.81)	40	40
S61	15½p	Pale violet (24.2.82)	50	50
S62	16p	Drab (27.4.83)	40	40

No.			U/M	F/U
S63	17p	Grey blue. Type I (23.10.84)	2.00	75
S63a		Type II (1.85)	1.00	70
S64	18p	Violet blue (8.4.81)	60	65
S65	19½p	Olive grey (24.2.82)	1.10	1.10

No.			U/M	F/U
S66	20½p	Ultramarine (27.4.83)	2.50	2.00
S67	22p	Blue (8.4.81)	2.00	2.00
S68	26p	Rosine Type I (24.2.82)	65	65

No.			U/M	F/U
S69	28p	Violet blue. Type II (27.4.83)	75	75
S70	31p	Bright purple. Type I (23.10.84)	1.20	1.20
S70a		Type II (6.85)	£77	£45
		First Day Cover (11½p, 14p, 18p, 22p)		3.00
		Presentation Pack 129b (28.10.81)		
		Contents: S45, 48, 51, 53/55, 61, 66, 69 (10v)	3.90	
		First Day Cover (12½p, 15½p, 19½p, 26p)		3.00
		First Day Cover (16p, 20½p, 28p)		3.00
		Presentation Pack 2 (3.8.83)		
		Contents: S50, 58, 63, 68, 70, 71 (6v)	8.50	

PCP/PVA

No.			U/M	F/U
S71	17p	Grey blue. Type II (25.6.85)	65	65

ACP/PVAD

No.			U/M	F/U
S72	16p	Drab (2.11.83)	4.00	30

No.			U/M	F/U
S73	22p	Yellow green. Type I (23.10.84)	1.50	1.50
S73a		Type II (6.86)	£22	£22
		First Day Cover (13p, 17p, 22p, 31p) (23.10.84)		3.00
		Presentation Pack 6 (23.10.84)		
		Contents: S50, 58, 63, 64, 70/72, 76(8v)	8.50	

				U/M	F/U
S82	**19p**	**2B** Orange red (21.3.89)		1.00	1.10
S83	**23p**	**2B** Bright green (21.3.89)		6.25	7.00

Printer: House of Questa in Litho

Type I   Type II
Large eye and mouth   Small eye and mouth

1986 (29 April) Decimal. Phosphor issue. No watermark. Perf. 15 x 14 One 4mm phosphor band or 'bar' on 12p, 13p, 14p, 15p, 17p and 18p.

FCP/PVAD

S74	**12p**	**LBar** Emerald (29.4.86)	1.00	1.00
S74a		Short band at top	£20	
S75	**13p**	**LBar** Pale chestnut Type II (4.11.86)	40	40
S75a		Short band at top	£15	

FCP/PVA

S76	**13p**	**LBar** Pale chestnut Type II (14.4.87)	60	
S76a		Short band at top	4.00	

S77	**14p**	**CBar** Dark blue (8.11.88)	40	40
S77a		Short band at top	4.00	
S77b		Short band at bottom	2.00	
S77c		Cream paper. Low OBA	4.50	
S77d		CB (21.3.89)	40	40
S78	**14p**	**LB** Dark blue (21.3.89)	50	50
S78a		Short band at top	£15	
S78b		Short band at bottom	£15	
S79	**15p**	**CBar** Bright blue (28.11.89)	35	40
S79a		Short band at top	3.50	
S79b		Short band at bottom	2.00	
S80	**17p**	**CBar** Dark blue (4.12.90)	45	50
S80a		Short band at top	1.50	
S80b		Short band at bottom	1.50	

S81	**18p**	**CBar** Bright green (3.12.91)	45	45
S81a		Short band at top	1.25	
S81b		Short band at bottom	1.25	
S81c		Perf error, (13½ x 14)	85	80
S81d		Perf error, Short band at top	1.50	
S81e		Perf error, Short band at bottom	1.50	
S81f		Perf error, Missing phosphor	£1250	

ACP/PVA

S84	**19p**	Orange red (25.4.89)	50	50

S85	**20p**	Black (28.11.89)	45	45
S85a		Low OBA	1.25	
S86	**22p**	Orange red (14.5.91)	70	
S87	**24p**	Indian red (28.11.89)	65	70

S88	**24p**	Chestnut (3.12.91)	75	80
S88a		Perf error, (13½ x 14) (10.92)	1.60	1.60
S89	**26p**	Stone (14.5.91)	1.10	
S90	**28p**	Blue grey (3.12.91)	55	55
S90a		Perf error, (13½ x 14) (10.92)	2.50	2.50

S91	**34p**	Slate (28.11.89)	90	95
S92	**37p**	Red (14.5.91)	95	1.00
S93	**39p**	Mauve (3.12.91)	1.00	1.10
S93a		Perf error, (13½ x 14) (4.92)	2.00	2.00

ACP/PVAD

S94	**17p**	Grey blue. Type II (29.4.86)	2.20	2.20

S95	**18p**	Olive grey. Type II (6.1.87)	50	50
S95a		Cream gum (29.3.88)	60	
S96	**19p**	Orange red (8.11.88)	50	30
S96a		Pale orange red (21.3.89)	50	50
S97	**22p**	Yellow green Type II (27.1.87)	70	75
S98	**22p**	Orange red (4.12.90)	55	60
S99	**23p**	Bright green (8.11.88)	60	65
S100	**26p**	Rosine. Type II (27.1.87)	1.75	1.85
S101	**26p**	Stone (4.12.90)	60	65
S102	**28p**	Violet blue. Type II (27.1.87)	60	65
S103	**31p**	Bright purple. Type II (29.4.86)	90	90

No.				U/M	F/U
S104	32p	**Deep greenish blue** (8.11.88)		85	90
S105	37p	**Red** (4.12.90)		1.00	
		First Day Cover (13p, 17p, 22p, 31p) (23.10.86)			3.00
		First Day Cover (18p) (6.1.87)			1.50
		First Day Cover (22p, 26p, 28p) (27.1.87)			3.00
		Presentation Pack 10 (3.3.87)			
		Contents: S78, 79, 100, 101, 103, 105, 107, 108 (8v)			
				8.75	
		First Day Cover (14p, 19p, 23p, 32p)			3.00
		First Day Cover (15p, 20p, 24p, 34p)			3.00
		First Day Cover (17p, 22p, 26p, 37p)			3.00
		First Day Cover (18p, 24p, 28p, 39p)			3.00

OFNP/PVA - C (Yellow) fluor

S106	18p	**LB Bright green** - SP62 (B. Potter book)			
		(10.8.93)		1.50	1.50
S107	24p	**2B Chestnut** - SP62 (B. Potter book)			
		(10.8.93)		1.30	1.30
S107a		Inset left band		4.50	4.00

For issues previously listed as S116 to S119 please see 'ellipticals' section

Wales

Printer: Harrison & Sons in Photogravure

3d, 4d, 5d   6d, 9d   1s3d, 1s6d

1958 (18 Aug.) Wmk. Multiple Crowns. Perf. 15 x 14

Cream paper/GA

WA1	3d	**Lilac**	45	25
WA2	6d	**Claret** (29.9.58)	75	40
WA3	1s 3d	**Green** (29.9.58)	2.25	1.00
		First Day Cover (3d)		£10

White paper/GA

WA4	3d	**Lilac** (30.4.62)	10	15
WA5	4d	**Ultramarine** (7.2.66)	10	15
WA6	6d	**Claret** (18.7.62)	25	15
WA7	1s 3d	**Green** (11.5.64)	30	30
WA7a		Deep green	25	50
WA7b		Myrtle green	£60	£15
		Set of 4	50	50

1967 (1 Mar.) Phosphor issue. Wmk. Multiple Crowns. Perf. 15 x 14

White paper/GA

WA8	3d	**CB Lilac** (16.5.67)	10	15
WA9	4d	**2B Ultramarine** (10.67)	10	10
WA10	9d	**2B Deep green** (1.3.67)	25	30
WA10a		Missing phosphor	£350	
WA11	1s 6d	**2B Grey blue** (1.3.67)	20	25
WA11a		Missing phosphor	£50	
		Set of 4	50	70
		First Day Cover (9d, 1s6d)		4.50

1967 (12 Dec.) Phosphor issue. No watermark. Perf. 15 x 14

Chalky paper/PVA

WA12	3d	**CB Lilac** (6.12.67)	10	15
WA12a		Missing phosphor	£60	

Chalky paper/PVA

WA13	4d	**2B Ultramarine** (21.6.68)	10	15
WA14	4d	**CB Sepia** (4.9.68)	10	15
WA15	4d	**CB Vermilion** (26.2.69)	10	15
WA15a		Missing phosphor	2.00	
WA16	5d	**2B Deep blue** (4.9.68)	15	15
WA16a		Missing phosphor	3.00	
WA17	1s 6d	**2B Grey blue** (12.12.68)	1.85	1.75
		Set of 6	2.25	2.40
		First Day Cover (4d sepia, 5d)		1.00
		Presentation Pack 24 (9.12.70)		
		Contents: WA10/12, 14/16 (6v)	1.40	

Printer: Harrison & Sons in Photogravure

1971 (7 July) Decimal. Phosphor issue. No watermark. Perf. 15 x 14.
Two 9.5mm phosphor bands or one 4mm centre band, unless stated otherwise.

OCP/PVA

WA18	2½p	**CB Magenta**	10	15
WA18a		Missing phosphor	6.00	
WA18b		Imperf. top margin	£175	
WA19	3p	**2B Ultramarine**	30	25
WA19a		Missing phosphor	£40	
WA20	5p	**2B Bright violet**	1.00	1.00
WA20a		Broad band	£75	
WA20b		Missing phosphor	£20	
WA21	7½p	**2B Chestnut**	1.20	1.25
WA21a		Missing phosphor	£80	
		First Day Cover		2.00
		Presentation Pack 28	1.50	

No.   U/M   F/U   No.   U/M   F/U

FCP/GA

			U/M	F/U
WA22	2½p	**CB Magenta** (22.9.72)	30	20
WA22a		Imperforate pair	£250	
WA23	3p	**2B Ultramarine** (6.6.73)	60	40
WA23a		Missing phosphor	£12	
WA23b		Right band (left band omitted)	£150	
WA23c		Left band (right band omitted)	£150	

FCP/PVA

WA24	2½p	**CB Magenta** (1973)	1.75	
WA25	3p	**2B Ultramarine** (2.73)	8.00	
WA25a		Broad band	£125	
WA26	3p	**CB Ultramarine** (23.1.74)	30	25
WA27	5p	**2B Bright violet** (6.73)	17.50	
WA27a		Missing phosphor	£75	

FCP/PVAD

WA28	3½p	**2B Bronze green** (23.1.74)	10	15
WA28a		Full stop before 'P' of value	1.50	
WA29	3½p	**CB Bronze green** (6.11.74)	10	15
WA29a		Full stop before 'P' of value	1.50	
WA30	4½p	**2B Steel blue** (6.11.74)	15	20
WA31	5½p	**2B Violet** (23.1.74)	15	15
WA31a		Missing phosphor	£175	
WA32	5½p	**CB Violet** (21.5.75)	15	15
WA32a		Imperf. pair	£400	

WA32b		Low emblem and value (ex cyl 2)	£300	

WA33	6½p	**CB Greenish blue** (14.1.76)	15	15
WA34	7p	**CB Red brown** (18.1.78)	15	15
WA35	8p	**2B Rose red** (23.1.74)	20	20
WA35a		Missing phosphor	£800	

WA36	8½p	**2B Yellow green** (14.1.76)	20	15
WA37	9p	**2B Violet** (18.1.78)	20	15
WA38	10p	**2B Orange brown** (20.10.76)	20	20
WA39	10p	**CB Orange brown** (23.7.80)	30	30

			U/M	F/U
WA40	10½p	**2B Steel blue** (18.1.78)	30	30
WA41	11p	**2B Scarlet** (20.10.76)	30	30
		First Day Cover (3p, 3½p, 5½p, 8p)		3.00
		Presentation Pack 63 (29.5.74)		
		Contents: WA26, 28, 31, 35 (4v)	1.10	
		First Day Cover (3½p, 4½p)		3.00
		Presentation Pack 63 (6.11.74)		
		Contents: WA26, 29/31, 35 (5v)	1.10	
		First Day Cover (6½p, 8½p)		3.00
		First Day Cover (10p, 11p)		3.00
		Presentation Pack 86 (20.10.76)		
		Contents: WA33, 36, 38, 41 (4v)	1.10	
		First Day Cover (7p, 9p, 10½p)		3.00

PCP/PVAD

WA42	12p	**Yellow green** (23.7.80)	40	40
WA43	13½p	**Red brown** (23.7.80)	40	40
WA44	15p	**Bright blue** (23.7.80)	40	40
		First Day Cover (12p, 13½p, 15p)		3.00
		First Day Cover (10p, 12p, 13½p, 15p)		3.00

Printer: House of Questa in Litho

1981 (8 April) Decimal. Phosphor issue. No watermark. Perf. 13½ x 14. One 4mm side band on 11½p and 12½p.

OCP/PVA

WA45	11½p	**LB Drab** (8.4.81)	50	50

Regionals Non Elliptical
No.

Wales
U/M   F/U   No.

Queen Elizabeth II
U/M   F/U

PCP/PVA

No.			U/M	F/U
WA46	14p	Grey blue (8.4.81)	40	35
WA47	18p	Violet blue (8.4.81)	70	75
WA48	22p	Blue (8.4.81)	65	65
		First Day Cover (11½p, 14p, 18p, 22p)		3.00
		Presentation Pack 129c (28.10.81)		
		Contents: WA34, 37, 40, 42/48 (10v)	3.90	

Type I   Type II
Thin wing-tips, tail and tongue   Thick wing-tips, tail and tongue

1984 (10 Jan) Decimal. Phosphor issue. No watermark. Perf. 15 x 14. One 4mm phosphor band or 'bar' on 12p, 12½p, 13p, 14p, 15p, 17p and 18p
Printer: House of Questa in Litho

FCP/PVAD

			U/M	F/U
WA49	12½p	LB Light emerald (24.2.82)	40	40

PCP/PVAD

			U/M	F/U
WA50	15½p	Pale violet (24.2.82)	50	50
WA50a		Lavender	1.50	75
WA51	16p	Drab (27.4.83)	90	90
WA52	19½p	Olive grey (24.2.82)	1.00	1.00

			U/M	F/U
WA53	20½p	Ultramarine (27.4.83)	2.00	2.00
WA54	26p	Rosine (24.2.82)	60	60
WA55	28p	Violet blue (27.4.83)	65	65
		First Day Cover (12½p, 15½p, 19½p, 26p)		3.00
		First Day Cover (16p, 20½p, 28p)		3.00
		Presentation Pack 3 (3.8.83)		
		Contents: WA39, 49, 51, 53/55 (6v)	8.50	

FCP/PVAD

			U/M	F/U
WA58	12p	LB Emerald (7.1.86)	90	90
WA58a		Short left 'bar' (7.86)	2.00	1.50
WA59	12½p	LB Light emerald (10.1.84)	3.00	3.00
WA60	13p	LB Pale chestnut Type I (23.10.84)	30	40
WA60a		Type II	2.50	1.75
WA60b		LBar Type II (1.87)	2.00	55
		First Day Cover (12p)		1.50

FCP/PVA

			U/M	F/U
WA62	13p	LBar Pale brown Type II (14.4.87)	1.20	1.00
WA62a		Short band at top	2.50	
WA62b		Short band at bottom	£25	

			U/M	F/U
WA63	14p	CBar Dark blue (8.11.88)	40	40
WA63a		Short band at top	7.50	
WA63b		Short band at bottom	2.50	
WA64	15p	CBar Bright blue (28.11.89)	30	30
WA64a		Missing phosphor	£90	
WA64b		Short band at top	3.00	
WA64c		Short band at bottom	3.00	
WA65	17p	CBar Dark blue (4.12.90)	40	40
WA65a		Missing phosphor	£18	
WA65b		Short band at top	2.00	

No.			U/M	F/U
WA66	**18p**	**CBar Bright green** (3.12.91)	30	30
WA66a		Short band at top	2.50	
WA66b		Short band at bottom	1.50	
WA66c		Perf error (13½ x 14) (12.92)	3.60	3.60
WA66d		Perf error, Short band at top	£15	
WA66e		Perf error, Short band at bottom	4.00	
WA66f		CB (25.2.92)	65	40
WA66g		Missing phosphor	£200	
WA67	**18p**	**RB Bright green** - SP55 (Wales book)		
		(25.2.92)	1.10	1.10
WA67a		Missing phosphor	£350	
WA68	**24p**	**2B Chestnut** - SP55 (Wales book)		
		(25.2.92)	75	90
WA68a		Short bands at top	6.00	
WA68b		Short bands at bottom	£12	
WA68c		Missing phosphor	£350	

PCP/PVAD

WA69	**16p**	**Drab** (10.1.84)	95	1.00

WA70	**17p**	**Grey blue**. Type I (23.10.84)	75	30
WA71	**31p**	**Bright purple**. Type I (23.10.84)	70	70

ACP/PVA

WA72	**19p**	**Orange red** (20.6.89)	65	
WA73	**20p**	**Black** (28.11.89)	45	45
WA73a		Low OBA	1.25	
WA74	**24p**	**Indian red** (28.11.89)	50	55

WA75	**24p**	**Chestnut** (3.12.91)	45	45
WA75a		Perf error (13½ x 14) (10.92)	2.00	2.00
WA76	**28p**	**Blue grey** (3.12.91)	75	75
WA77	**34p**	**Slate** (28.11.89)	80	85
WA78	**39p**	**Mauve** (3.12.91)	1.00	1.10

ACP/PVAD

WA79	**17p**	**Grey blue**. Type I (25.2.86)	50	50
WA79a		Type II (18.8.86)	£24	£22

WA81	**18p**	**Olive grey**. Type II (6.1.87)	45	45
WA81a		White gum (29.3.88)	70	
WA82	**19p**	**Orange red** (8.11.88)	50	55
WA83	**22p**	**Yellow green** Type II (23.10.84)	55	55
WA84	**22p**	**Orange red** (4.12.90)	50	55

WA85	**23p**	**Bright green** (8.11.88)	55	60
WA86	**26p**	**Rosine**. Type II (27.1.87)	3.50	3.50
WA87	**26p**	**Stone** (4.12.90)	70	75
WA88	**28p**	**Violet blue**. Type II (27.1.87)	75	80
WA89	**31p**	**Bright purple**. Type I (27.1.87)	70	70
WA90	**32p**	**Deep greenish blue** (8.11.88)	80	80
WA91	**37p**	**Red** (4.12.90)	1.00	1.10
		Presentation Pack 7 (23.10.84)		
		Contents: WA38, 54, 55, 60, 69/71, 85 (8v)	8.50	
		Presentation Pack 11 (3.3.87)		
		Contents: WA58, 60, 81, 83, 85, 87, 89, 90 (8v) 8.75		
		First Day Cover (13p, 17p, 22p, 31p) (23.10.84)		3.00
		First Day Cover (18p) (6.1.87)		1.50
		First Day Cover (14p, 19p, 23p, 32p)		3.00
		First Day Cover (15p, 20p, 24p, 34p)		3.00
		First Day Cover (17p, 22p, 26p, 37p)		3.00
		First Day Cover (18p, 24p, 28p, 39p)		3.00

OFNP/PVA - C (Yellow) fluor

WA92	**18p**	**LB Bright green** - SP62 (B. Potter book)		
		(10.8.93)	1.10	1.10
WA93	**24p**	**2B Chestnut** - SP62 (B. Potter book)		
		(10.8.93)	75	80
WA93a		Inset left band	4.50	4.00

For issues previously listed as WA94 to WA97 please see 'ellipticals' section

Regionals Elliptical
No.   U/M   F/U

Northern Ireland
No.   U/M   F/U

Queen Elizabeth II
U/M   F/U

Northern Ireland

Printer: House of Questa in Lithography

1993 (7 Dec.) Decimal. Perf. 15 x 14. Two phosphor bands, except where indicated.

OFNP/PVA - C (Yellow) fluor

			U/M	F/U
SLU88	19p	**CBar Olive-green**	50	50
SLU88a		Short band at top	2.50	2.50
SLU88b		Short band at bottom	6.00	6.00
SLU89	19p	**LB Olive-green** SP67, SP68 (N. Ireland book)		
		(26.7.94)	1.30	1.30
SLU89a		Inset left band	2.75	2.75
SLU89b		Short extra band at lower right	2.75	2.75
SLU89c		Missing phosphor	£950	
SLU89d		Broad band at left	£750	
SLU90	19p	**RB Olive-green** - SP71 (Nat. Trust book)		
		(25.4.95)	1.60	1.60
SLU91	25p	**2B 8mm Salmon-pink**	60	65
SLU91a		Short bands at top	9.50	
SLU91b		Short band at top right	4.50	4.50
SLU91c		Short band at top right and inset left band	4.50	4.50
SLU91d		Inset left band	2.50	2.50
SLU91e		Missing phosphor	£950	£375
SLU91f		Narrower gap between phosphor bands		
		(9.5 mm bands) (25.4.95)	80	80
SLU92	30p	**2B Grey-green**	80	85
SLU92a		Short bands at bottom	9.50	
SLU92b		Inset left band	3.25	3.25
SLU92c		Missing phosphor	£950	
SLU93	41p	**2B Stone**	1.10	1.15
SLU93a		Short bands at top	3.25	3.25
SLU93b		Missing phosphor	£950	
		First Day Cover (19p, 25p, 30p, 41p)		4.00

OFNP/PVA - D (Blue) fluor

			U/M	F/U
SLU94	19p	**CBar Olive-green** (1.2.96)	90	45
SLU84a		Short band at bottom	£10	

			U/M	F/U
SLU95	20p	**CB Bright green** (23.7.96)	1.00	1.00
SLU96	25p	**2B 8mm Salmon-pink** (27.2.96)	80	50
SLU96a		Narrower gap between phosphor bands		
		(9.5 mm bands) - SP76 (Euro Football book)		
		(14.5.96)	70	90

			U/M	F/U
SLU97	26p	**2B Red-brown** (23.7.96)	1.20	1.20
SLU98	37p	**2B Amethyst** (23.7.96)	2.00	2.00
SLU99	63p	**2B Light emerald** (23.7.96)	3.00	3.00
		First Day Cover (20p,26p,37p, 63p)		4.00

Printer: Walsall Security Printers in Gravure

OFNP/PVA - D (Blue) fluor

			U/M	F/U
SLU100	19p	**CB Olive-green** (8.6.99)	1.20	1.20
SLU101	20p	**CB Bright green** (1.7.97)	80	80
SLU102	20p	**RB Bright green** - SP86 (Breaking Barriers		
		book) (13.10.98)	1.00	1.10
SLU103	26p	**2B Red-brown** (1.7.97)	70	75
SLU103a		Perf 13½ - SP87 (Breaking Barriers		
		book) (13.10.98)	1.75	1.75
SLU104	37p	**2B Amethyst** (1.7.97)	1.50	1.50

			U/M	F/U
SLU105	38p	**2B Ultramarine** ((8.6.99)	1.50	1.50
SLU106	40p	**2B Greyish-blue** (25.4.00)	1.00	1.00
SLU107	63p	**2B Light emerald** (1.7.97)	2.50	2.50
SLU108	64p	**2B Sea green** (8.6.99)	3.00	3.00
SLU109	65p	**2B Greenish-blue** (25.4.00)	2.50	2.50
		First Day Cover (19p, 38p, 64p)		2.50
		First Day Cover (1st, 40p, 65p)		7.00

Printer: Harrison & Sons in Gravure

OFNP/PVA (Layflat) - D (Blue) fluor

			U/M	F/U
SLU110	26p	**2B Red-brown** - SP77 (BBC book)		
		(23.9.97)	1.50	1.50
SLU110	37p	**2B Amethyst** - SP77 (BBC book)		
		(23.9.97)	1.10	1.10

Regionals Elliptical
No.

Scotland
U/M   F/U   No.

Queen Elizabeth II
U/M   F/U

Scotland

Printer: House of Questa in Lithography

SLS124	26p	**2B Red-brown** (23.7.96)	1.20	1.20
SLS125	37p	**2B Amethyst** (23.7.96)	2.00	2.00
SLS126	63p	**2B Light emerald** (23.7.96)	2.50	2.50
		First Day Cover (20p,26p,37p, 63p)		4.00

Printer: Walsall Security Printers in Gravure

OFNP/PVA - D (Blue) fluor

SS127	20p	**CB Bright green** (1.7.97)	70	70
SS128	20p	**RB Bright green** - SP86 (Breaking Barriers		
		book) (13.10.98)	1.00	1.10
SS128	26p	**2B Red-brown** (1.7.97)	1.00	1.00
SS128a		Perf 13½ - SP87 (Breaking Barriers		
		book) (13.10.98)	1.00	1.10
SS129	37p	**2B Amethyst** (1.7.97)	1.50	1.50
SS130	63p	**2B Light emerald** (1.7.97)	2.00	2.00
		First Day Cover (19p, 38p, 64p)		2.50

Printer: Harrison & Sons in Gravure

OFNP/PVA (Layflat) - D (Blue) fluor

SS131	26p	**2B Red-brown** - SP77 (BBC book)		
		(23.9.97)	90	90
SS132	37p	**2B Amethyst** - SP77 (BBC book)		
		(23.9.97)	1.10	1.10

1993 (7 Dec.) Decimal. Perf. 15 x 14. Two phosphor bands, except where indicated.

OFNP/PVA - C (Yellow) fluor

SLS116	19p	**CBar Olive-green**	70	75
SLS116a		Short band at top	1.25	1.50
SLS116b		Short band at bottom	1.25	1.50
SLS117	19p	**RB Olive-green** - SP71 (Nat. Trust book)		
		(25.4.95))	1.60	1.60
SLS117a		Short band at top	£15	
SLS118	25p	**2B 8mm Salmon-pink**	70	75
SLS118a		Short bands at bottom	8.50	
SLS118b		Inset left band	7.50	
SLS118c		Narrower gap between phosphor bands		
		(9.5 mm bands) - SP71 (Nat. Trust book)		
		(25.4.95)	90	90
SLS118d		Short bands at top	8.50	
SLS119	30p	**2B Grey-green**	85	90
SLS119a		Right band inset	17.50	
SLS119b		Short bands at bottom	£10	
SLS120	41p	**2B Stone**	1.25	1.30
SLS120a		Missing phosphor	£300	
		First Day Cover (19p, 25p, 30p, 41p)		4.00

OFNP/PVA - D (Blue) fluor

SLS121	19p	**CBar Olive-green** (12.10.95)	1.00	1.00
SLS121a		Short band at top	7.50	
SLS121b		Short band at bottom	6.00	

SLS122	20p	**CB 4.75mm Bright green** (23.7.96)	70	75
SLS122a		4.5 mm CB (4.12.96)	2.50	2.50
SLS123	25p	**2B 8mm Salmon-pink** (3.8.95)	90	90
SLS123a		Narrower gap between phosphor bands		
		(9.5 mm bands) - SP76 (Euro Football book)		
		(14.5.96)	90	90

Regionals Elliptical
No.

Wales
U/M   F/U   No.

Queen Elizabeth II
U/M   F/U

Wales

Printer: House of Questa in Lithography

1993 (7 Dec.) Decimal. Perf. 15 x 14. Two phosphor bands, except where indicated.

OFNP/PVA - C (Yellow) fluor

No.			U/M	F/U
SLWA94	19p	**CBar Olive-green**	50	60
SLWA94a		Short band at top	2.50	2.50
SLWA94b		Short band at bottom	2.50	2.50
SLWA95	19p	**RB Olive-green** SP71 (Nat. Trust book)		
		(25.4.95)	1.70	1.75
SLWA96	25p	**2B 8mm Salmon-pink**	70	65
SLWA96a		Short bands at top	£20	
SLWA96b		Short bands at bottom	£10	£10
SLWA96c		Narrower gap between phosphor bands		
		(9.5 mm bands) - SP71 (Nat. Trust book)		
		(25.4.95)	90	90
SLWA96d		Broad left band (7.12.93)	£750	
SLWA97	30p	**2B Grey-green**	85	80
SLWA97a		Short bands at bottom	12.50	
SLWA98	41p	**2B Stone**	1.25	90
SLWA98a		Short bands at top	£20	
SLWA98b		Short bands at bottom	12.50	
SLWA98c		Weak phosphor and fluor	17.50	
		First Day Cover (19p, 25p, 30p, 41p)		4.00

OFNP/PVA - D (Blue) fluor

No.			U/M	F/U
SLWA99	19p	**CBar Olive-green** (2.11.95)	90	90
SLWA99a		Short band at top	£10	

No.			U/M	F/U
SLWA100	20p	**CB Bright green** (23.7.96)	60	60
SLWA101	25p	**2B 8mm Salmon-pink** (31.7.95)	90	90
SLWA101a		Narrower gap between phosphor bands		
		(9.5 mm bands) - SP76 (Euro Football book)		
		(14.5.96)	70	70

No.			U/M	F/U
SLWA102	26p	**2B Red-brown** (23.7.96)	1.25	1.25
SLWA103	37p	**2B Amethyst** (23.7.96)	2.00	2.00
SLWA104	41p	**2B Stone** (1.2.96)	1.25	90
SLWA105	63p	**2B Light emerald** (23.7.96)	3.00	3.00
		First Day Cover (20p,26p,37p, 63p)		4.00

1997. Decimal, without "p" in value. Perf. 15 x 14. Two phosphor bands, except where indicated.

Printer: Walsall Security Printers in Gravure

OFNP/PVA - D (Blue) fluor

No.			U/M	F/U
SWA106	20(p)	**CB Bright green** (1.7.97)	60	60
SWA106a		15-pin perforation variety	£13	
SWA107	20(p)	**RB Bright green** - SP86 (Breaking Barriers		
		book) (13.10.98)	1.20	1.25
SWA107	26(p)	**2B Red-brown** (1.7.97)	70	70
SWA107a		Perf 13½ - SP87 (Breaking Barriers		
		book) (13.10.98)	1.30	1.30
SWA108	37(p)	**2B Amethyst** (1.7.97)	1.25	1.25
SWA109	63(p)	**2B Light emerald** (1.7.97)	2.40	2.50
		First Day Cover (20p,26p,37p, 63p)		4.00
		First Day Cover (19p, 38p, 64p)		2.50

Printer: Harrison & Sons in computer engraved-gravure

OFNP/PVA (Layflat) - D (Blue) fluor

No.			U/M	F/U
SWA110	26(p)	**2B Red-brown** - SP77 (BBC book)		
		(23.9.97)	1.10	1.10
SWA111	37(p)	**2B Amethyst** - SP77 (BBC book)		
		(23.9.97)	1.75	1.75

Regionals Elliptical
No.

NVI's
U/M   F/U   No.

Queen Elizabeth II
U/M   F/U

Regional Machin NVI's

Printer: Walsall Security Printers in Gravure

2000 (15 Feb.) Two phosphor bands Perf 14

Northern Ireland

OFNP/PVA - D (Blue) fluor

UW1	1st	**2B Orange-red** - Pane SP100 (Special by Design book) (15.2.00)	1.20	1.20
UW1a		Short bands at bottom	4.50	
UW1b		Right band inset	9.50	
UW1c		Perf 15 x 14 - Sheets (25.4.00)	4.50	4.50

Scotland

OFNP/PVA - D (Blue) fluor

SW1	1st	**2B Orange-red** - Pane SP100 (Special by Design book) (15.2.00)	1.20	1.20
SW1a		Right band inset	9.50	

Wales

OFNP/PVA - D (Blue) fluor

WW1	1st	**2B Orange-red** - Pane SP100 (Special by Design book) (15.2.00)	1.20	1.20
WW1a		Right band inset	9.50	

England Pictorial

2001 (23 Apr.) Perf. 15 x 14. Two phosphor bands, except where indicated.

Printer: De La Rue in Gravure

				U/M	F/U
PEW2	2nd	**CBar Three Lions** (23.4.01)		45	45
PEW2a		Imperforate pair		£350	
PEW2b		Threee Lions, Bright fluor (10.4.03)		40	40
PEW1st	1st	**2B Crowned Lion** (23.4.01)		55	55
PEW1sta		Crowned Lion, Bright fluor (10.4.03)		50	50
PEWE	E	**2B Oak Tree** (23.4.01)		60	65
PEW65	65p	**2B Tudor Rose** (23.4.01)		1.20	1.30
PEW68	68p	**2B Tudor Rose** (4.7.02)		1.20	1.30
		First Day Cover (2nd, 1st, E, 65p)			3.00
		First Day Cover (68p)			3.00

Printer: House of Questa in Gravure

				U/M	F/U
PEQ2	2nd	**CB Three Lions**, from Across the Universe prestige book (24.9.02)		75	85
PEQ1	1st	**2B Crowned Lion**, from Across the Universe prestige book (24.9.02)		85	95

England Pictorial
reprinted with conventional white borders

2003 (14 Oct.) Perf. 15 x 14. Two phosphor bands, except where indicated.

Printer: De La Rue in Gravure

				U/M	F/U
PEDW2	2nd	**CB Three Lions** (14.10.03)		40	45
PEDW2a		Three Lions, Layflat gum (.04)		1.00	1.00
PEDW1	1st	**2B Crowned Lion** (14.10.03)		55	60
PEDW1a		Short band at bottom		7.50	
PEDW1b		Layflat gum (.04)		1.25	1.25
PEDWE	E	**2B Oak** (14.10.03)		1.50	1.50
PEDW40	40p	**2B Oak** (11.5.04)		80	80
PEDW42	42p	**2B Oak** (7.05)		70	75
PEDW44	44p	**2B** Oak (28.3.06)		1.25	1.25
PEDW48	48p	**2B** Oak (27.3.07)		80	85
PEDW68	68p	**2B Tudor Rose** (24.6.03)		1.10	1.20
PEDW68a		Right band inset		4.00	
PEDW68b		Sideways print - Pane SP132 (Letters by Night book) (16.3.04)		1.25	1.25
PEDW68c		Tudor Rose, Layflat gum (.04)		1.75	1.75
PEDW72	72p	**2B Tudor rose** (28.3.06)		1.60	1.65
PEDW78	78p	**2B Tudor rose** (27.3.07)		1.10	1.15
		First Day Cover (2nd, 1st, E, 68p)			3.00
		First Day Cover (40p)			2.00
		First Day Cover (42p)			2.00

Printer: Walsall in Gravure

				U/M	F/U
PEWW2	2nd	**CB Three Lions** - Pane SP141 (Bronte sisters book) (24.2.05)		50	50
PEWW40	40p	**2B Oak** - Pane SP141 (Bronte sisters book) (24.2.05)		80	80
PEWW42	42p	**2B Oak** (5.4.05)		70	70
		First Day Cover (42p)			2.00

Printer: De La Rue in Lithography

				U/M	F/U
PEDW78A	78p	**2B Tudor rose** (8.11.07)		1.00	1.10

Printer: Joh. Enschedé in Lithography

				U/M	F/U
PEEW1	1st	**2B Crowned Lion** - Pane SP167 (British Army Uniforms) (20.9.07)		75	80

Northern Ireland Pictorial

  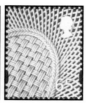

2001 (6 Mar.) - 03 Perf. 15 x 14. Two phosphor bands, except where indicated.

Printer: Walsall in Lithography

No.			U/M	F/U
PUW2	2nd	CB Giant's causeway (6.3.01)	40	45
PUW1	1st	2B Patchwork fields (6.3.01)	55	55
PUW1a		Missing phosphor	£35	
PUWE	E	2B Linen (6.3.01)	90	90
PUW65	65p	2B Parian china (6.3.01)	1.30	1.50
		First Day Cover (2nd, 1st, E, 65p)		3.00

Printer: Joh. Enschedé in Lithography

No.			U/M	F/U
PUE2	2nd	CB 4mm Giant's causeway - SP124		
		(Microcosmos book) (25.2.03)	90	90
PUE2a		Missing phosphor	£600	
PUE1	1st	2B Patchwork fields - SP124		
		(Microcosmos book) (25.2.03)	1.00	1.00
PUE1a		Missing phosphor	£700	
PUE1b		Right band inset	£20	

Printer: De La Rue in Lithography

No.			U/M	F/U
PUDE	E	2B Linen (15.10.02)	90	90
PUD68	68p	2B Parian china (4.7.02)	1.30	1.40
		First Day Cover (68p)		3.00
		First Day Cover (E)		3.00

Northern Ireland Pictorial
reprinted with conventional white borders

2003 (14 Oct.)-.Perf. 15 x 14. Two phosphor bands, except where indicated.

Printer: De La Rue in Lithography

No.			U/M	F/U
PUDW2	2nd	CB Giant's causeway (14.10.03)	35	35
PUDW1	1st	2B Patchwork fields (14.10.03)	50	55
PUDWE	E	2B Linen (14.10.03)	1.50	1.55
PUDW40	40p	2B Linen (11.5.04)	70	70
PUDW42	42p	2B Linen (7.05)	75	75
PUDW42	44p	2B Linen (28.3.06)	1.25	1.30
PUDW68	68p	2B Parian china (14.10.03)	1.20	1.20
PUDW72	72p	2B Parian china (28.3.06)	1.75	1.75
PUDW78	78p	2B Parian china (8.11.07)	1.00	1.10
		First Day Cover (2nd, 1st, E, 68p)		3.00
		First Day Cover (40p)		3.00

Printer: Walsall in Lithography

No.			U/M	F/U
PUWW42	42p	2B Linen (5.4.05)	70	70
		First Day Cover (42p)		4.00

Printer: De La Rue in Gravure

No.			U/M	F/U
PUDW48	48p	2B Linen (27.3.07)	75	75
PUDW72	78p	2B Parian china (27.3.07)	1.10	1.15

Printer: Joh. Enschedé in Lithography

No.			U/M	F/U
PUEW1	1st	2B Patchwork fields - Pane SP167		
		(British Army Uniforms) (20.9.07)	75	80

Scotland Pictorial

 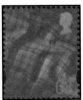

1999 (8 June) - Perf. 15 x 14. Two phosphor bands, except where indicated.

Scotland Pictorial
reprinted with conventional white borders

2003 (14 Oct.) - Perf. 15 x 14. Two phosphor bands, except where indicated.

Printer: Walsall in Gravure

No.		Description	U/M	F/U
PSW2	2nd	CB Flag of St. Andrew - Sheets (8.6.99)	45	45
PSW2a		Short band at bottom	1.20	
PSW1	1st	2B Lion of Scotland - Sheets (8.6.99)	60	60
PSW1a		Short bands at top	1.10	
PSW1b		Left band inset	£12	
PSW1c		Right band inset	7.50	
PSWE	E	2B Thistle - Sheets (8.6.99)	85	85
PSWEa		Short band at bottom	17.50	
PSWEb		Left band inset	£20	
PSWEc		Right band inset	£20	
PSW64	64p	2B Tartan - Sheets (8.6.99)	4.00	4.00
PSW65	65p	2B Tartan - Sheets (25.4.00)	1.80	1.80
PSW65a		Short bands at top	17.50	
PSW65b		Short bands at top, right band inset	£25	
PSW65c		Right band inset	£15	
		First Day Cover (2nd, 1st, E, 64p)		3.00
		First Day Cover (65p)		3.00

Printer: Questa in Gravure

No.		Description	U/M	F/U
PSQ2	2nd	CB Flag of St. Andrew (4.8.00)	1.00	1.00
PSQ2a		Pane SP103 (Life of the Century book) (4.8.00)	50	
PSQ1	1st	2B Lion of Scotland (22.10.01)	1.00	1.10
PSQ1a		Short bands at top	5.00	
PSQ1b		Short bands at top, left band inset	1.25	
PSQ1c		Left band inset	8.00	
PSQ1d		Pane SP115 (Unseen & unheard book) (22.10.01)	1.00	
PSQE	E	2B Thistle (22.10.01)	1.25	1.25
PSQEa		Short bands at top	5.00	
PSQEb		Left band inset	8.00	
PSQEc		Pane SP115 (Unseen & unheard book) (22.10.01)	1.25	
PSQ65	65p	2B Tartan (4.8.00)	2.75	2.75
PSQ65a		Left band inset	£20	
PSQ65b		Pane SP103 (Life of the Century book) (4.8.00)	1.80	

Printer: De La Rue in Gravure

No.		Description	U/M	F/U
PSD2	2nd	CB Flag of St. Andrew (5.6.02)	45	40
PSD2a		Flag of St. Andrew (Thick '2nd') (18.7.03)	45	
PSD1	1st	2B Lion of Scotland (5.6.02)	70	70
PSD1a		Lion of Scotland (Thick '1st') (10.9.03)	70	
PSD68	68p	2B Tartan (4.7.02)	1.30	1.15
		First Day Cover (2nd, 1st)		3.00
		First Day Cover (68p)		3.00

Printer: De La Rue in Gravure

No.		Description	U/M	F/U
PSDW2	2nd	CB Flag of St Andrew (14.10.03)	35	35
PSDW2a		Flag of St Andrew, Sideways print from Letters by Night prestige book (16.3.04)	65	65
PSDW2b		Flag of St Andrew. Coarse screen from Scottish Parliament min. sheet (5.10.04)	1.00	1.25
PSDW2c		Pane SP156 (World of Invention) (1.3.07)	70	75
PSDW1	1st	2B Lion of Scotland (14.10.03)	55	60
PSDW1a		Lion of Scotland. Thicker neck on bandeau Scottish Parliament min. sheet (5.10.04)	65	1.00
PSDWE	E	2B Thistle (14.10.03)	1.50	1.55
PSDW40	40p	2B Thistle (11.5.04)	70	80
PSDW40a		Thistle. Coarse screen from Scottish Parliament min. sheet (5.10.04)	90	1.10
PSDW42	42p	2B Thistle	65	70
PSDW44	44p	2B Thistle (28.3.06)	1.25	1.30
PSDW44	48p	2B Thistle (27.3.07)	80	85
PSDW68	68p	2B Tartan (14.10.03)	1.20	1.15
PSDW68a		Right band inset	5.00	
PSDW72	72p	2B Tartan (28.3.06)	1.75	1.80
PSDW78	78p	2B Tartan (27.3.07)	1.10	1.15
		First Day Cover (2nd, 1st, E, 68p)		3.00
		First Day Cover (40p)		3.00
		First Day Cover (42p)		3.00

Printer: Walsall in Gravure

No.		Description	U/M	F/U
PSWW42	42p	2B Thistle (5.4.05)	70	70
		First Day Cover (42p)		3.00

Printer: De La Rue in Lithography

No.		Description	U/M	F/U
PSDW78	78p	2B Tartan (8.11.07)	1.00	1.10

Printer: Joh. Enschedé in Lithography

No.		Description	U/M	F/U
PSEW1	1st	2B Lion of Scotland - Pane SP167 (British Army Uniforms) (20.9.07)	75	80

Wales Pictorial

1999 (8 June) -03 Perf. 15 x 14. Two phosphor bands, except where indicated.

Printer: Walsall in Gravure

			U/M	F/U
PWW2	2nd	CB Leek (8.6.99)	45	45
PWW2a		RB Leek from Trees prestige book		
		(18.9.00)	1.70	1.70
PWW2b		Right band inset	6.00	
PWW1	1st	2B Dragon(8.6.99)	55	65
PWWE	E	2B Daffodil (8.6.99)	1.00	1.00
PWW64	64p	2B Feathers (8.6.99)	3.60	3.60
PWW65	65p	2B Feathers (25.4.00)	1.70	1.70

Printer: De La Rue in Gravure

			U/M	F/U
PWD2	2nd	CB Leek (28.05.03)	45	45
PWD1	1st	2B Dragon (4.3.03)	60	60
PWD68	68p	2B Feathers (4.7.02)	1.10	1.20

Wales Pictorial
reprinted with conventional white borders

2003 (14 Oct.) - Perf. 15 x 14. Two phosphor bands, except where indicated.

Printer: De La Rue in Gravure

			U/M	F/U
PWDW2	2nd	CB Leek (14.10.03)	40	50
PWDW1	1st	2B Dragon (14.10.03)	60	60
PWDWE	E	2B Daffodil (14.10.03)	1.50	1.55
PWDW40	40p	2B Daffodil (11.5.04)	80	90
PWDW42	42p	2B Daffodil	85	85
PWDW44	44p	2B Daffodil (28.3.06)	1.25	1.30
PWDW44a		Pane SP156 (World of Invention) (1.3.07)	70	75
PWDW48	48p	2B Daffodil (27.3.07)	80	85
PWDW68	68p	2B Feathers (14.10.03)	1.10	1.20
PWDW72	72p	2B Feathers (28.3.06)	1.75	1.80
PWDW78	78p	2B Feathers (27.3.07)	1.10	1.15

Printer: Walsall in Gravure

			U/M	F/U
PWWW42	42p	2B Daffodil (5.4.05)	75	75

Printer: De La Rue in Lithography

			U/M	F/U
PWDW78	78p	2B Feathers (8.11.07)	1.00	1.10

Printer: Joh. Enschedé in Lithography

			U/M	F/U
PWEW1	1st	2B Dragon - Pane SP167 (British Army Uniforms) (20.9.07)	75	80

Postage Dues

Please note - *watermarks are illustrated as seen from the back of the stamp.*

Block Cypher Watermark
(sideways)   (sideways-inverted)

                                                   1924

(July) - 36 Wmk. Block Cypher (sideways). Perf. 14 x 15
Printer: Waterlow & Sons in Typo
Printer: Harrison & Sons in Typo (from 1934)

No.			U/M	M/M	F/U
P9	½d	**Emerald** (6.25)	1.30	40	20
P9a		Wmk. sideways-inverted	2.25	1.00	1.50
P10	1d	**Carmine** (4.25)	1.30	40	15
P10a		Wmk. sideways-inverted	-	-	£10
P11	1½d	**Chestnut** (10.24)	£75	£25	14.50
P11a		Wmk. sideways-inverted	-	-	£57
P12	2d	**Agate** (7.24)	5.00	80	25
P12a		Wmk. sideways-inverted	-	-	£12
P13	3d	**Violet** (10.24)	6.00	1.00	20
P13a		Wmk. sideways-inverted	£13	5.00	1.40
P13b		Printed on gummed side	£115	£70	
P14	4d	**Grey green** (10.24)	£27	8.50	2.25
P14a		Wmk. sideways-inverted	£40	£25	
P15	5d	**Bistre brown** (1.31)	£80	£24	£20
P16	1s	**Deep blue** (9.24)	£21	4.50	40
P16a		Wmk. sideways-inverted	-	-	£16
P17	2s 6d	**Purple** on yellow (10.24)	£185	£30	50
P17a		Wmk. sideways-inverted	-	-	£12
		Set of 9	£375	£95	£35

Experimental Block Cypher Watermark

1924 - 25 (?) Wmk. Experimental Block Cypher (sideways). Perf. 14 x 15
Printers: Waterlow & Sons in Typo on Experimental paper.

No.			U/M	M/M	F/U
P18	3d	**Violet**	£65	£40	£40

Royal Cypher Watermark
(sideways)   (sideways-inverted)

1914 (20 April) Wmk. Royal Cypher (sideways). Perf. 14 x 15
Printer: Somerset House in Typo (½d, 1d, 2d, 5d and 1s)
Printer: Harrison & Sons in Typo (½d - 5d and 1d chalky)

No.			U/M	M/M	F/U
P1	½d	**Emerald**	80	40	30
P1a		Wmk. sideways-inverted	1.20	60	30
P2	1d	**Carmine**	1.00	35	25
P2a		Wmk. sideways-inverted	90	35	50
P2b		Pale carmine	1.00	40	40
P2c		Wmk. sideways-inverted	1.80	60	90
P2d		Carmine. Chalky paper (1924)	7.50	3.50	3.00
P3	1½d	**Chestnut** (1923)	£90	£30	£11
P3a		Wmk. sideways-inverted	£95	£35	£14
P4	2d	**Agate**	1.00	30	25
P4a		Wmk. sideways-inverted	1.25	50	25
P5	3d	**Violet** (1918)	14.00	4.25	50
P5a		Wmk. sideways-inverted	16.00	6.50	45
P5b		Bluish violet	13.50	3.50	1.75
P5c		Wmk. sideways-inverted	£25	8.00	3.50
P6	4d	**Grey green** (1921)	£80	£17	£5
P6a		Wmk. sideways-inverted	£75	£20	5.50
P7	5d	**Bistre brown**	8.50	3.50	1.50
P7a		Wmk. sideways-inverted	£25	£15	£15
P8	1s	**Bright blue** (1915)	£80	18.50	2.50
P8a		Wmk. sideways-inverted	£75	£20	3.50
P8b		Deep bright blue	£80	18.50	2.50
P8c		Wmk. sideways-inverted	£75	£13	4.00
		Set of 8	£295	£65	£21

Multiple Crown E8R Watermark

1936 (Nov) - 37 Wmk. Multiple Crown E8R (sideways). Perf. 14 x 15
Printers: Harrison & Sons in Typo

P19	½d	**Emerald** (6.37)	6.00	5.00	5.50
P20	1d	**Carmine** (5.37)	1.00	70	1.00
P21	2d	**Agate** (5.37)	5.50	4.50	4.50
P22	3d	**Violet** (3.37)	1.50	1.00	1.50
P23	4d	**Grey green** (12.36)	£18	£12	£15
P24	5d	**Bistre brown** (11.36)	£35	£15	£24
P24a		Yellow brown (1937)	17.50	9.50	£22
P25	1s	**Deep blue** (12.36)	7.00	4.50	6.00
P26	2s 6d	**Purple** on yellow (5.37)	£195	£65	10.25
		Set of 8	£280	£90	£75

Multiple Crown GVIR Watermark
(sideways)   (sideways-inverted)

1937 - 50 Wmk. Multiple Crown G^{VI}R (sideways). Perf. 14 x 15
Printers: Harrison & Sons in Typo

P27	½d	**Emerald** (1938)	7.00	4.50	4.00
P28	1d	**Carmine** (1938)	1.50	70	20
P28a		Wmk. sideways-inverted	-	-	£12
P29	2d	**Agate** (1938)	1.00	70	25
P29a		Wmk. sideways-inverted	-	-	£12
P30	3d	**Violet** (1938)	5.00	3.00	20
P30a		Wmk. sideways-inverted	-	-	£12
P31	4d	**Grey green**	£55	£14	5.50
P31a		Wmk. sideways-inverted	-	-	£20
P32	5d	**Yellow brown** (1938)	6.75	3.00	60
P32a		Wmk. sideways-inverted	-	-	7.50
P33	1s	**Bright blue**	£42	£14	1.00
P33a		Wmk. sideways-inverted	-	-	£10
P34	2s 6d	**Purple** on yellow (1938)	£48	£12	1.50
		Set of 8	£160	£45	10.50

1951 (6 June) - 54 New Colours. Wmk. Multiple Crown G^{VI}R (sideways).
Perf. 14 x 15

P35	½d	**Orange** (18.9.51)	3.50	1.50	3.00
P36	1d	**Violet blue** (6.6.51)	1.50	70	50
P36a		Wmk. sideways-inverted	-		£28
P37	1½d	**Green** (11.2.52)	1.00	50	1.75
P37a		Wmk. sideways-inverted	9.00	4.00	£9
P38	4d	**Blue** (14.8.51)	£22	£12	£10
P38a		Wmk. sideways-inverted	-	-	£115
P39	1s	**Bistre brown** (6.12.51)	£16	9.00	2.50
P39a		Wmk. sideways-inverted	£2000	-	
		Set of 5	£39	£21	£16

Tudor Crown Watermark
(sideways)   (sideways-inverted)

1954 (Nov.) - 55 Wmk. Tudor Crown (sideways). Perf. 14 x 15

P40	½d	**Orange** (8.6.55)	7.00	7.00	7.50
P40a		Wmk. sideways-inverted	£15	£21	£22
P41	2d	**Agate** (28.7.55)	£45	£29	£16
P42	3d	**Violet** (4.5.55)	£30	£21	£26
P43	4d	**Blue** (14.7.55)	£20	£16	£15
P43a		Imperf. pair	£195		
P44	5d	**Yellow brown** (19.5.55)	£15	£13	£13
P45	2s 6d	**Purple** on yellow (11.54)	£50	£19	5.50
P45a		Wmk. sideways-inverted	-	-	£140
		Set of 6	£130	£85	£80

St. Edward's Crown Watermark
(sideways)   (sideways-inverted)

Multiple Crown Watermark
(sideways)   (sideways-inverted)

1955 (22 Nov.) - 58 Wmk. St. Edward's Crown (sideways). Perf. 14 x 15

No.			U/M	M/M	F/U
246	½d	**Orange** (16.7.56)	4.00	2.50	4.50
P46a		Wmk. sideways-inverted	£12	£10	£14
247	1d	**Violet blue** (7.6.56)	2.20	1.80	1.00
248	1½d	**Green** (13.2.56)	£10	9.00	10.50
P48a		Wmk. sideways-inverted	£15	£10	£11
249	2d	**Agate** (22.5.56)	£18	£10	2.20
249a		Wmk. sideways-inverted Note 1			£1500
250	3d	**Violet** (5.3.56)	3.50	2.50	1.50
250a		Wmk. sideways-inverted	£30	£12	£25
251	4d	**Blue** (24.4.56)	£11	7.50	1.80
251a		Wmk. sideways-inverted	£25	£13	£21
252	5d	**Yellow brown** (23.5.56)	£12	8.00	1.50
253	1s	**Ochre** (22.11.55)	£35	£15	1.50
253a		Wmk. sideways-inverted	-	-	£120
254	2s 6d	**Purple** on yellow (23.6.57)	£120	£40	4.50
254a		Wmk. sideways-inverted	-	-	£120
255	5s	**Scarlet** on yellow (25.11.55)	£52	£21	£12
255a		Wmk. sideways-inverted	£130	£95	£90
		Set of 10	£235	£90	£34

Note 1 This was found in November 2007. One used copy is known.

1959 (24 March) - 71 Wmk. Multiple Crown (sideways). Perf. 14 x 15
A. Cream Paper (½d - 1s)

No.			U/M	M/M	F/U
P56	½d	**Orange** (8.10.61)	30	20	30
P57	1d	**Violet blue** (9.5.60)	30	20	15
P58	1½d	**Green** (5.10.60)	1.20	60	1.50
P59	2d	**Agate** (14.9.59)	2.00	1.25	50
P60	3d	**Violet** (24.3.59)	50	35	20
P61	4d	**Blue** (17.12.59)	50	35	25
P62	5d	**Yellow brown** (6.11.61)	70	60	50
P62a		Wmk. sideways-inverted	£24	£14	£18
P63	6d	**Purple** (29.3.62)	80	55	1.00
P64	1s	**Ochre** (11.4.60)	2.50	1.00	35
P65	2s 6d	**Purple** on yellow (11.5.61)	2.00	75	35
P65a		Wmk. sideways-inverted	3.50	3.50	2.00
P66	5s	**Scarlet** on yellow (8.5.61)	3.50	1.20	40
P66a		Wmk. sideways-inverted	6.00	3.00	3.00
P67	10s	**Blue** on yellow (2.9.63)	£10	4.00	2.40
P67a		Wmk. sideways-inverted	£20	£15	9.00
P68	£1	**Black** on yellow (2.9.63)	£19	£10	3.50

B. White Paper (½d - 1s)

No.			U/M	M/M	F/U
P69	½d	**Orange** (22.9.64)	10	5	20
P69a		Wmk. sideways-inverted	50	40	60
P70	1d	**Violet blue** (1.3.65)	10	5	10
P70a		Wmk. sideways-inverted	5.00	4.00	5.00
P71	2d	**Agate** (1.3.65)	50	35	20
P71a		Wmk. sideways-inverted	£13	£11	£11
P72	3d	**Violet** (1.6.64)	20	10	15
P72a		Wmk. sideways-inverted	1.25	1.00	95
P73	4d	**Blue** (3.3.64)	20	10	15
P73a		Wmk. sideways-inverted	-	-	£35
P74	5d	**Yellow brown** (9.6.64)	25	15	30
P74a		Wmk. sideways-inverted	2.90	1.90	1.50
P75	6d	**Purple** (30.1.64)	30	15	15
P75a		Wmk. sideways-inverted	£10	-	£35
P76	1s	**Ochre** (28.8.64)	70	40	15
P76a		Wmk. sideways-inverted	6.00	3.90	2.50
		Set of 13	£32	£19	£7.75

1968 (11 April) - 70 No watermark. Chalky paper. Perf. 14 x 15
A. Gum Arabic

No.			U/M	M/M	F/U
P77	2d	**Agate** (11.4.68)	30		50
P78	4d	**Blue** (25.4.68)	15		20

B. PVA Gum

No.			U/M	F/U
P79	**2d**	**Agate** (26.11.68)	60	
P80	**3d**	**Violet** (5.9.68)	15	25
P81	**5d**	**Orange brown** (3.1.69)	3.20	3.80
P82	**6d**	**Purple** (5.9.68)	60	70
P83	**1s**	**Ochre** (19.11.68)	1.20	1.10
		Set of 6	4.90	5.00

1968 (3 Oct.) - 70 Small Format 21 x 17mm. Chalky paper. Perf. 14 x 15
PVA Gum

No.			U/M	F/U
P84	**4d**	**Blue** (12.6.69)	5.00	5.00
P85	**8d**	**Red** (3.10.68)	40	50
		Set of 2	5.20	5.20

1970 (12 June) - 84 No watermark. Perf. 14 x 15
A. Original Coated Paper. PVA Gum

No.			U/M	F/U
P86	**½p**	**Light turquoise blue** (15.2.71)	10	20
P87	**1p**	**Crimson** (15.2.71)	10	20
P88	**2p**	**Green** (15.2.71)	15	20
P89	**3p**	**Bright blue** (15.2.71)	15	15
P90	**4p**	**Light sepia** (15.2.71)	15	10
P91	**5p**	**Pale violet** (15.2.71)	15	10
P92	**10p**	**Cerise** (12.6.70)	20	15
P93	**20p**	**Olive green** (12.6.70)	70	35
P94	**50p**	**Blue** (12.6.70)	1.40	45
P95	**£1**	**Black** (12.6.70)	3.00	65
		Set of 10	5.30	2.00
		Presentation Pack 36 *Contents: P86/95 (10v)*	£15	

B. Fluorescent Coated Paper. PVA Gum

No.			U/M	F/U
P96	**1p**	**Crimson** (10.74)	30	
P97	**3p**	**Bright blue** (10.74)	1.50	
P98	**5p**	**Pale violet** (2.74)	1.50	
P99	**10p**	**Cerise** (2.74)	£30	
P100	**20p**	**Olive green** (10.74)	£35	
P101	**£5**	**Black and orange** (2.4.73)	£17	

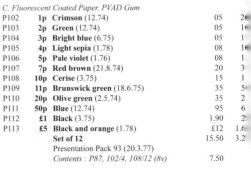

C. Fluorescent Coated Paper. PVAD Gum

No.			U/M	F/U
P102	**1p**	**Crimson** (12.74)	05	2
P103	**2p**	**Green** (12.74)	05	1
P104	**3p**	**Bright blue** (6.75)	05	1
P105	**4p**	**Light sepia** (1.78)	08	1
P106	**5p**	**Pale violet** (1.76)	08	1
P107	**7p**	**Red brown** (21.8.74)	20	3
P108	**10p**	**Cerise** (3.75)	15	1
P109	**11p**	**Brunswick green** (18.6.75)	35	5
P110	**20p**	**Olive green** (2.5.74)	35	2
P111	**50p**	**Blue** (12.74)	95	6
P112	**£1**	**Black** (3.75)	1.90	2
P113	**£5**	**Black and orange** (1.78)	£12	1.6
		Set of 12	15.50	3.2
		Presentation Pack 93 (20.3.77)		
		Contents : P87, 102/4, 108/12 (8v)	7.50	

D. Phosphor Coated Paper. PVAD Gum

No.			U/M	F/U
P114	**10p**	**Cerise** (6.80)	25	4
P115	**20p**	**Olive green** (6.80)	1.00	1.2

1982 (9 June) - 94 No watermark. Perf. 14 x 15
Fluorescent Coated Paper. PVAD Gum

No.			U/M	F/U
P116	1p	Crimson	20	25
P117	2p	Bright blue	20	5
P117a		Bright blue ACP/PVAD paper error	95.00	
P118	3p	Purple	20	25
P119	4p	Blue	20	25
P120	5p	Brown	20	25
P121	10p	Light brown	20	10
P122	20p	Sage green	30	20
P123	25p	Blue grey	40	50
P124	50p	Charcoal	95	95
P125	£1	Red	1.40	35
P126	£2	Turquoise	3.50	2.50
P127	£5	Dull orange	7.50	1.25
		Set of 12	£12.50	5.00
		Gutter pairs	£25	£10
		Presentation Pack 135	£24.50	

1994 (15 Feb.) - 94 OBA-Free non-phosphor paper PVA gum.
Perf. 15 x 14 (elliptical)
Printer: House of Questa in Lithography

No.			U/M	F/U
P128	1p	Yellow, orange-red and black	15	30
P129	2p	Magenta, purple and black	15	30
P130	5p	Yellow, brown and black	15	30
P131	10p	Yellow, green and black	30	30
P132	20p	Violet, emerald-green and black	1.00	1.00
P133	25p	Magenta, claret and black	1.50	1.00
P134	£1	Reddish pink, violet and black	5.50	5.50
P135	£1.20	Green, new blue and black	6.00	6.00
P136	£5	Green, charcoal and black	17.50	15.50
		Set of 9	27.50	28.50
		First Day Cover		£35
		Presentation Pack 32	£32	

Booklet Panes

Prices are for unmounted mint or fine used panes with full perforations all round plus selvedge. Lightly mounted panes at 25% less. Panes with clipped perfs are usually obtainable from 30% to 60% of the listed prices dependent on the number of stamps affected. Panes with cylinder numbers are worth considerably more, up to 150% in some cases.

King Edward VII

1904 (16 March) - 09 Wmk. Imperial Crown. Perf. 14 Printer: De La Rue

BP1	**6 x ½d**	**Yellow green** (6.06)	Upright	£75
BP1a			Inverted	£100

BP2	**5 x ½d**	**Yellow green** *plus* St. Andrew's		
BP2a		Cross label (6.06)	Upright	£450
			Inverted	£450

BP3	**6 x 1d**	**Scarlet**	Upright	£25
BP3a			Inverted	£40

1911 Wmk. Imperial Crown. Perf. 14 Printer: Harrison & Sons

BP4	**6 x ½d**	**Yellow green**	Upright	£80
BP4a			Inverted	£180
BP5	**5 x ½d**	**Yellow green** *plus* St. Andrew's		
		Cross label	Upright	£550
BP5a			Inverted	£550
BP6	**6 x 1d**	**Rose red**	Upright	£125
BP6a			Inverted	£125

King George V

1911 (Aug.) - 12 Wmk. Imperial Crown. Perf. 15 x 14. Die 1B

BP7	**6 x ½d**	**Green**	Upright	£75
BP7a			Inverted	£100
BP8	**6 x 1d**	**Carmine**	Upright	£75
BP8a			Inverted	£100
BP9	**6 x 1d**	**Scarlet** (6.12)	Upright	£175
BP9a			Inverted	£175
BP10		Aniline scarlet	Upright	£1800
BP10a			Inverted	£1800

King Edward VII & George V

1912 (Aug.) Wmk. Royal Cypher. Perf. 15 x 14. Die 1B

BP11	**6 x ½d**	**Green**	Upright	£300
BP11a			Inverted	£200
BP12	**6 x 1d**	**Scarlet**	Upright	£125
BP12a			Inverted	£125

1913 (April) - 24 Wmk. Royal Cypher. Perf. 15 x 14

BP13	**6 x ½d**	**Green**	Upright	£40
BP13a			Inverted	£40
BP14	**6 x 1d**	**Scarlet**	Upright	£40
BP14a			Inverted	£40
BP15	**6 x 1½d**	**Red brown** (10.18)	Upright	£50
BP15a			Inverted	£50

BP16	**4 x 1½d**	**Red brown** *plus* 2 x advert		
		labels (2.24)	Upright	£600
BP16a			Inverted	£600
BP17	**6 x 2d**	**Orange**. Die I (7.20)	Upright	£180
BP17a			Inverted	£180
BP18	**6 x 2d**	**Orange**. Die II(8.21)	Upright	£200
BP18a			Inverted	£200

1924 (Feb. - June) Wmk. Block Cypher. Perf. 15 x 14

BP19	**6 x ½d**	**Green**	Upright	£25
BP19a			Inverted	£25
BP20	**6 x 1d**	**Scarlet**	Upright	£25
BP20a			Inverted	£25
BP21	**6 x 1½d**	**Red brown**	Upright	£15
BP21a			Inverted	£20
BP22	**4 x 1½d**	**Red brown** *plus* 2 advert labels (6.24)	Upright	£200
BP22a			Inverted	£200

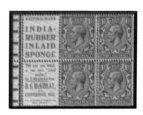

BP22b	**4 x 1½d**	**Red brown** *plus* 2 advert labels printed in green	Upright	£3500
BP22c	**4 x 1½d**	**Red brown** *plus* 2 advert labels printed in green	Inverted	£3500

1924 (Nov.) Wmk. Block Cypher (sideways). Perf. 15 x 14

BP23	**4 x 1½d**	**Red brown** *plus* 2 advert labels	Upright	£4000

1929 (May) Postal Union Congress. Wmk. Multiple Crown GvR.
Perf. 15 x 14

BP24	**6 x ½d**	**Green**	Upright	£70
BP24a			Inverted	£140
BP25	**6 x 1d**	**Scarlet**	Upright	£70
BP25a			Inverted	£140

BP26	**6 x 1½d**	**Red brown**	Upright	£30
BP26a			Inverted	£75
BP27	**4 x 1½d**	**Red brown** *plus* 2 advert labels	Upright	£275
BP27a			Inverted	£275

1935 (Jan) Photogravure. Wmk. Block Cypher. Perf. 15 x 14

A. Intermediate Format (stamps 18.3 x 22.2mm)

BP28	**6 x ½d**	**Green**	Upright	£150
BP28a			Inverted	£250
BP29	**6 x 1d**	**Scarlet**	Upright	£175
BP29a			Inverted	£225
BP30	**6 x 1½d**	**Red brown**	Upright	£80
BP30a			Inverted	£100
BP31	**4 x 1½d**	**Red brown** *plus* 2 advert labels	Upright	£600
BP31a			Inverted	£600

B. Small Format (stamps 18 x 21.7mm)

BP32	**6 x ½d**	**Green**	Upright	£40
BP32a			Inverted	£70
BP33	**6 x 1d**	**Scarlet**	Upright	£40
BP33a			Inverted	£70

BP34	**6 x 1½d**	**Red brown**	Upright	£20
BP34a			Inverted	£25

BP35	**4 x 1½d**	**Red brown** *plus* 2 advert labels	Upright	£140
BP35a			Inverted	£140

1935 (May) Silver Jubilee. Wmk. Multiple Crown GvR. Perf. 15 x 14

BP36	**4 x ½d**	**Green**	Upright	£30
BP36a			Inverted	£40

BP37	**4 x 1d**	**Scarlet**	Upright	£30
BP37a			Inverted	£45
BP38	**4 x 1½d**	**Red brown**	Upright	£10
BP38a			Inverted	£10

King Edward VIII

1936 (Oct.) Wmk. Multiple Crown E8R. Perf. 15 x 14

BP39	**6 x ½d**	**Green**	Upright	£15
BP39a			Inverted	£30
BP40	**6 x 1d**	**Scarlet**	Upright	£15
BP40a			Inverted	£30
BP41	**6 x 1½d**	**Red brown**	Upright	8.00
BP41a			Inverted	8.00
BP42	**2 x 1½d**	**Red brown**	Upright	£20
BP42a			Inverted	£20
BP43	**4 x 1½d**	**Red brown** *plus* 2 advert labels	Upright	£70
BP43a			Inverted	£70

Booklet Panes
No.   U/M   No.   # King George VI
                                                                  U/M

King George VI

1937 (May) - 38 Dark colours. Wmk. Multiple Crown GVIR. Perf. 15 x 14

BP44	6 x ½d	**Green**	Upright	£25
BP44a			Inverted	£45
BP45	2 x ½d	**Green** (2.38)	Upright	£50
BP45a			Inverted	£50
BP46	6 x 1d	**Scarlet**	Upright	£40
BP46a			Inverted	£175
BP47	2 x 1d	**Scarlet** (2.38)	Upright	£50
BP47a			Inverted	£50

BP48	6 x 1½d	**Red brown**	Upright	£20
BP48a			Inverted	£50
BP49	2 x 1½d	**Red brown** (1.38)	Upright	£30
BP49a			Inverted	£30
BP50	4 x 1½d	**Red brown** *plus* 2 advert labels	Upright	£125
BP50a			Inverted	£125
BP51	6 x 2d	**Orange**	Upright	£70
BP51a			Inverted	£300
BP52	6 x 2½d	**Ultramarine**	Upright	£50
BP52a			Inverted	£225

1940 (June) Wmk. Multiple Crown GVIR (sideways). Perf. 15 x 14.
Selvedge at top or bottom.   Top Bottom

BP53	4 x ½d	**Green** (2.38)	Upright	£45
BP53a			Inverted	£45
BP54	4 x 1d	**Scarlet**	Upright	£60
BP54a			Inverted	£60

1942 (March) - 47 Light colours. Wmk. Multiple Crown GVIR. Perf. 15 x 14

BP55	6 x ½d	**Pale green**	Upright	£20
BP55a			Inverted	£25
BP55b	4 x ½d	**Pale green** Selvedge at top or bottom		£1200
BP56	2 x ½d	**Pale green** (12.47)	Upright	£20
BP56a	4 x 1d	**Pale scarlet** Selvedge at top or bottom		£1200
BP57	2 x 1d	**Pale scarlet** (12.47)		£20
BP57a	4 x 1½d	**Pale red brown** Selvedge at top or bottom		£1200
BP58	2 x 1½d	**Pale red brown** (12.47)		£20
BP59	6 x 2d	**Pale orange**	Upright	£17
BP59a			Inverted	£25
BP60	6 x 2½d	**Light ultramarine**	Upright	£20
BP60a			Inverted	£25

1951 (May) - 54 New colours. Wmk. Multiple Crown GVIR. Perf. 15 x 14

BP61	6 x ½d	**Pale orange**		4.00
BP61a			Inverted	5.00
BP62	4 x ½d	**Pale orange**. Selvedge at top		£10
BP62a			Inverted	£10
BP62b		Selvedge at bottom		£10
BP63	2 x ½d	**Pale orange**		£12
BP64	6 x 1d	**Ultramarine** (1.53)		£20
			Inverted	£30
BP65	4 x 1d	**Ultramarine**. Selvedge at top		£10
BP65a		Selvedge at bottom		£10
BP66	2 x 1d	**Ultramarine**		£10

BP67	3 x 1d	**Ultramarine** *plus* 3 "PAPER RATE...." labels (17mm high) (3.52)		£10
BP67a			Inverted	£10
BP68	3 x 1d	**Ultramarine** *plus* 3 "PAPER RATE...." labels (15mm high) (3.53)		£70
BP68a			Inverted	£70
BP69	3 x 1d	**Ultramarine** *plus* 3 advert labels (1.54)		£60
BP69a			Inverted	£60
BP70	6 x 1½d	**Pale green** (3.52)		6.00
BP70a			Inverted	£20
BP71	4 x 1½d	**Pale green**. Selvedge at top		£10
BP71a			Inverted	£12
BP71b		Selvedge at bottom		£10
BP72	2 x 1½d	**Pale green**		£15
BP73	6 x 2d	**Pale red brown**		£10
BP73a			Inverted	£40
BP74	6 x 2½d	**Pale scarlet**	Inverted	5.00
BP74a				5.00

Queen Elizabeth II

Prices are for unmounted mint or fine used panes with full perforations all round plus selvedge. Lightly mounted panes at 25% less. Panes with clipped perfs are usually obtainable from 30% to 60% of the listed prices dependent on the number of stamps affected. Panes with cylinder numbers are worth considerably more, up to 150% in some cases.
Watermarks are illustrated upright from the back of the stamps.

Watermark Tudor Crown

1953 (2 Sept.) - 55   Perf. 15 x 14

No.				U/M
BP75	6 x ½d	Orange (3.54)	Upright	3.00
BP75a			Inverted	3.00
BP76	4 x ½d	Orange. (7.54)	Upright	6.00
BP76a			Inverted	6.50
BP77	2 x ½d	Orange	Upright	3.00
BP78	6 x 1d	Ultramarine (3.54)	Upright	22.50
BP78a			Inverted	37.50
BP79	4 x 1d	Ultramarine (7.54)	Upright	9.00
BP79a			Inverted	£25
BP80	2 x 1d	Ultramarine	Upright	3.00
BP81	3 x 1d	Ultramarine plus 3		
		"PAPER RATE...." labels (3.54)	Upright	£250
BP81a			Inverted	£250

BP82	3 x 1d	**Ultramarine** *plus* 3		
		"PLEASE POST EARLY...."		
		labels (4.54)	Upright	£25
BP82a			Inverted	£25
BP83	3 x 1d	**Ultramarine** *plus* 3		
		"PLEASE PACK YOUR PARCELS...."		
		labels (1.55)	Upright	£25
BP83a			Inverted	£25

BP84	6 x 1½d	**Green** (5.53)	Upright	2.50
BP84a			Inverted	2.50
BP85	4 x 1½d	**Green** (7.54)	Upright	7.50
BP85a			Inverted	6.50
BP86	2 x 1½d	**Green**	Upright	3.00
BP87	6 x 2d	**Red brown** (3.54)	Upright	£25
BP87a			Inverted	£125
BP88	6 x 2½d	**Carmine red**	Upright	3.50
BP88a			Inverted	2.50

Watermark St. Edwards Crown

1955 (Aug.) - 59   Perf. 15 x 14

BP89	6 x ½d	**Orange** (9.55)	Upright	1.50
BP89a			Inverted	1.75
BP90	4 x ½d	**Orange** (7.56)	Upright	6.00
BP90a			Inverted	6.00
BP91	2 x ½d	**Orange** (11.57)	Upright	12.50
BP92	6 x 1d	**Ultramarine** (3.54)	Upright	3.00
BP92a			Inverted	3.50
BP93	4 x 1d	**Ultramarine** (7.54)	Upright	6.00
BP93a			Inverted	6.00
BP94	2 x 1d	**Ultramarine** (11.57)	Upright	12.50
BP95	3 x 1d	Ultramarine *plus* 3		
		'PLEASE PACK YOUR PARCELS....'		
		labels	Upright	£10
BP95a			Inverted	£10
BP96	6 x 1½d	**Green**	Upright	2.50
BP96a			Inverted	1.50
BP97	4 x 1½d	**Green** (7.56)	Upright	6.00
BP97a			Inverted	6.50
BP98	2 x 1½d	**Green**	Upright	12.50

BP99	6 x 2d	**Red brown** (9.55)	Upright	22.50
BP99a			Inverted	£65
BP100	6 x 2d	**Light red brown** (1.57)	Upright	12.50
BP100a			Inverted	£30
BP101	6 x 2½d	**Carmine red** (9.55)	Upright	2.00
BP101a			Inverted	1.5
BP102	6 x 3d	**Violet** (10.57)	Upright	3.50
BP102a			Inverted	7.00
BP103	4 x 3d	**Violet** (4.59)	Upright	£15
BP103a			Inverted	£15

Watermark Multiple Crowns

1958 (Nov.) - 65   Perf. 15 x 14

Cream paper

BP104	6 x ½d	**Orange**	Upright	3.50
BP104a			Inverted	3.50
BP105	4 x ½d	**Orange** (8.59)	Upright	3.00
BP105a			Inverted	3.00
BP105b			Sideways left	8.00
BP105c			Sideways right	8.00

BP106	6 x 1d Ultramarine	Upright	3.50
BP106a		Inverted	3.50
BP107	4 x 1d Ultramarine (8.59)	Upright	3.00
BP107a		Inverted	3.00
BP107b		Sideays left	8.00
BP107c		Sideways right	8.00
BP108	6 x 1½d Green (12.58)	Upright	8.50
BP108a		Inverted	8.50
BP109	4 x 1½d Green (8.59)	Upright	3.00
BP109a		Inverted	3.00
BP109b		Sideways left	£40
BP109c		Sideways right	£35
BP110	6 x 2d Light red brown (4.61)	Upright	£60
BP110a		Inverted	£625
BP111	6 x 2½d Carmine red	Upright	8.00
BP111a		Inverted	£20
BP112	6 x 3d Violet	Upright	1.50
BP112a		Inverted	2.00
BP113	4 x 3d Violet	Upright	£15
BP113a		Inverted	£15
BP113b		Sideways left	5.00
BP113c		Sideways right	5.00

White paper

BP114	6 x ½d Orange (6.62)	Upright	£12
BP114a		Inverted	£12
BP115	4 x ½d Orange	Sideways left	8.00
BP115a		Sideways right	8.00

BP116	2 x ½d Orange *plus* 2 x 2½d		
	Carmine red (7.64)	Sideways left	1.25
BP116a		Sideways right	1.25
BP117	6 x 1d Ultramarine (4.62)	Upright	4.75
BP117a		Inverted	6.00
BP118	4 x 1d Ultramarine (6.62)	Sideways left	8.00
BP118a		Sideways right	8.00
BP119	2 x 1d Ultramarine *plus* 2 x 3d		
	Violet (1d at left)(8.65)	Sideways left	4.00
BP119a		Sideways right	4.00
BP120	2 x 3d Violet *plus* 2 x 1d		
	Ultramarine (1d at right)(8.65)	Sideways left	4.00
BP120a		Sideways right	4.00
BP121	6 x 1½d Green (4.62)	Upright	£16
BP121a		Inverted	£25
BP122	4 x 1½d Green	Sideways left	£40
BP122a		Sideways right	£40
BP123	6 x 2½d Carmine red (4.62)	Upright	£25
BP123a		Inverted	37.50
BP124	6 x 3d Violet	Upright	2.75
BP124a		Inverted	3.25
BP125	4 x 3d Violet (6.62)	Sideways left	5.00
BP125a		Sideways right	5.00
BP126	6 x 4d Deep ultramarine (6.65)	Upright	5.00
BP126a		Inverted	5.50
BP127	4 x 4d Deep ultramarine (8.65)	Sideways left	2.50
BP127a		Sideways right	2.50

Chalky paper

BP128	3 x ½d Orange *plus* 1 x 2½d		
	Carmine red (7.63)	Upright	8.00
BP128a		Inverted	8.00

| BP129 | 4 x 2½d Carmine red (7.63) | Upright | 1.00 |
| BP129a | | Inverted | 1.00 |

Graphite Lined Issue
Watermark Multiple Crowns

1959 (Aug.) Perf. 15 x 14

BP130	6 x ½d Orange	Upright	£50
BP130a		Inverted	£15
BP131	6 x 1d Ultramarine	Upright	£15
BP131a		Inverted	12.50
BP132	6 x 1½d Green	Upright	£425
BP132a		Inverted	£160
BP133	6 x 2½d Carmine red	Upright	£65
BP133a		Inverted	£275
BP134	6 x 3d Violet	Upright	3.00
BP134a		Inverted	3.00

Watermark Multiple Crowns
Green Phosphor

1960 (Aug.) - 67 Perf. 15 x 14

BP135	6 x ½d Orange (2B)	Upright	£15
BP135a		Inverted	£35
BP136	6 x 1d Ultramarine (2B)	Upright	£15
BP136a		Inverted	£35
BP137	6 x 1½d Green (2B)	Upright	17.50
BP137a		Inverted	67.50
BP138	6 x 2½d Carmine red	Upright	£65
BP138a		Inverted	£950
BP139	6 x 3d Violet (2B)	Upright	10.50
BP139a		Inverted	10.50

Watermark Multiple Crowns
Blue Phosphor - Cream Paper

No.				U/M
BP140	6 x ½d	Orange	Upright	3.00
BP140a			Inverted	5.50
BP141	4 x ½d	Orange	Sideways left	£35
BP141a			Sideways right	£35
BP142	6 x 1d	Ultramarine (2B) (6.63)	Upright	3.50
BP142a			Inverted	4.00
BP143	4 x 1d	Ultramarine	Sideways left	£12
BP143a			Sideways right	£12
BP144	6 x 1½d	Green (2B) (7.64)	Upright	7.50
BP144a			Inverted	£55
BP145	4 x 1½d	Green	Sideways left	£40
BP145a			Sideways right	£40
BP146	6 x 2½d	Carmine red (2B)	Upright	£70
BP146a			Inverted	£1000
BP147	6 x 2½d	Carmine red (LB)	Upright	£70
BP147a			Inverted	£160
BP148	6 x 3d	Violet	Upright	5.00
BP148a			Inverted	5.00
BP149	4 x 3d	Violet	Sideways left	£15
BP149a			Sideways right	£15

Watermark Multiple Crowns
Blue Phosphor - Whiter Paper

BP150	6 x ½d	Orange	Upright	£10
BP150a			Inverted	12.50
BP151	4 x ½d	Orange	Sideways left	37.50
BP151a			Sideways right	£35
BP152	6 x 1d	Ultramarine (2B) (6.63)	Upright	6.00
BP152a			Inverted	6.00
BP153	4 x 1d	Ultramarine	Sideways left	£12
BP153a			Sideways right	£12
BP154	2 x 1d	Ultramarine *plus* 2 x 3d		
		Violet (1d at left)	Sideways left	£60
BP154a			Sideways right	£60
BP155	2 x 3d	Violet (1d at left) *plus* 2 x 1d		
		Ultramarine	Sideways left	£60
BP155a			Sideways right	£60
BP156	6 x 1½d	Green (2B) (7.64)	Upright	£75
BP156a			Inverted	£175
BP157	4 x 1½d	Green	Sideways left	£40
BP157a			Sideways right	£40
BP158	6 x 2½d	Carmine red (LB)	Upright	£60
BP158a			Inverted	£175
BP159	6 x 3d	Violet	Upright	4.50
BP159a			Inverted	4.50
BP160	4 x 3d	Violet	Sideways left	18.50
BP160a			Sideways right	18.50
BP161	6 x 4d	Deep ultramarine (2B) (6.65)	Upright	£10
BP161a			Inverted	12.50
BP162	4 x 4d	Deep ultramarine	Sideways left	8.00
BP162a			Sideways right	8.00

Watermark Multiple Crowns
Violet Phosphor 8mm Bands

— 13mm —

BP163	6 x 1d	Ultramarine	Upright	6.00
BP163a			Inverted	6.00
BP164	2 x 1d	Ultramarine *plus* 2 x 3d		
		Violet (LB) (1d at left)	Sideways left	10.50
BP164a			Sideways right	10.50
BP165	2 x 3d	Violet (RB) (1d at left) *plus* 2 x 1d		
		Ultramarine	Sideways left	10.50
BP165a			Sideways right	10.50
BP166	2 x 3d	Violet (LB) *plus* 4 x 3d Violet (RB)	Upright	£20
BP166a			Inverted	£95
BP167	6 x 4d	Deep ultramarine (2B)	Upright	4.50
BP167a			Inverted	4.50
BP168	4 x 4d	Deep ultramarine Photogravure		
		phosphor	Sideways left	3.50
BP168a		Photogravure phosphor	Sideways right	3.50
BP168b		Typo phosphor	Sideways left	£50
BP168c		Typo phosphor	Sideways right	£50

Watermark Multiple Crowns
Violet Phosphor 9.5mm Bands

—11.5mm—

BP169	6 x 1d	Ultramarine	Upright	5.00
BP169a			Inverted	5.00
BP170	2 x 1d	Ultramarine *plus* 2 x 3d		
		Violet (2B) (1d at left)	Sideways left	4.50
BP170a			Sideways right	4.50
BP171	2 x 3d	Violet (2B) (1d at left) *plus* 2 x 1d		
		Ultramarine	Sideways left	4.50
BP171a			Sideways right	4.50
BP172	6 x 3d	Violet (CB)	Upright	6.00
BP172a			Inverted	£15
BP173	6 x 4d	Deep ultramarine (2B) (6.65)	Upright	2.50
BP173a			Inverted	2.50
BP174	4 x 4d	Deep ultramarine	Sideways left	1.50
BP174a			Sideways right	1.50

Pre-Decimal Machin Booklet Panes

1967 (Sept.) - 69 Machin series. No watermark. Perf. 15 x 14. Two phosphor bands, except where stated.

Gum Arabic (GA)

BP175	**6 x 4d**	**Sepia** (9.67)	8.00
BP175a		Missing phosphor	£20
BP175b		Deep olive brown (2.68)	9.00
BP175c		Missing phosphor	£22
BP176	**6 x 4d**	**Vermilion** (CB) (2.69)	£120

PVA

BP177	**6 x 1d**	**Olive** (3.68)	1.25
BP177a		Missing phosphor	£20
BP178	**4 x 1d**	**Olive** (CB) *plus* **2 x 4d** Sepia (CB) (9.68)	3.50
BP178a		Missing phosphor	£25

BP179	**4 x 1d**	**Olive** (CB) *plus* **2 x 4d** Vermilion (LB) (6.1.69)	3.00
BP179a		Missing phosphor	£150

BP180	**2 x 1d**	**Olive** (CB) *plus* **2 x 3d** Violet (1d at left) (4.68)	2.50
BP180a		Broad bands	£16
BP180b		Missing phosphor	£40

BP181	**2 x 1d**	**Olive** (CB) *plus* **2 x 3d** Violet (1d at right) (4.68)	2.50
BP181a		Broad bands	£12
BP181b		Missing phosphor	£40

BP182	**6 x 3d**	**Violet** (CB) (3.68)	£15
BP182a		Missing phosphor	£800
BP183	**6 x 4d**	**Deep Olive-brown** (2B) (3.68)	1.00
BP183a		Broad bands	£175
BP183b		Missing phosphor	£20
BP184	**6 x 4d**	**Deep olive** (CB) (9.68)	1.50
BP184a		Missing phosphor	£25

BP185	**4 x 4d**	**Deep Olive-sepia** (2B) (4.68)	1.00
BP185a		Broad bands	8.00
BP185b		Missing phosphor	8.00
BP186	**4 x 4d**	**Sepia** (CB) (9.68)	2.00
BP186a		Missing phosphor	

BP187	**2 x 4d**	**Sepia** (CB) *plus* 2 '£4,315....' labels (16.9.68)	2.50
BP187a		Missing phosphor	£70
BP188	**6 x 4d**	**Vermilion**, Head A (CB) (1.69)	2.00
BP188a		Missing phosphor	£40
BP188b		Pale vermillion	4.50
BP188c		Vermilion, Head B2	1.25
BP188d		Missing phosphor	£40
BP189	**4 x 4d**	**Vermilion** (CB) (3.69)	1.00
BP189a		Missing phosphor	£45
BP190	**2 x 4d**	**Vermilion** (CB) *plus* 2 '£4,315....' labels (3.69)	1.00
BP190a		Missing phosphor	£50

BP191	**6 x 5d**	**Deep blue** (2B) (11.68)	1.00
BP191a		Missing phosphor	£30
		First Day Cover (pane BP178)	2.25
		First Day Cover (pane BP170)	£12

Decimal Machin Booklet Panes

1971 (15 Feb.) - 74. Decimal Machin series. No watermark. Perf. 15 x 14.
Two 9.5mm phosphor bands except where stated.

OCP/PVA

MP1	**5 x ½p**	**Turquoise** (2B) *plus* 'B. Alan Ltd......' label	4.00	
MP1a		Missing phosphor	£300	

MP2	**5 x ½p**	**Turquoise** (2B) *plus* 'B. Alan Ltd......' blind label (17.9.71)	6.00	
MP3	**5 x ½p**	**Turquoise** (2B) *plus* 'Lick.....' label	3.75	
MP3a		Missing phosphor	£80	

MP4	**2 x ½p**	**Turquoise** (2B) *plus* **2 x 2p dark green** (2B) (½p below 2p)	3.75	
MP4a		Broad bands	£60	
MP4b		Missing phosphor	£300	
MP5	**2 x ½p**	**Turquoise** (2B) *plus* **2 x 2p dark green** (2B) (½p at right) (14.7.71)	7.50	
MP5a		Broad bands	£400	
MP5b		Missing phosphor	£400	

MP6	**2 x 1p**	**Crimson** (2B) *plus* **2 x 1½p black** (2B) (1p above 1½p)	3.75	
MP6a		Broad bands	£125	
MP7	**2 x 1p**	**Crimson** (2B) *plus* **2 x 1½p black** (2B) (1p at right) (14.7.71)	3.00	
MP7a		Broad bands	£225	

MP8	**4 x 2½p**	**Magenta** (CB) *plus* 2 x 'UNIFLO.....' labels	3.00	
MP8a		Missing phosphor	£275	
MP9	**4 x 2½p**	**Magenta** (CB) *plus* 2 x 'UNIFLO.....' blind labels	5.00	
MP9a		Missing phosphor	£250	
MP10	**5 x 2½p**	**Magenta** (CB) *plus* 'STICK.....' label	3.75	

MP11	**5 x 2½p**	**Magenta** (CB) *plus* 'STICK.....' blind label (17.9.71)	4.50	
MP12	**5 x 2½p**	**Magenta** (CB) *plus* 'TEAR OFF.....' label	3.75	
MP12a		Missing phosphor		

MP13	**2 x 2½p**	**Magenta** (LB) *plus* **4 x 3p ultramarine** (2B) (2½p at right)	3.50	
MP13a		Missing phosphor	£275	
MP13b		JET Phosphor		
MP14	**5 x 3p**	**Ultramarine** (2B) *plus* £4315.....' label (15.2.71)	1.50	
MP14a		Broad bands	£900	
MP14b		Missing phosphor	£300	

MP15	**5 x 3p**	**Ultramarine** (2B) *plus* £4315.....' blind label (23.7.71)	5.50	
MP16	**6 x 3p**	**Ultramarine** (2B)	3.50	
MP16a		Broad bands	£600	
MP16b		Missing phosphor	£200	
MP16c		JET Phosphor		

FCP/PVA

MP17	5 x ½p **Turquoise** (2B) *plus*	
	'LICK.....' blind label (17.9.71)	6.00

MP18	5 x ½p **Turquoise** (2B) *plus*	
	'MAKE YOUR LUCKY.....' blind label	
	(23.12.71)	2.00
MP18a	Missing phosphor	£525
MP18b	Thin paper	7.50
MP18c	JET Phosphor	
MP19	2 x½p **Turquoise** (2B) *plus* **2 x 2p** dark green	
	(2B) (½p at right) (6.10.71)	2.00
MP19a	Broad bands	£50
MP19b	Missing phosphor	£200
MP19c	JET Phosphor	
MP20	2 x 1p **Crimson** (2B) *plus* **2 x 1½p** black	
	(2B) (1p at right) (6.10.71)	2.00
MP20a	Broad bands	£120
MP20b	Missing phosphor	£300
MP20c	JET Phosphor	

MP21	4 x 2½p **Magenta** (CB) *plus* **2 x**	
	'DO YOU COLLECT.....' blind labels (23.12.71)	2.75
MP21a	Missing phosphor	£250
MP22	5 x 2½p **Magenta** (CB) *plus*	
	'TEAR OFF.....' blind label (17.9.71)	5.00
MP23	5 x 2½p **Magenta** (CB) *plus* 'STAMP COLLECTIONS.....'	
	blind label(23.12.71)	2.50
MP23a	Missing phosphor	£300
MP24	5 x 2½p **Magenta** Type I (CB) *plus*	
	'B. ALAN for.....' blind label (23.12.71)	2.50
MP24a	Missing phosphor	£30
MP25	5 x 2½p **Magenta** Type II (CB) *plus*	
	'B. ALAN for.....' blind label	£90
MP26	2 x 2½p **Magenta** (LB) *plus* **4 x 3p** ultramarine	
	(2B) (2½p at right) (17.9.71)	4.00
MP26a	Missing phosphor	£100
MP27	5 x 3p **Ultramarine** (2B) *plus* '£4315.....'	
	blind label (1.10.71)	2.25
MP27a	Missing phosphor	£300
MP27b	Thin paper	8.50
MP27c	Missing phosphor	£200

MP28	5 x 3p **Ultramarine** (CB) *plus*	
	blind label (14.11.73)	6.00

MP29	6 x 3p **Ultramarine** (2B) (17.9.71)	1.50
MP30	5 x 3½p **Olive-green** (2B) *plus* 'blind' label (14.11.73)	£10
MP30a	Missing phosphor	

FCP/PVAD

MP31	2 x ½p **Turquoise** (2B) *plus* **2 x 2p dark green**	
	(2B) (½p at right) (12.11.73)	60
MP31a	Broad bands	£28
MP32	2 x 1p **Crimson** (2B) *plus* **2 x 1½p black**	
	(2B) (1p at right) (12.11.73)	50
MP32a	Broad bands	£50
MP32b	Missing phosphor	£375
MP33	5 x 3p **Ultramarine** (CB) *plus* 'blind' label	
	(14.11.73)	3.00

MP34	5 x 3½p **Olive green** (2B) *plus* 'blind' label	
	(14.11.73)	1.50
MP34a	Missing phosphor	£30
MP35	5 x 3½p **Olive green** (CB) *plus* 'blind' label	
	(23.10.74)	1.50
MP35a	Miscut (label at top)	£12
MP35b	Missing phosphor	

MP36	5 x 4½p **Grey blue** (2B) *plus* blind label	
	(9.10.74)	2.00
MP36a	Missing phosphor	£400
MP36b	Phosphor under ink (white bands)	£50

Decimal Machin Booklet Panes

Important Note:

As these were not issued as a separate collectable item, these panes are therefore not priced; this listing is for reference purposes only.

1976 (3 Mar) - 95 Decimal Machin series. No watermark. Perf. 15 x 14.

Two phosphor bands or one CB except where stated. Panes are listed in order of paper/gum combination, size (panes of 4, 6, 10 etc.) and then in ascending order of face values, i.e. panes containing ½p are listed before panes containing 1p. There are two types of perforation used on the machine booklet panes and both are illustrated below. Usually the first pane listed has a single perforation hole extending into the Margin of the pane. Fully perforated margins are then listed within the grouping of that pane. Where a booklet pane exists in only one perf. type it is listed without perf. details.

All books are illustrated with the margins to the left. This means that all Vending (Machine) books show the Queen's portrait to the left; On Counter and Window books the Queen's portrait appears upright.

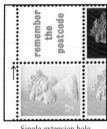 

Single extension hole   Perforated margin

Printed by Harrison in Photogravure

FCP/PVAD

Panes of 4

FP1	**2 x 1p**	**CB Crimson**, Type I and **8p CB** (short at top) **Rosine** (17.10.79)
FP1a		Perforated margin
FP1b		Miscut (8p at right)
FP2		Chambon printing (1p crimson, Type II) (4.8.80)
FP2a		Perforated margin
FP2b		Miscut (8p at right)

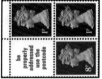

FP3	**1p**	**LB Crimson, 13p RB pale chestnut** and **2 x 18p 2B dull olive-grey** (20.10.86)
FP3a		Missing phosphor
FP3b		Reversed bands (1p RB and 13p LB) (20.10.86)
FP3c		'A' phosphor (27.1.87)
FP3d		Missing phosphor
FP3e		Reversed bands (1p RB and 13p LB) (27.1.87)

FP4	**4 x 13p**	**CB Pale chestnut**, margins all round (4.8.87)

FP5	**4 x 14p**	**CB Dark blue**, margins all round (23.8.88)
FP5a		Missing phosphor

FP6	**4 x 14p**	**CB Dark blue**, imperf. top and bottom (11.10.88)

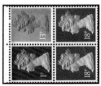

FP7	**4 x 14p**	**CB Dark blue**, imperf. on three sides (24.1.89)
FP7a		Missing phosphor

No.

No.

Panes of 6

FP8	**14p**	**RB Dark blue** and **2 x 19p 2B Orange-red** (2B) *plus* "Please use the postcode" label (5.9.88)
FP8a		Perforated margin
FP8b		Missing phosphor
FP8c		Miscut (14p at right)

FP13	**2 x ½p**	**2B Turquoise, 3 x 1p 2B Crimson** and **6p 2B Light green** with 12mm margin and cutting lines (8.2.78)
FP13a		Perforated margin
FP13b		Miscut (6p at right)
FP14		**Margin 5mm**
FP14a		Miscut (6p at right)
FP14b		Perforated margin
FP14c		Miscut (6p at right)

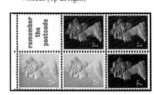

FP9	**2 x 15p**	**LB Light blue, 20p 2B Black** *plus* "Please use the postcode" label (2.10.89)
FP9a		Missing phosphor

FP15	**2 x ½p**	**CB Turquoise, 2 x 1p CB Crimson, 7p CB Purple-brown** *plus* "remember the postcode" label (8.2.78)
FP15a		Miscut (label at left)
FP15b		Perforated margin
FP15c		Missing phosphor
FP15d		Miscut (label at left)

FP10	**3 x 17p**	**2B Grey-blue** *plus* "Please use the postcode" label (12.8.86)
FP11		Multiple star underprint in blue (4.11.85)
FP11a		Missing phosphor

FP16	**½p**	**2B Turquoise, 1p 2B Crimson, 3 x 11½p (side band) Drab** and **14p 2B Grey-blue** (26.1.81). 11½p (RB) at left
FP16a		Perforated margin
FP16b		Missing phosphor
FP17		11½p (LB) at right
FP17a		Perforated margin
FP17b		Missing phosphor
FP17c		Miscut (2 x ½p, 2 x 1p and 2 x 14p)
FP17d		Miscut (6 x 11½p)

FP12	**2 x 17p**	**LB Dark blue, 17p RB Dark blue** *plus* "Please use the postcode" label (4.9.90)
FP12a		Missing phosphor

FP18	**1p**	**CB Crimson, 2 x 5p CB Claret** and **3 x 13p CB Pale chestnut** (20.10.86)
FP18a		'A' phosphor (27.1.87)

Standard Perforations

No.

FP19	Imperf. left and right sides (29.9.87)
FP19a	Missing phosphor
FP19b	4mm CB (29.9.87)

FP20	**2 x 1p CB Crimson** and **4 x 12p CB Emerald** (29.7.86)

FP21	**13p LB Pale chestnut** and **5 x 18p 2B Olive-grey** (2B) (20.1.86)
FP21a	'A' phosphor (27.1.87)

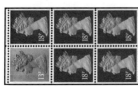

FP22	Imperf. left and right sides (29.9.87)

FP23	**2 x 14p RB Dark blue** and **4 x 19p 2B Orange-red** (narrow at right), imperf. left and right sides (5.9.88)
FP23a	Missing phosphor

Decimal Machin Booklet Panes

No.

Panes of 8

FP24	**½p 2B Turquoise, 4 x 3p 2B Bright magenta** and **3 x 12½p (side band) Light emerald** (1.2.82). 12½p (RB) at left
FP24a	Missing phosphor
FP25	12½p (LB) at right
FP25a	Missing phosphor
FP25b	Miscut (2 x ½p and 6 x 12½p)
FP25c	Miscut (8 x 3p)

FP26	**2 x 1p CB Crimson, 3 x 3½p CB Chestnut** and **3 x 12½p CB Light emerald** at right (5.4.83)
FP26a	Missing phosphor
FP26b	Miscut (3½p at right)

FP27	**3 x 1p CB Crimson, 2 x 4p CB Greenish blue** and **3 x 13p CB Pale chestnut** at right (3.9.84)
FP27a	Missing phosphor

Thick value	Thin value

FP28	**2 x 1p 2B Crimson, 3 x 7p (side band) purple-brown** and **3 x 9p 2B Dull violet** (13.6.77). 7p (RB) at left
FP28a	Thin value on 7p, Type III
FP29	7p (LB) at right
FP29a	Thin value on 7p, Type III

FP30   **2 x 2p**   **2B Dark green, 2 x 8p (side band) Rosine** and
       3 x 10p 2B Orange-brown *plus* "don't forget
       the postcode" label (28.8.79). 8p (RB) at left
FP30a   Missing phosphor
FP31   8p (LB) at right
FP31a   Missing phosphor
FP31b   Miscut (2 x 2p and 4 x 8p)
FP31c   Miscut (2 x 2p and 6 x 10p)

Panes of 10

FP39   **2 x ½p**   **2B Turquoise, 2 x 1p 2B Crimson, 2 x 6½p**
       (side band) Greenish-blue and **4 x 8½p 2B**
       Yellow-green (26.1.77).
       6½p (RB) at left
FP40   6½p (LB) at right

Normal printing   Chambon printing

FP32   **3 x 2p**   **2B Dark green, 2 x 10p (side band) Orange-brown**
       and **2 x 12p 2B Yellow-green** *plus*
       "don't forget the postcode" label (4.2.80).
       10p LB Orange brown at right
FP32a   Missing phosphor
FP33   **10p LB Orange brown** at right, Chambon
       printing. Lower set value on 12p (25.6.80)
FP33a   Missing phosphor
FP34   **10p RB Orange brown** at left
FP34a   Missing phosphor
FP35   **10p RB Orange brown** at left, Chambon
       printing. Lower set value on 12p (25.6.80)
FP35a   Missing phosphor

FP41   **10 x 6½p**   **CB Greenish blue** (14.7.76). Left margin
FP41a   Left margin - Miscut
FP41b   Left perforated margin
FP41c   Left perforated margin - Miscut
FP42   Right margin
FP42a   Right margin - Miscut
FP42b   Right perforated margin
FP42c   Right perforated margin - Miscut

FP36   **3 x 2½p**   **2B Rose-red, 2 x 4p 2B Green-blue** and **3 x 11½p**
       (side band) Drab (26.8.81). 11½p (RB) at left
FP36a   Perforated margin
FP37   **11½p drab** (LB) at right
FP37a   Perforated margin

FP43   **10 x 7p**   **CB Purple-brown** (13.6.77). Left margin
FP43a   Miscut
FP44   Right margin
FP44a   Miscut

FP45   **10 x 8p**   **CB Rosine** (3.10.79). Left margin
FP46   Right margin

FP38   **2 x 17p**   **RB Dark blue, 3 x 22p 2B Orange-red** *plus*
       3 x "Please use the postcode" labels, imperf. left and
       right sides (4.9.90)
FP38a   Missing phosphor

Standard Perforations

No.

FP47   **10 x 8½p** **2B Yellow-green** (14.7.76). Left margin
FP47a   Left margin - Miscut
FP47b   Left perforated margin
FP47c   Left perforated margin - Miscut
FP48   Right margin
FP48a   Right margin - Miscut
FP48b   Right perforated margin
FP48c   Right perforated margin - Miscut

FP49   **10 x 9p** **2B Deep violet** (13.6.77). Left margin
FP49a   Experimental fold between columns 2 and 3
FP49b   Miscut
FP50   Right margin
FP50a   Miscut

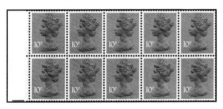

FP51   **10 x 10p** **CB Orange-brown** (4.2.80) Left margin
FP51a   Miscut
FP52   Right margin
FP53a   Miscut

FP54   **10 x 11½p** **CB Drab** (26.1.81). Left margin
FP55   Right margin

FP56   **4 x 11½p** **Drab (side band)** (2 left and 2 right bands) and
              6 x 14p 2B Grey blue (6.5.84). Left margin
FP57   Right margin

Decimal Machin Booklet Panes

No.

FP58   **10 x 12p** **CB Emerald** (14.1.86). Left margin
FP58a   Missing phosphor
FP59   Right margin
FP59a   Missing phosphor (on 8 stamps)
FP59b   Miscut

FP60   **4 x 12p** **(side band) Emerald** (2 left and 2 right bands) and
              6 x 17p 2B Grey blue (14.1.86). Left margin
FP61   Right margin

FP62   **10 x 12½p** **CB Light emerald** (1.2.82). Left margin
FP62a   Missing phosphor
FP63   Right margin
FP63a   Missing phosphor

FP64   **4 x 12½p** **(side band) Light emerald** (2 left and 2 right bands)
              and **6 x 15½p 2B Pale violet** (1.2.82). Left margin
FP64a   Missing phosphor
FP64b   Transposed phosphor bands
FP65   Right margin
FP65a   Missing phosphor
FP65b   Transposed phosphor bands

FP66	**4 x 12½p** **(side band) Light emerald** (2 left and 2 right bands)
	and **6 x 16p 2B Drab** (5.4.83). Left margin
FP66a	Missing phosphor
FP67	Right margin
FP67a	Missing phosphor

FP68	**10 x 13p** **CB Chestnut** (3.9.84). Left margin
FP68a	'A' phosphor (27.1.87)
FP68b	Missing phosphor
FP69	Star underprint in blue (2.12.86)
FP70	Right margin
FP70a	'A' phosphor (27.1.87)
FP70b	Missing phosphor
FP71	Star underprint in blue (2.12.86)

| FP72 | **10 x 13p** **CB Pale chestnut**, margins all round (4.8.87) |

FP73	**4 x 13p** **(side band) Pale chestnut** (2 left and 2 right bands)
	and **6 x 17p 2B Grey blue** (3.9.84). Left margin
FP73a	Transposed phosphor bands
FP74	Right margin
FP74a	Transposed phosphor bands

FP75	**10 x 14p** **CB Dark blue** (5.9.88). Left margin
FP75a	Missing phosphor
FP76	Right margin
FP76a	Missing phosphor

| FP77 | **10 x 14p** **CB Dark blue**, margins all round (23.8.88) |

FP78	**10 x 14p** **CB Dark blue**, imperf. top and bottom
	(11.10.88)
FP78a	Missing phosphor

Panes of 20

| FP79 | **10 x 7p** **CBar Purple brown** and **10 x 9p** |
| | **2Bars Dull violet** (15.11.78) |

FP80	**10 x 8p** **CBar Rosine** and **10 x 10p 2Bars**
	Orange brown (14.11.79)
FP80a	Miscut (8p above 10p)

Standard Perforations

No.

x 10 →

x 10 →

FP81   **10 x 10p**   **CBar Orange brown** and **10 x 12p**
         2Bars Yellow green (12.11.80)
FP81a   Missing phosphor

x 10 →

x 10 →

FP82   **10 x 11½p**   **CBar Drab** and **10 x 14p grey blue**
         2Bars (11.11.81)
FP82a   Miscut (11½p above 14p)

x 10 →

x 10 →

FP83   **10 x 12½p**   **CBar Light emerald** and **10 x 15½p pale violet**
         2Bars with blue ten point star underprint
         (10.11.82)
FP83a   Missing phosphor

x 10 →

x 10 →

FP84   **20 x 12½p**   **CB Light emerald** with 5 point star underprint in
         blue (9.11.83)
FP84a   Miscut
FP84b   Thin value, Type I
FP84c   Thin value, Type I, Miscut

Decimal Machin Booklet Panes

No.

PPP/PVAD

FP85   **10 x 10p**   **Orange brown** (3.10.79). Left margin
FP85a   Miscut
FP86   Right margin
FP86a   Miscut

PCP1/PVAD

FP87   **3 x 17p**   **Grey blue** (2B) *plus* 'Please use the postcode' label.
         Error (12.8.86)

FP88   **6 x 17p**   **Grey blue** (29.7.86)

FP89   **10 x 12p**   **Yellow green** (4.2.80). Left margin
FP89a   Miscut
FP90   Right margin
FP90a   Miscut

Standard Perforations

No.

FP91	**10 x 14p**	**Pale grey blue** (6.5.81). Left margin
FP91a		Fluorescent Brightener Omitted
FP92		Right margin
FP92a		Fluorescent Brightener Omitted

FP93	**10 x 15½p**	**Pale violet** Type II (1.2.82). Left margin
FP94		Right margin

FP95	**10 x 16**	**Pale drab** (5.4.83). Left margin
FP95a		Deep drab
FP96		'D' underprint in blue
FP96a		Miscut
FP97		Right margin
FP97a		Deep drab
FP98		'D' underprint in blue

FP99	**10 x 17p**	**Grey blue** (3.9.84). Left margin
FP100		'D' underprint in blue (5.3.85)
FP101		Right margin
FP102		'D' underprint in blue (5.3.85)

FP103	**10 x 18p**	**Olive grey** (20.10.86). Left margin
FP104		Right margin

Decimal Machin Booklet Panes

No.

PCP2/PVAD

FP106	**10 x 14p**	**Grey blue** (26.1.81). Left margin
FP107		Right margin
FP107a		Miscut

FP108	**10 x 15½p**	**Dull violet**, Type II (1.2.82). Left margin
FP109		Right margin

FP110	**10 x 18p**	**Olive grey** (20.10.86). Left margin
FP111		Right margin

ACP/PVAD

FP112	**2 x 1p**	**Crimson** and **2 x 24p chestnut** (10.9.91)
		Miscut

FP113	**2 x 2p**	**Deep green** and **4 x 24p chestnut** *plus*
		2 x "Please use the postcode" labels (10.9.91)

Standard Perforations

FP114   **4 x 18p   Dull grey olive**, margins all round (4.8.87)

FP115   **4 x 19p   Orange red**, margins all round (23.8.88)

FP116   **4 x 19p   Orange red**, imperf. top and bottom (11.10.88)

FP117   **4 x 19p   Orange red**, imperf. on three sides (24.1.89)

FP118   **4 x 26p   Red**, margins all round (4.8.87)

Decimal Machin Booklet Panes

FP119   **4 x 27p   Rust brown**, margins all round (23.8.86)

FP120   **4 x 27p   Rust brown**, imperf. top and bottom (11.10.88)

FP121   **5 x 20p   Black**, imperf. left and right sides *plus*
'Please use the postcode' label (2.10.89)

FP122   **10 x 18p   Dull olive grey** (27.1.87). Left margin
FP123   Right margin
FP123a   Miscut

FP124   **10 x 18p   Dull grey olive**, margins all round (4.8.87)

Standard Perforations

No.

FP125   **10 x 19p**   **Orange red** (5.9.88). Left margin
FP126   Right margin

FP127   **10 x 19p**   **Orange red**, margins all round (23.8.88)

FP128   **10 x 19p**   **Orange red**, imperf. top and bottom (11.10.88)

Printed by Questa in Lithography

1988 (11 Oct.) Perf. 15 x 14

FCP/PVA

LP1   **10 x 14p**   **CBar Dark blue**

ACP/PVA

LP2   **10 x 19p**   **Orange red**

Decimal Machin Booklet Panes

No.

Printed by Walsall in Lithography

1989 (25 April) Perf. 14

FCP/PVA

LP3   **2 x 14p**   **RB Dark blue** and **4 x 19p 2B Orange red**
            imperf. left and right sides
LP3a   Missing phosphor

LP4   **4 x 29p**   **2B Purple** imperf. on three sides (2.10.89)

ACP/PVA

LP5   **2 x 2p**   **Deep green** and **4 x 24p Chestnut** *plus*
            2 x "Please use the postcode" labels (9.2.93)
LP6   **4 x 29p**   **Purple** imperf. on three sides (17.4.90)
            Pane layout as LP4, but ACP

LP7   **4 x 31p**   **Bright blue**, imperf. top and bottom (17.9.90)
LP7a   Low OBA

LP8   **4 x 33p**   **Emerald**, imperf. top and bottom (16.9.91)

Elliptical Perforations

No.

LP9   **2 x 39p**   **Pale mauve**, imperf. top and bottom (28.7.92)

LP10   **4 x 39p**   **Deep mauve**, imperf. top and bottom (16.9.91)

ACP/PVAD

LP11   **4 x 33p**   **Emerald**, imperf. top and bottom (8.9.92)
         Pane layout as LP8, but ACP

Elliptical Perforations

Printed by Harrison in Photogravure

1993(1 Nov.) Perf. 15 x 14 elliptical

OFPP/PVAD

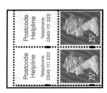

EP1   **2 x 25p**   **Salmon pink** *plus* 2 x "Postcode Helpline" label
EP1a   Miscut

EP2   **4 x 25p**   **Salmon pink** (26.4.94)

EP3   **8 x 25p**   **Salmon pink**

Decimal Machin Booklet Panes

No.

OFNP/PVAD

(The layout of panes EP4, EP5 and EP6 is the smae as EP1, EP2 and EP3 respectively.)

EP4   **2 x 25p**   **2B Salmon pink** C (Yellow) fluor
               plus 2 x 'Postcode Helpline' label
EP4a   Miscut

EP5   **4 x 25p**   **2B Salmon pink** C (Yellow) fluor
EP5a   D (Blue) fluor

EP6   **8 x 25p**   **2B Salmon pink** C (Yellow) fluor
EP6a   D (Blue) fluor

Printed by Walsall in Lithography

1993 (1 Nov.) No wmk. Perf. 15 x 14 elliptical

OFNP/PVA

EP7   **4 x 25p**   **2B Salmon pink** - C (Yellow) fluor (As EP2)

EP8   **4 x 35p**   **2B Yellow** - C (Yellow) fluor
EP8a   D (Blue) fluor

EP9   **4 x 37p**   **2B Amethyst** D (Blue) fluor

EP10   **4 x 41p**   **2B Stone** - C (Yellow) fluor
EP10a   D (Blue) fluor

EP11   **4 x 60p**   **2B Slate blue** - C (Yellow) fluor (9.8.94)
EP11a   D (Blue) fluor

Elliptical Peforations

No.

EP12   **4 x 63p**   **2B Light emerald** D (Blue) fluor
EP12a   Missing phosphor

Printed by Questa in Lithography

1996 (16 Jan.) Perf. 15 x 14 elliptical

OFNP/PVA (Blue) fluor

EP13   **4 x 25p**   **2B Salmon pink**

EP14   **3 x 26p**   **2B Red-brown** and **2 x 1p 2B Crimson** and
               1 x 20p CB Bright green *plus* two labels (8.7.96)
EP14a   Missing phosphor
EP14b   Miscut

EP15   **8 x 25p**   **2B Salmon-pink**

EP16   **7 x 26p**   **2B Red-brown** and **1 x 20p CB Bright green**
               (8.7.96)
EP16a   Missing phosphor

Decimal Machin Booklet Panes

No.

Printed by Walsall in Gravure

(Gravure is also sometimes refered to as EME or Computer engraved)

1997 (26 Aug.) Perf. 15 x 14 elliptical

OFNP/PVA - D (Blue) fluor

EP17   **4 x 30p**   **2B Grey-green** (5.5.98)

EP18   **4 x 37p**   **2B Amethyst** (26.8.97)

EP19   **4 x 38p**   **2B Ultramarine** (26.4.99)

EP20   **4 x 40p**   **2B Greyish blue** (27.4.00)

EP21   **4 x 63p**   **2B Light emerald** (26.8.97)

EP22   **4 x 64p 2B Sea green** (26.4.99)

EP23   **4 x 65p 2B Greenish blue** (27.4.00)

Printed by Questa in Gravure

OFNP/PVA - D(Blue) fluor

1998 (1Dec.) No Wmk. Perf 15 x 14 elliptical

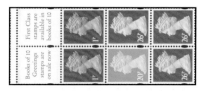

EP24   **3 x 26p 2B Red-brown** and **2 x 1p 2B Crimson** and
          1 x 20p CB Bright green *plus* two labels
EP24a   Miscut

1999 (26 Apr.) No Wmk. Perf 15 x 14 elliptical

EP25   **3 x 26p 2B Red-brown, 1 x 1p 2B Deep Crimson,
          1 x 2p CB Green** and **1 x 19p CB Olive-green**
EP25a   Miscut

1998 (1 Dec.) No Wmk. Perf 15 x 14 elliptical

EP26   **1 x 20p CB Bright green** and **7 x 26p
          2B Red-brown**
EP26a   Miscut

1999 (26 Apr.) No Wmk. Perf 15 x 14 elliptical

EP27   **1 x 19p CB Olive green** and **7 x 26p
          2B Red-brown**

Double Head (1d Black Anniversary)

No.

Double Head (1d Black Anniversary) Panes

Printed by Harrison in Photogravure

1990 (30 Jan.) 150th Anniversary of the Penny Black

FCP/PVAD

AP1   **2 x 15p   LB Bright blue, 20p 2B Black and buff** *plus*
'Please use the postcode' label

AP2   **10 x 15p   CB Bright blue**, imperf. top and bottom

ACP/PVAD

AP3   **4 x 20p   Black & buff**, imperf. on three sides (17.4.90)

AP4   **5 x 20p   Black & buff**, imperf. left and right sides *plus*
'Please use the postcode' label

AP5   **10 x 20p   Black & buff**, imperf. top and bottom

Decimal Machin Booklet Panes

No.

Printed by Questa in Lithography

Printed in Lithography. Perf. 15 x 14

FCP/PVA

AP6   **10 x 15p   CBar Bright blue** (17.4.90)

ACP/PVA

AP7   **10 x 20p   Black**. (17.4.90)
AP7a   ACP/Low OBA

Printed by Walsall in Lithography

Perf. 14

FCP/PVA

AP8   **4 x 15p   CB Bright blue**, imperf. on three sides (30.1.90)

AP9   **10 x 15p   CB Bright blue**, imperf. on three sides (12.6.90)

ACP/PVA

AP10   **5 x 20p   Black & buff**, imperf. left and right sides
plus "Please use the postcode" label (As AP4)

ACP/PVAD

AP11   **4 x 20p Black & buff**, imperf. on three sides (30.1.90)

AP12   **10 x 20p Black & buff**, imperf. on three sides (12.6.90)

Standard Perforations

No.

Printed by Harrison in Photogravure

1989 (22 Aug.) Perf. 15 x 14

FCP/PVAD

CP1   **4 x 2nd CB Bright blue**, imperf. on three sides (28.11.89)

CP2   **10 x 2nd CB Bright blue**, imperf. at top and bottom

CP3   **10 x 2nd CB Dark blue**, imperf. at top and bottom (7.8.90)

ACP/PVAD

CP4   **4 x 1st Black**, imperf. on three sides (5.12.89)

CP5   **10 x 1st Black**, imperf. at top and bottom

NVI Machin Booklet Panes

No.

CP6   **10 x 1st Orange red**, imperf. top and bottom (7.8.90)

Printed by Questa in Lithography

Perf. 15 x 14

FCP/PVA

CP7   **10 x 2nd CBar Bright blue,** Perf. margin (19.8.89)

CP7a   **10 x 2nd CBar Bright blue,** Imperf. margin

CP8   **10 x 2nd CBar Dark blue** (7.8.90)

ACP/PVA

CP9	**10 x 1st Black**. Perf. margin (19.9.89)
CP9a	Low OBA
CP9b	Imperf. margin
CP9c	Low OBA

Standard Perforations

No.

CP10   **10 x 1st   Orange red** (6.8.91)

ACP/PVAD

CP11   **10 x 1st   Orange red** (7.8.90) As CP10 above

Printed by Walsall in Lithography

Perf. 14

FCP/PVA

CP12   **4 x 2nd   CB Bright blue**. Imperf. on three sides (22.8.89)

CP13   **4 x 2nd   CB Dark blue**. Imperf. at top and bottom (7.8.90)

CP14   **4 x 2nd   CB Bright blue**. Imperf. at top and bottom (6.8.91)

CP15   **4 x 1st   2B Black**. Imperf. on three sides (22.8.89)
CP15a   Missing phosphor

NVI Machin Booklet Panes

No.

CP16   **10 x 2nd   CB Dark blue**. Imperf. at top and bottom (7.8.90)

CP17   **10 x 2nd   CB Bright blue**. Imperf. at top and bottom (6.8.91)

FCP/PVAD

CP18   **10 x 2nd   CB Bright blue**. Imperf. at top and bottom (16.3.93) As CP17 above

ACP/PVA

CP19   **4 x 1st   Orange red**. Imperf. at top and bottom (7.8.90)
CP19a   Low OBA

CP20   **10 x 1st   Orange red**. Imperf. at top and bottom (7.8.90)
CP20a   Low OBA

Perf. 13 in error

CP21   **4 x 1st   Orange red**. Imperf. at top and bottom (10.90)
CP21a   Low OBA

ACP/PVAD

CP22   **4 x 1st   Orange red.** Imperf. at top and bottom Pane layout as CP 19 (16.3.93)
CP23   **10 x 1st   Orange red**. Imperf. at top and bottom Pane layout as CP20 (9.2.93)

Elliptical Perforations

NVI Machin Booklet Panes

Printed by Harrison in Photogravure

1993 (6 April) Perf. 15 x 14 elliptical

OFNP/PVAD

CP24   **4 x 2nd**   **CB Bright blue** (7.9.93)
     C (Yellow) fluor
CP24a   **4 x 2nd**   **CB Bright blue** (18.7.95)
     D (Blue) fluor

CP25   **10 x 2nd**   **CB Bright blue** (12.12.95)
     D (Blue) fluor

CP26   **10 x 1st**   **2B Orange red** (4.4.95)
     C (Yellow) fluor

CP26a   **10 x 1st**   **2B Orange red** (18.7.95)
     D (Blue) fluor

OFPP/PVAD

CP27   **4 x 1st**   **Orange red** (6.4.93)
CP28   **10 x 1st**   **Orange red,** (6.4.93) Pane layout as CP26

OFNP/PVA (Layflat)

CP29   **10 x 2nd**   **CB Bright blue,** Pane layout as CP25
CP30   **10 x 1st**   **2B Orange-red,** Pane layout as CP26

Printed by Questa in Lithography

Perf. 15 x 14 elliptical

OFNP/PVA

CP31   **10 x 2nd**   **CBar Bright blue** (6.4.93)
CP31a   Missing phosphor
CP32   **10 x 2nd**   **CB Bright blue** (1.11.93)
     C (Yellow) fluor. As CP31
CP32a   **10 x 2nd**   **CB Bright blue** (.7.95)
     D (Blue) fluor. As CP31

CP33   **10 x 1st**   **2B Orange red** (1.11.93)
     C (Yellow) fluor
CP33a   **10 x 1st**   **2B Orange red** (.7.95)
     D (Blue) fluor

Commemorative issue

CP34   **4 x 1st**   **2B Orange red** *plus* '300 years
     of The Bank of England' label (27.7.94)
CP34a   Missing phosphor

No.   No.

Printed by Walsall in Lithography

Commemorative issues

Perf. 15 x 14 elliptical

OFNP/PVA

CP35	4 x 2nd	CB Bright blue (6.4.93)
		C (Yellow) fluor
CP35a	4 x 2nd	CB Bright blue (.7.95)
		D (Blue) fluor

CP36	10 x 2nd	CB Bright blue (1.11.93)
		C (Yellow) fluor
CP36a	10 x 2nd	CB Bright blue (.7.95)
		D (Blue) fluor

CP37	4 x 1st	2B Orange red
		C (Yellow) fluor
CP38	4 x 1st	2B Orange red
		D (Blue) fluor

CP39	10 x 1st	2B Orange red (6.4.93)
		C (Yellow) fluor
CP39a		Missing phosphor
CP39b		Broad band
CP40	10 x 1st	2B Orange red
		D (Blue) fluor

CP41	4 x 1st	2B Orange red *plus* 'R. J. Mitchell'
		label (16.5.95)

CP41A	4 x 1st	2B Orange red *plus* 'Queen's 70th Birthday'
		label (16.4.96)

CP41B	4 x 1st	2B Orange red *plus* 'Hong Kong 97'
		label (12.2.97)

CP41C	4 x 1st	2B Orange red *plus* 'Heads of Government'
		label (21.10.97)

CP41D	4 x 1st	2B Orange red *plus* 'Prince's Trust'
		label (14.11.98)

Elliptical Perforations

CP41E   **4 x 1st   2B Orange red** *plus* 'Berlin Airlift'
label (12.5.99)

CP41F   **4 x 1st   2B Orange red** *plus* 'Rugby World Cup'
label (1.10.99)

CP41G   **4 x 1st   2B Millennium** *plus* 'Postman Pat'
label (21.3.00)

CP41H   **4 x 1st   2B Millennium** *plus* 'Botanical'
label (4.4.00)

Printed by Harrison/De La Rue in Gravure

1997 (21 April) Perf. 15 x 14 elliptical

OFNP/PVA (Layflat) - D (Blue) fluor

CP42   **10 x 2nd   CB Bright-blue**

NVI Machin Booklet Panes

CP43   **10 x 1st   2B Orange-red**

CP44   **10 x 1st   2B Gold** (21.4.97)

Printed by Walsall in Gravure

Perf. 15 x 14 elliptical

OFNP/PVA - D (Blue) fluor

CP45   **4 x 2nd   CB Bright blue** (26.8.97)

CP46   **4 x 1st   2B Bright orange red** (26.8.97)
CP46a   Missing phosphor

CP47   **4 x E   2B Dark blue**

Elliptical Perforations

CP48   **10 x 1st   2B Gold**

CP49   **10 x 1st   2B Bright orange red** (18.11.97)

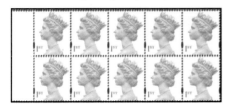

CP50   **10 x 1st   2B Millennium** (6.1.00)

Printed by Questa in Gravure

Perf. 15 x 14 elliptical

OFNP/PVA - D (Blue) fluor

CP51   **10 x 2nd   CB Bright-blue** (1.12.98)
CP51a   Miscut

CP52   **10 x 1st   2B Bright orange red** (1.12.98)
CP52a   Miscut

NVI Machin Booklet Panes

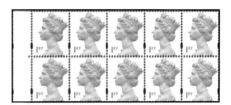

CP53   **10 x 1st   2B Millennium** (6.1.00)
CP53a   Missing phosphor

2000 (27 Apr.) No Wmk. Perf 15 x 14 elliptical

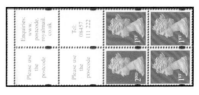

CP54   **1 x 2nd   CB Bright blue, 3 x 1st 2B Orange-red** and
                 four labels (Postcode) (27.4.00)
CP54a   Miscut

2000 (27 Apr.) No Wmk. Perf 15 x 14 elliptical

CP55   **2 x 2nd   CB Bright blue** and **6 x 1st 2B Orange-red**
CP55a   Broad band left

2001 (17 Apr.) No Wmk. Perf 15 x 14 elliptical

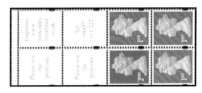

CP56   **1 x 2nd   CB Bright blue, 3 x 1st 2B Orange-red** and
                 four labels (Postcodes)

Booklets

King Edward VII

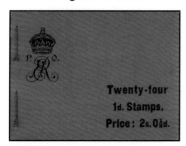

1904 (16 March) Printed by De La Rue. Sold with ½d premium for the booklet. Grease-proof paper interleaving. *Contents* BP3/3/3/3
BK1   **2s 0½d   Black on red**   £325

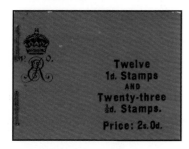

1906 (June) Face value of stamps 1s 11½d *Contents* BP3/3/1//1/1/2
BK2   **2s   Black on red**   £1100

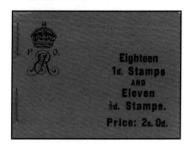

1907 (Aug.) *Contents* BP3/3/3/1/2
BK3   **2s   Black on red**   £1800

1908 (Aug) Interleaving printed in red on grease-proof paper.
Contents BP3/3/3/1/2
BK4   **2s   Black on red**   £1400

1909 (Aug) Interleaving printed in green on normal paper.
Contents BP3/3/3/1/2
BK5   **2s   Black on red**   £1100

1911 (June) Printed by Harrison & Sons. *Contents* BP6/6/6/4/5
BK6   **2s   Black on red**   £1250

King George V

All booklets were printed by Harrison & Sons unless otherwise stated.

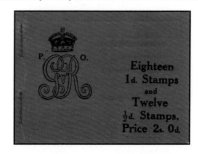

1911 (Aug.) Value of contents now 2s *Contents* BP8/8/8/7/7
BK7   **2s   Black on red**   £850

1912 (April) Redrawn cover design. *Contents* BP8/8/8/7/7
BK8   **2s   Black on red**   £1000

1912 (Sept.) *New contents* BP12/12/12/11/11
BK9   **2s   Black on red**   £750

Inscribed 'RATES OF POSTAGE'

1912 (Nov.) *Contents* BP12/12/12/11/11
BK10   **2s   Black on red**   £900

Edition No. added to cover (8)

1913 (Jan.) Edition Nos. 8 and 9 added to cover.
Contents BP12/12/12/11/11
BK11   **2s   Black on red**   £850

1913 (April) Edition Nos. 10-35. *Contents* BP14/14/14/13/13
BK12   **2s   Black on red**   £600

Inscribed 'NEW RATES OF POSTAGE'

1915 (Nov.) Edition Nos. 36-42. *Contents* BP14/14/14/13/13
BK13   **2s   Black on red**   £700

1916 (May) Interleaves printed in black. Edition Nos. 43-45.
Contents BP14/14/14/13/13
BK14   **2s   Black on red**   £750

1916 (July) Edition Nos. 46-64. *Contents* BP14/14/14/13/13
BK15   **2s   Black on orange**   £600

Advertisement on cover

1917 (Sept.) Edition Nos. 65-81. *Contents* BP14/14/14/13/13
BK16   **2s   Black on orange**   £600

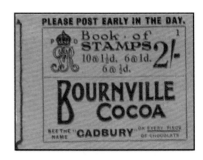

Inscribed 'Book of STAMPS'

1924 (Feb.) Edition Nos. 1 and 2. *Contents* BP16/15/14/13
BK17   **2s   Black on blue**   £1300

1924 (June) Printed by Waterlow & Sons Ltd. Edition Nos. 3-102, 108-254.
Contents BP22/21/20/19
BK18   **2s   Black on blue**   £525

1924 (Nov.) Printed by Waterlow & Sons Ltd. Edition No. 15.
Contents BP23/21/20/19
BK19   **2s   Black on blue**   £4000

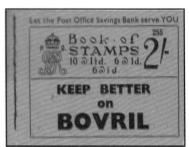

1934 (Feb.) Edition Nos. 255-287.
Contents BP22/21/20/19
BK20   **2s   Black on blue**   £550

1935 (Jan.) Photogravure intermediate format. Edition Nos. 288-297.
Contents BP31/30/29/28
BK21   **2s   Black on blue**   £1400

1935 (July) Photogravure small format. Edition Nos. 305-353. *Contents*
BP35/34/33/32
BK22   **2s   Black on blue**   £375

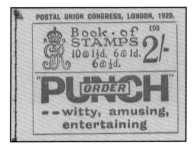

1929 (May) Postal Union Congress. Printed by Waterlow & Sons Ltd.
Edition Nos. 103-107. *Contents* BP27/26/25/24
BK23   **2s   Blue on buff**   £375

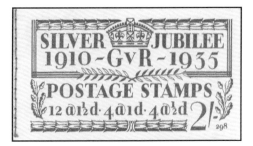

1935 (May) Silver Jubilee. Edition Nos. 298-304.
Contents BP38/38/38/37/36
BK24   **2s   Blue on buff**   £75

1918 (Oct.) Edition Nos. 1-11. *Contents* BP15/15/14/14/13/13
BK25   **3s   Black on orange**   £750

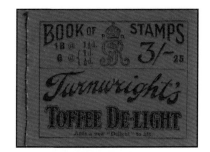

1919 (July) Edition Nos. 12-28. *Contents* BP15/15/15/14/13
BK26   **3s   Black on orange**   £750

1921 (April) Edition Nos. 35 and part 37. *Contents* BP17/17/17
BK27   **3s   Black on blue**   £1000
1921 (Dec.) Edition Nos. 12, 13 and part 37. *Contents* BP18/18/18
BK28   **3s   Black on blue**   £1100

1922 (May) Edition Nos. 19, 20, 22, 23 and 25-54.
Contents BP15/15/15/14/13
BK29   **3s   Black on scarlet**   £950

1922 (June) Edition Nos. 21 and 24. *Contents* BP15/15/15/15
BK30   **3s   Black on blue**   £1100

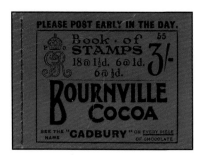

1924 (Feb.) Printed by Waterlow & Sons Ltd. Edition Nos. 55-167 and 173-273. *Contents BP21/21/21/20/19*

BK31   **3s   Black on scarlet**   £350

1934 (March) Edition Nos. 274 - 288.
Contents BP21/21/21/20/19

BK32   **3s   Black on scarlet**   £425

1935 (Jan.) Photogravure intermediate format. Edition Nos. 289-293.
Contents BP30/30/30/29/28

BK33   **3s   Black on scarlet**   £1300

1935 (July) Photogravure small format. Edition Nos. 298-319. *Contents* BP34/34/34/33/32

BK34   **3s   Black on scarlet**   £350

1929 (May) Postal Union Congress. Printed by Waterlow & Sons Ltd. Edition Nos. 168-172. *Contents BP26/26/26/25/24*

BK35   **3s   Red on buff**   £300

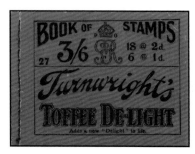

1935 (May) Silver Jubilee. Edition Nos. 294-297.
Contents BP38/38/38/38/38/37/36

BK36   **3s   Red on buff**   £75

1920 (July) Edition Nos. 27-32. *Contents* BP17/17/17/17/14

BK37   **3s6d   Black on orange**   £1000

1921 (Jan.) Edition Nos. 33, 34, 36 and 38. *Contents* BP17/17/15/14/13
BK38   **3s6d**   **Black on orange**   £1000

1921 (July) Edition Nos. 1, 2 & 4 *Contents* BP17/17/15/14/13
BK39   **3s6d**   **Black on orange**   £1000

1921 (July) Edition Nos. 3, 5-11,14-18 *Contents* BP18/18/15/14/13
BK39a   **3s6d**   **Black on orange**   £1000

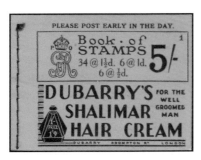

1931 (Aug.) Printed by Waterlow & Sons Ltd. Edition No. 1.
Contents BP22/21/21/21/21/21/20/19
BK40   **5s**   **Black on green**   £3750

1932 (June) Printed by Waterlow & Sons Ltd. Edition Nos. 2-6.
Contents BP22/21/21/21/21/21/20/19
BK41   **5s**   **Black on buff**   £2250

1934 (July) Edition Nos. 7 and 8.
Contents BP22/21/21/21/21/21/20/19
BK42   **5s**   **Black on buff**   £1250

1935 (Feb.) Photogravure intermediate format. Edition No. 9.
Contents BP31/30/30/30/30/30/29/28
BK43   **5s**   **Black on buff**   £3000

1935 (July) Photogravure small format. Edition Nos. 10-15.
Contents BP35/34/34/34/34/33/32
BK44   **5s**   **Black on buff**   £350

King Edward VIII

1936 Plain cover. *Contents* BP42/42
BK45   **6d Buff**   £40

1936 (Oct.) Edition Nos. 354-385. *Contents* BP43/41/40/39
BK46   **2s Black on scarlet**   £85

1936 (Nov.) Edition Nos. 320-332. *Contents* BP41/41/41/40/39
BK47   **3s Black on scarlet**   £70

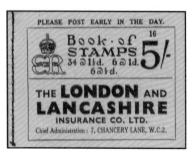

1937 (March) Edition Nos. 16 and 17.
Contents BP43/41/41/41/41/41/40/39
BK48   **5s Black on buff**   £200

King George VI

1938 (Jan.) Plain cover. *Contents* BP49/49
BK49   **6d Buff cover**   £45

1938 (Feb.) Plain cover. *Contents* BP49/47/45
BK50   **6d Pink cover**   £275

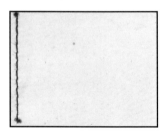

1940 (June) Plain cover. *Contents* BP54/53
BK51   **6d Green cover**   £90

1947 (Dec.) Plain cover. *Contents* BP56/56/57/57/57/58/58
BK52   **1s Cream cover**   £15

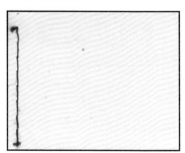

1948 (Nov.) Plain cover. *Contents* BP55b/56a/57a
BK52a   **1s Cream cover**   £5000

1951 (May) Plain cover. *Contents* BP63/63/66/66/72/72
BK53   **1s Cream cover**   £15
1951 (May) Plain cover. *Contents* BP62/65/71. Selvedge at top or bottom
BK54   **1s Cream cover**   £15

1952 (Dec.) Round G.P.O. emblem. *Contents* BP62/65/71.
BK55   **1s   Cream cover**   £10

1954 Oval G.P.O. emblem. *Contents* BP62/65/71.
BK56   **1s   Cream cover**   £12

1937 (Aug.) Edition Nos. 386-412. *Contents* BP50/48/46/44.
BK57   **2s   Black on blue**   £450

1938 (April) G.P.O. emblem added to cover. Edition Nos. 413-508.
Contents BP50/48/46/44.
BK58   **2s   Black on blue**   £450

1940 (June) Edition Nos. 1-7. *Contents* BP52/51/44.
BK59   **2s6d   Black on scarlet**   £1000

1940 (Sept.) Edition Nos. 8-13.
Contents BP52/51/44.
BK60   **2s6d   Black on blue**   £1000

Note: An example of edition 8 has been found on red card before production
changed to blue card. This is the only known example.

1940 (Oct.) Edition Nos. 14-94. *Contents* BP52/51/44
BK61   **2s6d   Black on green**   £500

1942 (March) Edition Nos. 95-214. *Contents* BP60/59/55
BK62   **2s6d   Black on green**   £525

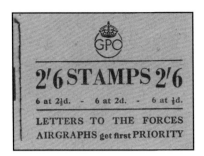

1943 (Aug.) Introduction of dated editions and G.P.O. emblem placed centrally. Edition dates Aug. 1943 - Feb. 1951 (90). *Contents* BP60/59/55

BK63   **2s6d   Black on green**   From £50 to £120

1951 (May) Edition dates May 1951 - Feb. 1952 (10). *Contents* BP74/73/61

BK64   **2s6d   Black on green**   £28

1952 (March) Edition dates Mar. 1952 - May 1953 (15). *Contents* BP74/70/67/61

BK65   **2s6d   Black on green**   £28

Composite Booklets

1953 (May). Edition dates May - Sept. 1953 (5). *Contents* BP88/84/67/61
BK66   **2s6d   Black on green**   From £20
1953 (Sept.) Edition date Sept. 1953. *Contents* BP88/84/68/61
BK67   **2s6d   Black on green**   £60

1953 (Oct.) Edition dates Oct. - Dec. 1953 (3). *Contents* BP88/84/67/61
BK68   **2s6d   Black on green**   From £20
1953 (Oct.) Edition dates Oct. - Nov. 1953 (2). *Contents* BP88/84/68/61
BK69   **2s6d   Black on green**   From £50
1954 (Jan.) Edition dates Jan. - Feb. 1954 (2). *Contents* BP88/84/69/61
BK70   **2s6d   Black on green**   £40
1954 (March) Edition date Mar. 1954. *Contents* BP88/84/67/75
BK71   **2s6d   Black on green**   £400
1954 (March) Edition date Mar. 1954. *Contents* BP88/84/69/75
BK71a   **2s6d   Black on green**   £3500

1937 (Aug.) Edition Nos. 333-343. *Contents* BP48/48/48/46/44
BK72   **3s   Black on scarlet**   £87

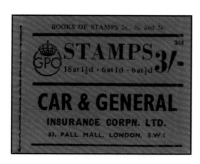

1938 (April) Edition Nos. 344-377. *Contents* BP48/48/48/46/44

BK73   **3s   Black on scarlet**   £875

1937 (Aug.) Edition Nos. 18-20. *Contents* BP50/48/48/48/48/48/46/44

BK74   **5s   Black on buff**   £1000

1938 (May) Edition Nos. 21-29. *Contents* BP50/48/48/48/48/48/46/44

BK75   **5s   Black on buff**   £950

1940 (July) Edition Nos. 1-16. *Contents* BP52/52/52/51/44

BK76   **5s   Black on buff**   £1000

1942 (March) Edition Nos. 16-29 (part). *Contents* BP60/60/60/59/55

BK77   **5s   Black on buff**   £1000

1943 (Feb.)
Edition Nos. 29(part) -36. *Contents* BP60/60/60/59/55

BK77a   **5s   Black on buff** unglazed covers   £1250

1943 (Sept.) Edition dates Sept. 1943 - Dec. 1950 (49).
Contents BP60/60/60/59/55

BK78   **5s   Black on buff**   From £65 to £120

1951 (May) Edition dates May 1951 - Jan. 1952 (5).
Contents BP74/74/74/73/61

BK79   **5s   Black on buff**   £40

1952 (March) Edition dates Mar. - Nov. 1952 (5).
Contents BP74/74/74/70/67/67/61

BK80   **5s   Black on buff**   £30

1953 (Jan.) Edition dates Jan. - Mar. 1953 (2). *Contents* 74/74/73/70/64/61
BK81   **5s   Black on buff**   £35

1944 (April) Edition dates Apr. - June 1944 (2). *Contents*
BP60/60/60/59/55
BK82   **5s   Black on buff**   £1600

1953 (May) Edition dates May - Sept. 1953 (3). *Contents*
BP88/88/73/84/64/61
BK83   **5s   Black on buff**   From £25

1953 (Nov.) Edition dates Nov. 1953 - Jan. 1954 (2). *Contents*
BP88/88/73/84/64/61
BK84   **5s   Black on buff**   From £25
1954 (March) Edition date Mar. 1954.*Contents* BP88/88/73/84/64/75
BK85   **5s   Black on buff**   £600
1954 (March) Edition date Mar. 1954.*Contents* BP88/88/73/84/78/75
BK86   **5s   Black on buff**   £125

Queen Elizabeth II Wilding Booklets

1953 (Sept.) Plain cover. *Contents* BP86/86/80/80/77/77
BK87   **1s   White cover**   2.00
1957 (Nov.) Plain cover. *Contents* BP98/98/94/94/91/91
BK88   **1s   White cover**   £10

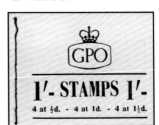

1954 (July) Oval G.P.O. emblem. *Contents* BP85/79/76
BK89   **1s   Black on white**   3.00
1956 (July) *Contents* BP97/93/90
BK90   **1s   Black on white**   2.50
1959 (Aug.) *Contents* BP109/107/105
BK91   **1s   Black on white**   2.75

1959 (22 April) *Contents* BP103/97/93/90
BK92   **2s   Black on salmon**   4.00

1960 (Nov.) Small G.P.O. emblem. *Contents* 113/109/107/105
BK93   **2s   Black on salmon**   6.0
BK94   **2s   Black on lemon (2.61)**   3.0

1961 (April) Edition dates Apr. 1961 - Apr. 1965 (17).
Contents BP125/124/123/122 or BP132/131/128/126
BK95   **2s   Black on lemon**   £25
1961 (April). Phosphor issue. Edition dates Apr. 1961 - Apr. 1965 (13).
Contents BP156/155/154/153 or BP164/163/158/157
BK96   **2s   Black on lemon**   From £45

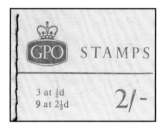

BK97 Black stitching

BK98 White stitching

1963 (July) Holiday resorts issue. *Contents* BP121/121/120
BK97   **2s   Red on lemon** (black stitching)   1.75
BK98   **2s   Red on lemon** (white stitching)   2.25
1964 (July) Holiday resorts issue. *Contents* BP127/127/127/127
BK99   **2s   Red on lemon**   3.00

1965 (Aug.) Edition dates July 1965 - Jan. 1967 (7).
Contents BP133/129 or 130
BK100   **2s   Black on orange**   1.25

1965 (Aug.) Phosphor issue. Edition dates July 1965 - Oct. 1967 (10).
Contents BP165/159 or 160
BK101   **2s   Black on orange**   From 3.00

1965 (Dec.) Christmas Cards issue. *Contents* BP132/132
BK102   **2s   Red on orange**   50

1967 (Nov.) Edition dates Jan. - Mar. 1968 (2). *Contents* BP165/161 or 162
BK103   **2s   Black on orange**   1.50

1954 (March) Edition date Mar. 1954. *Contents* BP88/84/81/75
BK104   **2s6d   Black on green**   £200
1954 (April) Edition dates Apr. 1954 - Jan. 1955 (10).
Contents BP88/84/82/75
BK105   **2s6d   Black on green**   £25
1955 (Jan.) Edition dates Jan. - Aug. 1955 (8). *Contents* BP88/84/83/75
BK106   **2s6d   Black on green**   £25
1955 (Aug.) Edition dates Aug. 1955 - June 1956 (8).
Contents BP88/84/83/75 or BP101/96/95/89 or mixed
BK107   **2s6d   Black on green**   £20
1956 (Feb.) Edition dates Feb.1956 - Mar. 1957 (12).
Contents BP101/96/95/89
BK108   **2s6d   Black on green**   £15
1957 (April) Edition dates Apr. - Dec. 1957 (9). *Contents* BP101/100/89
BK109   **2s6d   Black on green**   £15

1958 (Jan.) Edition dates Jan. - Nov. 1958 (9). *Contents* BP102/96/92/89
BK110   **3s   Black on red**   £12

1958 (Nov.) Edition dates Nov.1958 - Jan. 1959 (3).
Contents BP102/96/92/89 or BP112/108/106/104 or mixed
BK111   **3s   Black on red**   £15
1958 (Dec.) Edition dates Dec. 1958 - Sept. 1959 (5).
Contents BP112/108/106/104
BK112   **3s   Black on red**   £15

1959 (Aug.) Graphite lined issue. Edition dates Aug. - Sept. 1959 (2).
Contents BP138/136/135/134
BK113   **3s   Black on red**   £125

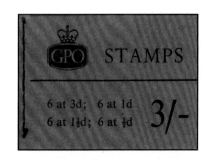

1959 (Oct.) Small G.P.O. emblem. Edition dates Oct. 1959 - Nov. 1960 (14). *Contents* BP112/108/106/104

BK114   **3s**   **Black on brick red**   £20

1959 (Oct.) Graphite lined issue. Edition dates Oct. 1959 - Apr. 1960 (4). *Contents* BP138/136/135/134

BK115   **3s**   **Black on brick red**   £140

1960 (Aug.) Phosphor issue. Edition dates Aug. & Nov. 1960 (2). *Contents* BP144/141/140/139

BK116   **3s**   **Black on brick red**   £35

1960 (Dec.) Large G.P.O. emblem. Edition dates Dec. 1960 - May 1965 (46). *Contents* BP112/108/106/104 or BP118/116/115/114

BK117   **3s**   **Black on brick red**   From £25

1960 (Dec.) Phosphor issue Edition dates Dec. 1960 - May 1965 (34). *Contents* BP144/141/140/139 or BP149/147/146/145

BK118   **3s**   **Black on brick red**   From £35

1953 (Nov.) Edition dates Nov. 1953 - Dec. 1955 (10). *Contents* BP88/88/88

BK119   **3s9d**   **Black on red**   £20

1955 (Oct.) Edition dates Oct. and Dec. 1955 (2). *Contents* BP88/88/88 or BP101/101/101 or mixed

BK120   **3s9d**   **Black on red**   £20

1955 (Oct.) Edition dates Oct. 1955 - Aug. 1957 (12). *Contents* BP101/101/101

BK121   **3s9d**   **Black on red**   £15

1957 (Oct.) Edition dates Oct. 1957 - Dec. 1958 (7). *Contents* BP102/102/102

BK122   **4s6d**   **Black on purple**   £15

1958 (Oct.) Edition date Dec. 1958. *Contents* BP112/112/112

BK123   **4s6d**   **Black on purple**   £60

1959 (Feb.) Small G.P.O. emblem. Edition dates Feb. - Dec. 1959 (5). *Contents* BP112/112/112

BK124   **4s6d**   **Black on purple**   £18

1959 (Feb.) Edition dates Feb.1959 - Oct. 1960 (9). *Contents* BP112/112/112

BK125   **4s6d**   **Black on violet**   £18

1959 (April) Edition dates Apr.1959 - Apr. 1960 (4). *Contents* BP138/138/138

BK126   **4s6d**   **Black on violet**   £18

1959 (Aug.) Edition date Aug. 1959 (5). *Contents* BP138/138/138

BK127   **4s6d**   **Black on purple**   £15

1960 (Aug.) Edition date Aug. 1960. *Contents* BP144/144/144

BK128   **4s6d**   **Black on violet**   £20

1960 (Dec.) Large G.P.O. emblem. Edition dates Dec. 1960 - Apr. 1965 (36). *Contents* BP112/112/112 or BP118/118/118

BK129   **4s6d**   **Black on violet**   £20

1961 (Feb.) Phosphor issue Edition dates Feb. 1961 - Mar. 1965 (31). *Contents* BP144/144/144 or BP149/149/149

BK130   **4s6d**   **Black on violet**   £30

1965 (July) New contents. Edition dates July 1965 - Mar. 1967 (7). *Contents* BP119/119/115

BK131   **4s6d**   **Black on slate blue**   £1

1965 (July) Phosphor issue. Edition dates July 1965 - Mar. 1968 (13). *Contents* BP152/152/146

BK132   **4s6d**   **Black on slate blue**   £1

1954 (Mar.) Edition dates Mar. 1954 - Sept. 1955 (10).
Contents BP88/88/87/84/78/75
BK133   **5s Black on buff**   From £25
1955 (Sept.) Edition dates Sept. 1955 - May 1956 (4)
Contents BP88/88/87/84/78/75 or BP101/101/99/96/92/89 mixed
BK134   **5s Black on buff**   From £25
1955 (Sept.) Edition dates Sept. 1955 - Jan. 1957 (9).
Contents BP101/101/99/96/92/89
BK135   **5s Black on buff**   From £20
1957 (Jan.) Edition dates Jan. - Nov. 1957 (6).
Contents BP101/101/100/96/92/89
BK136   **5s Black on buff**   From £15
1958 (Jan.) Edition dates Jan. - Nov. 1958 (5).
Contents BP102/102/101/92/89
BK137   **5s Black on buff**   From £15
1958 (July) Edition dates July - Nov. 1958 (2).
Contents BP102/102/101/92/89 or BP112/112/111/106/104 mixed
BK138   **5s Black on buff**   From £15

1958 (Jan.) Small G.P.O. Cypher. Edition date Jan. 1959
Contents BP112/112/92/89 or BP112/112/111/106/104 mixed
BK139   **5s Black on buff**   £15

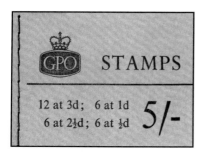

1959 (Jan.) Edition dates Jan. 1959 - Nov. 1960 (10)
Contents BP112/112/111/104
BK140   **5s Black on blue**   From £20

1959 (July) Graphite lined issue. Edition dates July 1959 - Sept. 1960 (3)
Contents BP138/138/137/134
BK141   **5s Black on blue**   From £75

1960 (Sept.) Phosphor issue. Edition dates Sept. 1960.
Contents BP144/144/142/140/139
BK142   **5s Black on blue**   £60

1961 (Jan.) Large G.P.O. Cypher. Edition dates Jan. 1961 - May 1965 (27). *Contents* BP112/112/111/106/104 cream or whiter paper.
BK143   **5s Black on blue**   From £25

1961 (Mar.) Phosphor issue. Edition dates Mar. 1961 - Jan. 1962 (4).
Contents BP144/144/142/140/139
BK144   **5s Black on blue**   From £65
1962 (Mar.) Edition dates Mar. 1962 - May 1965 (20). *Contents* BP144/143/140/139 cream or whiter paper.
BK145   **5s Black on blue**   From £50

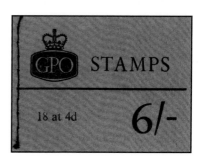

965 (June) Large G.P.O. Cypher. Edition dates June 1965 - Apr. 1967 (23).
Contents BP119/119/119
BK146   **6s Black on claret**   From £20

1965 (June) Phosphor issue. Edition dates June 1965 - Aug. 1967 (27).
Contents BP152/152/152
BK147   **6s Black on claret**   From £20

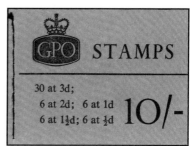

1961 (April) Undated. *Contents* BP112/112/112/112/112/110/108/106/104
BK148   **10s Black on green**   £75

1961 (Oct.) Edition date Oct. 1961. *Contents* BP112/112/112/112/112/110/106/104
BK149   **10s Black on green**   £85

1961 (April) Edition dates Apr. 1962 - Dec. 1964 (7).
Contents BP118/118/118/118/118/117/116/115
BK150   **10s Black on green**   From £55

1965 (Aug.) Edition dates Aug. 1965 - Nov. 1966 (5).
Contents BP119/119/119/119/118/115
BK151   **10s   Black on ochre**   £15

Machin Issues 1968 – 70

1968 (6 April) No watermark. Edition dates May - Aug. 1968 (3).
Contents BP176/171 or 172
BK154   **2s   Black on orange**   75

1967 (Feb.) Edition date Feb. 1967. *Contents* BP152/152/152/152/150/146
BK152   **10s   Black on buff**   5.00
1967 (Aug.) Edition dates Aug. 1967 and Feb. 1968 (2).
Contents BP152/152/152/152/150/146
BK153   **10s   Black on buff**   5.00

1968 (16 Sept.) Edition dates Sept. 1968 & Jan. 1969 (2).
Contents BP176/178
BK155   **2s   Black on grey**, Sept. 1968   60
BK155a   Jan. 1969   £130
1968 (16 Sept.) Edition dates Sept. 1968 & Jan. 1969 (3)
Contents BP177/178
BK156   **2s   Black on grey**   60
BK156a   Sept. 1968   £350
1969 (3 March) Edition dates Mar. - Dec. 1970 (12).
Contents BP180/181
BK157   **2s   Black on grey**   2.00

1968 (1 May) Large G.P.O. Cypher. Edition date May 1968.
Contents BP174/174/168
BK158   **4s6d   Black on slate blue**   6.00

1968 (July) - 70 Ships series. Printed in black on blue cover. G.P.O. emblem. *Contents* BP174/174/168

| BK159 | **4s6d The Cutty Sark**, July 1968 | 1.50 |

Contents BP175/175/168

| BK160 | **4s6d Golden Hind**, Sept. 1968 (16.9.68) | 1.50 |
| BK161 | **4s6d Discovery**, Nov. 1968 | 1.50 |

Contents BP179/179/168

BK162	**4s6d Queen Elizabeth 2**, Jan. 1968 (6.1.69)	1.50
BK163	**4s6d Sirius**, Mar. 1969	1.80
BK163a	May 1969	2.20
BK164	**4s6d Dreadnought**, July 1969	2.40
BK164a	Sept. 1969	4.00
BK165	**4s6d Mauretania**, Nov. 1969	3.50
BK165a	Jan. 1970	4.00
BK166	**4s6d Victory**, Mar. 1970	3.00
BK166a	May 1970	7.00

1970 (Aug.) Crown emblem. *Contents* BP179/179/168

| BK167 | **4s6d The Sovereign of the Seas**, Aug. 1970 | 3.00 |
| BK167a | Oct. 1970 | 8.00 |

1968 (27 Nov.) - 69 English Homes series. Printed in black on cinnamon cover. G.P.O. emblem. *Contents* BP182/182

BK168	**5s Igtham Mote**, Dec. 1968	1.75
BK169	**5s Little Moreton Hall**, Feb. 1969	1.50
BK170	**5s Long Melford Hall**, Apr. 1969	2.50
BK170a	June 1969	2.50
BK170b	Aug. 1969	3.00

1969 (Oct.) - 70 Crown emblem. *Contents* BP182/182

BK171	**5s Mompesson House**, Oct. 1969	2.50
BK171a	Dec. 1969	2.75
BK172	**5s Cumberland Terrace**, Feb. 1970	2.50
BK173	**5s The Vineyard**, Saffron Waldon, June 1970	2.40
BK173a	Aug. 1970	2.40
BK174	**5s Mereworth Castle**, Oct. 1970	3.50
BK174a	Dec. 1970	3.50

1970 (3 March) Philympia 1970, London. Red stitching. *Contents* BP182/182

| BK175 | **5s** Black on cinnamon | 1.50 |

1967 (21 Sept.) - 68 Edition dates Sept. 1967 - Jan. 1968 (5). *Contents* BP166/166/166

| BK176 | **6s Black on claret** | £28 |

1968 (Feb.) Edition dates Feb. - May 1968 (4). *Contents* BP166b/166b/166b

| BK177 | **6s Black on claret** | From £15 |

1968 (May) - 68 Edition date May 1968. *Contents* BP174/174/174

| BK178 | **6s Black on claret** | £215 |

1968 (4 June) - 69 Birds series. Printed in black on orange cover. G.P.O. emblem. *Contents* BP174/174/174

BK179	**6s Kingfisher**, June 1968	1.80
BK179a	July 1968	4.00
BK180	**6s Peregrine Falcon**, Aug. 1968	1.50

Contents BP175/175/175

BK181	**6s**	**Peregrine Falcon**, Sept. 1968	2.00
BK182	**6s**	**Pied Woodpecker**, Oct. 1968	2.00
BK182a		Nov. 1968	2.25
Bk183	**6s**	**Great Crested Grebe**, Dec. 1968	2.25
Bk184	**6s**	**Barn Owl**, Jan. 1969	2.25

Contents BP167/167/167 (Gum Arabic)

BK185	**6s**	**Barn Owl**, Feb. 1969	£150

Contents BP167/167/167 or BP179/179/179 mixed

BK186	**6s**	**Barn Owl**, Feb. 1969	From £50
BK187	**6s**	**Jay**, Mar. 1969	£50

Contents BP179/179/179 (PVA Gum)

BK188	**6s**	**Barn Owl**, Feb. 1969	2.00
BK189	**6s**	**Jay**, Mar. 1969	2.25
BK189a		May 1969	2.50
BK190	**6s**	**Puffin**, July 1969	2.50
BK190a		Sept. 1969	4.50

1969 (Nov.) - 70 Crown emblem. *Contents* BP179/179/179

BK191	**6s**	**Cormorant**, Nov. 1969	3.00
BK191a		Jan. 1970	3.90
BK192	**6s**	**Wren**, Apr. 1970	3.00
BK193	**6s**	**Golden Eagle**, Aug. 1970	3.00
BK193a		Oct. 1970	3.90

1968 (25 Mar.) Explorers series. Printed in black on purple cover. G.P.O. emblem. *Contents* BP174/174/174/174/173/168

BK194	**10s**	**Livingstone**, May 1968	5.50
BK194a		Aug. 1968	5.50

1968 (16 Sept.) Printed in black on yellow green cover.
Contents BP182/182/175/175/169

BK195	**10s**	**Scott**, Sept. 1968	3.75

Contents BP182/182/179/179/170

BK196	**10s**	**Mary Kingsley**, Feb. 1969 (1.69)	3.00
BK196a		May 1969	4.50
BK197	**10s**	**Shackleton**, Aug. 1969	4.50
BK197a		Nov. 1969	5.25

Contents BP182/182/179/167/170 or BP182/182/167/179/170

BK198	**10s**	**Mary Kingsley**, May 1969	£75

1970 (2 Feb.) Crown emblem. *Contents* BP182/182/179/179/170

BK199	**10s**	**Frobisher**, Feb. 1970	6.00
BK200	**10s**	**Captain Cook**, Nov. 1970	6.50

Decimal Machin Stitched Booklets

1971 (15 Feb.) - 74 Pillar Box series. Printed in black on old gold cover.
Contents 2 x ½p *plus* 2 x 2p (½p below 2p), 2 x 1p *plus* 2 x 1½p (1p above 1½p). Panes MP4/MP6 (OCP/PVA)

MB1	✓ 10p	**London Pillar Box 1855**, Feb. 1971	1.75
MB2		April 1971 (19.3.71)	1.75
MB3	10p	**Giant Pillar Box 1856**, June 1971 (1.6.71)	1.75

Contents 2 x ½p *plus* 2 x 2p (½p at right), 2 x 1p *plus* 2 x 1½p (1p at right). Panes MP5/MP7 (OCP/PVA)

MB4	10p	**Giant Pillar Box 1856**, Aug. 1971 (14.7.71)	2.50
MB5	10p	**Standard Pillar Box 1857**, Oct. 1971 (27.8.71)	2.50

Contents Panes MP19/MP20 (FCP/PVA)

MB6	10p	**Standard Pillar Box 1857**, Dec. 1971	£25
MB6a		*Panes* OCP/PVA, FCP/PVA	£40
MB6b		*Panes* OCP/PVA, OCP/PVA	3.00
MB7	10p	**Penfold Pillar Box 1866**, Feb. 1972 (8.12.71)	3.00
MB7a		*Panes* OCP/PVA, FCP/PVA	£40
MB7b		*Panes* FCP/PVA, OCP/PVA	£25
MB8	10p	**April 1972** (24.2.72)	2.25
MB8a		*Panes* OCP/PVA, FCP/PVA	£25
MB9	10p	**Double Aperture Box 1899**, June 1972 (12.4.72)	2.25
MB10		Aug. 1972 (8.6.72)	2.25
MB11	10p	**Mellor Pillar Box 1968**, Oct. 1972 (2.8.72)	2.25
MB12		Dec. 1972 (30.10.72)	2.25
MB13	10p	**King Edward VIII 1936**, Feb. 1973 (5.1.73)	2.25
MB14		April 1973	2.75
MB15	10p	**Standard Pillar Box 1952**, June 1973 (18.4.73)	2.00
MB16		Aug. 1973 (4.7.73)	£15
MB17	10p	**Double Aperture Mellor Box**, Oct. 1973 (16.8.73)	2.25
MB18		Dec. 1973 (12.11.73)	4.50
MB18a		*Panes* FCP/PVA, FCP/Dex	£10
MB18b		*Panes* FCP/Dex, FCP/PVA	
MB18c		*Panes* FCP/Dex, FCP/Dex	2.00

Contents Panes MP31/MP32 (FCP/Dex)

MB19	10p	**Double Aperture Mellor Box**, Feb. 1974 (17.12.79)	1.75
MB19a		*Panes* FCP/PVA, FCP/PVA	12.50
MB19b		*Panes* FCP/PVA, FCP/Dex	£10
MB19c		*Panes* FCP/Dex, FCP/PVA	3.00
MB20	10p	**Philatelic Posting Box 1974**, April 1974 (22.2.74)	1.75
MB20a		*Panes* FCP/PVA, FCP/PVA	12.50
MB20b		*Panes* FCP/PVA, FCP/Dex	£10
MB20c		*Panes* FCP/Dex, FCP/PVA	3.00
MB21		June 1974 (23.4.74)	1.75

1974 (23 July) - 76 Postal Uniforms series. Printed in black on old gold cover. *Contents* 2 x ½p *plus* 2 x 2p (½p at right), 2 x 1p *plus* 2 x 1½p (1p at right). Panes MP31/MP32 (FCP/Dex)

MB22	10p	**General Letter Carrier 1793**, Aug. 1974	1.20
MB23		Oct. 1974 (27.8.74)	1.20
MB24	10p	**District Letter Carrier 1837**, Dec. 1974 (25.10.74)	1.20
MB25		Feb. 1975, (12.1.74)	1.20
MB26	10p	**Letter Carrier 1855**, April 1975 (26.3.75)	1.20
MB27		June 1975 (21.5.75)	1.20
MB28		Aug. 1975 (27.6.75)	1.25
MB29		Oct. 1975 (3.10.75)	75
MB30		Jan. 1976 (16.3.76)	75

1971 (15 Feb.) - 73 Veteran Transport series. Printed in black on mauve cover.

Contents 5 x 2½p *plus* label, 4 x 2½p *plus* labels, 5 x ½p *plus* label. Panes MP10 or 11/MP8 or 9/MP1 or 2 (OCP/PVA)

MB31	✓ 25p	**Knife-board Omnibus 1850**, Feb. 1971	2.50
MB32	25p	**B.-type Omnibus 1910**, June 1971 (11.6.71)	3.50
MB33		Aug. 1971 (17.9.71)	6.50
MB34	25p	**Showman's Engine 1886**, Oct. 1971 (22.11.71)	6.00

Contents Panes MP24 or 25/MP21/MP18 (FCP/PVA)

MB35	25p	**Royal Mail Van 1913**, Feb. 1972 (23.12.71)	5.00
MB36		April 1972 (13.3.72)	5.50
MB37	25p	**Motor Wagonette 1901**, June 1972 (24.4.72).	5.50
MB38		Aug. 1972 (14.6.72)	6.00
MB39	25p	**London Taxi Cab 1913**, Oct. 1972 (17.7.72)	4.50
MB40		Dec. 1972 (19.10.72)	6.50
MB41		Dec. 1972 Issue 'S' (6.11.72)	4.50
MB42	25p	**Norwich Tramcar**, Feb. 1973 (26.2.73)	5.50

1971 (19 March) '80 Years of British Stamp Books'
Contents 5 x ½p *plus* label, 4 x 2½p *plus* labels, 5 x ½p *plus* label.
Panes MP10/MP8/MP1 (OCP/PVA)
MB43   **25p Black on mauve**, April 1971   2.50

1973 (7 June) 'Save the Children Fund'.
Contents 5 x ½p *plus* label, 4 x 2½p *plus* labels, 5 x ½p *plus* label.
Panes MP25/MP21/MP18 (FCP/PVA)
MB44   **25p Black on mauve**, June 1973   5.00

1973 (10 Aug.) Cover colours changed to black on buff.
Contents Panes MP27/MP27 (FCP/PVA)
MB61   **30p Oyster Catcher**, Aug. 1973   4.00

1971 (19 March) '80 Years of British Stamp Books'.
Contents Panes MP14/MP14 (FCP/PVA)
MB62   **30p Black on cerise**, April 1971   4.00

1974 (30 Jan.) 'Save the Children Fund'. *Contents* 5 x 3p CB *plus* label,
5 x 3p CB *plus* label. Panes MP28/MP28 (FCP/Dex)
MB63   **30p Black on red**, Spring 1974   8.00
MB63a   *Panes* FCP/PVA, FCP/PVA   3.00
MB63b   *Panes* FCP/PVA, FCP/Dex   £30
MB63c   *Panes* FCP/Dex, FCP/PVA   £20

1974 (21 June) 'Canada Life'. *Contents* Panes MP28/MP28 (FCP/Dex)
MB64   **30p Black on red**, June 1974   3.50

1971 (15 Feb.) - 73. British Birds series. Printed in black on cerise cover.
Contents 5 x 3p *plus* label, 5 x 3p *plus* label. Panes MP14 or 15 (OCP/PVA)
MB45   **30p Curlew**, Feb 1971   3.50
MB46   **30p Lapwing**, June 1971 (26.5.71)   3.50
MB47   Aug. 1971 (23.7.71)   3.50
Contents Panes MP27/MP27 (FCP/PVA)
MB48   **30p Robin**, Oct. 1971 (1.10.71)   3.50
MB49   Dec. 1971 (10.11.71)   4.00
MB49a   *Panes* OCP/PVA, OCP/PVA   £10
MB50   **30p Pied Wagtail**, Feb. 1972 (21.12.71)   3.50
MB51   April 1972 (9.2.72)   3.50
MB52   **30p Kestrel**, June 1972 (12.4.72)   3.50
MB53   Aug. 1972 (8.6.72)   3.50
MB54   **30p Black Grouse**, Oct. 1972 (31.7.72)   3.70
MB55   Dec. 1972 (30.10.72)   3.70
MB56   Dec. 1972 Issue 'S' (6.12.72)   4.00
MB57   **30p Skylark**, Feb. 1973 (29.1.73)   4.00
MB58   April 1973 (2.4.73)   3.60
MB59   **30p Oyster Catcher**, June 1973 (8.5.73)   3.60
MB60   Aug. 1973 (7.6.73)   7.00

1973 (12 Dec.) - 74. British Coins series. Printed in black on blue cover. *Contents* 5 x 3½p *plus* label, 5 x 3½p *plus* label. Panes MP34/MP34 (FCP/Dex)

MB65	**35p**	**Cuthred Penny 798-807**, Autumn 1973	2.00
		Panes FCP/PVA, FCP/PVA	6.00
		Panes FCP/PVA, FCP/Dex	9.00
		Panes FCP/Dex, FCP/PVA	7.25
MB66		April 1974 (10.4.74)	3.75
		Panes FCP/PVA, FCP/PVA	6.00
		Panes FCP/PVA, FCP/Dex	12.50
		Panes FCP/Dex, FCP/PVA	£10
MB67	**35p**	**Silver Groat 1279**, June 1974 (4.7.74)	2.50
		Panes FCP/PVA, FCP/PVA	£15
		Panes FCP/PVA, FCP/Dex	9.00
		Panes FCP/Dex, FCP/PVA	9.00

1974 (23 Oct.) 'Canada Life'. *Contents* 5 x 3½p CB *plus* label, 5 x 3½p CB *plus* label. Panes MP35/MP35 (FCP/Dex)

MB68	**35p**	**Black on blue**, Sept. 1974	2.50

1974 (9 Oct.) British Coins series continued. Printed in black on buff cover. *Contents* 5 x 4½p *plus* label, 5 x 4½p *plus* label. Panes MP36/MP36 (FCP/Dex)

MB69	**45p**	**Gold Crown 1592-5**, Sept. 1974	3.50
MB70		Dec. 1974 (1.11.74)	3.50

1974 (26 Nov.) Cover colours changed to black on orange-brown

MB71	**45p**	**Gold Crown 1592-5**, Dec. 1974	9.00

1971 (15 Feb.) - 72. British Flowers series. Printed in black on apple-green cover. *Contents* 6 x 3p, 4 x 3p *plus* 2 x 2½p, 5 x 2½p *plus* label, 5 x ½p *plus* label. Panes MP16/MP13/MP12/MP3 (OCP/PVA)

MB72	✓	**50p**	**Large Bindweed**, Feb. 1971	6.00
MB73		**50p**	**Primrose**, May 1971 (24.3.71)	6.50
MB74		**50p**	**Honeysuckle**, Aug. 1971 (28.6.71)	6.50

Contents Panes MP29/MP26/MP22/MP17 (FCP/PVA)

MB75	**50p**	**Hop**, Nov. 1971 (17.9.71)	6.00
		Panes OCP/OCP/FCP/FCP	£45
		Panes OCP/FCP/FCP/FCP	£75

Contents Panes MP29/MP26/MP23/MP18 (FCP/PVA)

MB76	**50p**	**Common Violet**, Feb. 1972 (24.12.71)	6.00
MB77	**50p**	**Lords and Ladies**, May 1972 (13.3.72)	6.00
MB78	**50p**	**Wood Anemone**, Aug. 1972 (31.5.72)	6.50
MP79	**50p**	**Deadly Nightshade**, Nov. 1972 (15.9.72)	6.50

1973 (19 Jan.) - 74. 'Canada Life'. *Contents* Panes MP29/MP26/MP23/MP18 (FCP/PVA)

MB80	**50p**	**Black on apple-green**, Feb. 1973	5.00
MB81		April 1973 (26.2.73)	6.50
MB82		May 1973 (2.4.73)	6.50
MB83		Aug 1973 (14.6.73)	9.50

Contents 5 x 3½p *plus* label, 5 x 3p *plus* label, 5 x 3p CB *plus* label.
Panes MP34/MP34/MP33 (FCP/Dex)

MB84	**50p**	**Black on moss-green**, Autumn 1973 (14.11.73)	
		Panes PVA/PVA/PVA	5.50
		Panes PVA/PVA/Dex	£12
		Panes PVA/Dex/Dex	17.50
		Panes PVA/Dex/PVA	£25
		Panes Dex/PVA/PVA	£20
		Panes Dex/PVA/Dex	17.50
		Panes Dex/Dex/PVA	£12
MB85		**March 1974** (18.2.74)	3.50
		Panes PVA/PVA/Dex	£15
		Panes PVA/Dex/Dex	£15

1974 (13 Nov.) 'Canada Life'.
Contents 5 x 4½p *plus* label, 5 x 4½p *plus* label, 5 x 4½p *plus* label, 5 x 3½p
CB *plus* label. Panes MP36/MP36/MP35 (FCP/Dex)

MB86	**85p**	**Black on cerise**, Sept. 1974	6.00

Prestige Books and Panes

Prestige Books and Panes

Prices for panes are for the complete pane including stubs

1969 £1 'Stamps for Cooks'

1969 (1 Dec.) £1 'Stamps for Cooks' booklet. No watermark. Perf. 15 x 14

| PB1 | Complete Book, stitched | 7.50 |
| PB1a | Complete book stapled | £250 |

Pane printed by Harrison on OCP/PVA

SP1	**15 x 5d 2B Deep blue** *plus* 'Method.....' label. **Stitched.**	3.00
SP1a	Broad bands	£550
SP1b	Missing phosphor	£110
SP1c	Uncoated paper	£200
SP1d	**Stapled**	£10
SP1e	Uncoated paper	£200
	First Day Covers (4)	£18
SP1f	'Specimen' overprint	£450

Pane printed by Harrison on OCP/PVA

SP2	**15 x 4d CB Vermillion. Stitched.**	2.50
SP2a	Missing phosphor	£75
SP2b	Uncoated paper	£200
SP2c	**Stapled**	£10
SP2d	'Specimen' overprint	£325

SP3	**15 x 4d Red (CB)** *plus* 'Method.....' label. **Stitched.**	2.50
SP3a	Missing phosphor	£100
SP3b	Uncoated paper	£110
SP3c	**Stapled**	£10
SP3d	'Specimen' overprint	£325

Pane printed by Harrison on OCP/PVA

SP4	**6 x 1d 2B Yellow-olive, 3 x 4d LB Vermillion, 3 x 4d RB Vermillion, 3 x 5d 2B Deep blue. Stitched.**	£10
SP4a	Missing phosphor	£150
SP4b	Uncoated paper	£750
SP4c	**Stapled**	£30
SP4d	Missing phosphor (stapled)	£350
SP4e	'Specimen' overprint	£1400

1972 £1 'The Story of Wedgwood'

1972 (24 May). £1 'The Story of Wedgwood' booklet. No Wmk. Perf. 15 x 14

| PB2 | Complete book | 38.00 |

Pane printed by Harrison on FCP/PVA

SP5	**12 x 3p 2B Ultramarine** plus label	2.75
SP5a	Broad bands	£165
SP5b	Missing phosphor	£175

Pane printed by Harrison on FCP/PVA

SP6   **3 x 2½p CB Magenta, 3 x 2½p RB Magenta**
        and 6 x 3p 2B Ultramarine   5.00
SP6a   Missing phosphor
SP6b   Broad bands   £375

Pane printed by Harrison on FCP/PVA

SP7   **3 x ½p 2B Turquoise, 3 x 2½p LB Magenta,**
        3 x 2½p CB Magenta and 3 x 2½p RB Magenta   6.00
SP7a   Missing phosphor   £1750
SP7b   Phosphor bands are printed on the back   £2500
SP7c   Broad bands   £375

Pane printed by Harrison on FCP/PVA

SP8   **3 x ½p 2B Turquoise, ½p LB Turquoise**
        and 2 x 2½p LB Magenta   £37
SP8a   Broad band left
SP8b   Missing phosphor

1980 £3 'The Story of Wedgwood'

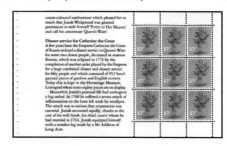

1980 (16 April). £3 'The Story of Wedgwood' booklet. No wmk. Perf. 15 x 14

PB3   Complete book   3.75

Pane printed by Harrison on FCP/PVAD

SP9   **9 x 12p 2B Yellow green**   2.25
SP9a   Broad bands   £220
SP9b   Missing phosphor   £27
SP9c   Phosphor printed on the back only   £950

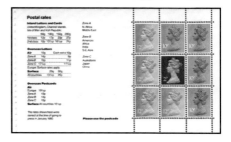

Pane printed by Harrison on FCP/PVAD

SP10   **9 x 10p CB Orange**   2.25
SP10a   Missing phosphor   £33
SP10b   Phosphor bands printed on the back only   £650

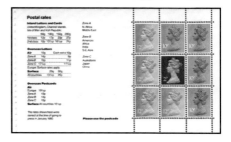

Pane printed by Harrison on FCP/PVAD

SP11   **6 x 2p 2B Deep green**   50
SP11a   Broad bands at centre   £250
SP11b   Missing phosphor   £43
SP11c   Phosphor bands also printed on the back   £600
SP11d   6 x 2p Missing red (£1 Royal Mail Stamps, etc.)
        from booklet illustration on label.   £1300

Pane printed by Harrison on FCP/PVAD

SP12	**2p 2B Deep green, 10p LB Orange,**	
	3 x 10p CB Orange and 4 x 12p 2B	
	Yellow green plus label	2.50
SP12a	Missing phosphor	£38
SP12b	Phosphor bands also printed on the back	£950
SP12c	Broad band	

1982 £4 'Story of Stanley Gibbons'

1982 (19 May) £4 'Story of Stanley Gibbons' booklet. No wmk. Perf. 15 x 14

| PB4 | Complete book | 5.75 |

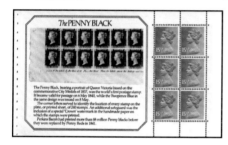

Pane printed by Harrison on FCP/PVAD

SP13	**6 x 15½p 2B Pale violet**	2.25
SP13a	Broad bands at centre	£135
SP13b	Missing phosphor	£65
SP13c	Phosphor bands also printed on the back	£350

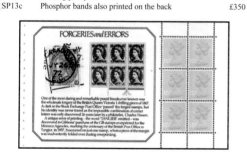

Pane printed by Harrison on FCP/PVAD

SP14	**3 x 12½p LB Light emerald and 3 x 12½p RB**	
	Light emerald	2.00
SP14a	Broad bands	£500
SP14b	Missing phosphor	£35
SP14c	Phosphor bands also printed on the back	£475

Pane printed by Harrison on FCP/PVAD

SP15	**2p 2B Deep green, 3p 2B Magenta,**	
	3 x 12½p LB Light emerald, 12½p CB Light emerald	
	and 3 x 12½p RB Light emerald	3.00
SP15a	Broad bands at centre	£395
SP15b	Missing phosphor	£160
SP15c	Phosphor bands also printed on the back	

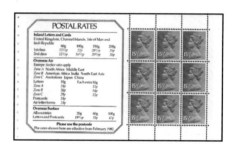

Pane printed by Harrison on FCP/PVAD

SP16	**9 x 2B 15½p Pale violet**	2.05
SP16a	Broad bands	£200
SP16b	Missing phosphor	£40
SP16c	Two phosphor bands also printed on the back	£950

1983 £4 'Story of the Royal Mint'

1983 (14 Sept.) £4 'The Story of the Royal Mint' booklet. Perf. 15 x 14

| PB5 | Complete book | 5.00 |

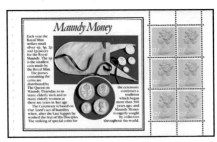

Pane printed by Harrison on FCP/PVAD

SP17	**3 x 12½p LB Light emerald** and **3 x 12½p RB**	
	Light emerald	1.50
SP17a	Broad band on column 2	£595
SP17b	Missing phosphor	£375
SP17c	Phosphor bands also printed on the back	£550

Pane printed by Harrison on FCP/PVAD

SP18	**3 x 12½p LB Light emerald** and **3 x 12½p RB**	
	Light emerald	1.50
SP18a	Broad band on column 2	£375
SP18b	Missing phosphor	£390
SP18c	Phosphor bands also printed on the back	£550

Pane printed by Harrison on ACP/PVAD

| SP19 | **3p Magenta, 3½p Dull chestnut** and **6 x 16p Deep drab** | 3.50 |

1984 £4 'The Story of our Christian Heritage'

1984 (4 Sept.). £4 'The Story of our Christian Heritage' booklet. Perf. 15 x 14

| PB6 | Complete book | £15 |

Pane printed by Harrison on ACP/PVAD

SP21	**6 x 17p Grey blue**	2.50
	First Day Cover (pane SP21 - stamps only)	4.50
	First Day Covers (4)	£13

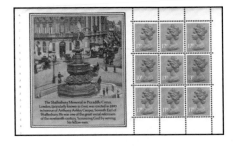

Pane printed by Harrison on FCP/PVAD

| SP22 | **3 x 13p LB Chestnut** and **3 x 13p RB Chestnut** | 2.25 |
| SP22a | Missing phosphor | £230 |

Pane printed by Harrison on ACP/PVAD

| SP20 | **9 x 16p Deep drab** | 3.00 |

Pane printed by Harrison on FCP/PVAD

SP23	**10p 2B Orange**, Type II, **13p Deep chestnut LB**	
	and **7 x 17p 2B Grey blue**	£20
SP23a	Missing phosphor	
SP23b	Phosphor bands also printed on the back	

Pane printed by Harrison on FCP/PVAD

SP24	**3 x 13p LB Chestnut** and **3 x 13p RB Chestnut**	2.25
SP24a	Broad band on column 2	£350
SP24b	Missing phosphor	£275

1985 £5 'The Story of The Times'

1985 (8 Jan.) £5 'The Story of The Times' booklet. Perf. 15 x 14

PB7	Complete book	£10

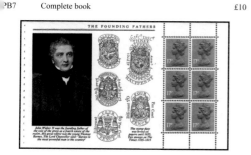

Pane printed by Harrison on ACP/PVAD

SP25	**6 x 17p Grey blue**	2.50

Pane printed by Harrison on FCP/PVAD

SP26	**9 x 13p CB Chestnut**	2.70
SP26a	Missing phosphor	£495
SP26b	Phosphor bands also printed on the back	£895

Pane printed by Harrison on FCP/PVAD

SP27	**4p LB Greenish blue**, **4p RB Greenish blue**,	
	2 x 13p LB Chestnut, **2 x 13p RB Chestnu**,	
	2 x 17p 2B Grey blue and **34p 2B Ochre brown**	6.50
SP27a	Broad bands on columns 2 and 3	£1350
SP27b	Missing phosphor	£1895
SP27c	Phosphor bands also printed on back	£3000

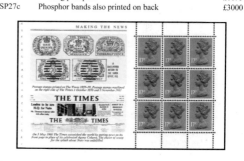

Pane printed by Harrison on ACP/PVAD

SP28	**9 x 17p Grey blue**	2.50

1986 £5 'The Story of British Rail'

1986 (18 March) £5 'The Story of British Rail' booklet. Perf. 15 x 14

PB8	Complete book	12.50

Pane printed by Harrison on ACP/PVAD
| SP29 | **9 x 17p Grey blue** | 2.70 |
| SP29a | 9 x 17p Missing yellow from label (inscription, etc.) | £1350 |

Pane printed by Harrison on FCP/PVAD
SP30	**9 x 12p CB Emerald**	2.50
SP30a	Missing phosphor	£165
SP30b	Phosphor bands also printed on the back	£595

Pane printed by Harrison on FCP/PVAD
SP31	**3 x 12p LB Emerald, 3 x 12p RB Emerald,**	
	2 x 17p 2B Grey blue and 31p 2B Mauve	£10
SP31a	Broad bands	£1500
SP31b	Missing phosphor	£1150
SP31c	Phosphor bands also printed on the back	£1300

Pane printed by Harrison on FCP/PVAD
| SP32 | **6 x 17p 2B Grey blue** | 2.50 |

1987 £5 'The Story of P & O'

1987 (3 March) £5 'The Story of P & O' booklet. No wmk. Perf. 15 x 14

'A' phosphor ink.

| PB9 | Complete book | 10.95 |

Pane printed by Harrison on ACP/PVAD
| SP33 | **9 x 18p Olive grey** | 3.00 |

Pane printed by Harrison on FCP/PVAD.
| SP34 | **9 x 13p CB Pale chestnut** | 2.50 |

Pane printed by Harrison on FCP/PVAD.

| SP35 | **1p Crimson** (RB), **2 x 13p Pale chestnut** (RB), **5 x 18p Olive grey** (2B) and **26p Rosine** (2B) | 7.75 |

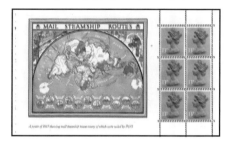

Pane printed by Harrison on FCP/PVAD.

| SP36 | **6 x 13p CB Pale chestnut** *plus* label | 2.20 |

1989 £5 'The Story of The Financial Times'

1988 (9 Feb.) £5 'The Story of The Financial Times' booklet. Perf. 15 x 14

| PB10 | Complete book | 16.00 |

Pane printed by Questa on ACP/PVAD

SP37	**9 x 18p Grey olive**	3.50
	First Day Cover (pane SP38 - stamps only)	4.50
	First Day Covers (4)	£14

Pane printed by Questa on FCP/PVA

| SP38 | **6 x 13p CB Pale chestnut** | 2.60 |
| SP38a | Missing phosphor | £500 |

Pane printed by Questa on FCP/PVA

SP39	**3 x 13p LB Pale chestnut, 3 x 13p RB Pale chestnut, 18p 2B Deep grey-olive, 22p 2B Yellow green and 34p 2B Ochre brown**	£11
SP39a	Broad bands	£1150
SP39b	Missing phosphor	£1150
SP39c	18p printed in blackish olive	£85
SP39d	Double print of 18p *1	£750

*1 This variety varies considerably due to the position of the second print

Pane printed by Questa on ACP/PVAD

| SP40 | **6 x 18p Grey olive** | 2.75 |

1989 £5 'The Scots Connection'

1989 (21 Mar.) £5 'The Scots Connection' booklet. No wmk. Perf. 15 x 14

| PB11 | Complete book | £12 |

No.   U/M   No.   U/M

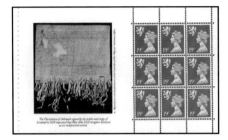

Pane printed by Questa on ACP/PVAD

SP41   **9 x 19p Orange red**   3.00
         First Day Cover (pane SP42 - stamps only)   4.50
         First Day Covers (4)   £14

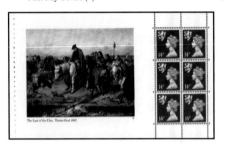

Pane printed by Questa on FCP/PVA

SP42   **6 x 14p CB Dark blue**   1.80

Pane printed by Questa on FCP/PVA

SP43   **5 x 14p LB Dark blue, 2 x 19p 2B Orange red**
         and 23p 2B Bright green *plus* label   9.50
         Imperforate   £1400
         Error. Perforated as a pane of six   £2000

Pane printed by Questa on ACP/PVAD

SP44   **6 x 19p Scotland Orange red**   2.50

1990 £5 'London Life'

1990 (20 Mar.) £5 'London Life' booklet. No wmk. Perf. 15 x 14

PB12   Complete book   13.50

Pane printed by Harrison on ACP/PVAD

SP45   **4 x 20p Alexandra Palace**   2.00

Pane printed by Harrison on ACP/PVAD

SP46   **6 x 20p Black** Penny Black Anniversary stamp   2.50
         First Day Cover (pane SP45 - stamps only)   5.00
         First Day Covers (4)   £16

Pane printed by Harrison on FCP/PVAD

SP47   **15p RB Light blue, 20p 2B Black, 50p 2B Bistre,**
         2nd RB Light blue, 1st 2B Black, 15p 2B Light blue
         & 20p Black (Penny Black Anniversary stamps),
         20p 2B Black, 29p 2B Purple *plus* label   £1.

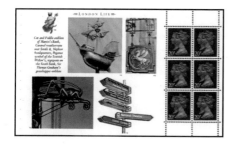

Pane printed by Harrison on ACP/PVAD

SP48   **6 x 20p Black** Penny Black Anniversary stamp   2.50

Pane printed by Questa on ACP/PVA

SP51 **6 x 22p Orange red, 2 x 33p Emerald** *plus* label   5.50

1991 £6 'Alias Agatha Christie'

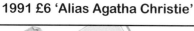

Pane printed by Questa on FCP/PVA

SP52   **6 x 17p CB Dark blue**   2.25
SP52a   Missing phosphor

1991 (19 March) £6 'Alias Agatha Christie' booklet. Perf. 15 x 14

PB13   Complete book   9.50

1992 £6 'Cymru Wales'

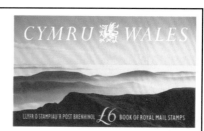

1992 (25 Feb.) £6 'Cymru Wales' booklet. Perf 15 x 14

PB14   Complete book   9.00

Pane printed by Questa on FCP/PVA

SP49   **6 x 17p CB Dark blue**   2.25
SP49a   Missing phosphor

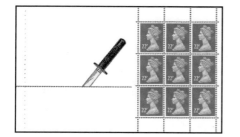

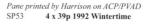

Pane printed by Questa on ACP/PVA

SP50   **9 x 22p Orange red** *plus* label   4.00
       First Day Cover (pane SP51 - stamps only)   5.00
       First Day Covers (4)   £14

Pane printed by Harrison on ACP/PVAD

SP53   **4 x 39p 1992 Wintertime**   3.00

No.   U/M   No.   U/M

Pane printed by Questa on FCP/PVA

| SP54 | **6 x 18p CBar Bright green** | 2.50 |
| SP54a | Missing phosphor | |

Pane printed by Questa on FCP/PVA

SP55	**1 x 2nd RB Bright blue, 1st 2B Orange red, 2 x 33p 2B Emerald, Wales 2 x 18p RB Bright green, 2 x 24p 2B Chestnut**	8.00
SP55a	Missing phosphor	£3000
SP55b	Solid all over phosphor	£2500

Pane printed by Questa on ACP/PVA

| SP56 | **6 x 24p Wales Chestnut** | 2.75 |

1992 £6 'Tolkien'

1992 (27 Oct.) £6 'Tolkien' booklet. Perf. 15 x 14

| PB15 | Complete book | 9.00 |

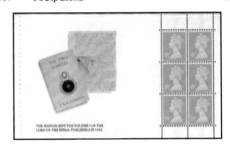

Pane printed by Questa on ACP/PVA

| SP57 | **6 x 24p Brown** | 2.50 |

Pane printed by Questa on FCP/PVA

| SP58 | **6 x 18p CB Bright green** | 2.30 |

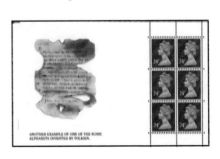

Pane printed by Questa on FCP/PVA

| SP59 | **2 x 18p RB Bright green, 2 x 24p 2B Chestnut, 2 x 39p 2B Bright mauve, 2nd CB Bright blue, 1st 2B Orange red** | 7.50 |

Pane printed by Questa on ACP/PVA

| SP60 | **6 x 24p Chestnut** | 2.5 |

1993 £6 'The Story of Beatrix Potter'

1993 (10 Aug.) £6 'The Story of Beatrix Potter' booklet. Perf. 15 x 14

PB16   Complete book   £10

Pane printed by Harrison on OFNP/PVAD
SP61   **4 x 1st 2B 1994 Greetings**   1.70

Pane printed by Questa on OFNP/PVA
SP62   **3 x 18p LB Bright green, 3 x 24p 2B Chestnut**
         from Northern Ireland, Scotland and Wales   6.00

Pane printed by Questa on OFNP/PVA
SP63   **3 x LB 2nd Bright blue, 3 x 1st 2B Orange red**   3.30

Pane printed by Questa on OFNP/PVA
SP64   **2 x 18p LB Bright green, 2 x 33p 2B Emerald,**
         2 x 39p 2B Mauve, 2nd LB Bright blue,
         plus label   5.50
SP64a   Missing phosphor   £2250

1994 £6.04 'Northern Ireland'

1994 (26 July) £6.04 'Northern Ireland' booklet

PB17   Complete book   11.50

Pane printed by Harrison in Photogravure on OFPP/PVAD
SP65   **4 x 30p Mourne Mountains**   2.50

No.   U/M   No.   U/M

Pane printed by Questa in Lithography on OFNP/PVA
SP66   **6p 2B Lime green, 19p LB Bistre,**
         4 x 25p 2B Salmon pink   7.50
SP66a   6p Misplaced left

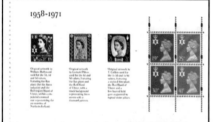

Pane printed by Questa in Lithography on OFNP/PVA
SP67   **2 x 19p LB Bistre, 4 x 25p 2B Salmon pink,**
         30p 2B Sage green, 41p 2B Stone *plus label*   4.00

Pane printed by Questa in Lithography on OFNP/PVA
SP68   **19p LB Bistre, 25p 2B Salmon pink, 30p 2B Sage green**
         41p 2B Stone   3.20
SP68a   Missing phosphor

1995 £6 'The National Trust'

1995 (25 April) £6 'The National Trust' booklet

PB18   Complete book   £11

Pane printed by Harrison in Gravure on OFNP/PVAD
SP69   **6 x 25p 2B 1995 National Trust**   2.60

Pane printed by Questa in Lithography on OFNP/PVA
SP70   **10p 2B Dull orange, 19p LB Bistre, 19p RB Bistre,**
         2 x 25p 2B Salmon pink, 30p 2BSage green,
         35p 2B Yellow, 41p 2B Stone *plus label*   £11
SP70a   Missing phosphor

Pane printed by Questa in Lithography on OFNP/PVA
SP71   **3 x 19p RB Bistre, 3 x 25p 2B Salmon pink** from
         Northern Ireland, Scotland and Wales   4.00

Pane printed by Questa in Lithography on OFNP/PVA
SP72   **3 x 19p LB Bistre, 3 x 19p RB Bistre**   5.00

1996 £6.48 'European Football Championship'

1996 (14 May) £6.48 'European Football Championship' booklet
Perf. 14½ x 14

PB19	Complete book	9.50

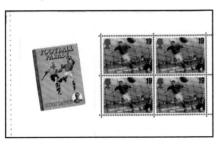

Pane printed by Questa in Lithography on OFNP/PVA

SP73	**4 x 19p CB 1996 Football**	1.75
SP73a	Missing phosphor	

Pane printed by Questa in Lithography on OFNP/PVA

SP74	**4 x 25p 2B 996 Football**	2.25
SP74a	Missing phosphor	

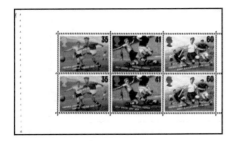

Pane printed by Questa in Lithography on OFNP/PVA

SP75	**2 x 35p 2B , 2 x 41p 2B , 2 x 60p 2B 1996 Football**	4.50

Pane printed by Questa in Lithography on OFNP/PVA

SP76	**2 x 25p 2B Salmon-pink, and 2 each x 25p** from Northern Ireland, Scotland and Wales (all 2B) *plus* label	3.50

1997 £6.15 '75 Years of the BBC'

1997 (23 Sept.) £6.15 '75 years of the BBC' booklet
Perf. 15 x 14 elliptical

PB20	Complete book	9.50

Pane printed by Harrison in Gravure on OFNP/PVA

SP77	**1 each x 26p 2B Red-brown** and **37p 2B Amethyst** from Northern Ireland, Scotland and Wales	3.75

Pane printed by Harrison in Gravure on OFNP/PVA

SP78   **4 x 26p 2B Gold, 4 x 1st 2B Gold** *plus* label   4.00

Pane printed by Walsall in Gravure on OFNP/PVA

SP81   **9 x 26p 2B Brown** (wilding design)   4.00

Pane printed by Harrison in Gravure on OFNP/PVA

SP79   **3 x 20p RB Bright green, 3 x 26p 2B Reddish brown**   3.00

Pane printed by Walsall in Gravure on OFNP/PVA

SP82   **3 x 20p LB Pastel green, 3 x RB Pastel green**
          (Wilding design)   3.00

Pane printed by Harrison in Gravure on OFNP/PVA

SP80   **4 x 20p CB 1996 Television**   2.50

1998 £7.49 'The Definitive Portrait'

Pane printed by Walsall in Gravure on OFNP/PVA

SP83   **2 x 20p LB Bright green, 2 x 20p RB Bright green**
          (Wilding design), 2 x 26p 2B Brown (Wilding design),
          2 x 37p 2B Red-purple (Wilding design) *plus*
          'National symbols' label   5.50

1998 (10 Mar.) £7.49 'The Definitive Portrait' booklet
Perf. 15 x 14 elliptical

PB21   Complete book   12.50

Pane printed by Walsall in Gravure on OFNP/PVA

SP84   **3 x 26p 2B Brown** (wilding design),
          3 x 37p 2B Red-purple (wilding design)   4.50

1998 £6.16 'Breaking Barriers'

1998 (13 Oct.) £6.16 'Breaking Barriers' Booklet
Perf. 15 x 14 elliptical

PB22   Complete book   £13

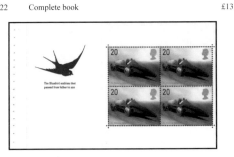

Pane printed by Walsall in Gravure on OFNP/PVA
SP85   **2 x 20p LB Multicoloured** and **2 x 20p RB**
       Multicoloured   4.00

Pane printed by Walsall in Gravure on OFNP/PVA
SP86   **1 x 20p RB** Country stamp from each of Scotland, Wales and
       Northern Ireland and **3 x 43p 2B Sepia-brown**   5.50

Pane printed by Walsall in Gravure on OFNP/PVA
SP87   **3 x 2nd RB Bright blue** plus **1 x 26p 2B** Country stamp
       each from Scotland, Wales and N. Ireland   4.50

Pane printed by Walsall in Gravure on OFNP/PVA
SP88   **2 x 10p 2B Deep orange, 3 x 2nd LB Bright blue,**
       3 x 43p 2B Chocolate-brown *plus* label   5.50

1999 £7.54 'Profile on Print'

1999 (16 Feb.) £7.54 'Profile on Print' Booklet

PB23   Complete book   £16

Pane printed by De La Rue in Gravure on OFNP/PVA
SP89   **8 x 1st 2B Orange red** *plus* label   3.50
SP89a   Broad band left   £80

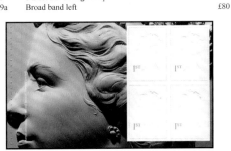

Pane printed by Walsall, Litho and embossed, on OFNP/PVA
SP90   **4 x 1st**   5.00

Pane printed by Enschedé in Intaglio on Uncoated paper/PVA

SP91   **4 x 1st 2B Greyish-black**   5.00

Pane printed by Questa in Gravure on OFNP/PVA

SP94   **4 x 20p CB** Special stamps   1.60

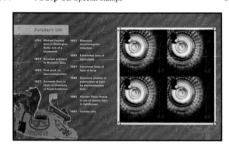

Pane printed by Harrison by Letterpress on Uncoated paper/PVA

SP92   **4 x 1st 2B Black**   5.00
SP92a   Missing phosphor

Pane printed by Questa in Lithography on OFNP/PVA

SP95   **4 x 44p 2B** Special stamps   8.50

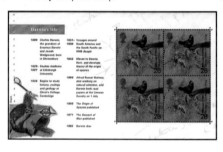

Pane printed by Questa in Litho on OFNP/PVA

SP93   **9 x 1st 2B Orange-red**   4.50

Pane printed by Questa in Lithography on OFNP/PVA

SP96   **4 x 26p 2B** Special stamps   6.50

1999 £6.99 'World Changers'

1999 (21 Sep.) £6.99 'World Changers' Booklet

PB24   Complete book   £15

Pane printed by Questa in Gravure on OFNP/PVA

SP97   **4 x 63p 2B** Special stamps   9.00

Pane printed by Questa in Gravure on OFNP/PVA

SP98   **4 x 1p 2B Crimson, 3 x 19p CB Bistre,**
        1 x 26p 2B Chestnut *plus* label   2.50

Pane printed by Walsall in Gravure on OFNP/PVA

SP101   **4 x 19p RB Bistre** and **2 x 38p 2B Ultramarine**   9.50

2000 £7.50 'Special by Design'

2000 (15 Feb.) £7.50 'Special by Design' Booklet

PB25   Complete book   £17

Pane printed by Walsall in Gravure on OFNP/PVA

SP102   **6 x 1st 2B Black & buff**   7.00

2000 £7.03 'The Life of the Century'

2000 (4 Aug.) £7.03 'The Life of the Century' booklet

PB26   Complete book   12.50

Pane printed by Walsall in Gravure on OFNP/PVA

SP99   **8 x 1st 2B Millennium** *plus* label   3.50

Pane printed by Walsall in Gravure on OFNP/PVA

SP100   **3 x 1st 2B Orange-red Scotland, 3 x 1st 2B Orange-red**
        Wales and **3 x 1st 2B Orange-red N. Ireland**   5.50

Pane printed by Questa in Gravure on OFNP/PVA

SP103   **6 x 2nd CB Scotland emblem, 2 x 65p 2B Scotland**
        emblem *plus* label   4.50

Pane printed by Questa in Gravure on OFNP/PVA
SP104   **9 x 1st 2B Millennium**   4.00

Pane printed by Walsall in Gravure on OFNP/PVA
SP107   **2 x 65p 2B Special stamps**   2.10

Pane printed by Questa in Gravure on OFNP/PVA
SP105   **4 x 27p 2B Special stamps**   5.50

Pane printed by Walsall in Gravure on OFNP/PVA
SP108   **4 x 45p 2B Special stamps**   2.50

Pane printed by Questa in Gravure on OFNP/PVA
SP106   **4 x 27p 2B Special stamps**   5.50

Pane printed by Walsall in Gravure on OFNP/PVA
SP109   **2 x 65p 2B Special stamps**   2.50

2000 £7 'A Treasury of Trees'

Pane printed by Walsall in Gravure on OFNP/PVA
SP110   **4 x 1st 2B Millennium, 4 x 2nd CB Wales emblem**
            plus label   6.50

2000 (18 Sep.) £7.00 'A Treasury of Trees' Booklet

PB27   Complete book   £14

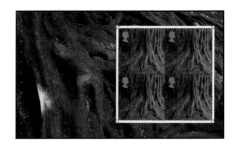

Pane printed by Walsall in Gravure on OFNP/PVA

SP111   **4 x 2nd CB Special stamps**   2.00

Pane printed by Questa in Gravure on OFNP/PVA

SP114   **4 x 1st 2B Special stamps**   3.00

2001 £6.76 'Unseen and Unheard'

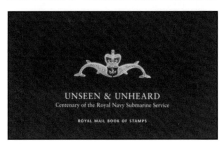

Pane printed by Questa in Gravure on OFNP/PVA

SP115   **4 x 1st 2B Scotland emblem, 4 x 'E' 2B Scotland
         emblem *plus* label**   4.50

2001 (22 Oct.) £6.76 'Unseen and Unheard' Booklet

PB28   Complete book   17.50

2002 £7.29 'A Gracious Accession'

Pane printed by Questa in Gravure on OFNP/PVA

SP112   **2 x 1st 2B Special stamps and 2 x 65p 2B Special
         stamps**   9.00

2002 (6 Feb) £7.29 'A Gracious Accession' Booklet

PB29   Complete book   £14

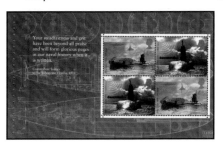

Pane printed by Questa in Gravure on OFNP/PVA

SP113   **2 x 2nd CB Special stamps and 2 x 45p 2B Special
         stamps**   9.00

Pane printed by Enschedé in Gravure on OFNP/PVA

SP116   **4 x 'E' 2B Dark blue, 4 x 2nd CB Bright blue
         plus label**   3.70

Pane printed by Enschedé in Gravure on OFNP/PVA

SP117   **1 x 2nd CB, 1 x 1st 2B, 1 x 'E' 2B and
1 x 45p 2B** Special stamps   5.00

Pane printed by Enschedé in Gravure on OFNP/PVA

SP118   **1 x 1st 2B, 1 x 'E' 2B, 1 x 45p 2B and
1 x 65p 2B** Special stamps   6.00

Pane printed by Enschedé in Gravure on OFNP/PVA

SP119   **4 x 1st 2B (Wilding), 4 x 2nd CB (Wilding)**
plus **blank label**   7.00

2002 £6.83 'Across the Universe'

2002 (24 Sep.) £6.83 'Across the Universe' Booklet

PB30   Complete book   £13

Pane printed by Questa in Gravure on OFNP/PVA

SP120   **4 x 1st 2B England emblem, 4 x 2nd CB England
emblem and 1 x 1st 2B Scotland emblem**   4.00

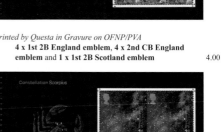

Pane printed by Questa in Gravure on OFNP/PVA

SP121   **4 x 1st 2B** Special stamps   3.00

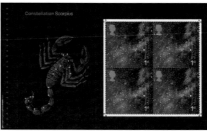

Pane printed by Questa in Gravure on OFNP/PVA

SP122   **4 x 1st 2B Gold, 4 x 'E' 2B** *plus* **label**   3.50

Pane printed by Questa in Gravure on OFNP/PVA

SP123   **4 x 1st 2B** Special stamps   3.00

2003 £6.99 'Microcosmos'

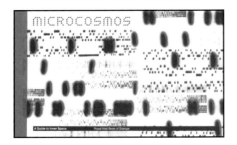

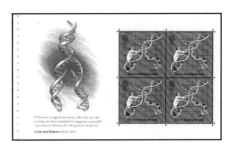

Pane printed by Enschedé in Lithography on OFNP/PVA
SP127   **4 x E 2B Special stamps**   3.00

2003 (25 Feb.) £6.99 'Microcosmos' Booklet
PB31   Complete book   11.50

2003 £7.46 'A Perfect Coronation'

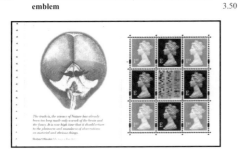

Pane printed by Enschedé in Lithography on OFNP/PVA
SP124   **4 x 1st 2B N. Ireland emblem, 5 x 2nd CB N. Ireland
           emblem**   3.50

2003 (2 June) £7.46 'A Perfect Coronation'

PB32   Complete book   £32

Pane printed by Enschedé in Gravure on OFNP/PVA.
SP125   **4 x 1st 2B Gold, 4 x 'E' 2B Dark blue**
           plus label   4.50

Pane printed by Walsall in Gravure on OFNP/PVA
SP128   **4 x 1st 2B Gold, 4 x 2nd CB Bright blue**
           plus label   3.50

Pane printed by Enschedé in Lithography on OFNP/PVA
SP126   **2 x 2nd CB Special stamps** and **2 x 1st 2B
           Special stamps**   2.00

Pane printed by Walsall in Gravure on OFNP/PVA
SP129   **4 x 1st 2B Special stamps**   2.50

Pane printed by Walsall in Gravure on OFNP/PVA
SP130   **4 x 1st 2B Special stamps**   2.50

Pane printed by Walsall in Gravure on OFNP/PVA
SP131   **2 x 47p 2B Wilding design, 2 x 68p 2B Wilding design**
           and £1 2B 'Dulac' design   £32

2004 £7.44 'Letters by Night'

2004 (16 Mar.) £7.44 'Letters by Night'

PB33   Complete book   £12
PB33a   Pane 6 omitted plus 2 copies of Pane 5   35.00

Pane printed by De la Rue in Gravure on OFNP/PVA
SP132   **3 x 2nd CB Scotland emblem and 3 x 68p 2B**
           England emblem (2B)   4.50

Pane printed by De la Rue in Lithography on OFNP/PVA
SP133   **1 x 28p 2B Locomotive, 1 x 'E' 2B Locomotive**
           and 1 x 42p 2B Locomotive   4.50

Pane printed by De la Rue in Gravure on OFNP/PVA
SP134   **4 x 1st 'The station' 2B**   2.50

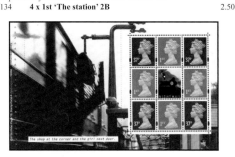

Pane printed by De la Rue in Gravure on OFNP/PVA
SP135   **4 x 37p 2B Black, 4 x 1st 2B Gold** *plus* label   5.50

2004 £7.23 'The Glory of the Garden'

2004 (25 May) £7.23 'The Glory of the Garden'

PB34   Complete book   £18

Pane printed by Enschedé in Gravure on OFNP/PVA
SP136   **4 x 1st 2B Gold, 2 x 42p 2B Sage-green,**
          2 x 47p 2B Sea green *plus label*   4.50

Pane printed by Enschedé in Gravure on OFNP/PVA
SP137   **1 x 2nd CB 1 x 'E' 2B , 1 x 68p 2B and 1 x 42p 2B**
          Special stamps   3.00

Pane printed by Enschedé in Lithography on OFNP/PVA
SP138   **4 x 1st 2B 'Flowers'** Special stamps   3.00

Pane printed by Enschedé in Gravure on OFNP/PVA
SP139   **4 x 47p 2B** Special stamps   5.50

2005 £7.47 'The Bronte Sisters'

2005 (Feb. 24) £7.47 'The Bronte Sisters' Booklet

PB35   Complete book   12.50

Pane printed by Walsall in Gravure on OFNP/PVA
SP140   **4 x 2nd CB Bright blue, 2 x 39p 2B Light grey,**
          2 x 42p 2B Sage green *plus* label   4.50

Pane printed by Walsall in Gravure on OFNP/PVA
SP141   **2 x 2nd CB England emblem, 2 x 40p 2B England**
          emblem *plus* label   3.00

Pane printed by Walsall in Lithography on OFNP/PVA
SP142   **2 x 1st 2B** and **2 x 2nd CB** Special stamps   2.25

Pane printed by Walsall in Lithography on OFNP/PVA
SP143   **1 x 40p 2B, 1 x 57p 2B, 1 x 68p** 2B and
           1 x £1.12 2B special stamps   4.60

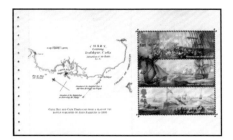

Pane printed by Cartor Security Printing in Lithography on OFNP/PVA.
SP146   **1 x 1st 2B, 1 x 42p 2B** and **1 x 68p 2B**
           Special stamps   2.50

2005 £7.26 'Battle of Trafalgar'

2005 (18 Oct.) £7.26 'Battle of Trafalgar'

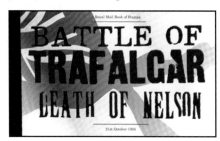

PB36   Conplete book   11.50

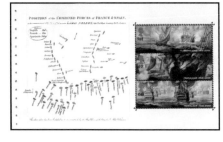

Pane printed by Cartor Security Printing in Lithography on OFNP/PVA.
SP147   **1 x 1st 2B, 1 x 42p 2B** and **1 x 68p 2B**
           Special stamps   2.50

2006 £7.40 'Brunel'

2006 (23 Feb.) £7.40 'Brunel'

Pane printed by Cartor Security Printing in Lithography on OFNP/PVA.
SP144   **3 x 1st 2B Special stamps**   3.60

PB37   Conplete book   £12

Pane printed by Walsall in Gravure on OFNP/PVA..
SP145   **4 x 1st 2B Gold, 2 x 50p 2B Ochre, 2 x 68p 2B Stone**
           plus label   5.00

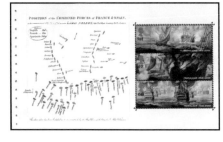

Pane printed by Enschedé in Lithography on OFNP/PVA
SP148   **1 x 1st 2B, 1 x 42p AOP, 1 x 68p 2B** Special stamps   2.75

Pane printed by Enschedé in Lithography on OFNP/PVA
SP149   **1 x 40p 2B, 1 x 60p 2B, 1 x 47p**
         Special stamps   3.00

Pane printed by Enschedé in Lithography on OFNP/PVA
SP152   **1 x 64p AOP, 1 x 64p AOP,**
         1 x 72p AOP Special stamps   3.00

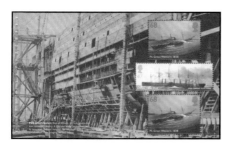

Pane printed by Enschedé in Lithography on OFNP/PVA
SP150   **2 x 68p 2B, 1 x 47p 2B**
         Special stamps   5.00

Pane printed by Enschedé in Lithography on OFNP/PVA
SP153   **1 x 1st AOP, 1 x 64p AOP, 1 x 72p AOP**
         Special stamps   **3.00**

Pane printed by Enschedé in Gravure on OFNP/PVA
SP151   **4 x 1st 2B Gold, 2 x 35p CB Lime green, 2 x 40p 2B**
         Greenish-blue *plus* label   5.00

Pane printed by Enschedé in Lithography on OFNP/PVA
SP154   **4 x 1st 2B PiP Gold, 4 x 50p 2B Ochre**
         plus label   5.50

2006 £7.44 'Victoria Cross'

2006 (21 Sep.) £7.44 'Victoria Cross'

PB38   Conplete book   £12

Pane printed by Enschedé in Gravure on OFNP/PVA
SP155   **4 x 20p AOP** Special stamps   3.50

2007 £7.49 'World of Invention'

2007 (1 March) £7.49 'World of Invention'

Pane printed by De La Rue in Gravure on OFNP/PVA
SP159   **2 x 1st 2B, 2 x 72p 2B** Special stamps   3.50

PB39   Conplete book   £12

2007 £7.66 'Machin Anniversary'

2007 (5 June) £7.66 'Machin 40th Anniversary'

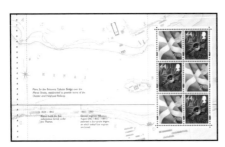

Pane printed by De La Rue in Gravure on OFNP/PVA
SP156   **3 x 2nd CB Scotland, 3 x 44p 2B Wales**   3.50

PB40   Complete book

Pane printed by De La Rue in Gravure on OFNP/PVA
SP157   **4 x 1st 2B PiP, 4 x 5p 2B Claret**
           plus label   2.50

Pane printed by De La Rue in Gravure on OFNP/PVA
SP160   **4 x 2p 2B, 2 x 46p 2B, 2 x 48p 2B** *plus* label

Pane printed by De La Rue in Gravure on OFNP/PVA
SP161   **2 x £1 Ruby** *plus* label

Pane printed by De La Rue in Gravure on OFNP/PVA
SP158   **2 x 1st 2B, 2 x 64p 2B** Special stamps   3.00

Pane printed by De La Rue in Gravure on OFNP/PVA
SP162   **2 x 1st Special stamps (portrait),**
          2 x 1st Special stamps (4d Machin)   2.50

Pane printed by De La Rue in Gravure on OFNP/PVA
SP163   **2 x 1st Large PiP, 2 x 2nd Large PiP, 1 x 1st PiP,**
          1 x 2nd PiP *plus* label   3.50

2007 £7.49 'British Army Uniforms'

2007 (20 Sep) £7.49 'British Army Uniforms'

PB41   Complete book   12.50

Pane printed by Enschedé in Lithography on OFNP/PVA
SP164   **3 x 78p 2B** Special stamps   3.95

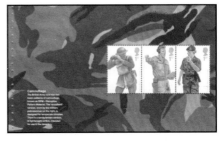

Pane printed by Enschedé in Lithography on OFNP/PVA
SP165   **3 x 1st 2B** Special stamps   2.50

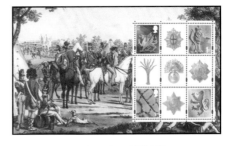

Pane printed by Enschedé in Gravure on OFNP/PVA
SP166   **2 x 1p 2B, 4 x 46p 2B, 2 x 54p 2B** *plus* label   3.95

Pane printed by Enschedé in Lithography on OFNP/PVA
SP167   **1 x 1st Wales, 1 x 1st England, 1 x 1st N. Ireland**
          1 x 1st Scotland *plus* 5 x labels   2.95

Christmas Books

1978 (15 Nov.)

Contents 10 x 7p CB below 10 x 9p 2B. Pane FP79

			Plain	Cyl.
FC1	**£1.60**	**Greetings**, August 1978	3.00	4.50

1979 (15 Nov.)

Contents 10 x 8p CB below 10 x 10p 2B. Pane FP80

FC2	**£1.80**	**Christmas cracker**, Oct. 1979	3.50	5.00
C2a		Miscut pane	£95	£145

1980 (12 Nov.)

Contents 10 x 10p CB below 10 x 12p 2B. Pane FP81

FC3	**£2.20**	**Nativity**, Sept 1980	4.50	5.00
FC3a		Missing phosphor (Partial)	£125	£275

1981 (11 Nov.)

Contents 10 x 11½p CB below 10 x 14p 2B. Pane FP82

FC4	**£2.55**	**Ice-skaters**, Jan 1981	6.00	-
FC4a		Miscut pane	£1000	-

1982 (10 Nov.) .

Contents 10 x 12½p CB below 10 x 15½p 2B, with 'star' underprint (£2.80). Pane FP83

FC5	**£2.80**	**Christmas mummers**, Feb. 1982	6.50	6.75

1983 (9 Nov.)

Contents 20 x 12½p with 'star' underprint (£2.50). Pane FP84

FC6	**£2.50**	**Pantomimes**, April 1983	6.50	6.50
FC6a		Miscut pane	£3500	
FC6b		Thin value, Type 1	9.00	£19

1984 (20 Nov.)

Contents 20 x 13p Christmas commemorative with 'star' underprint (£2.60)

FC7	**£2.60**	**The Nativity**, Sept. 1984	6.00	6.50
FC7a		Miscut pane	£20	

No.   Plain   Cyl.   No.   Plain   Cyl.

1985 (19 Nov.)

Contents 20 x 12p Christmas commemorative with 'star' underprint.
FC8   **£2.40 The Pantomime**   6.00   6.50

1986 (2 Dec.)

Contents 10 x 13p CB with 'star' underprint (£1.30). Pane FP69 or FP71
FC9   **£1.30 Shetland Yule Cakes.** Left margin   4.00   5.00
FC9a   Right margin   7.00   £15

1990 (13 Nov.)

Contents 20 x 17p Christmas commemorative, imperf. at top or bottom.
FC10   **£3.40 Snowman**   7.00   7.50

1991 (12 Nov.)

Contents 20 x 18p Christmas commemorative
FC11   **£3.60 Holly**   7.00   7.50

1992 (10 Nov.)

Contents 20 x 18p Christmas commemorative
FC12   **£3.60 Santa Claus**   6.00   6.50

1993 (9 Nov.)

Contents 10 x 25p Christmas commemorative
FC13   **£2.50 Santa Claus**   5.50   7.50

Contents 20 x 19p Christmas commemorative
FC14   **£3.80 Santa Claus**   7.00   8.00

1994 (1 Nov.)
Contents 10 x 25p Christmas commemorative
FC15   **£2.50   Christmas play props**   5.00   7.50

Contents 20 x 19p Christmas commemorative
FC16   **£3.80**   6.50   8.00

1995 (30 Oct.)

Contents 4 x 60p 2B
FC17   **£2.40   Robins**   4.50   5.50

Contents 10 x 25p Christmas commemorative
FC18   **£2.50   Robins**   4.50   6.50

Contents 20 x 19p Christmas commemorative
FC19   **£3.80   Robins**   7.00   8.00

1996 (28 Oct.)

Contents 10 x 1st
FC20   **£2.60   Nativity**   6.50   7.75

Contents 20 x 2nd
FC21   **£4.00   Nativity**   7.00   8.00

1997 (27 Oct.)

Contents 10 x 1st
FC22   **£2.60   Father Christmas & crackers**   6.50   7.50

No.   Plain Cyl. No.   Plain Cyl.

Contents 20 x 2nd
FC23 **£4.00 Father Christmas & crackers** 7.00 8.00

1998 (2 Nov.)

Contents 10 x 26p
FC24 **£2.60 Angels** 6.50 7.50

Contents 20 x 20p
FC25 **£4 Angels** 6.50 7.00

1999 (2 Nov.)

Contents 10 x 26p
FC26 **£2.60 King James's Bible** 4.50 5.50

Contents 20 x 19p
FC27 **£1.90 Hark the Herald Angels Sing** 6.00 7.00

2000 (7 Nov.)

Contents 10 x 1st
FC28 **£2.70 Spirit and Faith** 6.50 7.50

Contents 20 x 2nd
FC29 **£4.00 Spirit and Faith** 5.50 6.50

**Christmas books from 2001 onwards are of the
self adhesive type and are listed elsewhere.**

Greetings Stamp Books

1989 (31 Jan.) Cover with various designs.

			Plain	Cyl.
Contents 10 x 19p Greetings stamps *plus* 12 x labels.				
GB1	**£1.90**	**Sept. 1988**	£30	£35

1990 (6 Feb.)

Contents 10 x 20p Greetings stamps *plus* 12 x labels. Loose in folder.				
GB2	**£2**	**"Smiles"**	£19	-

1991 (5 Feb.)

Contents 10 x 1st Greetings stamps *plus* 12 x labels.				
GB3	**£2.20**	**"Good Luck"** charms	6.50	7.00

1991 (26 March)

Contents 10 x 1st Greetings stamps *plus* 12 x labels.				
GB4	**£2.20**	**Laughing letter box**	5.50	6.50
GB4a		Reprint. Revised instructions on use of NVI stamps on overseas mail (3.3.92)	7.50	9.50

1992 (28 Jan.)

Contents 10 x 1st Greetings stamps *plus* 12 x labels.				
GB5	**£2.40**	**Memories**	5.50	6.00

1993 (2 Feb.)

Contents 10 x 1st Greetings stamps *plus* 20 x labels.				
GB6	**£2.40**	**Rupert Bear and Wilfrid**	6.50	7.50
GB6a		Reprint. 'Thompson' corrected to 'Thomson'	7.00	£12
GB6b		Reprint. Revised text and spelling of 'Sorrell'	8.00	£12

1994 (1 Feb.)

Contents 10 x 1st Greetings stamps *plus* 20 x labels.
GB7　　**£2.50　Rupert Bear and Paddington Bear**　　6.50　7.00

1995 (21 March)

Contents 10 x 1st Greetings stamps *plus* 20 x labels.
GB8　　**£2.50　Noted Art Works**　　　　　　　6.50　7.50
GB8a　　　　　Alteration to event dates in inside cover -
　　　　　　　'Pull open' removed from yelow strip　8.00　9.00

1996 (26 Feb.)

Contents 10 x 1st Greetings stamps (All over phosphor) *plus* 20 x labels.
GB9　　**£2.50　More! Love**　　　　　　　　6.50　8.00

1996 (11 Nov.)
Contents 10 x 1st Greetings stamps (2 x D (Blue) phosphor bands) *plus*
20 x labels.
GB10　　**£2.60　More! Love**　　　　　　　　£10　£10

1997 (6 Jan.)

Contents 10 x 1st Greetings stamps *plus* 20 x labels.
GB11　　**£2.60　19ᵗʰ Century Flower Paintings**　　6.50　8.00

1997 (3 Feb)

GB12　　**£2.60　19ᵗʰ Century Flower Paintings**　　6.50　8.00

1998 (5 Jan.)

Contents 10 x 1st Greetings stamps *plus* 20 x labels.
GB13　　**£2.60　19ᵗʰ Century Flower Paintings**　　6.50　8.00

No.   Plain   Cyl.   No.   Plain   Cyl

1998 (7 Sep.)

Contents 10 x 1st Greetings stamps *plus* 20 x labels.
GB14   **£2.60   19th Century Flower Paintings**   6.50   7.50

Folded (Counter) Books

First issued on 14 July 1976, these Swedish style books were introduced as a convenient method for the public to buy a small supply of the more common denominations that they required. They were eventually replaced by the now familiar 'Window' books which are listed elsewhere.

The panes of stamps in these books are attached by either the left or right margins and are listed simply as Left or Right. Please note that a dash '-' in the price column denotes that this does not exist.

There are wide number of varieties to be found in these books and many collections have been assembled based on this area of GB alone. In this new edition we have now included the price of the cheapest cylinder book, and also miscut panes, missing and displaced phosphors bands, but a complete listing of these fascinating books can be found in the Machin Collectors Club Specialised Catalogue featured at the beginning of this book.

Left margin plain normal pane - guillotine marks at top and bottom

Left margin
cylinder 11 Dot pane

Left margin miscut -
guillotine mark in centre

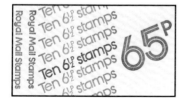

976 (14 July) 'Royal Mail Stamps' design
Contents 10 x 6½p CB. Pane FP41 or FP42

			Plain	Cyl.
B1	65p	March 1976, Left	7.50	£10
B1a		Miscut pane	8.50	£35
B1b		Perforated margin	5.00	£15
B1c		Miscut pane	8.00	£45
B2		Right	5.00	-
B2a		Miscut pane	6.00	-
B2b		Perforated margin	3.50	-
B2c		Miscut pane	£10	-

1977 (13 June) 'Royal Mail Stamps' design
Contents 10 x 7p CB. Pane FP43 or FP44.

			Plain	Cyl.
FB3	70p	June 1977. Left	4.00	4.50
FB3a		Miscut pane	£10	£25
FB4		Right	3.75	-
FB4a		Miscut pane	£15	-

1978 (8 Feb.) Country Crafts.
Contents 10 x 7p CB. Pane FP43 or FP44

			Plain	Cyl.
FB5	70p	Horse-shoeing, 1st Left	£20	£25
F5aa		Miscut pane	5.50	£20
FB6		Right	3.75	-
FB6a		Miscut pane	7.00	-

FB7	70p	Thatching, 2nd (3.5.78). Left	£95	£95
FB8		Right	4.00	

FB9	70p	Dry-stone walling, 3rd (9.8.78). Left	£150	£195
FB10		Right	4.00	-

				Plain	Cyl.
FB11	70p	**Wheel making**, 4th (25.10.78). Left		4.50	7.00
FB12		Right		4.50	-

FB13	70p	**Wattle fence making**, 5th (10.1.79). Left	12.50	17.50
FB14		Right	4.00	-
FB14a		Miscut pane	£150	-

FB15	70p	**Basket making**, 6th (4.4.79). Left	6.00	7.50
FB16		Right	4.50	-

1979 (5 Feb.) Derby Letter Office.
Contents 10 x 7p CB. Pane FP43 or FP44

FB17	70p	**Kedlestone Hall**, Left	5.00	8.00
FB18		Right	5.50	-

1979 (3 Oct.) Military Aircraft.
Contents 10 x 8p CB. Pane FP45 or FP46

FB19	80p	**BE2B 1914**, Vickers Gun Bus 1915, 1st.		
		Left	3.00	3.50
FB20		Right	3.00	-

1976 (14 July) 'Royal Mail Stamps' design
Contents 10 x 8½p 2B. Pane FP47 or FP48.

FB21	85p	**March 1976,** Left	7.50	£10
FB21a		Miscut pane	29.50	£150
FB21b		Perforated margin	£20	10.50
FB21c		Miscut pane	£200	£350
FB22		Right	7.50	-
FB22a		Miscut pane	29.50	-
FB22b		Perforated margin	£20	-
FB22c		Miscut pane		-

1977 (13 June) 'Royal Mail Stamps' design
Contents 10 x 9p 2B. Pane FP49 or FP50.

FB23	90p	**June 1977,** Left	4.00	5.00
FB23a		Miscut pane	£17	£85
FB24		Right	4.50	-
FB24a		Miscut pane	£10	-

1978 (8 Feb.) British Canals.
Contents 10 x 9p 2B. Pane FP49 or FP50

FB25	90p	**Grand Union Canal**, (8.1.78) 1st Left	£20	27.50
FB25a		Miscut pane	£25	
FB26		Right	4.50	-
FB26a		Miscut pane	12.50	-

FB27	90p	**Llangollen Canal**, 2nd (3.5.78) Left	3.50	5.00
FB28		Right	£275	-

Plain   Cyl.   Plain   Cyl.

				Plain	Cyl.
FB29	90p	**Kennet & Avon Canal**, 3rd (9.8.78) Left	£10	17.50
FB30		Right	6.50	-

FB31	90p	**Caledonian Canal**, 4th (25.10.78) Left	4.00	6.00
FB32		Right	6.00	-

FB33	90p	**Regents Canal**, 5th (10.01.79) Left	8.50	£10
FB33a		Experimental fold between cols. 2 & 3	£25	£28
FB34		Right	7.50	-
FB34a		Miscut pane	£350	

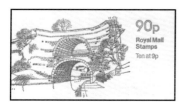

FB35	90p	**Leeds and Liverpool Canal**, 6th (4.4.79).		
		Left	4.50	£10
FB35a		Miscut pane	£50	£175
FB36		Right	4.50	

1979 (5 Feb.) Derby Letter Office.
Contents 10 x 9p 2B. Pane FP49 or FP50

FB37	90p	**Tramway Museum**, Crich. Left	6.00	12.50
FB38		Right	6.00	-

1979 (3 Oct.) Industrial Archaeology.
Contents 10 x 10p PPP. Pane FP85 or FP86

FB39	£1	**Ironbridge**, Telford, 1st Left	3.50	4.25
FB39a		Miscut pane	£15	£55
FB40		Right	3.50	-
FB40a		Miscut pane	9.50	-

1980 (4 Feb) Military Aircraft.
Contents 10 x 10p CB. Pane FP51 or FP52.

FB41	£1	**Sopwith Camel**, 2nd (4.2.80) Left	3.25	4.00
FB41a		Miscut pane	27.50	
FB42		Right	3.25	-
FB42a		Miscut pane	£20	-

FB43	£1	**Hawker Fury**, 3rd (25.6.80). Left	3.25	4.50
FB43a		Right	3.25	-

FB44	£1	**Hurricane**, 4th (24.9.80). Left	3.25	6.00
FB44a		Right	3.25	-

1981 (26 Jan.) Military Aircraft.
Contents 10 x 11½p CB. Pane FP54 or FP55.

| FB45 | **£1.15** | **Spitfire & Lancaster**, 5th. (26.1.81) Left | 3.50 | 5.00 |
| FB45a | | Right | 3.50 | - |

| FB46 | **£1.15** | **Lightning and Vulcan**, 6th (18.3.81). Left | 4.00 | 5.00 |
| FB46a | | Right | 3.75 | - |

1981 (6 May - Sept.) Museums.
Contents 10 x 11½p CB. Pane FP54 or FP55

| FB47 | **£1.15** | **Natural History Museum**, 1st, Left | 3.50 | 5.00 |
| FB48 | | Right | 3.50 | |

FB49	**£1.15**	**The National Museum of Antiquities of Scotland**,		
		2nd (30.9.81). Left	3.50	5.00
FB50		Right	3.50	

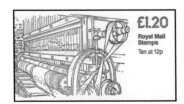

1980 (4 Feb. - Sept.) Industrial Archaeology.
Contents 10 x 12p PCP1. Pane FP89 or FP90

FB51	**£1.20**	**Beetle Mill**, 2nd. Left	3.75	4.50
FB51a		Miscut pane	6.00	17.50
FB52		Right	3.75	-
FB52a		Miscut pane	6.50	-

| FB53 | **£1.20** | **Tin Mines**, 3rd (25.6.80). Left | 4.00 | 4.50 |
| FB54 | | Right | 4.00 | - |

| FB55 | **£1.20** | **Bottle Kilns**, 4th (24.9.80). Left | 4.00 | 5.00 |
| FB56 | | Right | 4.00 | - |

1986 (14 Jan.) Pillar Box.
Contents 10 x 12p CB. Pane FP58 or FP59

FB57	**£1.20**	**Pillar Box**. Left	3.50	4.00
FB58		Right	3.50	4.00
FB58a		Miscut pane	£195	£575

1986 (29 April) National Gallery.
Contents 10 x 12p CB. Pane FP58 or FP59

FB59	**£1.20**	**National Gallery**. Left Margin	3.50	4.00
FB59a		Missing phosphor	£60	£85
FB60		Right	3.50	4.00
FB60a		Missing phosphor	£175	£250

1986 (29 July) Graphology.
Contents 10 x 12p CB. Pane FP58 or FP59

| FB61 | **£1.20** | **"Maybe"**. Left | 3.50 | 4.00 |
| FB62 | | Right | 3.50 | 4.00 |

1982 (1 Feb.) Museums Series.
Contents 10 x 12½p CB. Pane FP62 or FP63

FB63	£1.25	**The Ashmolean Museum**, 3rd. Left	3.50	-
FB64		Right	3.50	-

FB65	£1.25	**National Museum of Wales**, 4th (6.5.82).		
		Left	3.50	-
FB66		Right	3.75	-

?B67	£1.25	**Ulster Museum**, 5th (11.8.82). Left	3.50	£350
?B68		Right	3.50	-

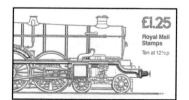

?69	£1.25	**Castle Museum**, 6th (6.10.82). Left	3.50	4.00
?70		Right	3.50	4.00

?983 (16 Feb) Railway Engines.
?ontents 10 x 12½p CB. Pane FP62 or FP63

?71	£1.25	**GWR Isambard Kingdom Brunel**, 1st.		
		Left	4.00	5.50
?72		Right	3.50	4.50

FB73	£1.25	**LMS Class 4P Passenger Tank Engine**, 2nd (5.4.83).		
		Left	4.00	5.00
FB74		Right	4.50	5.00
FB74a		Rate corrected to "36p" (200g). Left	£37	£35
FB74b		Right	£55	£45

FB75	£1.25	**LNER Mallard**, 3rd (27.7.83). Left	4.00	4.50
FB76		Right	4.00	4.50

FB77	£1.25	**SR/BR Clan Line**, 4th (26.10.83). Left	4.00	4.50
FB78		Right	4.00	4.50

1981 (6 May) Postal History.
Contents 4 x 11½p SB and 6 x 14p 2B. Pane FP56 or FP57

FB79	£1.30	**The Penny Black** 1840/41, 1st. Left	4.25	-
FB80		Right	4.50	-

FB81	£1.30	**The Downey Head 1911**, 2nd (30.9.81).		
		Left	4.75	-
FB82		Right	12.00	-

1984 (3 Sept.) Trams Series
Contents 10 x 13p CB. Pane FP68 or FP70

| FB83 | **£1.30** | **Swansea/Mumbles**, 1st. Left | 3.50 | 4.00 |
| FB84 | | Right | 3.50 | 4.00 |

| FB85 | **£1.30** | **Glasgow**, 2nd (15.1.85). Left | 4.00 | 4.00 |
| FB86 | | Right | 3.50 | 4.00 |

| FB87 | **£1.30** | **Blackpool**, 3rd (23.4.85). Left | 3.50 | 4.00 |
| FB88 | | Right | 3.50 | 3.75 |

| FB89 | **£1.30** | **London**, 4th (23.7.85). Left | 3.50 | 4.00 |
| FB90 | | Right | 3.25 | 3.75 |

1986 (20 Oct.) Special Offer series.
Contents 10 x 13p CB. Pane FP68 or FP70

FB91	**£1.30**	**Bears**. "My Day" work book. Left	4.00	4.50
FB91a		All over phos. (2), streaks (6)	£25	
FB92		Right	4.00	4.50

1987 (27 Jan.) Special Offer series.
Contents 10 x 13p CB, 'A' phosphor. Pane FP68a or FP70a.

| FB93 | **£1.30** | **"Keep in Touch"** pack. Left | 3.50 | 4.50 |
| FB94 | | Right | 3.50 | 4.50 |

1987 (14 April) Special Offer series.
Contents 10 x 13p CB. 'A' phosphor. Pane FP68a or FP70a

| FB95 | **£1.30** | **"Ideas for your Garden"**. Left | 3.50 | 4.75 |
| FB96 | | Right | 3.50 | 4.00 |

1987 (14 July) Special Offer series.
Contents 10 x 13p CB 'A' phosphor. Pane FP68a or FP70a

| FB97 | **£1.30** | **"Brighter Writer"** pack. Left | 3.50 | 4.50 |
| FB98 | | Right | 3.50 | 4.50 |

1987 (29 Sept.) Special Offer series.
Contents 10 x 13p CB. 'A' phosphor. Pane FP68a or FP70a

FB99	**£1.30**	**"Jolly Postman"** pack. Left	3.50	4.00
FB99a		Missing phosphor	£35	£50
FB100		Right	3.50	3.75
FB100a		Missing phosphor	£75	£175

1986 (26 Jan.) Special Offer series.
Contents 10 x 13p CB, 'A' phosphor. Pane FP68a or FP70a

FB101 **£1.30** **Natural History Postcards (Linnean Society).**

Left	3.50	4.00
FB102 | Right | 3.50 | 4.00 |

1988 (12 April) Special Offer series.
Contents 10 x 13p CB. 'A' phosphor. Pane FP68a or FP70a

FB103	**£1.30**	**Recipe Cards**. Left	3.25	4.00
FB104		Right	3.25	4.00

1988 (5 July) Special Offer series.
Contents 10 x 13p CB. 'A' phosphor. Pane FP68a or FP70a

FB105	**£1.30**	**Children's party pack**. Left	3.25	4.00
FB105a		All over phosphor error on 6 stamps	7.50	
FB106		Right	3.25	4.00
FB106a		All over phosphor error	£10	

1981 (26 Jan Industrial Archaeology.
Contents 10 x 14p PCP2. Pane FP106 or FP107

FB107	**£1.40**	**Preston Mill**, 5th. Left	3.75	4.00
FB108		Right	3.50	

FB109	**£1.40**	**Talyllyn Railway**, 6th (18.3.81). Left	4.00	4.50
FB110		Right	4.00	-
FB110a		Miscut pane	£500	-

1981 (6 May) Nineteenth Century Women's Costume.
Contents 10 x 14p PCP2. Pane FP106 or FP107

FB111	**£1.40**	**1800 - 1815**, 1st. Left PCP2	4.25	4.75
FB111a		PCP1. Pane FP91	£45	47.50
FB112		Right PCP2	4.25	-
FB112a		Fluorescent Brightener Omitted.	£15	-
FB112b		PCP1. Pane FP92	£37	-

FB113	**£1.40**	**1815 - 1830**, 2nd (20.9.81). Left PCP2	4.00	5.50
FB113a		PCP1. Pane FP91	32.00	37.00
FB114		Right PCP2	4.50	-
FB114a		Fluorescent Brightener Omitted	£30	-
FB114b		PCP1. Pane FP92	£27	-

1988 (5 Sept.) Special Offer series.
Contents 10 x 14p CB. 'A' phosphor. Pane FP73 or FP74

FB115	**£1.40**	**'Pocket Planner'**. Left	3.75	4.00
FB115a		Missing phosphor	£150	£200
FB116		Right	3.75	4.00

1989 (24 Jan.) 'William Henry Fox Talbot'
Contents 10 x 14p CB. 'A' phosphor. Pane FP73 or FP74

FB117	**£1.40**	**William Henry Fox Talbot**. Left	3.75	4.50
FB118		Right	3.75	4.50

1982 (1 Feb.) - 83 Postal History.
Contents 4 x 12½p SB and 6 x 15½p 2B. Pane FP64 or FP65

| FB119 | £1.43 | **James Chalmers**, 3rd. Left | 3.75 | - |
| FB120 | | Right | 3.75 | - |

FB121	£1.43	**Edmund Dulac**, 4th (6.5.82). Left	3.75	8.00
FB121a		Transposed phosphor bands	£195	£260
FB122		Right	3.75	8.00

| FB123 | £1.43 | **Forces Postal Service**, 5th (21.7.82). Left | 3.50 | 4.75 |
| FB124 | | Right | 3.50 | 5.00 |

| FB125 | £1.43 | **The £5 Orange**, 6th (6.10.82). Left | 3.75 | 5.50 |
| FB126 | | Right | 3.75 | 7.00 |

| FB127 | £1.43 | **Postmark History**, 7th (16.2.83). Left | 3.75 | 7.00 |
| FB128 | | Right | 3.75 | 5.50 |

1982 (12 July) The Holiday Postcard Stamp Book.
Contents 4 x 12½p SB and 6 x 15½p 2B. Pane FP64 or FP65

| FB129 | £1.43 | **The Golden Hinde** (replica). Left | 3.50 | 4.00 |
| FB130 | | Right | 3.75 | 4.25 |

1983 (10 Aug.) Britain's Countryside.
Contents 10 x 16p PCP1 with 'D' underprint (£1.60). Pane FP96 or FP98

FB131	£1.45	**Lyme Regis**, Dorset. Left	4.50	6.00
FB131a		Miscut	£1250	£1500
FB132		Right	4.50	7.00

1983 (5 April - Oct.) Postal History.
Contents 4 x 12½p SB and 6 x 16p 2B. Pane FP66 or FP67

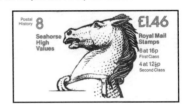

FB133	£1.46	**Seahorse High Values**, 8th. Left	7.50	8.00
FB133a		Rate corrected to '36p' (200g). Left	£20	£25
FB134		Right	7.50	8.50
FB134a		Rate corrected to '36p' (200g). Right	£14	£15

| FB135 | £1.46 | **Parcel Post**, 9th (27.7.83). Left | 6.50 | 7.00 |
| FB136 | | Right | 6.50 | 7.00 |

| FB137 | £1.46 | **Regional Stamps**, 10th (26.10.83). Left | 6.50 | 7.0 |
| FB138 | | Right | 7.50 | 8.0 |

Folded (Counter) Books

1986 (14 Jan.) Special Offer series.
Contents 4 x 12p SB and 6 x 17p 2B. Pane FP60 or FP61
FB139	**£1.50**	**Pillar Box**. 'Write Now' Letter-pack. Left	3.75	4.25
FB140		Right	3.75	4.00

1986 (29 April) Special Offer series.
Contents 4 x 12p SB and 6 x 17p 2B. Pane FP60 or FP61
FB141	**£1.50**	**National Gallery**. Left	3.75	4.50
FB142		Right	3.75	4.75

1986 (29 July) Graphology. Special Offer series.
Contents 4 x 12p SB and 6 x 17p 2B. Pane FP60 or FP61
FB143	**£1.50**	**'No'**. Left	4.00	4.50
FB144		Right	4.00	5.00

1985 (30 July) Royal Mail, 350 years of service to the public.
Contents 10 x 17p PCP commemorative with 'D' underprint (£1.70).
FB145	**£1.53**	**Datapost van and aircraft**	4.50	6.50

1984 (3 Sept.) Postal History.
Contents 4 x 13p SB and 6 x 17p 2B. Pane FP73 or FP74

Queen Elizabeth II

FB146	**£1.54**	**To Pay Labels**, 11th. Left	3.50	4.00
FB146a		Transposed phosphor bands	£28	£30
FB147		Right	3.50	4.00
FB147a		Transposed phosphor bands	£60	£70

FB148	**£1.54**	**Embossed Stamps**, 12th (15.1.85). Left	3.50	4.00
FB149		Right	3.50	4.00

FB150	**£1.54**	**Surface Printed Stamps** 13th (23.4.85).		
		Left	3.50	4.00
FB151		Right	3.50	4.00

FB152	**£1.54**	**350 Years of Service to the Public**, 14th (23.7.85).		
		Left	3.50	4.00
FB153		Right	3.50	4.50

1982 (1 Feb.) Nineteenth Century Women's Costume.
Contents 10 x 15½p PCP1. Pane FP93 or FP94

FB154	**£1.55**	**1830 - 1850**, 3rd. Left	4.50	-
FB154a		PCP2. Pane FP108	£60	-
FB155		Right	4.50	-
FB155a		PCP2. Pane FP109	£95	-

Plain   Cyl.   Plain   Cyl.

FB156	**£1.55**	**1850 - 1860**, 4th (6.5.82). Left	4.75	25.00
FB156a		PCP2. Pane FP108	£150	£200
FB157		Right	4.75	17.50
FB157a		PCP2. Pane FP109	£80	£125

FB158	**£1.55**	**1860 - 1880**, 5th (11.8.82). Left	4.00	9.00
FB158a		PCP2. Pane FP108	£250	£300
FB159		Right.	4.00	6.00
FB159a		PCP2. Pane FP109	£250	£300

FB160	**£1.55**	**1880 - 1900**, 6th (6.10.82) Left	4.00	5.50
FB160a		PCP2. Pane FP108	£40	£60
FB161		Right	4.00	5.50
FB161a		PCP2. Pane FP109	£35	39.50

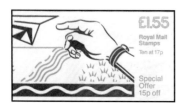

1985 (5 March) Social Letter Writing.
Contents 10 x 17p PCP1 with 'D' underprint (£1.70). Panes FP100 or FP102

FB162	**£1.55**	**Letters abroad**, 2nd. Left	5.00	5.50
FB163		Right	5.00	6.00

1983 (5 April) Special Offer series.
Contents 10 x 16p PCP1. Pane FP95 or FP97

FB164	**£1.60**	**'Birthday Box'** Left	5.00	6.00
FB164a		Rates corrected to '36p' (200g) Left	35.00	35.00
FB165		Right	5.00	7.00
FB165a		Rates corrected to '36p' (200g) Right	45.00	45.00

1983 (21 Sept.) Britain's Countryside.
Contents 10 x 16p PCP1. Pane FP95 or FP97

FB166	**£1.60**	**Cotswolds Arlington Row**, Left	4.00	4.50
FB167		Right	4.00	4.50

1984 (14 Feb.) Special Offer series.
Contents 10 x 16p PCP1. Pane FP95 or FP97

FB168	**£1.60**	**'Write it'** wallet. Left	4.50	5.00
FB169		Right	4.50	5.00

1984 (3 Sept.) Social Letter Writing.
Contents 10 x 17p PCP1. Pane FP99 or FP101

FB170	**£1.70**	**Love letters**, 1st. Left (3.9.84)	4.50	4.50
FB171		Right	4.50	5.00

FB172	**£1.70**	**Fan letters**, 3rd. Left (9.4.85)	3.75	4.25
FB173		Right	3.75	4.25

Folded (Counter) Books

Queen Elizabeth II

1985 (8 Oct.) Special Offer series.
Contents 10 x 17p PCP1. Pane FP99 or FP101

FB174	**£1.70**	**Pillar Box**. 'Write Now' letter pack. Left	4.00	5.25
FB175		Right	4.00	6.00
FB176	**£1.70**	**Revised rate '12p'** (60g) and BBC copyright on back		
		cover. Left	£10	£15
FB177		Right	£10	£12

1986 (29 April) Special Offer series.
Contents 10 x 17p PCP1. Pane FP99 or FP101. Cover as £1.20 booklet

FB178	**£1.70**	**National Gallery**. Left	4.00	4.50
FB179		Right	4.00	4.50

1986 (28 July) Graphology. Special Offer series.
Contents 10 x 17p PCP1. Pane FP99 or FP101

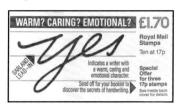

FB180	**£1.70**	**"Yes"**. Left	4.00	4.50
FB181		Right	3.50	4.00

1986 (20 Oct.) Special Offer series.
Contents 10 x 18p PCP1. Pane FP103 or FP104

FB182	**£1.80**	**Rabbits**. 'My Day' word book. Left	5.00	6.00
FB182a		PCP2. Pane FP110	£20	47.50
FB183		Right	5.00	5.50
FB183a		PCP2. Pane FP111	17.50	19.50

1987 (27 Jan.) Special Offer series.
Contents 10 x 18p PCP1. Pane FP103 or FP104

FB184	**£1.80**	**'Keep in touch'** pack. Left	5.25	8.00
FB184a		ACP. Pane FP122	6.50	7.00
FB185		Right	7.00	7.50
FB185a		ACP. Pane FP123	7.50	

1987 (14 April) Special Offer series.
Contents 10 x 18p ACP. Pane FP122 or FP123

FB186	**£1.80**	**'Ideas for your Garden'**. Left	5.50	6.50
FB187		Right	5.50	6.50

1987 (14 July) Special Offer series.
Contents 10 x 18p ACP. Pane FP122 or FP123

FB188	**£1.80**	**'Brighter Writer'** pack. Left	5.00	6.50
FB189		Right	5.00	6.50

1987 (29 Sept.) Special Offer series.
Contents 10 x 18p ACP. Pane FP122 or FP123

FB190	**£1.80**	**'Jolly Postman'** pack. Left	4.75	4.75
FB191		Right	4.75	5.25
FB191a		Miscut	£118	£450

Plain   Cyl.

Plain   Cyl.

1988 (26 Jan.) Special Offer series.
Contents 10 x 18p ACP. Pane FP122 or FP123

FB192	**£1.80**	**Natural History Postcards** (Linnean Society)		
		'for three 18p stamps (54p)'. Left	4.75	5.50
FB192a		Miscut pane	£125	£500
FB193		Right	4.75	5.50
FB194		Error '...for four 13p stamps (52p)'. Left	12.00	12.50
FB195		Right	11.00	12.50

1988 (12 April) Special Offer series.
Contents 10 x 18p ACP. Pane FP122 or FP123

| FB196 | **£1.80** | **Recipe Cards**. Left | 4.75 | 5.50 |
| FB197 | | Right | 4.75 | 5.50 |

1988 (5 July) Special Offer series.
Contents 10 x 18p ACP. Pane FP122 or FP123

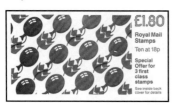

FB198	**£1.80**	**Children's party pack**. Left	5.00	5.50
FB198a		All over phosphor (6 stamps)		
FB199		Right	5.00	5.50
FB199a		All over phosphor		

1988 (5 Sept.) Special Offer series.
Contents 10 x 19p ACP. Pane FP125 or FP126

| FB200 | **£1.90** | **Pocket Planner**. Left | 5.25 | 6.25 |
| FB201 | | Right | 5.25 | 6.75 |

1989 (24 Jan.). .

| FB202 | **£1.90** | **William Henry Fox Talbot**. Left | 5.25 | 6.25 |
| FB203 | | Right | 5.25 | 6.25 |

Machine (Vending) Books

The notes on the decimal booklet panes are applicable to this listing of booklets and the numbers quoted for panes are taken from that section of the catalogue. A short description of the pane is included for ease.

There are wide number of varieties to be found in these books and many collections have been assembled based on this area of GB alone. In this new edition we have now included the price of the cheapest cylinder book, and also miscut panes and missing phosphor books, but a complete listing of these fascinating books can be found in the Machin Collectors Club Specialised Catalogue featured at the beginning of this book.

Miscut books are easily identified by the misplaced 'guillotine' line. On a normal book these are at each side, but on a miscut book this line is at the centre as illustrated below. Another feature of these issues is a Black or Red Back Marker Bar (BMB) which is printed on the spine of the book. These are printed every 25th book as an aid in the packing process.

Please note that a dash '-' in the price column denotes that this variety does not exist.

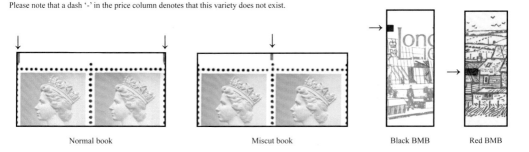

Normal book   Miscut book   Black BMB   Red BMB

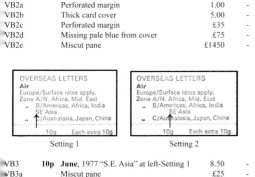

1976 (10 March) - 77. 10p Plain Cover.
Contents 2 x ½p 2B, 3 x 1p 2B and 6p 2B. Pane FP13 (VB1/2) or FP14 (VB3)

			Plain	Cyl.
VB1	10p	**White card**, Nov. 1975	1.20	-
VB1a		Perforated margin	1.00	-
VB1b		Cream card cover	1.25	-
VB1c		Perforated margin	1.50	-
VB2	10p	**Thin card cover**, Mar. 1976 (9.6.76)	1.00	-
VB2a		Perforated margin	1.00	-
VB2b		Thick card cover	5.00	-
VB2c		Perforated margin	£35	-
VB2d		Missing pale blue from cover	£75	-
VB2e		Miscut pane	£1450	-

OVERSEAS LETTERS
Air
Europe/Surface rates apply.
Zone A/N. Africa, Mid. East
  ,,   B/Americas, Africa, India
      SE Asia
  ,, ↑/Australasia, Japan, China
     10g   Each extra 10g

Setting 1

OVERSEAS LETTERS
Air
Europe/Surface rates apply.
Zone A/N. Africa, Mid. East
  ,,   B/Americas, Africa, India
      SE Asia
  ,,   C/Australasia, Japan, China
     10g   Each extra 10g

Setting 2

√VB3	10p	**June**, 1977 "S.E. Asia" at left-Setting 1	8.50	-
√VB3a		Miscut pane	£25	-
√VB3b		Perforated margin	2.00	-
√VB3c		Miscut pane	6.50	-
√VB3d		"S.E. Asia" at right-Setting 2	3.00	-
√VB3e		Miscut pane	3.50	-
√VB3f		Perforated margin	£25	-
√VB3g		Miscut pane	7.50	-

1978 (8 Feb.) - 79. Farm Buildings.
Contents 2 x ½p CB, 2 x 1p CB and 7p CB. Pane FP15.

VB4	10p	**Oast houses**, 1st (8.2.78)	75	-
VB4a		Perforated margin	60	-
VB4b		Miscut pane	£60	-

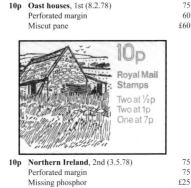

VB5	10p	**Northern Ireland**, 2nd (3.5.78)	75	-
VB5a		Perforated margin	75	-
VB5b		Missing phosphor	£25	-
VB5c		Miscut pane	£120	-

Plain Cyl.

Plain Cyl.

| VB6 | **10p Yorkshire**, 3rd (9.8.78) | 90 | - |
| VB6a | Perforated margin | 75 | - |

VB7	**10p Wales**, 4th (25.10.78)	75	-
VB7a	Missing turquoise from cover	£95	-
VB7b	Perforated margin	75	-

VB8	**10p Scotland**, 5th (10.1.79)	65	-
VB8a	Perforated margin	50	-
VB8b	Miscut pane	£12	-

VB9	**10p Sussex**, 6th (4.4.79)	75	-
VB9a	Miscut pane	£275	-
VB9b	Perforated margin	60	-

1979 (17 Oct.) - 80 "London 1980".
Contents 2 x 1p CB and 8p CB *plus* label. Panes FP1 or FP2 (VB12)

| VB10 | **10p Aug. 1979** (17.10.79) | 50 | - |
| VB10a | Miscut pane | 7.00 | - |

1p Jumelle   1p Chambon

VB11	**10p Jan. 1980**, Jumelle (12.1.80)	50	-
VB11a	Miscut pane	3.50	-
VB12	**10p Jan. 1980**, Chambon (4.8.80)	1.25	-
VB12a	Perforated margin	1.00	-
VB12b	Miscut pane	£350	-

1977 (26 Jan. - June) Plain cover.
Contents 2 x ½p 2B, 2 x 1p 2B, 2 x 6½p SB and 4 x 8½p 2B. Pane FP39
or FP40.

VB13	**50p March 1976** (26.1.77). 6½p (right band)		
	at left	2.50	-
VB13a	6½p (left band) at right	2.50	-

OVERSEAS LETTERS
Air
Europe/Surface rates apply.
Zone A/N. Africa, Mid. East
   ,, B/Americas, Africa, India
      SE Asia
   ,, C/Australasia, Japan, China
     10g   Each extra 10g

Setting 1

OVERSEAS LETTERS
Air
Europe/Surface rates apply.
Zone A/N. Africa, Mid. East
   ,, B/Americas, Africa, India
      SE Asia
   ,, C/Australasia, Japan, China
     10g   Each extra 10g

Setting 2

Contents 2 x 1p 2B, 3 x 7p SB and 3 x 9p 2B. Pane FP28 or FP29.
Setting 1

VB14	**50p June 1977** (13.6.77). 7p (right band) at left	7.50	-
VB14a	Thin value on 7p's	15.00	-
VB14b	7p (left band) at right	7.50	-
VB14c	Thin value on 7p's	10.00	-

Setting 2

VB14	**50p June 1977** (13.6.77). 7p (right band) at left	4.50	-
VB14a	Thin value on 7p's	9.00	-
VB14b	7p (left band) at right	3.00	-
VB14c	Thin value on 7p's	9.50	-

1978 (2 Aug.) - 79 Commercial Vehicles.
Contents 2 x 1p 2B, 3 x 7p SB and 3 x 9p 2B. Pane FP28 or FP29.

VB15	**50p**	**Clement-Talbot van**, 1st (8.2.78). 7p (right band)		
		at left	4.50	-
VB15a		Thin value on 7p's	7.00	-
VB15b		7p (left band) at right	2.50	-
VB15c		Thin value on 7p's	6.00	-
VB15d		Missing bistre-yellow from cover	£60	

VB16	**50p**	**Austin Cape taxi**, 2nd (3.5.78) 7p (right band)		
		at left	4.50	-
VB16a		7p (left band) at right	2.75	-

VB17	**50p**	**Morris Royal Mail van**, 3rd (9.8.78) 7p (right band)		
		at left	4.50	-
VB17a		Thin value on 7p's	8.00	-
VB17b		7p (left band) at right	3.00	-
VB17c		Thin value on 7p's	8.00	-

VB18	**50p**	**Guy Electric dustcart**, 4th (25.10.78) 7p (right band)		
		at left	4.50	-
VB18a		Thin value on 7p's	8.00	-
VB18b		7p (left band) at right	3.50	-
VB18c		Thin value on 7p's	7.50	-

VB19	**50p**	**Albion Van**, 5th (10.1.79) 7p (right band)		
		at left	6.00	-
VB19a		Thin value on 7p's	£25	-
VB19b		7p(left band) at right	5.00	-
VB19c		Thin value on 7p's	17.50	-

VB20	**50p**	**Leyland Fire engine**, 6th (4.4.79) 7p (right band)		
		at left	4.50	-
VB20a		7p (left band) at right	2.75	-

Contents 2 x 2p 2B. 2 x 8p SB and 3 x 10p 2B *plus* label. Pane FP30 or FP31.

VB21	**50p**	**Leyland Fire engine**, 6th (28.8.79) 8p (right band)		
		at left	1.50	-
VB21a		8p (left band) at right	1.50	-

1979 (3 Oct.) - 81. Veteran Cars.
Contents 2 x 2p 2B, 2 x 8p SB and 3 x 10p 2B *plus* label. Pane FP30 or FP31.

VB22	**50p**	**1907 Rolls Royce Silver Ghost**, 1st (3.10.79).		
		8p (right band) at left	2.00	-
VB22a		Miscut (2 x 2p & 4 x 8p)	£2250	-
VB22b		8p (left band) at right	2.00	-
VB22c		Miscut pane	£2250	-

Plain   Cyl.

Plain   Cyl.

Contents 3 x 2p 2B, 2 x 10p SB and 2 x 12p 2B *plus* label. Panes FP32/33 or FP34/35 (VB24/25)

VB23	**50p**	**1908 Grand Prix Austin**, 2nd (4.2.80). 10p (right band)		
		at left	2.75	-
VB23a		10p (left band) at right	2.25	-

VB24	**50p**	**1905 Vauxhall**, 3rd (25.6.80) 10p (right band)		
		at left	1.50	-
VB24a		Missing phosphor	£50	-
VB24b		10p (left band) at right	1.50	-
VB24c		Missing phosphor	£50	-

VB25	**50p**	**1897 - 1900 Daimler**, 4th (24.9.80) 10p (right band)		
		at left	1.50	-
VB25a		Missing phosphor	£60	-
VB25b		10p (left band) at right	1.50	-
VB25c		Missing phosphor	£60	-

Contents ½p 2B, 1p 2B, 3 x 11½p SB and 14p 2B. Pane FP16 or FP17

VB26	**50p**	**1896 Lanchester**, 5th (26.1.81). 11½p (right band)		
		at left	1.95	-
VB26a		Perforated margin	1.75	-
VB26b		Missing phosphor	£50	-
VB26c		Missing phosphor, Perforated margin	£35	-
VB26d		Miscut (6 x 11½p)	£4000	-
VB26e		11½p (left band) at right	1.95	-
VB26f		Perforated margin	1.75	-
VB26g		Missing phosphor	£50	-
VB2h		Missing phosphor, Perforated margin	£35	-
VB26i		Miscut (2 x ½p, 2 x 1p & 2 x 14p)	£3000	-

VB27	**50p**	**1913 Bullnose Morris**, 6th (18.3.81). 11½p (right band)		
		at left	4.00	-
VB27a		Perforated margin	2.25	-
VB27b		11½p (left band) at right	3.75	-
VB27c		Perforated margin	2.25	-

1981 (6 May) - 82 Follies.
Contents ½p 2B, 1p 2B, 3 x 11½p SB and 14p 2B. Pane FP16 or FP17

VB28	**50p**	**Mugdock Castle**, 1st (6.5.81). 11½p (right band)		
		at left	3.75	-
VB28a		Perforated margin	1.75	-
VB28b		Missing phosphor	£60	-
VB28c		11½p (left band) at right	3.75	-
VB28d		Perforated margin	1.75	-
VB28e		Missing phosphor	£60	-

Contents 3 x 2½p 2B, 2 x 4p 2B and 3 x 11½p SB. Pane FP36 or FP37

VB29	**50p**	**Mugdock Castle**, 1st (26.8.81). 11½p (right band)		
		at left	2.75	-
VB29a		Perforated margin	£20	-
VB29b		11½p (left band) at right	5.00	-
VB29c		Perforated margin	£60	-

VB30	**50p**	**Mow Cop Castle**, 2nd (30.9.81). 11½p (right band)		
		at left	3.00	-
VB30a		11½p (left band) at right	3.00	-

Contents ½p 2B, 4 x 3p 2B and 3 x 12½p SB. Pane FP24 or FP25

Plain   Cyl.

Plain   Cyl.

VB31	**50p**	**Paxton's Tower**, 3rd (1.2.82) 12½p (right band)		
		at left	1.50	-
VB31a		Miscut (2 x ½p & 6 x 12½p)	£400	-
VB31b		12½p (left band) at right	1.50	-
VB31c		Miscut (8 x 3p)	£400	-

VB32	**50p**	**Temple of the Winds**, 4th (6.5.82) 12½p (right band)		
		at left	1.50	-
VB32a		12½p (left band) at right	1.50	-

VB33	**50p**	**Temple of the Sun**, 5th (11.8.82) 12½p (right band)		
		at left	1.50	-
VB33a		12½p (left band) at right	1.75	-

VB34	**50p**	**Water Gardens**, 6th (6.10.82) 12½p (right band)		
		at left	1.50	-
VB34a		12½p (left band) at right	2.00	-

1983 (16 Feb. - Oct.) Rare Farm Animals.
Contents ½p 2B, 4 x 3p 2B and 3 x 12½p SB. Pane FP24 or FP25

VB35	**50p**	**Bagot Goat**, 1st (16.2.83). 12½p (right band)		
		at left	2.50	-
VB35a		12½p (left band) at right	2.25	-

Contents 2 x 1p CB, 3 x 3½p CB and 3 x 12½p CB at right. Pane FP26

VB36	**50p**	**Gloucester Old Spot Pig**, 2nd (5.4.83)	3.00	-
VB36a		Missing phosphor	£12	-
VB36b		Miscut 12½p CB at left	£220	-
VB36c		Rate corrected to '36p' (200g)	6.00	-

VB37	**50p**	**Toulouse Goose**, 3rd (27.7.83)	3.00	-

VB38	**50p**	**Orkney Sheep**, 4th (26.10.83)	3.00	-
VB38a		Missing phosphor	£450	-

1984 (3 Sept.) - 85. Orchids. Printed in yellow-green and light violet.
Contents 3 x 1p CB, 2 x 4p CB and 3 x 13p CB. Pane FP27

			Plain	Cyl.
VB39	**50p**	**Dendrobium**, 1st (3.9.84)	1.50	1.75
VB39a		Missing phosphor	£200	£250

VB40	**50p**	**Cypripedium**, 2nd (15.1.85)	1.50	1.75

VB41	**50p**	**Bifrenaria**, 3rd (23.4.85)	1.50	1.75

VB42	**50p**	**Cymbidium**, 4th (23.7.85)	1.50	2.25

1985 (4 Nov.) Special Offer series. Printed in grey-black and light scarlet.
Contents 3 x 17p 2B *plus* label with 'stars' underprint (51p). Pane FP11

VB43	**50p**	**Pillar Box**, Nov. 1985 (4.11.85)	2.00	2.25
VB43a		Missing phosphor	£33	£50

1986 (20 May) - 87. Pond Life. Printed in dull blue and light blue-green.
Contents 3 x 17p 2B *plus* label with 'stars' underprint (51p). Pane FP11

VB44	**50p**	**Emperor Dragonfly**, 1st (20.5.86)	1.80	1.75
VB44a		Missing phosphor	£50	£95

Contents 3 x 17p 2B *plus* label with 'stars' underprint (51p). Pane FP10
VB45	**50p**	**Common frog**, 2nd (29.7.86)	2.50	2.75

Contents 3 x 17p 2B *plus* label without 'stars' underprint (51p). Pane FP10
VB46	**50p**	**Common frog**, 2nd (12.8.86)	1.80	2.75
VB46a		Error. PCP1 paper. Pane FP87	£190	£195

Contents 1p CB, 2 x 5p CB and 3 x 13p CB. Pane FP18
VB47	**50p**	**Moorhen**, 3rd (20.10.86) 'A' phosphor. Pane FP18a		
			4.00	4.50

VB48	**50p**	**Giant Pond Snail**, 4th (27.1.87)	3.50	3.75

Plain   Cyl.   Plain   Cyl.

1986 (29 July) - 87. Roman Britain.

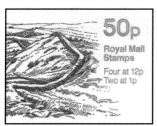

Contents 2 x 1p CB and 4 x 12p CB. Pane FP20

				Plain	Cyl.
VB49	**50p**	**Hadrian's Wall**, 1st (29.7.86)		3.50	4.00

				Plain	Cyl.
VB53	**50p**	**Ashes urn**, 2nd (14.7.87)		2.00	3.00
VB53a		Error. Old phosphor ink		£145	£295

Contents 1p LB, 13p RB and 2 x 18p 2B. Pane FP3

VB50	**50p**	**Roman Theatre**, St. Albans, 2nd (20.10.86)		2.50	3.00
VB50a		Broad bands		£595	£750
VB50b		Missing phosphor		£275	£550
VB50c		Reversed phosphor bands		£30	£50

VB54	**50p**	**Lord's Pavillion**, 3rd (29.9.87)		1.95	2.50
VB54a		Missing phosphor		£55	£125
VB54b		Reversed phosphor bands		£40	£65

Contents 1p LB, 13p RB and 2 x 5p 2B. 'A' phosphor. Pane FP3c

VB51	**50p**	**Portchester Castle**, 3rd (27.1.87)		2.25	2.95
VB51a		Reversed phosphor bands		£125	£175

VB55	**50p**	**England Badge**, 4th (26.1.88)		2.00	2.50

1987 (14 April) - 88. MCC Bicentenary.
Contents 1p LB, 13p RB and 2 x 18p 2B. Pane FP3c

1987 (14 April) - 86. Botanical Gardens.
Contents 1p CB, 2 x 5p CB and 3 x 13p CB. Pane FP18

VB56	**50p**	**Bodnant**, 1st (14.4.87)		3.00	3.75

VB52	**50p**	**Father Time**, 1st		1.95	3.00
VB52a		Missing phosphor		£75	£120
VB52b		Error. Old phosphor ink		4.50	£12

VB57	**50p**	**Edinburgh**, 2nd (14.7.87)		3.00	4.00
		Imperf. sides. Pane FP19			

Plain   Cyl.   Plain   Cyl.

			Plain	Cyl.
VB58	**50p**	**Mount Stuart** (Incorrect spelling), 4.5mm Phosphor band 3rd (29.9.87)	3.00	4.00
VB58a		4mm Phosphor band	4.50	10.00
VB59	**50p**	**Mount Stewart** (Corrected spelling), 4.5mm Phosphor band 3rd (30.10.87)	3.00	3.75
VB59a		4mm Phosphor band	4.00	4.75
VB59b		Missing phosphor	£225	£325

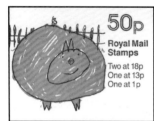

			Plain	Cyl.
VB60	**50p**	**Kew**, 4.5mm Phosphor band 4th (26.1.88)	2.50	3.00
VB60a		4mm Phosphor band	£15	£20

1988 (12 April - 5 July) London Zoo.
Contents 1p LB, 13p RB and 2 x 18p RB. Pane FP3c

			Plain	Cyl.
VB61	**50p**	**Pigs**, 1st	2.00	2.25
VB61a		Missing phosphor	£45	£75

Contents 1p CB, 2 x 5p CB and 3 x 13p CB. Pane FP19

			Plain	Cyl.
VB62	**50p**	**Birds**, 4.5mm Phosphor band, 2nd	2.50	3.00
VB62a		4mm Phosphor band	10.00	12.50

			Plain	Cyl.
Contents 1p LB, 13p RB and 2 x 18p 2B. Pane FP3c				
VB63	**50p**	**Elephants**, 4th (5.7.88)	2.00	2.50

1988 (5 July) - 89 Marine Life. Printed in dull blue and light orange-brown.
Contents 1p CB, 2 x 5p CB and 3 x 13p CB. Pane FP19

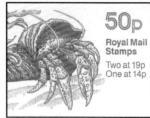

			Plain	Cyl.
VB64	**50p**	**Parasitic anemone**, 1st	2.00	2.25

Contents 14p RB and 2 x 19p 2B *plus* label. Pane FP10

			Plain	Cyl.
VB65	**50p**	**Common hermit crab**, 2nd (18.7.89). APS perf	2.00	2.50
VB65a		Reprint. Comb perf (8.8.89)	2.75	4.00

1988 (5 Sept.) - 89 Gilbert and Sullivan. Printed in salmon and black.
Contents 14p RB and 2 x 19p 2B *plus* label. Pane FP8a

			Plain	Cyl.
VB66	**50p**	**The Yeoman of the Guard**, 1st	1.75	2.50
VB66a		Missing phosphor	7.50	17.50
VB66b		Miscut pane	£950	£1200

Plain Cyl.

			Plain	Cyl.
VB67	**50p**	**The Pirates of Penzance**, 2nd (24.1.89)	2.50	2.75
VB67a		Missing phosphor	£95	£145
VB67b		Miscut	£1200	

			Plain	Cyl.
VB68	**50p**	**The Mikado**, 3rd (25.4.89)	3.00	£25
VB68a		Missing phosphor	£35	£60

1989 (2 Oct.) - 91 Aeroplanes. Printed in blue-green and brown.
Contents 2 x 15p LB and 20p 2B *plus* label. Pane FP9

			Plain	Cyl.
VB69	**50p**	**HP42**, 1st	3.75	7.00
VB69a		Missing phosphor	£400	£500

Contents 2 x 15p LB and 20p 2B Anniversary stamps *plus* label. Pane AP1

VB70	**50p**	Vickers Viscount 806, 2nd (30.1.90)	3.50	5.00

Contents 2 x 17p LB and 17p RB *plus* label. Pane FP12

			Plain	Cyl.
VB71	**50p**	BAC1-11, 3rd (4.9.90)	2.50	2.75
VB71a		Missing phosphor	£35	£70

VB72	**50p**	BAe ATP, 4th (25.6.91)	2.75	3.00

1991 (10 Sept.) - 92 Archaeology.
Contents 2 x 1p, 2 x 24p ACP. Pane FP112

VB73	**50p**	**Sir Arthur Evans**, 1st. 100g @ 35p	1.75	2.25
VB73a		Miscut	£135	£295
VB73b		Rates corrected. 100g @ 36p (10.91)	1.75	2.25

VB75	**50p**	**Howard Carter**, 2nd (21.1.92)	1.75	2.25

VB76	**50p**	**Sir Austen Layard**, 3rd (28.4.92)	1.50	2.25

Machine (Vending) Books

			Plain	Cyl.

VB77   **50p**   **Sir Flinders Petrie**, 4th (28.7.92)   2.00   2.25

1992 (22 Sept.) Sheriff's Millennium.
Contents 2 x 1p, 2 x 24p. Pane FP112

VB78   **50p**   **Crest**   1.50   2.25

1993 (9 Feb.) Postmarks.
Contents 2 x 1p, 2 x 24p ACP. Pane FP112

VB79   **50p**   **Airmail**, 1st   1.50   2.25

VB80   **50p**   **Ship mail**, 2nd (6.4.93)   1.50   2.25

VB81   **50p**   **Registered mail**, 3rd (6.7.93)   1.50   2.25

			Plain	Cyl.

Contents 2 x 25p OFPP *plus* 2 x labels. Pane EP1

VB82	**50p**	**'Paid'**, 4th (1.11.93)	1.50	2.25
VB82a		Miscut	£45	£150

1994 (25 Jan.) Coaching Inn Signs.
Contents 2 x 25p OFPP *plus* 2 x labels. Pane EP1

VB83   **50p**   **'Swan with Two Necks'**, 1st   1.50   2.25

VB84   **50p**   **'Bull and Mouth'**, 2nd (26.4.94)   1.50   2.25

VB85   **50p**   **'Golden Cross'**, 3rd (6.6.94)   1.50   2.25

VB86   **50p**   **'Pheasant Inn'**, 4th (6.9.94)   1.50   2.50

Plain   Cyl.   Plain   Cyl.

1995 (7 Feb.) Sea Charts.
Contents 2 x 25p OFPP *plus* 2 x labels. Pane EP1

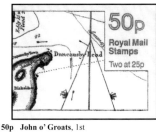

			Plain	Cyl.
VB87	**50p**	**John o' Groats,** 1st	1.50	2.25

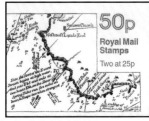

			Plain	Cyl.
VB88	**50p**	**Land's End,** 2nd (4.4.95)	1.50	2.00

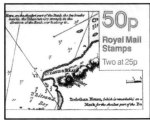

			Plain	Cyl.
VB89	**50p**	**St. David's Head,** 3rd (6.6.95)	2.75	3.25

			Plain	Cyl.
VB90	**50p**	**Giant's Causeway,** 4th (4.9.95)	3.00	3.50

1986 (29 July) - 87. Musical Instruments. Printed in red and black.

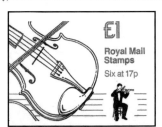

Contents 6 x 17p PCP1 (£1.02). Pane FP88

			Plain	Cyl.
VB114	**£1**	**Violin,** 1st	3.50	5.00

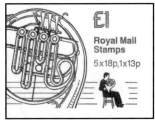

Contents 13p LB and 5 x 18p 2B. Pane FP21

			Plain	Cyl.
VB115	**£1**	**French horn,** 2nd (20.10.86) '	5.00	5.50

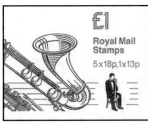

A' phosphor. Pane FP21a

			Plain	Cyl.
VB116	**£1**	**Bass clarinet,** 3rd (27.1.87)	3.50	4.00

1987 (14 April) - 88 Sherlock Holmes.
Contents 13p LB and 5 x 18p 2B. Pane FP21a

			Plain	Cyl.
VB117	**£1**	**A Study in Scarlet,** 1st	5.00	5.50

			Plain	Cyl.
VB118	**£1**	**The Hound of the Baskervilles,** 2nd (14.7.87)	4.50	5.00

Plain   Cyl.

Plain   Cyl.

VB119	**£1**	**The Adventure of the Speckled Band**, 3rd (29.9.87)	4.50	5.00

Contents 2 x 14p RB and 4 x 19p 2B, imperf. sides. Pane FP23

VB123	**£1**	**Nicholas Nickleby**, 2nd (5.9.88). APS perf.	4.50	4.75
VB123a		Comb perf	£45	£145

VB120	**£1**	**The Final Problem**, 4th (26.1.88)	4.00	4.25

VB124	**£1**	**David Copperfield**, 3rd (24.1.89).		
		Comb perf.	3.00	3.25
VB124a		APS perf. (3.89)	9.50	£45

1988 (12 April) London Zoo. Drawings by children. Printed in black and brown. *Contents* 13p LB and 5 x 18p 2B, imperf. sides. Pane FP22

VB121	**£1**	**Bears**, 3rd	4.00	4.25

Contents 2 x 14p RB and 4 x 19p 2B, imperf. sides. Pane LP3
Printer: Walsall in Lithography.

VB125	**£1**	**Great Expectations**, 4th (25.4.89)	4.00	4.50
VB125a		Missing phosphor	£1100	£1500

1988 (5 July) - 89 Charles Dickens.
Contents 13p LB and 5 x 18p 2B, imperf. sides. Pane FP22

1989 (18 July) Marine Life.
Contents 2 x 14p RB and 4 x 19p 2B, imperf. sides. Pane FP23

VB122	**£1**	**Oliver Twist**, 1st	4.00	4.25

VB126	**£1**	**Edible sea urchin**, 3rd	3.00	3.50

1989 (2 Oct.) - 91 Mills.
Contents 5 x 20p imperf sides *plus* label. Pane FP121

VB127	**£1**	**Wicken Fen**, 1st	4.00	4.50

Printer: Walsall in Lithography. Printed on glossy card.
Contents 5 x 20p Anniversary stamp *plus* label. Pane AP10

VB128	**£1**	**Wicken Fen**, 1st (30.1.90)	10.00	12.00

Contents 5 x 20p Anniversary stamps *plus* label. Pane AP4

VB129	**£1**	**Click Mill**, 2nd (30.1.90)	3.50	3.75

Contents 2 x 17p RB and 3 x 22p 2B *plus* 3 x labels. Pane FP38

VB130	**£1**	**Jack and Jill Mills**, 3rd (4.9.90)	2.50	3.50
VB130a		Missing phosphor	£60	£85

VB131	**£1**	**Howell Mill**, 4th (25.6.91)	2.00	3.00

1991 (10 Sept.) - 92 'Punch'.
Contents 2 x 2p, 4 x 24p imperf sides *plus* 2 x labels. Pane FP113

VB132	**£1**	**1st**. 100g @ 35p	3.00	3.50
VB132a		Rates corrected 100g @ 36p	3.00	3.50

VB133	**£1**	**2nd** (21.1.92)	2.75	3.00

VB134	**£1**	**3rd** (28.4.92)	2.75	3.00

VB135	**£1**	**4th** (28.7.92)	2.75	3.00

1992 (22 Sept.) Sheriff's Millennium.
Contents 2 x 2p, 4 x 24p imperf sides *plus* 2 x labels. Pane FP113

VB136	**£1**	**Crest**	2.75	3.00

1993 (9 Feb.) Educational Institutions.
Contents 2 x 2p, 4 x 24p imperf sides *plus* 2 x labels. Pane LP5
Printer: Walsall in Lithography

			Plain	Cyl.
VB137	**£1**	**University of Wales**, 1st	3.50	4.00

VB138	**£1**	**St. Hilda's College**, 2nd (6.4.93)	3.50	4.00

VB139	**£1**	**Marlborough College**, 3rd (6.7.93)	3.50	4.00

Contents 4 x 25p (2 bands). Pane EP4

VB140	**£1**	**University of Edinburgh**, 4th (1.11.93)	3.50	3.50

1994 (25 Jan.) British Prime Ministers.
Contents 4 x 25p (2 bands). Pane EP4
Printer: Walsall in Lithography

			Plain	Cyl.
VB141	**£1**	**Asquith**, 1st	2.75	3.00

Contents 4 x 25p OFPP. Pane EP2
Printer: Harrison

VB142	**£1**	**Lloyd-George**, 2nd (26.4.94)	2.50	3.00

VB143	**£1**	**Churchill**, 3rd (6.6.94)	2.50	2.75
VB143a		Miscut	£725	£1250

VB144	**£1**	**Attlee**, 4th (6.9.94)	2.50	3.00

1995 (7 Feb.) 'Inspiration for Victory'.
Contents 4 x 25p OFPP. Pane EP2

VB145	**£1**	**Violette Szabo**, 1st	2.50	3.00
VB145a		Miscut	£350	£400

			Plain	Cyl.
VB146	**£1**	**Dame Vera Lynn**, 2nd (4.4.95)	2.50	3.00
VB146a		Miscut	£375	£1250
VB146b		4 x 25p 2B Yellow fluor	£75	£150

			Plain	Cyl.
VB147	**£1**	**R J Mitchell**, 4 x 25p 2B Yellow fluor 3rd (16.5.95)	2.50	3.00
VB147a		Miscut	£150	£350
VB147b		4 x 25p 2B Blue fluor	3.00	3.50

			Plain	Cyl.
VB148	**£1**	**Archibald McIndoe**, 4th (4.9.95)	3.00	3.50
VB148a		Miscut	£450	£1200
VB148b		Missing phosphor	£85	£145

1996 (16 Jan.) Varnished Cover
Contents 4 x 25p 2B. Pane EP2

			Plain	Cyl.
VB149	**£1**	**Multicoloured**	3.00	3.50

1996 (8 July) Varnished Cover
Contents 3 x 26p 2B, 1 x 20p CB, 2 x 1p 2B. Pane EP Printed in Litho. Pane EP14

			Plain	Cyl.
VB150	**£1**	**Multicoloured**	3.00	3.50
VB150a		Corrected rate (4.2.97)	3.00	4.00
VB150b		'Textphone' inscription added (5.5.98)	3.00	3.50

1998 (1 Dec.) Varnished Cover
Contents 2 x 1p 2B, 1 x 20p CB, 3 x 26p 2B Printed in Gravure. Pane EP19

			Plain	Cyl.
VB151	**£1**	**Multicoloured**	3.00	3.50
VB151a		Miscut	£2750	£3000

1999 (26 Apr.) Varnished Cover
Contents 1 x 1p 2B, 1 x 2p 2B, 1 x 19p CB, 3 x 26p 2B Printed in Gravure. Pane EP20

			Plain	Cyl.
VB152	**£1**	**Multicoloured**	3.00	3.50
VB152a		Miscut	£1750	£2000

2000 (27 Apr.) Varnished Cover
Contents 1 x 2nd CB, 3 x 1st 2B and two lables. Pane CP49

			Plain	Cyl.
VB153	£1	Multicoloured (Postcode) (27.4.00) *1	3.50	4.50
VB153a		Miscut	£350	£1250

2001 (17 Apr.) Varnished
Contents 1 x 2nd CB, 3 x 1st 2B and two lables. Pane CP51

			Plain	Cyl.
VB154	£1	Multicoloured (Postcodes) (17.4.01) *2	3.50	4.50
VB154a		Miscut	£1000	£1750

*1 Web address is www.postcode.royalmail.co.uk on label 2
*2 Web address is www.postcodes.royalmail.co.uk on label 2

Plain   Cyl.

Plain   Cyl.

1993 (1 Nov.) - 94 Postal Vehicles.
Contents 8 x 25p OFPP. Pane EP3

			Plain	Cyl.
VB230	**£2**	**Motorised Cycle**, 1st	3.75	4.00
VB230a		Miscut	12.50	£55

VB231	**£2**	**Experimental Motor Mail Van**, 2nd (26.4.94)	3.00	4.00

VB232	**£2**	**Experimental Electric Mail Van**, 3rd (6.9.94)	3.00	4.00

1995 (7 Feb.) Rowland Hill Birth Bicentenary.
Contents 8 x 25p OFPP. Pane EP3

VB233	**£2**	**London and Brighton Railway**, 1st	3.00	4.00

			Plain	Cyl.
VB234	**£2**	**Hill's Educational Reform**, 2nd (4.4.95)	3.75	4.25
VB234a		Miscut	£300	£350

VB235	**£2**	**Postal Districts**, 3rd (6.6.95)	4.50	5.00
VB235a		Miscut		

VB235a was confirmed in April 2004 - only one copy known.

VB236	**£2**	**Uniform Penny Postage**, 4th (4.9.95)		
		Yellow fluor	4.50	5.00
VB236a		Blue fluor	6.00	7.00

1996 (16 Jan.) Varnished Cover
Contents 8 x 25p 2B. Pane EP15

VB237	**£2**	**Multicoloured**	4.00	4.50

Plain Cyl.

Plain Cyl.

1996 (8 July) Varnished Cover
Contents 7 x 26p 2B, 1 x 20p CB, Printed in Litho. Pane EP16

VB238	**£2**	**Multicoloured**	4.50	5.50
VB238a		Corrected rate (4.2.97)	4.50	5.00
VB238b		'Textphone' inscription added (5.5.98)	4.00	4.50

1998 (1 Dec.) Varnished Cover
Contents 7 x 26p 2B 1 x 20p CB, Printed in Gravure. Pane EP23

VB239	**£2**	**Multicoloured**	5.50	6.50
VB239a		Miscut	£1250	£1750

1999 (26 Apr.) Varnished Cover
Contents 1 x 19p CB and 7 x 26p 2B Printed in Gravure. Pane EP24

VB240	**£2**	**Multicoloured**	4.00	5.00

2000 (27 Apr.) Varnished Cover
Contents 2 x 2nd CB and 6 x 1st 2B Printed in Gravure. Pane CP55

VB241	**£2**	**Multicoloured**	4.00	5.00

Window Books

Window booklets made their appearance on 4 August 1987. They were designed for sale through the usual Post Office counters and supermarkets, stationers and similar retail outlets. The term "window" was applied because of the transparent "window" through which an example of the stamp contents could be viewed. The idea has been dropped and the booklets now have a printed 'stamp' on the cover. The term 'window' appears to have stayed and the booklets are now referred to as 'window' or 'bar code' booklets.

On the reverse of each booklet cover is a Bar Code moreover, on the early booklets, a Code Letter in the lower right hand corner. The code letter has since been dropped but it is important for sorting the earlier booklets and is therefore included in the listings. The early booklets can also be sorted by the locking 'tab' designed to keep the contents secure. The first 'tab' was square and this was altered to a round 'tab' on the first reprint.

The booklets have since moved on, and some covers adapted to promotions for leading retailers or Post Office promotions. The cover designs in later years were aimed at 'the high street' and the greetings books especially, have included eye catching characters, familiar to the great British public.

Window books were superseded by Self Adhesive books from 29 January 2001.

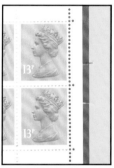
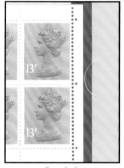

Square tab   Round tab

1987 (4 Aug.) Large Format Booklets. Covers printed in red, yellow and black with a laminated finish and transparent 'window'. Perf. 15 x 14 Printer: Harrison & Sons in Photogravure

A. Window booklets with square tab (60mm high)

WB1	**4 x 13p Chestnut** CB. Code E	FP4	2.50	2.75
WB2	**4 x 13p Chestnut** CB. Code F	FP4	2.50	2.75
WB3	**4 x 18p Grey-green** ACP. Code A	FP114	2.75	3.00
WB4	**4 x 18p Grey-green** ACP. Code B	FP114	2.75	3.00
WB5	**4 x 26p Red** ACP. Code I	FP118	9.00	9.50
WB6	**4 x 26p Red** ACP. Code J	FP118	9.00	9.50
WB7	**10 x 13p CB Chestnut** Code G	FP72	3.75	6.00
WB8	**10 x 13p CB Chestnut** Code H	FP72	3.25	4.50
WB9	**10 x 18p Grey-green** ACP. Code C	FP124	4.50	4.75
WB10	**10 x 18p Grey-green** ACP. Code D	FP124	4.75	6.50

B. Window booklets with round tab (60mm high) (1.88)

WB11	**4 x 13p CB Chestnut** Code E	FP4	8.50	12.50
WB12	**4 x 13p CB Chestnut** Code F	FP4	£10	£15
WB13	**4 x 18p Grey-green** ACP. Code A	FP114	£11	£25
WB14	**4 x 18p Grey-green** ACP. Code B	FP114	6.50	8.50
WB15	**4 x 26p Red** ACP Code I	FP118	£14	£15
WB16	**10 x 13p CB Chestnut** Code G	FP72	£11	£11
WB17	**10 x 13p CB Chestnut** Code H	FP72	£11	£11
WB18	**10 x 18p Grey-green** ACP. Code C	FP124	£15	£15
WB19	**10 x 18p Grey-green** ACP. Code D	FP124	£14	£15

Pane   Plain   Cyl.

Pane   Plain   Cyl.

1988 (11 Oct.) Small Format Booklets with printed 'stamp' (48mm high)
Printer: Harrison & Sons in Photogravure. Perf. 15 x 14

WB38	4 x 14p CB Dark blue	FP6	4.50	6.00
WB39	4 x 19p Orange-red ACP.	FP116	5.00	5.50
WB39a	Error of contents (10 x 19p)		£800	£1300
WB40	4 x 27p Red-brown ACP.	FP120	£20	£20
WB41	10 x 14p CB Dark blue - Bar code 100104	FP78	8.00	7.50
WB42	10 x 14p CB Dark blue - Bar code 200101	FP78	£15	£10
WB42a	Missing phosphor		£180	£250
WB42c	Error of contents (4 x 14p)	FP6	£850	£1200

Contents FP128

WB43	10 x 19p Orange-red ACP. - Bar code 200088	FP128	6.50	6.50
WB43b	Plain - Error of contents (4 x 19p)	FP116	£1200	£1200
WB44	10 x 19p Orange-red ACP. - Bar code 100081	FP128	8.00	9.00

Printer: House of Questa in Lithography. Perf. 15 x 14

WB45	10 x 14p CB Dark blue	LP1	£11	-
WB46	10 x 19p Orange-red ACP. Plain	LP2	£11	-

1988 (23 Aug.) Slightly smaller booklets with a reduced margin around the pane and new code letters. Round tab (56mm high). Perf. 15 x 14
Printer: Harrison & Sons in Photogravure

WB20	4 x 14p CB Dark blue Code O	FP5	4.50	4.50
WB20a	Error of contents (4 x 19p) Code O	FP115	£345	£500
WB20b	Missing phosphor	FP5a	£250	£400
WB21	4 x 14p CB Dark blue Code P	FP5	4.50	4.50
WB22	4 x 19p Orange-red ACP. Code K	FP115	4.00	4.25
WB23	4 x 19p Orange-red ACP. Code L	FP115	4.00	4.25
WB24	4 x 27p CB Red-brown Code S	FP119	8.50	8.50
WB24a	4 x 27p CB Red-brown Code S - Error Blank inside back cover	FP119	£20	£35
WB25	4 x 27p CB Red-brown Code T	FP119	8.50	8.50
WB26	10 x 14p CB Dark blue Code Q	FP77	6.00	7.00
WB27	10 x 14p CB Dark blue Code R	FP77	7.50	7.75
WB28	10 x 19p Orange-red ACP. Code M	FP127	9.50	9.50
WB28a	10 x 19p Orange-red ACP/ Low OBA, Code M	FP127	9.50	9.50
WB29	10 x 19p Orange-red ACP. Code N	FP127	9.50	9.50
WB29a	10 x 19p Orange-red ACP/ Low OBA, Code N	FP127	£95	9.50

1989 (24 Jan.)
Booklet covers printed by Walsall Security Printers Ltd.
Stamps Printed by Harrison & Sons in Photogravure Perf. 15 x 14

WB47	4 x 14p CB Dark blue Imperf. on three sides	FP7	£15	-
WB47a	4 x 14p Dark blue. Imperf. on three sides Missing phosphor	FP7a	17.50	
WB48	4 x 19p Orange-red ACP. Imperf. on three sides.	FP117	£17	-

1988 (11 Oct.)
Printer: House of Questa in Lithography

WB30	10 x 14p CB Dark blue Code Q	LP1	£11	-
WB31	10 x 14p CB Dark blue Code R	LP1	£11	-
WB32	10 x 19p Orange-red ACP. Code M	LP2	12.50	-
WB33	10 x 19p Orange-red ACP. Code N	LP2	12.50	-

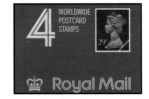

1989 (2 Oct.) Worldwide postcards. Perf. 14
Printer: Walsall in Lithography

Booklet covers printed by Walsall Security Printers Ltd.
Stamps printed by Harrison & Sons in Photogravure Perf. 15 x 14.

WB34	4 x 14p CB Dark blue Code O	FP5	4.00	3.25
WB35	4 x 14p CB Dark blue Code P	FP5	4.00	3.25
WB36	4 x 19p Orange-red ACP. Code K	FP115	4.50	3.75
WB37	4 x 19p Orange-red ACP. Code L	FP115	4.50	3.75

WB49	4 x 29p 2B Purple	LP4	7.50	8.00
WB50	4 x 29p Purple ACP. (17.4.90)	LP6	6.50	7.00

1990 (17 Sep.) Worldwide Postcard Books

WB51	4 x 31p Ultramarine ACP.	LP7	3.50	5.00
WB51a	4 x 31p Ultramarine ACP./Low OBA	LP7a	5.00	9.50
WB51b	4 x 31p Ultramarine ACP./Low OBA New revised locking tab without side slits	LP7a	3.50	4.00

	Pane	Plain	Cyl.

	Pane	Plain	Cyl.

1991 (16 Sept.) Worldwide postcards and Airmail stamps. Perf. 14
Printer: Walsall in Lithography

| WB52 | **4 x 33p Light emerald** PVA gum. | LP8 | 2.50 | 3.50 |
| WB52a | Error. PVAD gum. No text on postcard rate. | LP11 | 6.00 | 8.50 |

Reprint.

| WB53 | **4 x 33p Light emerald** PVAD gum.. Text - postcard rate is 33p | LP11 | 2.75 | 3.50 |
| WB54 | **4 x 39p Bright mauve** ACP | LP10 | 2.75 | 4.00 |

1992 (28 July) Kellogs Overseas Rate. Perf. 14
Printer: Walsall in Lithography

| WB55 | **2 x 39p Bright mauv**e ACP. | LP9 | 2.00 | 3.00 |

1993 (1 Nov.) - 94 Worldwide postcards and Airmail stamps.
Printer: Walsall in Lithography. Perf. 15 x 14 elliptical

| WB56 | **4 x 35p 2B Yellow** (Yellow fluor). | EP8 | 3.50 | 3.75 |
| WB57 | **4 x 41p 2B Stone** (Yellow fluor). | EP10 | 3.75 | 4.00 |

| WB58 | **4 x 60p 2B Slate-blue** (Yellow fluor). (9.8.94) | EP11 | 5.50 | 6.00 |

| WB59 | **4 x 60p 2B Slate-blue** (Yellow fluor). Christmas edition (4.10.94) | EP11 | 5.50 | 6.50 |

1995 (16 May) Worldwide postcards and Airmail stamps.
Printer: Walsall in Lithography. Perf. 15 x 14 elliptical.

WB60	**4 x 35p 2B Yellow** (Yellow fluor).	EP8	3.50	4.00
WB60b	**4 x 35p 2B Yellow** (Blue fluor) (10.10.94)	EP8a	3.00	4.00
WB61	**4 x 41p 2B Drab** (Yellow fluor).	EP10	3.75	4.25
WB62	**4 x 60p 2B Slate-blue** (Yellow fluor).	EP11	4.50	5.50

1996 (19 Mar.) Worldwide postcards and Airmail stamps. Olympics.
Printer: Walsall in Lithography. Perf. 15 x 14 elliptical.

WB63	**4 x 35p 2B Deep yellow** (Blue fluor).	EP8a	6.00	7.50
WB64	**4 x 41p 2B Stone** (Blue fluor).	EP10a	7.00	7.50
WB65	**4 x 60p 2B Slate-blue** (Blue fluor).	EP11a	7.50	8.00

1996 (8 July) Worldwide postcards and Airmail stamps. Cover as WB63
Printer: Walsall in Lithography. Perf. 15 x 14 elliptical.

WB66	**4 x 37p 2B Amethyst** (Blue fluor).	EP9	4.00	5.00
WB67	**4 x 63p 2B Light emerald** (Blue fluor).	EP12	5.00	6.00
	Missing Phosphor	EP12a	£1200	£1200

Pane   Plain   Cyl.   Pane   Plain   Cyl.

1997 (4 Feb.) Worldwide postcards and Airmail stamps. Text 'Worldwide Airmail Stamps' ranged to the left and 'International' omitted.
Printer: Walsall in Photogravure

WB68	4 x 37p 2B Amethyst (Blue fluor).	EP9	4.00	5.00
WB69	4 x 63p 2B Light emerald (Blue fluor).	EP12	5.00	6.00

1997 (26 Aug.) Worldwide postcards and Airmail stamps with table of postage rates
Printer: Walsall in computer-engraved gravure. Perf. 15 x 14 elliptical.

WB70	4 x 37p 2B Amethyst (Blue fluor).	EP9	2.50	3.50
WB71	4 x 63p 2B Light emerald (Blue fluor). Cover as WB69	EP12	3.50	4.50

1998 (5 May) European Airmail stamps.

WB72	4 x 30p 2B Grey-green (Blue fluor).	EP14	2.50	3.25
WB73	4 x 63p 2B Light emerald (Blue fluor).	EP18	3.75	4.50
WB74	4 x 38p 2B Ultramarine (Blue fluor). (26.4.99)	EP16	2.75	3.50
WB75	4 x 64p 2B Sea green (Blue fluor). (26.4.99)	EP19	3.75	4.50

1998 (5 May) Worldwide postcards and Airmail stamps.

Cover as WB70 but *without* table of postal rates (above)

WB76	4 x 37p 2B Amethyst (Blue fluor).	EP15	2.75	3.50

1998 (3 Aug.) Worldwide postcards and Airmail stamps Create-a-Card

WB77	4 x 30p 2B Grey-green (Blue fluor)	EP14	3.00	3.75
WB78	4 x 37p 2B Amethyst (Blue fluor)	EP15	3.25	4.00

These have a revised telephone number beginning with 0845

2000 (27 Apr.) European Airmail stamps.

WB79	4 x 40p 2B Greyish-blue (Blue fluor).	EP17	2.75	3.50
WB80	4 x 65p 2B Greenish-blue (Blue fluor).	EP20	3.75	4.50

Penny Black Anniversary Books

Non Value Indicator (NVI) Books

1990 (30 Jan. - 12 June) Printer: Harrison & Sons in Photogravure

AB1	**10 x 15p CB Bright blue**	AP2	5.50	6.00
AB2	**10 x 20p Black & buff** ACP.	AP5	6.00	6.50

Printer: House of Questa in Lithography

AB3	**10 x 15p CB Bright blue** (17.4.90)	AP6	£11	-
AB4	**10 x 20p Black & buff** ACP. (17.4.90)	AP7	£700	-
AB4a	**10 x 20p Black & buff** ACP/Low OBA	AP7a	£10	-

Printer: Walsall Security Printers Ltd in Lithography

AB5	**4 x 15p CB Bright blue**	AP8	3.75	4.25
AB5a	Yellow Queen Victoria head on cover	AP8	4.50	7.50
AB6	**4 x 20p Black & buff** ACP.	AP11	4.00	4.25
AB7	**10 x 15p CB Bright blue** (12.6.90)	AP9	5.75	5.75
AB7a	Incorrect rates on inside cover	AP9a	8.50	£10
AB8	**10 x 20p Black & buff** ACP. (12.6.90)	AP12	7.50	7.50

1990 (17 April) Booklet covers printed by Walsall Security Printers Ltd Stamps printed by Harrison & Sons in Photogravure

Contents

AB9	**4 x 20p Black & buff** ACP	AP3	4.50	-
AB9a	Missing cream from Queen Victoria head on cover	AP3	7.50	-

1989 (22 Aug.) - 90 Printer: Harrison & Sons in Photogravure. Perf. 15 x 14

CB1	**10 x 2nd CB Bright blue**	CP2	6.00	6.00
CB1a	Reprint. Full postal rates	CP2	6.00	7.00
CB2	**10 x 1st Black** ACP.	CP5	7.50	8.00
CB2a	Reprint. Full postal rates	CP5	8.00	8.50

Printer: House of Questa in Lithography. Perf. 15 x 14

CB3	**10 x 2nd CB Bright blue** Perforated margin (19.9.89)	CP7	6.50	-
CB3a	Imperf. margin	CP7a	£60	-
CB4	**10 x 1st Black** ACP. Perforated margin (19.9.89)	CP9	9.75	-
CB4a	Perforated margin - Low OBA	CP9a	£16	-
CB4b	Imperf. margin	CP9b	10.50	-
CB4c	Imperf margin - Low OBA	CP9c	£16	-

Printer: Walsall Security Printers Ltd in Lithography. Perf. 14

CB5	**4 x 2nd CB Bright blue**	CP12	4.00	5.00
CB6	**4 x 1st 2B Black**	CP15	4.50	5.50

1989 (28 Nov.) Booklet covers printed by Walsall Security Printers Ltd. Stamps printed by Harrison & Sons in Photogravure. Perf. 15 x 14

CB7	**4 x 2nd CB Bright blue**	CP1	9.00	-
CB8	**4 x 1st Black** ACP.	CP4	£11	-

		Pane	Plain	Cyl.

1990 (7 Aug.) - 91 New 'Royal Mail' logo. Perf. 15 x 14
Printer: Harrison & Sons in Photogravure.

CB9	**10 x 2nd CB Dark blue**.	CP3	4.75	5.25
CB10	**10 x 1st Orange-red** ACP.	CP6	6.00	6.50

Printer: House of Questa in Lithography. Perf. 15 x 14

CB11	**10 x 2nd CB Dark blue**	CP8	6.00	-
CB12	**10 x 1st Orange-red** ACP.	CP11	6.00	-

Printer: Walsall Security Printers Ltd in Lithography. Perf. 14

CB13	**4 x 2nd CB Dark blue**	CP13	3.50	4.00
CB14	**4 x 1st Orange-red** ACP.	CP19	4.00	4.50
CB14a	**4 x 1st Orange-red** ACP./Low OBA	CP19a	3.50	5.00
CB15	**4 x 1st Orange-red** ACP. Perf 13. (10.90)	CP21	7.00	8.50
CB15a	**4 x 1st Orange-red** ACP/Low OBA. Perf 13	CP21a	7.00	8.50
CB16	**10 x 2nd CB Dark blue**	CP16	4.75	5.50
CB17	**10 x 1st Orange-red** ACP.	CP20	6.00	6.50
CB17a	**10 x 1st Orange-red** ACP./Low OBA	CP20a	7.50	8.50

Without side slits - Newcastle address on inside cover

Printer: Walsall Security Printers Ltd in Lithography. Perf. 14

CB18	**4 x 2nd CB Dark blue**	CP13	3.50	4.00
CB19	**4 x 1st Orange-red** ACP.	CP19	4.00	4.25
CB20	**10 x 2nd CB Dark blue**	CP16	5.50	5.75
CB21	**10 x 1st Orange-red** ACP.	CP20	6.00	6.50

Without side slits - London address on inside cover

1991 (6 Aug.)
Printer: House of Questa in Lithography. Perf. 15 x 14

CB22	**10 x 2nd CB Bright blue**	CP7	4.75	6.00
CB23	**10 x 1st Orange-red** ACP.	CP11	6.00	6.50

Printer: Walsall Security Printers Ltd in Lithography. Perf. 15

CB24	**4 x 2nd CB Bright blue**	CP12	3.50	4.00
CB25	**4 x 1st Orange-red** ACP.	CP19	4.00	4.25
CB26	**10 x 2nd CB Bright blue**	CP17	4.75	5.50
CB27	**10 x 1st Orange-red** ACP.	CP20	6.00	6.50

		Pane	Plain	Cyl.

Printer: Harrison & Sons in Photogravure. Perf 15 x 14

Contents

CB28	**10 x 1st Orange-red** ACP.	CP6	6.00	6.75

1992 (21 Jan.) British Olympic and Paralympic teams logo.
Printer: Harrison & Sons in Photogravure. Perf. 15 x 14

CB29	**10 x 1st Orange-red** ACP.	CP6	6.00	6.25

Printer: House of Questa in Lithography. Perf. 15 x 14

CB30	**10 x 2nd CB Bright blue** (31.3.92)	CP7	5.00	5.50

Printer: Walsall Security Printers in Lithography. Perf. 14

CB31	**4 x 2nd CB Bright blue**	CP14	3.50	4.00
CB32	**4 x 1st Orange-red** ACP.	CP19	4.00	4.50
CB33	**10 x 2nd CB Bright blue**	CP17	4.75	5.50
CB34	**10 x 1st Orange-red** ACP.	CP20	6.00	6.75

1993 (9 Feb.) Rupert Bear Promotion. Perf. 14
Printer: Walsall Security Printers in Lithography

CB35	**10 x 1st Orange-red** ACP.	CP23	6.00	6.50
CB36	**10 x 1st 2B Orange-red** 'C' Yellow fluor. (1.11.93)	CP39	6.00	6.75

1993 (6 April) Security booklets Type 1.
These books have a single line of text at left of inside cover

Printer: Harrison & Sons in Photogravure. Perf. 15 x 14 elliptical

CB37	**4 x 1st Orange-red** OFPP.	CP27	4.00	5.2.
CB38	**10 x 1st Orange-red** OFPP.	CP28	6.00	7.0.

Pane   Plain Cyl.

Pane   Plain Cyl.

Printer: House of Questa in Lithography. Perf. 15 x 14 elliptical

| CB39 | **10 x 2nd CB Bright blue** | CP31 | 4.75 | 5.75 |
| CB39a | Missing phosphor | | £1250 | £1400 |

Printer: Walsall Security Printers Ltd in Lithography. Perf. 15 x 14 elliptical

CB40	**4 x 2nd CB Bright blue**	CP35	3.50	4.50
CB41	**4 x 1st 2B Orange-red**	CP37	4.00	5.50
CB42	**10 x 1st 2B Orange-red**	CP39	6.00	6.50
CB42a	Missing phosphor	CP39a	£1000	£1200

1993 (17 Aug.) Security Booklets Type 2
These books have two lines of text at left of inside cover

Printer: Walsall Security Printers in Lithography. Perf. 15 x 14 elliptical

CB43	**4 x 2nd CB Bright blue** C(Yellow) fluor.	CP35	3.50	4.75
CB44	**4 x 1st 2B Orange-red** C(Yellow) fluor.	CP37	4.00	4.50
CB45	**10 x 2nd CB Bright blue** C(Yellow) fluor.	CP36	4.75	5.75
CB46	**10 x 1st 2B Orange-red** C(Yellow) fluor.	CP39	6.00	7.00

Printer: House of Questa in Lithography. Perf. 15 x 14 elliptical

| CB47 | **10 x 2nd CB Bright blue** C(Yellow) fluor | CP32 | 4.75 | 6.25 |
| CB48 | **10 x 1st 2B Orange-red** C(Yellow) fluor | CP33 | 6.00 | 7.00 |

Printer: Harrison & Sons in Photogravure. Perf. 15 x 14 elliptical

| CB49 | **4 x 2nd CB Bright blue** (7.9.93) | CP24 | 3.50 | 4.75 |
| CB50 | **10 x 1st Orange-red** OFPP. | CP28 | 6.00 | 7.50 |

1993 (17 Aug.) Security Booklets Type 3
These books have three lines of text at left of inside cover

Printer: House of Questa in Lithography. Perf. 15 x 14 elliptical

| B51 | **10 x 2nd CB Bright blue** | CP32 | 4.75 | 6.75 |
| B52 | **10 x 1st 2B Orange-red** C (Yellow) fluor. | CP33 | 6.00 | 8.50 |

1994 (22 Feb.) Free Postcards (text on tab at right). Perf. 15 x 14 elliptical
Printer: Walsall Security Printers in Lithography

CB53	**10 x 1st 2B Orange-red** CP39 *plus* additional pane			
	detailing 'Free Greetings Postcards' offer	CP39	6.00	7.25
CB53a	Broad band	CP39a	£750	£850

1994 (1 July) W H Smith free kite offer. OPEN NOW Chance to win a kite (text on tab at right).
Printer: Walsall Security Printers in Lithography Perf 15 x 14 elliptical

CB54	**10 x 1st 2B Orange-red**	CP39		
	Better Luck Next Time (text on inside back cover)		6.00	7.50
	You've Won! (text on inside back cover)		6.00	7.00

1994 (27 July) Bank of England. Perf. 15 x 14 elliptical
Printer: House of Questa in Lithography.

| CB55 | **4 x 1st 2B Orange-red** | CP34 | 4.00 | 5.50 |
| CB55a | Missing phosphor | CP34a | £950 | £1250 |

1994 (6 Sept.) STAMPERS™.
Printer Walsall Security Printers in Lithography. Perf. 15 x 14 elliptical

	10 x 1st 2B Orange-red	CP39.		
CB56	* Do not open until.....		6.00	7.50
CB57	* Keep in Touch		6.00	7.50
CB58	* Happy birthday		6.00	7.50
CB59	* What's Happenin'?		6.00	7.50

	Pane	Plain	Cyl.

	Pane	Plain	Cyl.

1995 (14 Feb.) Thorntons Sun Chocolates.
Printer: Walsall Security Printers in Lithography. Perf. 15 x 14 elliptical

CB75	10 x 1st 2B Orange-red	CP39	6.00	7.50
CB75a	Missing phosphor	CP39a	£1000	£1200

1995 (10 Jan.) New cover designs.
Printer: Harrison & Sons in Photogravure. Perf. 15 x 14 elliptical

C (Yellow) fluor phosphor

CB60	4 x 2nd CB Bright blue	CP24	3.50	4.50
CB61	10 x 1st Orange-red OFPP.	CP28	6.00	7.50
CB62	10 x 1st 2B Orange-red (4.4.95)	CP26	6.00	6.50

Printer: House of Questa in Lithography. Perf. 15 x 14 elliptical

CB63	10 x 2nd CB Bright blue	CP32	4.75	5.75
CB64	10 x 1st CB Orange-red	CP33	6.00	7.50

Printer: Walsall Security Printers Ltd in Lithography. Perf. 15 x 14 elliptical

CB65	4 x 1st 2B Orangre-red	CP37	4.00	5.00
CB66	10 x 1st 2B Orange-red	CP39	5.50	6.00

D (Blue) fluor phosphor

Printer: Harrison & Sons in Photogravure. Perf. 15 x 14 elliptical

CB67	4 x 2nd CB Bright blue	CP24a	3.50	4.50
CB68	10 x 1st 2B Orange-red	CP26a	6.00	7.00
CB69	10 x 2nd CB Bright blue	CP25	4.75	5.75

Printer: House of Questa in Lithography. Perf. 15 x 14 elliptical

CB70	10 x 2nd CB Bright blue	CP32a	4.75	5.75
CB71	10 x 1st 2B Orange-red	CP33a	7.00	8.00

Printer: Walsall Security Printers Ltd in Lithography. Perf. 15 x 14 elliptical

CB72	4 x 1st 2B Orange-red	CP38	4.00	5.00
CB73	10 x 1st 2B Orange-red	CP40	5.50	6.00
CB74	4 x 2nd CB Bright blue	CP35a	3.50	4.50

1995 (24 April) W H Smith Special Offer. (text on tab at right)
Printer: Walsall Security Printers in Lithography. Perf. 15 x 14 elliptical

CB76	10 x 1st 2B Orange-red	CP39	6.00	8.50

1995 (16 May) R J Mitchell. (label attached to stamps)
Printer: Walsall Security Printers in Lithography. Perf. 15 x 14 elliptical

CB77	4 x 1st 2B Orange-red	CP41	4.00	5.50

1995 (26 June) Sainsbury's Promotion. (text on tab at right)
Printer: House of Questa in Lithography. Perf. 15 x 14 elliptical

CB78	10 x 1st 2B Orange-red	CP33	9.00	9.50

	Pane	Plain	Cyl.

	Pane	Plain	Cyl.

1995 (4 Sept.) Someone special. (Royal Mail)
Printer: Harrison & Sons in Photogravure. Perf. 15 x 14 elliptical

CB79	**10 x 1st 2B Orange-red**	CP26a	6.00	7.00

1996 (6 Feb.) Olympic Symbols. (on reverse)
Printer: Walsall Security Printers in Lithography. Perf. 15 x 14 elliptical

CB80	**4 x 2nd CB Bright blue**	CP35a	3.50	4.50
CB81	**4 x 1st 2B Orange-red**	CP38	4.00	4.75
CB82	**10 x 1st 2B Orange-red**	CP40	4.75	6.25

Printer: Harrison & Sons/De La Rue in Photogravure

CB83	**10 x 2nd CB Bright blue**	CP25	4.75	6.75
CB84	**10 x 1st 2B Orange-red** (19.3.96)	CP26a	6.00	8.00

Printer: House of Questa in Lithography

CB85	**10 x 2nd CB Bright blue**	CP32a	4.75	6.25

1996 (19 Feb.) Promotional. Perf. 15 x 14 elliptical
Printer: Harrison & Sons/De La Rue in Photogravure

CB86	**10 x 1st 2B Orange-red**	CP26a	6.00	7.50

1996 (16 April) Queen's 70th Birthday. (label attached to stamps)
Perf. 15 x 14 elliptical
Printer: Walsall Security Printers in Lithography

CB87	**4 x 1st Orange-red** 2B.	CP41A	4.00	5.50

1996 (13 May.) Olympics. Perf. 15 x 14 elliptical
Printer: Harrison & Sons in Photogravure

CB88	**10 x 1st 2B Orange-red** Shot Put	CP26a	6.00	7.50
CB89	**10 x 1st 2B Orange-red** Hurdles	CP26a	6.00	7.50
CB90	**10 x 1st 2B Orange-red** Archery	CP26a	6.00	7.50

1996 (15 July) W H Smith/Olympic Symbols. (on reverse)
Perf. 15 x 14 elliptical
Printer: Walsall Security Printers in Lithography

CB91	**10 x 1st 2B Orange-red**	CP39	6.00	8.00

Printers Initial added to bottom right corner of reverse

1996 (6 Aug.) (New Rates) Olympic Symbols and printer's intial on reverse)
Perf. 15 x 14 elliptical
Printer: Harrison & Sons/De La Rue in Photogravure

CB92	**10 x 2nd CB Bright blue**	CP25	4.75	5.50
CB93	**10 x 1st 2B Orange-red** (16.8.96)	CP26a	6.00	7.50

Diagonal line on stamp omitted and printers initial added

Printer: House of Questa in Lithography

CB94	10 x 2nd CB Bright blue		CP32a	4.75	8.50

Printer: Walsall Security Printers in Lithography

CB95	10 x 1st 2B Orange-red (6.8.96)		CP40	6.00	7.00

1996 (9 Sept.) Promotional. Perf. 15 x 14 elliptical
Printer: Walsall Security Printers in Lithography

CB96	10 x 1st 2B Orange-red		CP40	6.00	7.00

1996 (7 Oct.) ASDA ('Offer inside' on tab)/**Olympic Symbols.** (on reverse)
Perf. 15 x 14 elliptical
Printer: Walsall Security Printers Ltd in Lithography

CB97	10 x 1st 2B Orange-red		CP40	6.00	7.00

1997 (4 Feb.) New Cover (no diagonal line across stamp) Perf. 15 x 14 elliptical
Printer: Harrison & Sons in Photogravure

CB98	10 x 2nd CB Bright blue		CP25	6.00	6.50
CB99	10 x 1st 2B Orange-red		CP26a	6.50	7.00

Printer: House of Questa in Lithography

CB100	10 x 2nd CB Bright blue		CP32a	4.75	6.75

Printer: Walsall Security Printers in Lithography

CB101	4 x 2nd CB Bright blue		CP35a	3.50	4.00
CB102	4 x 1st 2B Orange-red		CP38	4.25	4.25
CB103	10 x 1st 2B Orange-red		CP40	6.00	6.50

Printer: Walsall Security Printers in Gravure

CB104	4 x 2nd CB Bright blue 26.8.97		CP45	3.50	4.25
CB105	4 x 1st 2B Orange-red (26.8.97)		CP46	4.00	5.00
CB106	10 x 1st 2B Orange-red (18.11.97)		CP49	5.75	6.25
CB107	10 x 1st 2B Gold		CP48	6.00	6.75

Printer: Harrison & Sons in Gravure

CB108	10 x 1st 2B Gold (21.4.97)		CP44	5.00	6.50
CB109	10 x 2nd CB Bright blue (29.4.97)		CP42	4.75	5.75
CB110	10 x 1st 2B Orange-red (18.11.97)		CP43	6.00	6.75

1997 (12 Feb.) Hong Kong 97. (label attached to stamps) Perf. 15 x 14 elliptical
Printer: Walsall Security Printers in Lithography

CB111	4 x 1st 2B Orange-red		CP41B	4.00	5.00

1997 (15 Sept.) First Class Travel ('Open for details' on tab) Perf. 15 x 14 elliptical
Printer: Harrison & Sons in Gravure

CB112	10 x 1st 2B Gold		CP44	6.00	6.5

Pane   Plain   Cyl.

Pane   Plain   Cyl.

1997 (21 Oct.) Heads of Government. (label attached to stamps)
Perf. 15 x 14 elliptical
Printer: Walsall Security Printers Ltd in Lithography

CB113	**4 x 1st 2B Orange-red** + Label	CP41C	4.00	5.00

1998 (2 Feb.) Disney ('See reverse…' on tab) Perf. 15 x 14 elliptical
Printer: De La Rue in Gravure

CB114	**10 x 1st 2B Orange-red**	CP43	6.00	6.75

1998 (April) Woolworths Perf. 15 x 14 elliptical
Printer: De La Rue in Gravure

CB115	**10 x 1st 2B Orange-red**	CP43	6.00	6.50

1998 (5 May) New Inscriptions (textphone for hard of hearing)
Perf. 15 x 14 elliptical

Printer: Walsall Security Printers in Gravure

CB116	**4 x 1st 2B Orange-red**	CP46	4.00	5.00
CB117	**4 x 2nd CB Bright blue**	CP45	3.50	4.00
CB118	**10 x 1st 2B Orange-red**	CP49	6.00	6.50

Printer: De La Rue in Gravure

CB119	**10 x 2nd CB Bright blue**	CP42	4.75	5.25
CB120	**10 x 1st 2B Orange-red**	CP43	6.00	6.50

Printer: The House of Questa in Gravure

CB121	**10 x 2nd CB Bright blue** (1.12.98)	CP51	4.75	5.25
CB121a	Miscut	CP51a	£15	£20
CB122	**10 x 1st 2B Orange-red**	CP52	6.00	7.00
CB122a	Miscut	CP52a	£25	£100

1998 (5 May) Smaller Covers (cover 48mm deep)

Printer: Walsall Security Printers Ltd in Gravure

CB123	**4 x 2nd CB Bright blue**	CP45	3.50	4.50
CB124	**4 x 1st 2B Orange-red**	CP46	4.00	5.00

Printer: The House of Questa in Lithography

CB125	**10 x 2nd CB Bright blue**	CP32a	4.75	5.25
CB126	**10 x 1st 2B Orange-red** (7.09.98)	CP33a	6.00	6.50

1998 (1 July) JVC Perf. 15 x 14 elliptical
Printer: De La Rue in gravure

CB127	**10 x 1st 2B Orange-red**	CP43	6.00	6.50

1998 (3 Aug.) Create - a - Card
Printer: De La Rue in gravure

CB128	**10 x 1st 2B Orange-red**	CP43	6.00	6.50

1998 (14 Nov.) Princes Trust
Printer: Walsall Security Printers in Lithography

CB129   **4 x 1st 2B Orange-red** + Label   CP41D 4.00 5.00

1999 (16 Mar.) Revised Validity on inside cover
Printer: Walsall Security Printers in Gravure

CB130   **10 x 1st 2B Orange-red**   CP49 11.50 17.50

1999 (16 Mar,) Smaller Covers with Revised Validity on Inside Cover
Printer: Walsall Security Printers Ltd.in Gravure

CB131   **4 x 1st 2B Orange-red**   CP46 4.00 4.75
CB132   **10 x 1st 2B Orange-red**   CP49 11.50 17.50

Printer: The House of Questa in Gravure

CB133   **10 x 1st 2B Orange-red**   CP52 6.00 6.50

1999 (12 May) Berlin Airlift
Printer: Walsall Security Printers in Gravure

CB134   **4 x 1st 2B Orange-red** + Label   CP41E 4.00 4.75

1999 (1 Oct.) Rugby Union World Cup
Printer: Walsall Security Printers in Gravure

CB135   **4 x 1st 2B Orange-red** + Label   CP41F 4.00 4.75

2000 (6 Jan.) Millennium Cover with Revised Validity Notice
Printer: Walsall Security Printers in Gravure

CB136   **10 x 1st 2B Millennium**   CP50 6.00 6.50

2000 (6 Jan.) Millennium Cover with Revised Text
Printer: The House of Questa in Gravure

CB137   **10 x 1st 2B Millennium**   CP53 6.00 6.75

2000 (14 Mar.) Millennium Cover with Revised Telephone Number (Number changed to 08457 111 222)
Printer: Walsall Security Printers in Gravure

CB138   **10 x 1st 2B Millennium**   CP50 6.00 7.00

These stamps are valid whatever the current
postage rate and may be used for Second Class
items up to 60g within the UK. They can also be
used as part payment for postage on any item
to any country provided the full cost of postage
is paid. Information on postage rates is available
from post offices.

Postcode enquiries www.postcodes.royalmail.co.uk
or tel: 08457 111 222
Customer Services Helpline tel: 08457 740 740
Telephone 0845 600 0606 (for the deaf and hard of hearing)

2nd class book -Inside cover
1st class has similar layout but text refers to 1st class items.

2000 (14 Mar.) Revised Telephone Number
Printer: Walsall Security Printers in Gravure

CB139	**4 x 2nd CB Bright blue**	CP45	3.50	4.50
CB140	**4 x 1st 2B Orange-red**	CP46	4.00	4.75

Printer: The House of Questa in Gravure

CB141	**10 x 2nd CB Bright blue**	CP51	4.75	5.25
CB142	**10 x1st 2B Millennium**	CP53	6.00	7.00
CB142a	Missing Phosphor	CP53a	£40	£45

2000 (21 Mar.) Postman Pat
Printer: Walsall Security Printers in Gravure

CB143	**4 x 1st 2B Millennium** + Label	CP41G	4.00	4.50

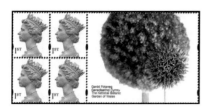

2000 (4 Apr.) National Botanical Garden of Wales
Printer: Walsall Security Printers in Gravure

CB144	**4 x 1st 2B Millennium** + Label	CP41H	4.00	4.75

Single Self Adhesive Stamps

Self adhesive un-mounted mint stamps are assumed to have the 'backing' attached. In general, the backing paper will be square cut around the stamp giving a distinct border. Original printings came with the surplus paper surrounding the stamps (the matrix) still attached. However the norm is now for this paper surplus (matrix) to be stripped away during stamp production. Singles from some presentation packs have been prepared specially in that the die-cutting has been punched through the backing paper giving true 'stamp' shapes.

Landscape Design

Printer: Walsall in Lithography

Matrix intact, Perf 14 x 15 with ellipses

| S1 | 1st | **2B Orange-red** - Book (19.10.93) | 70 |
| S1a | | Missing phosphor | £150 |

Printer: Joh. Enschedé in Gravure

Matrix removed, Perf 14 x 15 with ellipses

S2	2nd	**CB Bright blue** - Coil (18.3.97)	75
S2a		Larger sized 'frame' of stamp - Coil (Used only)	£135
S3	1st	**2B Orange-red** - Coil (18.3.97)	90

Portrait Design

Printer: Enschedé in Gravure

Matrix removed, Perf 15 x 14 with ellipses

S4	2nd	**CB Bright blue** - Translucent backing paper - Coil (6.4.98)	1.25
S4a		Yellow translucent backing paper - Coil (.11.05)	1.25
S5	1st	**2B Orange-red** - Translucent backing paper - Coil (6.4.98)	90
S24	1st	**2B Gold** - Yellow translucent backing paper - Coil(06.06)	75

Printer: Enschedé, Questa or Walsall in Gravure

Matrix intact, Perf 15 x 14 with ellipses

S6	2nd	**CB Bright blue** - Unprinted backing - Bus. sheets (22.6.98)	50
S6a		Imperforate	
S6b		'Dagger' perfs	£125
S6c		Orange-red printed backing paper (29.1.01) - Booklets	50
S6d		Imperforate	
S6e		Missing phosphor	
S7	1st	**2B Orange-red** - Unprinted backing - Bus. sheets (25.6.98)	70
S7a		Imperforate	
S7b		'Dagger' perfs	£125
S7c		Orange-red printed backing paper (29.1.01) - Booklets	70
S7d		Imperforate	£125
S7e		Missing phosphor	£125
S7f		Grey/white printed backing paper (13.2.01) - Booklets	2.00
S14	1st	**2B Gold** - Unprinted backing - Bus. sheets (4.7.02)	70

Printer: De La Rue, Questa or Walsall in Gravure

Matrix removed, Perf 15 x 14 with ellipses

S9	1st	**2B Gold** - Printed backing paper - Booklets (5.6.02)	70
S9a		Imperforate	
S9b		Unprinted backing - Bus. sheets (18.3.02)	70
S9c		Die cut through, unprinted backing - Presentation Packs (6.9.05)	1.00
S10	2nd	**CB Bright blue** - Printed backing paper - Booklets (4.7.02)	50
S10a		Unprinted backing - Bus. sheets (18.9.03)	50
S10b		Imperforate	
S10c		Missing colour	£150
S10d		Die cut through, unprinted backing - Presentation Packs (6.9.05)	1.30

S11	E	**2B Dark blue** - Printed backing paper - Booklets (4.7.02)	95
S12	42p	**2B Sage** - Printed backing paper - Booklets (4.7.02)	1.10
S13	68p	**2B Stone** - Printed backing paper - Booklets (4.7.02)	2.20

S15	Eur.	**2B Ultramarine & Red** - Printed backing paper - Booklets (27.3.03)	90
S15a		Die cut through - Printed backing paper - Presentation Packs (27.3.03)	1.80
S15b		Die cut through - Unprinted backing paper - Presentation Packs (6.9.05)	1.80
S16	W/W	**2B Red & Ultramarine** - Printed backing paper - Booklets (27.3.03)	1.70
S16a		Die cut through - Printed backing paper - Presentation Packs (27.3.03)	2.50
S16b		Die cut through - Unprinted backing paper - Presentation Packs (6.9.05)	2.00

| S17 | Post. | **2B Grey, Red & Blue** - Printed backing paper - Booklets (1.4.04) | 1.00 |
| S17a | | Die cut through - Unprinted backing paper - Presentation Packs (1.4.04) | 1.90 |

Large Portrait Design

Printer: Walsall in Lithography and Embossing

| S8 | **1st** | **White** - Phosphor printed background - Pane SP90, Profile on Print Prestige book (16.2.99) | 2.70 |

Definitive Sized 'Smilers' design

Printer: Walsall in Gravure

First Definitive 'Smilers' as issued in booklet - matrix removed

S18	**1st**	**Flower** - Printed backing paper - Booklet (4.10.05)	60
S19	**1st**	**Hello** - Printed backing paper - Booklet (4.10.05)	60
S20	**1st**	**Love** - Printed backing paper - Booklet (4.10.05)	60
S20a		**Love** - Elliptical perfs - Booklet (16.01.07)	60
S21	**1st**	**Flag** - Printed backing paper - Booklet (4.10.05)	60
S22	**1st**	**Bear** - Printed backing paper - Booklet (4.10.05)	60
S23	**1st**	**Robin** - Printed backing paper - Booklet (4.10.05)	60

Printer: Cartor in Lithography

From Generic 'For life's Special Moments' Smilers sheet with matrix intact- Non elliptical perfs

S25	**1st**	**Flower** - Unprinted backing paper - Generic sheet (4.7.06)	60
S26	**1st**	**Hello** - Unprinted backing paper - Generic sheet (4.7.06)	60
S27	**1st**	**Love** - Unprinted backing paper - Generic sheet (4.7.06)	60
S28	**1st**	**Flag** - Unprinted backing paper - Generic sheet (4.7.06)	60
S29	**1st**	**Bear** - Unprinted backing paper - Generic sheet (4.7.06)	60
S30	**1st**	**Robin** - Unprinted backing paper - Generic sheet (4.7.06)	60

These stamps were originally issued in Personalised Smilers sheets from 4.10.05

PiP Design

Printer: Walsall in Gravure

S31	**2nd**	**Large 2B Bright blue** - Printed backing paper (15.8.06)	70
S31a		Unprinted backing paper - Bus. sheets (27.3.07)	70
S32	**1st**	**Large 2B Gold** - Printed backing paper (15.8.06)	85
S32a		Unprinted backing paper - Bus. sheets (27.3.07)	85

Printer: Walsall or Enschedé in Gravure

S33	**2nd**	**CB Bright blue** - Printed backing paper, booklets (12.9.06)	50
S33a		Unprinted backing paper, Bus. sheets (12.9.06)	50
S35	**2nd**	**CB Bright blue** Yellow translucent backing paper - Coil (Oct. 06)	75
S34	**1st**	**2B Gold** - Printed backing paper, booklets (12.9.06)	60
S34a		Unprinted backing paper, Bus. sheets (12.9.06)	60

Definitive Sized 'Smilers' design

Printer: Walsall in Gravure

Second Definitive 'Smilers' as issued in booklet - matrix removed

S36	**1st**	**New baby** - Printed backing paper - Booklet (17.10.06)	60
S37	**1st**	**Best wishes** - Printed backing paper - Booklet (17.10.06)	60
S38	**1st**	**Thank you** - Printed backing paper - Booklet (17.10.06)	60
S39	**1st**	**Balloons** - Printed backing paper - Booklet (17.10.06)	60
S40	**1st**	**Firework** - Printed backing paper - Booklet (17.10.06)	60
S41	**1st**	**Butterflies** - Printed backing paper - Booklet (17.10.06)	60

Printer: Cartor in Lithography

From Generic 'Extra Special Moments' Smilers sheet with matrix intact- Non elliptical perfs

S42	**1st**	**New baby** - Unprinted backing paper - Generic sheet (17.10.06)	60
S43	**1st**	**Best wishes** - Unprinted backing paper - Generic sheet (17.10.06)	60
S44	**1st**	**Thank you** - Unprinted backing paper - Generic sheet (17.10.06)	60
S45	**1st**	**Balloons** - Unprinted backing paper - Generic sheet (17.10.06)	60
S46	**1st**	**Firework** - Unprinted backing paper - Generic sheet (17.10.06)	60
S47	**1st**	**Butterflies** - Unprinted backing paper - Generic sheet (17.10.06)	60

Country Designs

Printer: Cartor in Lithography

From Generic 'Country' Smilers sheet with matrix intact - Non elliptical perfs

S48	**1st**	**2B Wales Dragon** - Unprinted backing paper (1.03.07)	65
S49	**1st**	**2B England Lion** - Unprinted backing paper (23.4.07)	65
S50	**1st**	**2B Scotland Lio**n - Unprinted backing paper (30.11.07)	65

Self Adhesive Issues

These are arranged in issue date order and include all the basic types. There are many varieties on these which are beyond the scope of this catalogue, but full details can be found in the Machin Collectors Club Specialised catalogue.

Details of some of the varieties known to date are indicated by the following abbreviations at the right of the *Contents* line:-

MP-Missing phosphor   ILB-Inset Left Band   IRB-Inset Right Band
SBT-Short Band Top   SBB-Short Band Bottom
IMP-Imperforate (Kiss die-cut omitted)

1993 (19 Oct.)   **20 x 1st class Sheet**

Printer: Walsall Security Printers in Lithography
Contents 20 x 1st Orange-red 2B. - Pane SB1   MP - SBT

SAB1	Complete Book	8.00
	Double print of phosphor	65.00

1998 (22 June) 100 x 2nd class Business sheet

Printer: Walsall Security Printers in Gravure
Contents 100 x 2nd Bright blue CB. - Pane SS1   SBT - SBB

SAS1	Complete sheet	40.00
	Top panel of four	7.50

100 x 1st class Business sheet

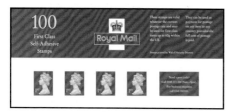

Printer: Walsall Security Printers in Gravure
Contents 100 x 1st Orange-red 2B. - Pane SS2

SAS2	Complete sheet	50.00
	Top panel of four	12.50

2000 (4 Sep.)   **100 x 2nd class Business sheet**

Printer: Walsall Security Printers in Gravure
Contents 100 x 2nd Bright blue CB. - Pane SS3   SBT - SBB

SAS3	Complete sheet	35.00
	Top panel of four	

2000 (4 Sep.)   **100 x 1st class Business sheet**

Printer: House of Questa in Gravure
Contents 100 x 1st class Orange-red 2B - Pane SS4   ILB - IRB -IMP

SAS4	Complete sheet	43.00
	Top panel of four	9.50

2001 (29 Jan.)   **6 x 2nd class book - Walsall**

Printer: Walsall Security Printers in Gravure
Contents 6 x 2nd Bright blue CB. - Pane SB2

SAB2	Complete book	3.00

10 x 2nd class book - Questa

Printer: House of Questa in Gravure
Contents 10 x 2nd class Bright blue CB - Pane SB3

SAB3	Complete book	3.00

2 x 2nd class book - Questa

Printer: House of Questa in Gravure
Contents 12 x 2nd class Bright blue CB - Pane SB4   IMP
SAB4   Complete book   3.60

6 x 1st class book - Walsall

Printer: Walsall Security Printers in Gravure
Contents 6 x 1st class Orange-red 2B - Pane SB5   ILB - IRB - IMP

SAB5   Complete book   3.50

6 x 1st Victoria label

Printer: Walsall Security Printers in Gravure
Contents 6 x 1st Orange-red 2B. - Pane SB6   ILB

SAB6   Complete book   4.00

10 x 1st class book - Questa

Printer: House of Questa in Gravure
Contents 10 x 1st class Orange-red 2B. - Pane SB7

SAB7   Complete book   4.40

12 x 1st class book - Questa

Printer: House of Questa in Gravure
Contents 12 x 1st class Orange-red 2B - Pane SB8

SAB8   Complete book   6.00

12 x 1st class book - Walsall

Printer: Walsall Security Printers in Gravure
Contents 12 x 1st Orange-red 2B. Pane - SB9   ILB - IRB - MP - IMP

SAB9   Complete book   6.00

2001 (13 Feb.)   **10 x 1st Cats and Dogs**

Printer: Walsall Security Printers in Gravure
Contents 10 x 1st Cats and Dogs designs 2B. - Pane SB10   IMP

SAB10   Complete book   10.00

12 x 1st Cats and Dogs

Printer: Walsall Security Printers in Gravure
Contents 10 x 1st Cats and Dogs designs 2B plus 2 x 1st Orange-red 2B.
Pane SB11   ILB

SAB11   Complete book   18.00

2001 (17 Apr.)   **6 x 1st Submarines**

Printer: House of Questa in Gravure
Contents 2 x 1st Submarines stamps plus 4 x 1st Orange-red 2B
Pane SB12   IMP

SAB12   Complete book   60.00

2001 (1 Aug.)   **Revised Text on Back Covers**

6 x 2nd book - Walsall

Printer: House of Questa in Gravure - Revised text on back cover
Contents 6 x 2nd Bright blue CB - Pane SB2

SAB2a   Complete book`   3.00

12 x 2nd book - Questa

Front of cover as SAB4 - Back of cover as SAB2a (above)

Printer: House of Questa in Gravure - Revised text on back cover
Contents 12 x 2nd Bright blue CB - Pane SB4

SAB4a   Complete book   3.60

6 x 1st book - Walsall

Front of cover as SAB5 - Back of cover as SAB2a (above)

Printer: Walsall Security Printers in Gravure - Revised text on back cover
Contents 6 x 1st Orange-red 2B - Pane SB5

SAB5a   Complete book   3.50

12 x 1st book - Walsall

Front of cover as SAB9 - Back of cover as SAB2a (above)

Printer: Walsall Security Printers in Gravure - Revised text on back cover
Contents 12 x 1st Orange-red 2B - Pane SB9   ILB

SAB9a   Complete book   4.75

12 x 1st book - Questa

Front of cover as SAB8 - Back of cover as SAB2a (above)

Printer: House of Questa in Gravure - Revised text on back cover
Contents 12 x 1st Orange-red 2B - Pane SB8

SAB8a   Complete book   5.75

2001 (4 Sep.)   **6 x 1st Punch & Judy**

Printer: House of Questa in Gravure
Contents 2 x 1st Punch & Judy stamps plus 4 x 1st Orange-red 2B -
Pane SB13

SAB13   Complete book   14.00

2001 (22 Oct.)   **6 x 1st Flags & Ensigns**

Printer: House of Questa in Gravure
Contents 2 x 1st Flag stamps plus 4 x 1st Orange-red 2B - Pane SB14   IMP

SAB14   Complete book   14.00

2001 (6 Nov.)   **24 x 2nd Christmas**

Printer: De La Rue in Gravure
Contents 24 x 2nd Christmas stamps - Pane SS5

SAS5   Complete sheet   6.50

12 x 1st Christmas

Printer: De La Rue in Gravure
Contents 12 x 1st Christmas stamps - Pane SS6

SAS6   Complete sheet   4.75

2002 (15 Jan.)   10 x 1st Kipling - Just So stories

Printer: Walsall Security Printers in Gravure
Contents 10 x 1st Special stamps 2B - Pane SB15

SAB15   Complete book   7.00

2002 (2 May) Airliners

Printer: House of Questa in Gravure
Contents 2 x 1st Special stamps 2B plus 4 x 1st Orange-red 2B -
Pane SB16

SAB16   Complete book   5.00

2002 (9 May) 100 x 2nd Business sheet - Enschedé

Printer: Joh. Enschedé in Gravure
Contents 100 x 2nd Bright blue CB - Business sheet SS7

SAS7   Complete sheet   30.00
           Top panel of four   6.50

100 x 1st Business sheet

Printer: Joh. Enschedé in Gravure
Contents 100 x 1st Orange-red 2B - Business sheet SS8

SAS8   Complete sheet   42.50
           Top panel of four   12.00

2002 (21 May)   6 x 1st World Cup

Printer: Walsall Security Printers in Gravure
Contents 2 x 1st Special stamps 2B plus 4 x 1st Orange-red 2B -
Pane SB17   ILB - IRB - SBB

SAB17   Complete book   3.50

2002 (5 June)   6 x 1st Book - Questa

Printer: House of Questa in Gravure
Contents 6 x 1st Gold 2B - Pane SB18

SAB18   Complete book   3.50

6 x 1st book - Walsall

Printer: Walsall Security Printers in Gravure
Contents 6 x 1st Gold 2B - Pane SB19   SBT - SBB

SAB19   35mm Printers imprint, Complete book   3.50
SAB19a   29mm Printers imprint, Complete book (15.1.04)   3.50
SAB19b   'Hello' label, Complete book (27.1.05)   3.50
SAB19c   'Love' label, Complete book (26.7.05)   3.50

12 x 1st book - Walsall

Printer: Walsall Security Printers in Gravure
Contents 12 x 1st Gold 2B - Pane SB20   SBT - SBB

| SAB20 | 35mm Printers imprint, Complete book | 6.00 |
| SAB20a | 29mm Printers imprint, Complete book (15.1.04) | 6.00 |

2002 (4 July)

12 x 2nd - Questa

Printer: House of Questa in Gravure
Contents 12 x 2nd Bright blue CB - Pane SB21

| SAB21 | Complete book | 4.50 |

6 x 1st - Questa

Printer: House of Questa in Gravure
Contents 6 x 1st Orange-red 2B - Pane SB22

| SAB22 | Complete book | 3.50 |

100 x 2nd Business sheet - Enschedé

Printer: Joh. Enschedé in Gravure
Contents 100 x 2nd Bright blue CB - Business sheet SS9

| SAS9 | Complete sheet | 40.00 |
| | Top panel of four | 6.50 |

100 x 1st Business sheet - Enschedé

Printer: Joh. Enschedé in Gravure
Contents 100 x 1st Gold 2B - Business sheet SS10   SBT - SBB

| SAS10 | Complete sheet | 42.50 |
| | Top panel of four | 7.50 |

6 x E European - Walsall

Printer: Walsall Security Printers in Gravure
Contents 6 x E stamps 2B - Pane SB23   SBB

| SAB23 | Complete book | 4.50 |

6 x 42p - Walsall

Printer: Walsall Security Printers in Gravure
Contents 6 x 42p stamps 2B - Pane SB24   SBT

| SAB24 | Complete book | 4.50 |

6 x 68p - Walsall

Printer: Walsall Security Printers in Gravure
Contents 6 x 68p stamps 2B - Pane SB25   SBB

| SAB25 | Complete book | 7.00 |

2002 (10 Sep.)   **6 x 1st Bridges of London**

Printer: House of Questa in Gravure
Contents 2 x 1st Bridges stamps plus 4 x 1st Gold 2B - Pane SB26

SAB26   Complete book   5.00

2002 (5 Nov.)   **24 x 2nd Christmas**

Printer: De La Rue in Gravure
Contents 24 x 2nd Christmas stamps - Pane SS11

SAS11   Complete sheet   6.00

           12 x 1st Christmas

Printer: De La Rue in Gravure
Contents 12 x 1st Christmas stamps - Pane SS12

SAS12   Complete sheet   4.50

2003 (4 Mar.)   **6 x 1st Hello - Questa**

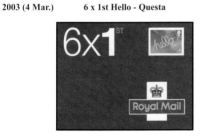

Printer: House of Questa in Gravure
Contents 2 x 1st Hello stamps plus 4 x 1st Gold 2B - Pane SB27

SAB27   Complete book   7.50

2003 (18 Mar.)   **100 x 2nd Business sheet**

Printer: Walsall Security Printers in Gravure
Contents 100 x 2nd Bright blue CB - Business sheet SS13

SAS13   Complete sheet   35.00
              Top panel of four   6.50

           100 x 1st Business sheet

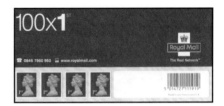

Printer: Walsall Security Printers in Gravure
Contents 100 x 1st Gold 2B - Business sheet SS14

SAS14   Complete sheet   42.50
              Top panel of four   7.50

2003 (25 Mar.)   **Fruit & Veg Pack**

There are two versions of this pack. The post office version which is a plain pack and a second type sold by Sainsbury's which has a cut-out at the top of the pack for display purposes (shown below).

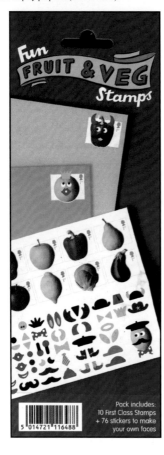

Printer: Walsall Security Printers in Gravure
Contents 10 x 1st Multi-coloured Fruit & Veg stamps 2B - Pane SB28

SAB28	Complete pack - Post Office version	6.50
SAB28a	Complete pack - Sainsbury's version	6.50

2003 (27 Mar.)

12 x 2nd book - The Real Network ™ added

Printer: Walsall Security Printers in Gravure
Contents 12 x 2nd Bright blue CB - Pane SB29   SBB

SAB29	Complete book	4.50

6 x 1st book - The Real Network ™ added

Printer: Walsall Security Printers in Gravure
Contents 6 x 1st Gold 2B - Pane SB19a

SAB30	Complete book	2.50

12 x 1st book - The Real Network ™ added

Printer: Walsall Security Printers in Gravure
Contents 12 x 1st Gold 2B - Pane SB20a   SBB

SAB31	Complete book	6.00

4 x Europe book - The Real Network ™ sdded

Printer: Walsall Security Printers in Gravure
Contents 4 x Europe 2B - Pane SB30   SBT - SBB - ILB - IRB

SAB32	Complete book	2.80

4 x Worldwide book - The Real Network ™ added

Printer: Walsall Security Printers in Gravure
Contents 4 x Worldwide 2B - Pane SB31   SBT - SBB

SAB33	Complete book	6.70

2003 (29 Apr.)   **6 x 1st Extreme Endeavours**

Printer: De La Rue in Gravure
Contents 2 x 1st Special stamps plus 4 x 1st Gold 2B - Pane SB32

SAB34   Complete book   4.50

2003 (28 May) 6 x E The Real Network ^{TM} added

Printer: Walsall Security Printers in Gravure
Contents 6 x E 2B - Pane SB23

SAB35   Complete book   5.00

6 x 42p The Real Network ^{TM} added

Printer: Walsall Security Printers in Gravure
Contents 6 x 42p 2B -Pane SB24

SAB36   Complete book   4.50

6 x 68p The Real Network ^{TM} added

Printer: Walsall Security Printers in Gravure
Contents 6 x 68p 2B - Pane SB25

SAB37   Complete book   7.00

2003 (15 July)   **6 x 1st Scotland**

Printer: De La Rue in Gravure
Contents 2 x 1st Special stamps plus 4 x 1st Gold 2B- Pane SB33

SAB38   Complete book   2.80

2003 (18 Sep)   **6 x 1st Transports of Delight**

Printer: De La Rue in Gravure
Contents 2 x 1st Special stamps plus 4 x 1st Gold 2B -Pane SB34

SAB39   Complete book   7.50

2003 (4 Nov.)   **24 x 2nd Christmas**

Printer: De La Rue in Gravure
Contents 24 x 2nd Christmas stamps - Pane SS15

SAS15   Complete sheet   6.25

12 x 1st Christmas

Printer: De La Rue in Gravure
Contents 12 x 1st Christmas stamps - Pane SS16

SAS16   Complete sheet   4.50

2004 (16 Mar.)   **6 x 1st Northern Ireland**

Printer: De La Rue in Gravure
Contents 2 x 1st Special stamps plus 4 x 1st Gold 2B - Pane SB35

SAB40   Complete book   2.80

2004 (1 Apr.)   **4 x Postcard**

Printer: Walsall Security Printers in Gravure
Contents 4 x Postcard 2B - Pane SB36   SBB

SAB41   Complete book   3.50

2004 (13 Apr.)   **6 x 1st Ocean Liners**

Printer: De La Rue in Gravure
Contents 2 x 1st Special stamps plus 4 x 1st Gold 2B -Pane SB37

SAB42   Complete book   4.00

2004 (15 June) 12 x 2nd book - The Real Network [TM] removed

Printer: Walsall Security Printers in Gravure
Contents 12 x 2nd Bright blue CB - Pane SB29a

SAB43   Complete book   4.50

6 x 1st Wales

Printer: De La Rue in Gravure
Contents 2 x 1st Special stamps plus 4 x 1st Gold 2B - Pane SB38

SAB46   Complete book   4.50

4 x Europe - The Real Network [TM] removed

Printer: Walsall Security Printers in Gravure
Contents 4 x Europe 2B - Pane SB30a   SBT

SAB44   Complete book   4.00

4 x Worldwide - The Real Network [TM] removed

Printer: Walsall Security Printers in Gravure
Contents 4 x Worldwide 2B - Pane SB31a   SBB

SAB45   Complete book   4.50

6 x 1st Olympic

Printer: Walsall Security Printers in Gravure
Contents 6 x 1st Gold 2B -Pane SB39

SAB47   Complete book   3.50

100 x 2nd Business sheet - The Real Network ᵀᴹ removed

Printer: Walsall Security Printers in Gravure
Contents 100 x 2nd Bright blue CB - Business sheet SS17

| SAS17 | Complete sheet | 35.00 |
| | Top panel of four | 5.00 |

100 x 1st Business sheet - The Real Network ᵀᴹ removed

Printer: Walsall Security Printers in Gravure
Contents 100 x 1st Gold 2B - Business sheet SS18

| SAS18 | Complete sheet | 42.50 |
| | Top panel of four | 6.50 |

2004 (2 Nov.)   24 x 2nd Christmas

Printer: De La Rue in Gravure
Contents 24 x 2nd Christmas stamps - Pane SS19

| SAS19 | Complete sheet | 6.25 |

12 x 1st Christmas

Printer: De La Rue in Gravure
Contents 12 x 1st Christmas stamps - Pane SS20

| SAS20 | Complete sheet | 4.50 |

2005 (4 Oct.)   6 x 1st 'Smilers'

Printer: Walsall Security Printers in Gravure
Contents 6 x 1st 2B Multicoloured - Pane SB42

| SAB48 | Complete book | 7.00 |

2005 (1 Nov.)   24 x 2nd Christmas

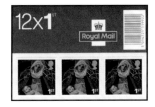

Printer: De La Rue in Gravure
Contents 24 x 2nd Christmas stamps - Pane SS21

| SAS21 | Complete sheet | 6.25 |

12 x 1st Christmas

Printer: De La Rue in Gravure
Contents 12 x 1st Christmas stamps - Pane SS22

| SAS22 | Complete sheet | 4.50 |

2006 (25 Apr.)   12 x 2nd PiP Validity

Printer: Walsall Security Printers in Gravure
Contents 12 x 2nd Bright blue CB - Pane SB29b

| SAB49 | Complete book | 5.00 |

2006 (25 Apr.)   **6 x 1st PiP Validity**

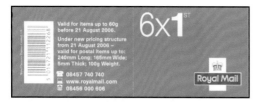

Printer: Walsall Security Printers in Gravure
Contents 6 x 1st Gold PiP 2B - Pane SB19d

SAB49   Complete book   3.60

2006 (25 Apr.)   **12 x 1st PiP Validity**

Printer: Walsall Security Printers in Gravure
Contents 12 x 1st Gold PiP 2B - Pane SB20c

SAB49   Complete book   7.00

2006 (16 May)   **100 x 2nd PiP Business sheet**

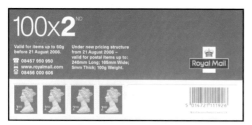

Printer: Walsall Security Printers in Gravure
Contents 100 x 2nd Bright blue PiP CB - Pane SS23

SAS23   Complete sheet   35.00
         Top panel of four   5.50

2006 (16 May)   **100 x 1st PiP Business sheet**

Printer: Walsall Security Printers in Gravure
Contents 100 x 1st Gold PiP CB - Pane SS24

SAS24   Complete sheet   45.00
         Top panel of four   6.50

2006 (15 Aug.)   **4 x 2nd Large PiP**

Printer: Walsall Security Printers in Gravure
Contents 4 x 2nd Bright blue Large PiP 2B - Pane SB43

SAB53   Complete book   7.00

2006 (15 Aug.)   **4 x 1st Large PiP**

Printer: Walsall Security Printers in Gravure
Contents 4 x 1st Gold Large PiP 2B - Pane SB44

SAB54   Complete book   7.00

2006 (12 Sep.)   **12 x 2nd PiP**

Printer: Walsall Security Printers in Gravure
Contents 12 x 2nd Bright blue PiP CB - Pane SB45

SAB55   Complete book   5.00

2006 (12 Sep.)   **6 x 1st PiP**

Printer: Walsall Security Printers in Gravure
Contents 6 x 1st Gold PiP 2B - Pane SB46

SAB56   Complete book   3.50
SAB56a   Complete book with 'Loveastamp' label (2.10.06) 3.50
SAB56b   Complete book with 'Postalcode' label (1.02.07) 3.50

2006 (12 Sep.)   **12 x 1st PiP**

Printer: Walsall Security Printers in Gravure
Contents 12 x 1st Gold PiP 2B - Pane SB47

SAB57   Complete book   5.00

2006 (12 Sep.)   **100 x 2nd PiP**

Printer: Walsall Security Printers in Gravure
Contents 100 x 2nd Bright blue PiP CB - Pane SS25

SAS25   Complete sheet   35.00
            Top panel of four   5.50

2006 (12 Sep.)   **100 x 1st PiP**

Printer: Walsall Security Printers in Gravure
Contents 100 x 1st Gold PiP 2B - Pane SS26

SAS26   Complete sheet   45.00
            Top panel of four   6.50

2006 (17 Oct.)   **6 x 1st Smilers 2**

Printer: Walsall Security Printers in Gravure
Contents 6 x 1st 2B Multicoloured - Pane SB49

SAB58   Complete book   3.50

2006 (7 Nov.)   **12 x 2nd Christmas**

Printer: De La Rue in Gravure
Contents 12 x 2nd Christmas stamps - Pane SB50

SAB59   Complete book   4.90

2006 (7 Nov.)   **12 x 1st Christmas**

Printer: De La Rue in Gravure
Contents 12 x 1st Christmas stamps - Pane SB51

SAB60   Complete book   6.50

2007 (16 Jan.)   **5 x 1st PiP & 1 x 1st 'Love' stamp**

Printer: Walsall Security Printers in Gravure
Contents 5 x 1st Gold PiP 2B + 1 x 1st 'Love' stamp - Pane SB52

SAB61   Complete book   3.50

2007 (27 Mar.)   **50 x 2nd Large PiP**

Printer: Walsall Security Printers in Gravure
Contents 50 x 2nd Bright blue Large PiP 2B - Pane SS27

| SAS27 | Complete sheet | 25.00 |
| | Top panel of four | 6.90 |

2007 (27 Mar.)   **50 x 1st Large PiP**

Printer: Walsall Security Printers in Gravure
Contents 50 x 2nd Bright blue Large PiP 2B - Pane SS28

| SAS28 | Complete sheet | 32.00 |
| | Top panel of four | 7.90 |

2007 (5 Jun.)   **12 x 2nd (Non PiP stamps)**

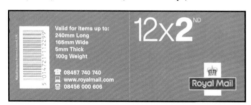

Printer: Walsall Security Printers in Gravure
Contents 12 x 2nd Bright blue CB - Pane SB29c

| SAB62 | Complete book | 5.00 |

2007 (5 Jun.)   **6 x 1st (Non PiP stamps)**

Printer: Walsall Security Printers in Gravure
Contents 6 x 1st Gold 2B - Pane SB55

| SAB64 | Complete book | 3.50 |
| SAB64a | Complete book - Bi-lingual label (20.9.07) | 3.50 |

2007 (5 Jun.)   **12 x 1st (Non PiP stamps)**

Printer: Walsall Security Printers in Gravure
Contents 12 x 1st Gold 2B - Pane SB20d

| SAB65 | Complete book | 5.00 |

2007 (5 Jun.)   **6 x 1st (Machin Anniversary)**

Printer: Walsall Security Printers in Gravure
Contents 6 x 1st Gold 2B - Pane SB54

| SAB63 | Complete book | 3.50 |

2007 (5 June)   **100 x 2nd (Non PiP stamps)**

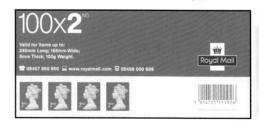

Printer: Walsall Security Printers in Gravure
Contents 100 x 2nd Bright blue CB - Pane SS29

| SAS29 | Complete sheet | 35.00 |
| | Top panel of four | 5.50 |

2007 (5 June)   **100 x (Non PiP stamps)**

Printer: Walsall Security Printers in Gravure
Contents 100 x 1st Gold 2B - Pane SS30

| SAS30 | Complete sheet | 45.00 |
| | Top panel of four | 6.50 |

2007 (28 Aug)   **6 x 1st (Harry Potter)**

Printer: Walsall Security Printers in Gravure
Contents 6 x 1st Gold 2B - Pane SB56

| SAB66 | Complete book | 3.50 |

2007 (6 Nov.)   **12 x 2nd Christmas**

Printer: De La Rue in Gravure
Contents 12 x 2nd Christmas stamps - Pane SB58

| SAB67 | Complete book | 4.90 |

2007 (6 Nov.)   **12 x 1st Christmas**

Printer: De La Rue in Gravure
Contents 12 x 1st Christmas stamps - Pane SB59

| SAB68 | Complete book | 6.50 |

Coil Issues

1997 (18 Mar.)   **100 x 2nd - Landscape**

Printer: Joh. Enschedé in Gravure
Contents 100 x 2nd Bright blue CB

SAC1   Complete box of 100
            Vertical coil strip of 4   4.00

100 x 1st - Landscape

Printer: Joh. Enschedé in Gravure
Contents 100 x 1st Orange-red 2B

SAC2   Complete box of 100
            Vertical coil strip of 4   4.00

1998 (6 Apr.)   **200 x 2nd - Portrait**

Printer: Joh. Enschedé in Gravure
Contents 200 x 2nd Bright blue CB

SAC3   Complete box of 200
            Vertical coil strip of 4   5.00

200 x 1st - Portrait

Printer: Joh. Enschedé in Gravure
Contents 200 x 1st Orange-red 2B

SAC4   Complete box of 200
            Vertical coil strip of 4   5.00

2005 (Apr.)   **10,000 x 2nd - Portrait**

Printer: Joh. Enschedé in Gravure
Contents: 10,000 x 2nd Bright blue CB

SAC3a   2 x Vertical coil strip of 5 (with and without number)   £20

2005 (Apr.)   **10,000 x 1st - Portrait**

Printer: Joh. Enschedé in Gravure
Contents: 10,000 x 1st Gold 2B

SAC5   Complete box of 10,000
            Vertical strip of four   5.00

2006 (Jun.)   **10,000 x 2nd PiP- Portrait**

Printer: Joh. Enschedé in Gravure
Contents: 10,000 x 2nd Bright blue CB

SAC6   Complete box of 10,000
            Vertical strip of four   4.00

		Appendix 1 - Panes and Single Reference			
Book Pane		Description	Process	Printer	Single No.
SB1		20 x 1st Orange-red	Litho	Walsall	S1
SB1a		Missing phosphor			S1a
SP90		4 x 1st (Large format)	Emb/Litho	Walsall	S8
SB2		6 x 2nd	Gravure	Walsall	S6c
SB2a		Missing phosphor			S6e
SB3		10 x 2nd		Questa	S6c
SB4		12 x 2nd		Questa	S6c
SB4a		Imperforate			S6d
SB5		6 x 1st Orange-red	Gravure	Walsall	S7c
SB5a		Imperforate			S7d
SB6		6 x 1st Orange-red - Victoria label		Walsall	S7c
SB7		10 x 1st Orange-red		Questa	S7c
SB8		12 x 1st Orange-red		Questa	S7c
SB9		12 x 1st Orange-red		Walsall	S7c
SB9a		Missing phosphor			S7e
SB9b		Imperforate			S7d
SB10		10 x 1st Cats & Dogs		Walsall	
SB10a		Imperforate			
SB11		10 x 1st Cats & Dogs / 2 x 1st Orange-red		Walsall	S7f
SB12		6 x 1st Orange-red / Submarines		Questa	S7c
SB12a		Imperforate			
SB13		6 x 1st Orange-red / Punch & Judy		Questa	S7c
SB14		6 x 1st Orange-red / Flags & Ensigns		Questa	S7c
SB14a		Imperforate			
SB15		10 x 1st Kiplimg		Walsall	
SB16		6 x 1st Orange-red / Airliners		Questa	S7c
SB17		6 x 1st Orange-red / World Cup		Walsall	S7c
SB18	*	6 x 1st Gold		Questa	S9
SB19	*	6 x 1st Gold - 35mm Printers imprint		Walsall	S9
SB19a	*	'The Real Network' Strap-line on cover		Walsall	S9
SB19b		Imperforate			S9a
SB19c	*	'The Real Network' removed - 29mm Printers imprint		Walsall	S9
SB19d	*	6 x 1st - back cover PiP validity notice text (25.4.06)		Walsall	S9
SB20	*	12 x 1st Gold - 35mm Printers imprint		Walsall	S9
SB20a	*	'The Real Network' Strap-line on cover		Walsall	S9
SB20b	*	'The Real Network' removed - 29mm printers imprint		Walsall	S9
SB20c	*	12 x 1st - back cover PiP validity notice text (25.4.06)		Walsall	S9
SB20d	*	12 x 1st - PiP rates on back cover (5.6.07)		Walsall	S9
SB21	*	12 x 2nd		Questa	S10
SB22		6 x 1st Orange-red		Questa	S7c
SB23	*	6 x E		Walsall	S11
SB24	*	6 x 42p		Walsall	S12
SB25	*	6 x 68p		Walsall	S13
SB26	*	6 x 1st Gold / London Bridges		Questa	S9
SB27	*	6 x 1st Gold / Hello		Questa	S9
SB28		10 x 1st Fruit & Veg		Walsall	
SB28a		Imperforate			
SB29	*	12 x 2nd 'The Real Network' Strap-line on cover		Walsall	S10

* Indicates the matrix has been stripped away during manufacture

Book Pane		Description	Process	Printer	Single No.
SB29a	*	'The Real Network' removed		Walsall	S10
SB29b	*	12 x 2nd - back cover PiP validity notice text (25.4.06)		Walsall	S10
SB29c	*	12 x 2nd - PiP rates on back cover (5.6.07)		Walsall	S10
SB30	*	4 x Europe		Walsall	S15
SB30a	*	'The Real Network' removed - Labels spaced wider		Walsall	S15
Book Pane		Description	Process	Printer	Single No.
SB31	*	4 x Worldwide	Gravure	Walsall	S16
SB31a	*	'The Real Network' removed		Walsall	S16
SB32	*	6 x 1st Gold / Endeavours		De La Rue (Byfleet)	S9
SB33	*	6 x 1st Gold / Scotland		De La Rue (Byfleet)	S9
SB34	*	6 x 1st Gold / Toy Transport		De La Rue (Byfleet)	S9
SB35	*	6 x 1st Gold / Northern Ireland		De La Rue	S9
SB36	*	4 x Postcard		Walsall	S17
SB37	*	6 x 1st Gold / Ocean Liners		De La Rue	S9
SB38	*	6 x 1st Gold / Wales		De La Rue	S9
SB39	*	6 x 1st Gold ' Support London 2012' label		Walsall	S9
SB40	*	6 x 1st Gold 'Smilers - Hello' label		Walsall	S9
SB41	*	6 x 1st Gold 'Smilers - Love' label		Walsall	S9
SB42	*	6 x 1st Definitive sized 'Smilers'		Walsall	S18, S19, S20, S21, S22, S23
SB42a	*	Smilers 1 - back cover PiP validity text (17.7.06)		Walsall	S18, S19, S20, S21, S22, S23
SB43	*	4 x 2nd Large PiP (15.8.06)		Walsall	S31
SB44	*	4 x 1st Large PiP (15.8.06)		Walsall	S32
SB45	*	12 x 2nd PiP back cover PiP text (12.9.06)		Walsall	S33
SB46	*	6 x 1st PiP back cover PiP tet (12.9.06)		Walsall	S34
SB47	*	12 x 1st PiP back cover PiP text (12.9.06)		Walsall	S34
SB48	*	6 x 1st PiP 'loveastamp' label (2.10.06)		Walsall	S34
SB49	*	6 x 1st Smilers 2 (17.10.06)		Walsall	S36, S37, S38 S39, S40, S41
SB50	*	12 x 2nd Christmas 2006 (7.11.06)		De La Rue	
SB51	*	12 x 1st Christmas 2006 (7.11.06)		De La Rue	
SB52	*	5 x 1st PiP; 1 x 1st 'Love' Valentine 1 (16.1.07)		Walsall	S34, S20a
SB53	*	6 x 1st PiP Postcode label (1.2.07)		Walsall	S34
SB54	*	6 x 1st Machin label (5.6.07)		Walsall	S9
SB55	*	6 x 1st Postcode label (5.6.07)		Walsall	S9
SB56	*	6 x 1st Harry Potter label (28.8.07)		Walsall	S9
SB57	*	6 x 1st Bi-lingual Postcode label (20.9.07)		Walsall	S9
SB58	*	12 x 2nd Christmas 2007 (6.11.07)		De La Rue	
SB59	*	12 x 1st Christmas 2007 (6.11.07)		De La Rue	

Z Folded Sheets

SS1		100 x 2nd Business sheets	Gravure	Walsall	S6
SS2		100 x 1st Orange-red Business sheets		Walsall	S7
SS3		100 x 2nd Business sheets		Walsall	S6
SS3a		Imperforate			
SS4		100 x 1st Orange-red Business sheets		Questa	S7
SS4a		Imperforate			
SS5		24 x 2nd Christmas 2001		De La Rue (High Wycombe)	
SS6		12 x 1st Christmas 2001		De La Rue (High Wycombe)	
SS7		100 x 2nd Business sheets		Enschedé	S6

* Indicates the matrix has been stripped away during manufacture

SS8		100 x 1st Orange-red Business sheets		Enschedé	S7
SS9		100 x 2nd Business sheets		Enschedé	S6
SS10		100 x 1st Gold Business sheets		Enschedé	S14
SS11		24 x 2nd Christmas 2002		De La Rue (High Wycombe)	
SS12		12 x 1st Christmas 2002		De La Rue (High Wycombe)	
SS13	*	100 x 2nd Business sheets 'The Real Network'		Walsall	S10a
SS14	*	100 x 1st Gold Business sheets 'The Real Network'		Walsall	S9b
SS15	*	24 x 2nd Christmas 2003		De La Rue (Byfleet)	
SS16	*	12 x 1st Christmas 2003		De La Rue (Byfleet)	
SS17	*	100 x 2nd ('The Real Network' removed)		Walsall	S10a
SS17a		Imperforate			S10b
SS17b	*	Missing colour			S10c
SS18	*	100 x 1st Gold ('The Real Network' removed)		Walsall	S9b
SS19	*	24 x 2nd Christmas 2004		De La Rue	
SS20	*	12 x 1st Christmas 2004		De La Rue	
SS21	*	24 x 2nd Christmas 2005		De La Rue	
SS22	*	12 x 1st Christmas 2005		De La Rue	
SS23	*	100 x 2nd - PiP validity text Business sheet (16.5.06)		Walsall	S10a
SS24	*	100 x 1st - PiP validity text Business sheet (16.5.06)		Walsall	S9b
SS25	*	100 x 2nd PiP Business sheet (12.9.06)		Walsall	S33a
SS26	*	100 x 1st PiP Business sheet (12.9.06)		Walsall	S34a
SS27	*	50 x 2nd Large Business sheet (27.3.07)		Walsall	S31a
SS28	*	50 x 1st Large Business sheet (27.3.07)		Walsall	S32a
SS29	*	100 x 2nd PiP rate text Business sheet (5.6.07)		Walsall	S10a
SS30	*	100 x 1st PiP rate text Business sheet (5.6.07)		Walsall	S9b
Coils					
SC1	*	100 x 2nd (Landscape design)	Gravure	Enschedé	S2
SC2	*	100 x 1st Orange-red (Landscape design)		Enschedé	S3
SC3	*	200 x 2nd (Portrait design)		Enschedé	S4
SC3a	*	10,000 x 2nd (Portrait design)		Enschedé	S4a
SC4	*	200 x 1st Orange-red (Portrait design)		Enschedé	S5
SC5	*	10,000 x 1st Gold coil (June 06)		Enschedé	S24
SC6	*	10,000 x 2nd PiP coil (October 06)		Enschedé	S35

* Indicates the matrix has been stripped away during manufacture

Book No.	Description	Process	Printer	Pane No.
	Appendix 2 - Complete Books and Pane Reference			
SAB1	20 x 1st Orange-red	Litho	Walsall	SB1
	Missing phosphor			SB1a
SAB2	6 x 2nd	Gravure	Walsall	SB2
	Missing phosphor			SB2a
SAB2a	6 x 2nd Revised text on back cover		Walsall	SB2
SAB3	10 x 2nd		Questa	SB3
SAB4	12 x 2nd		Questa	SB4
	Imperforate			SB4a
SAB4a	12 x 2nd - Revised text on back cover		Questa	SB4
SAB5	6 x 1st Orange-red	Gravure	Walsall	SB5
	Imperforate			SB5a
SAB5a	6 x 1st Orange-red - Revised text on back cover		Walsall	SB5
SAB6	6 x 1st Orange-red Victoria label		Walsall	SB6
SAB7	10 x 1st Orange-red		Questa	SB7
SAB8	12 x 1st Orange-red		Questa	SB8
SAB8a	12 x 1st Orange-red - Revised text on back cover		Questa	SB8
SAB9	12 x 1st Orange-red		Walsall	SB9
	Missing phosphor			SB9a
	Imperforate			SB9b
SAB9a	12 x 1st Orange-red - Revised text on back cover		Walsall	SB9
SAB10	10 x 1st Cats & Dogs		Walsall	SB10
	Imperforate			
SAB11	10 x 1st Cats & Dogs / 2 x 1st Orange-red Machin		Walsall	SB11
SAB12	6 x 1st Orange-red / Submarines		Questa	SB12
	Imperforate			
SAB13	6 x 1st Orange-red / Punch & Judy		Questa	SB13
SAB14	6 x 1st Orange-red / Flags & Ensigns		Questa	SB14
	Imperforate			
SAB15	10 x 1st Kipling		Walsall	SB15
SAB16	6 x 1st Orange-red / Airliners		Questa	SB16
SAB17	6 x 1st Orange-red / World Cup		Walsall	SB17
SAB18	6 x 1st Gold - Re-branded cover		Questa	SB18
SAB19	6 x 1st Gold - 35mm Printers imprint - Re-branded cover		Walsall	SB19
SAB19a	'The Real Network' removed - 29mm printers imprint		Walsall	SB19c
SAB19b	6 x 1st Gold with 'Smilers - Hello' label inside		Walsall	SB40
SAB19c	6 x 1st Gold with 'Smilers - Love' label inside		Walsall	SB41
SAB20	12 x 1st Gold - 35mm Printers imprint - Re-branded cover		Walsall	SB20
SAB20a	'The Real Network' removed - 29mm Printers imprint		Walsall	SB20b
SAB21	12 x 2nd - Re-branded cover		Questa	SB21
SAB22	6 x 1st Orange-red		Questa	SB22
SAB23	6 x E		Walsall	SB23
SAB24	6 x 42p		Walsall	SB24
SAB25	6 x 68p		Walsall	SB25
SAB26	6 x 1st Gold / London Bridges		Questa	SB26
SAB27	6 x 1st Gold / Hello		Questa	SB27
SAB28	10 x 1st Fruit & Veg		Walsall	SB28
	Imperforate			SB28a
SAB29	12 x 2nd 'The Real Network' Strap line on cover		Walsall	SB29
SAB30	6 x 1st Gold 'The Real Network' strap line on cover		Walsall	SB19a
	Imperforate			SB19b

SAB31	12 x 1st Gold 'The Real Network' strap line on cover	Gravure	Walsall	SB20a
SAB32	4 x Europe 'The Real Network' strap line on cover		Walsall	SB30
SAB33	4 x Worldwide - 'The Real Network' strap line on cover		Walsall	SB31
SAB34	6 x 1st Gold / Endeavours		De La Rue (Byfleet)	SB32
SAB35	6 x E 'The Real Network' strap line on cover		Walsall	SB22
SAB36	6 x 42p 'The Real Network' strap line on cover		Walsall	SB23
SAB37	6 x 68p 'The Real Network' strap line on cover		Walsall	SB24
SAB38	6 x 1st Gold / Scotland		De La Rue (Byfleet)	SB33
SAB39	6 x 1st Gold / Toy Transport		De La Rue (Byfleet)	SB34
SAB40	6 x 1st Gold / Northern Ireland		De La Rue (Byfleet)	SB35
SAB41	4 x Worldwide Postcard		Walsall	SB36
SAB42	6 x 1st Gold / Ocean Liners		De La Rue (Byfleet)	SB37
SAB43	12 x 2nd 'The Real Network' removed		Walsall	SB29a
SAB44	4 x Europe The Real Network' removed; Labels spaced wider		Walsall	SB30a
SAB45	4 x Worldwide 'The Real Network' removed; Labels spaced wider		Walsall	SB31a
SAB46	6 x 1st Gold / Wales		De La Rue (Byfleet)	SB38
SAB47	6 x 1st Gold ' Support London 2012'		Walsall	SB39
SAB48	6 x 1st Definitive sized 'Smilers'		Walsall	SB42
SAB49	12 x 2nd - back cover PiP validity notice text (25.4.06)		Walsall	SB29b
SAB50	6 x 1st - back cover PiP validity notice text (25.4.06)		Walsall	SB19d
SAB51	12 x 1st - back cover PiP validity notice text (25.4.06)		Walsall	SB20c
SAB52	Smilers 1 - back cover PiP validity notice text (17.7.06)		Walsall	SB42a
SAB53	4 x 2nd Large PiP (15.8.06)		Walsall	SB43
SAB54	4 x 1st Large PiP (15.8.06)		Walsall	SB44
SAB55	12 x 2nd PiP back cover PiP text (12.9.06)		Walsall	SB45
SAB56	6 x 1st Pip back cover PiP text (12.9.06)		Walsall	SB46
SAB56a	6 x 1st PiP 'loveastamp' label (2.10.06)		Walsall	SB48
SAB56b	6 x 1st PiP Postcode lable (1.2.07)		Walsall	SB53
SAB57	12 x 1st PiP back cover PiP text (12.9.06)		Walsall	SB47
SAB58	6 x 1st Smilers 2 (17.10.06)		Walsall	SB49
SAB59	12 x 2nd Christmas 2006 (7.11.06)		De La Rue	SB50
SAB60	12 x 1st Christmas 2006 (7.11.06)		De La Rue	SB51
SAB61	5 x 1st PiP; 1 x 1st 'Love' Valentine 1 (16.1.07)		Walsall	SB52
SAB62	12 x 2nd - PiP text on back cover (5.6.07)		Walsall	SB29c
SAB63	6 x 1st Machin label (5.6.07)		Walsall	SB54
SAB64	6 x 1st Postcode label (5.6.07)		Walsall	SB55
SAB64a	6 x 1st Bi-lingual Postcode label (20.9.07)		Walsall	SB57
SAB65	12 x 1st - PiP text on back cover (5.6.07)		Walsall	SB20d
SAB66	6 x 1st Harry Potter label (28.8.07)		Walsall	SB56
SAB67	12 x 2nd Christmas 2007 (6.11.07)		De La Rue	SB58
SAB68	12 x 1st Christmas 2007 (6.11.07)		De La Rue	SB59

Z Folded (Business) Sheets and Pane References

SAS1	100 x 2nd Business sheet	Gravure	Walsall	SS1
SAS2	100 x 1st Orange-red Business sheet		Walsall	SS2
SAS3	100 x 2nd Business sheet		Walsall	SS3
	Imperforate			
SAS4	100 x 1st Orange-red Business sheet		Questa	SS4
	Imperforate			
SAS5	24 x 2nd Christmas 2001		De La Rue (High Wycombe)	SS5
SAS6	12 x 1st Christmas 2001		De La Rue (High Wycombe)	SS6
SAS7	100 x 2nd Business sheet		Enschedé	SS7
SAS8	100 x 1st Orange-red Business sheet		Enschedé	SS8
SAS9	100 x 2nd Business sheet - Re-branded cover		Enschedé	SS9
SAS10	100 x 1st Gold Business sheet - Re-branded cover		Enschedé	SS10
SAS11	24 x 2nd Christmas 2002		De La Rue (High Wycombe)	SS11
SAS12	12 x 1st Christmas 2002		De La Rue (High Wycombe)	SS12
SAS13	100 x 2nd Business sheet - 'The Real Network'		Walsall	SS13
SAS14	100 x 1st Gold Business sheet - 'The Real Network'		Walsall	SS14
SAS15	24 x 2nd Christmas 2003		De La Rue (Byfleet)	SS15
SAS16	12 x 1st Christmas 2003		De La Rue (Byfleet)	SS16
SAS17	100 x 2nd - 'The Real Network' removed		Walsall	SS17
	Imperforate			
	Missing colour			
SAS18	100 x 1st Gold - 'The Real Network' removed		Walsall	SS18
SAS19	24 x 2nd Christmas 2004		De La Rue (Byfleet)	SS19
SAS20	12 x 1st Christmas 2004		De La Rue (Byfleet)	SS20
SAS21	24 x 2nd Christmas 2005		De La Rue (Dunstable)	SS21
SAS22	12 x 1st Christmas 2005		De La Rue (Dunstable)	SS22
SAS23	100 x 2nd - PiP validity text Business sheet (16.5.06)		Walsall	SS23
SAS24	100 x 1st - PiP validity text Business sheet (16.5.06)		Walsall	SS24
SAS25	100 x 2nd PiP Business sheet (12.9.06)		Walsall	SS25
SAS26	100 x 1st PiP Business sheet (12.9.06)		Walsall	SS26
SAS27	50 x 2nd Large Business sheet (27.3.07)		Walsall	SS27
SAS28	50 x 1st Large Business sheet (27.3.07)		Walsall	SS28
SAS29	100 x 2nd - PiP rate text Business sheet (5.6.07)		Walsall	SS29
SAS30	100 x 1st - PiP rate text Business sheet (5.6.07)		Walsall	SS30

Complete Coils and References

SAC1	100 x 2nd (Landscape Design)	Gravure	Enschedé	SC1
SAC2	100 x 1st Orange-red (Landscape Design)		Enschedé	SC2
SAC3	200 x 2nd (Portrait Design)		Enschedé	SC3
SAC3a	10,000 x 2nd (Portrait Design)		Enschedé	SC3a
SAC4	200 x 1st Orange-red (Portrait Design)		Enschedé	SC4
SAC5	10,000 x 1st Gold coil		Enschedé	SC5
SAC6	10,000 x 2nd PiP Design coil		Enschedé	SC6

Stamps of issues 1841-1901 used in offices abroad.
Compiled by Paul Dauwalder

British stamps were sent to various agencies mainly in the Americas, Mediterranean, North Africa and Mesopotamia usually through British Consulate Appointments and mail distributed via British Packet Mail Boat lines.

The system carried on in embryonic form until the various countries established their own postal service and postage labels. D65 is known to be used at Pisagua, Peru on 2/- blue and various GB stamps were used with local non numerical cancels in Nigeria, Niger Coast, Egypt and Ionian Islands.

This listing is by no means exhaustive. We have detailed numeral cancels only and illustrate some typical cancels employed. Various barred cancels may be found freely from each office.

Prices are estimates of values of clearly legible postmarks on stamps only, but please note the operative word 'from'. Stamps on cover are worth considerably more. An asterisk thus * indicates that a cancel is known on stamp or cover. For more information we refer the reader to Stanley Gibbons British Commonwealth Catalogue 1840 - 1952.

We welcome further information of incidence of cancels within the territories shown below.

Stamp Face value	Comments and thoughts
4d, 6d and 1s	By far the commonest three values encountered, the 4d value is slightly more difficult from west coast offices and vice versa for the 6d but certainly not difficult. The early 1862 issues are generally very difficult, which to be expected as the offices were not open, the obvious exception being Buenos Ayres.
3d, 9d, 10d, 2s and 5s	Still fairly easy values to obtain, varies from office to office but generally regularly seen, the comments about the 1862 issues apply here as well.
1d, 2d, 1½d and ½d (Line engraved)	Surprisingly difficult at times, it is infinitely easier to find a 2s or 5s used abroad than it is a 1d plate. The scarcest is the ½d mainly due to its size and getting a legible strike of the postmark.
½d - 5d (1880 issue) Lilac & Green issue	Very tricky. The only one that commonly appears is the 1½d Venetian red used in Greytown, the rest are much rarer. The Lilac & Green issue is only found in Panama and really are an abnormal usage from Naval mail. We don't actually list them here but they definitely exist
8d	This is one of the key values used abroad from this area. The only ones seen with any regularity are, as you would expect, St. Thomas, Callao and Valparaiso. Never underestimate this value!
2½d Rosy mauve	This is a major rarity and a surprise for most people. The writer has only seen 4 or 5 used in Valparaiso and a couple used in Panama. Do not underestimate this stamp - it is very common used in Malta, Gibraltar etc, and the exact opposite in South America.
10s & £1	Vary rare as to be expected. Six 10s used in Valparaiso (2 reperforated and 2 badly damaged) are known; The 10s for Greytown is believed unique. The 10s listed for Port Au Prince is very rare and three £1 used in Valparaiso are known (they all have faults!)

Comparative Rarity

In this section we endeavour to give an idea of the rarity of one office to another, as we feel it is this balance which is most important - and most difficult to obtain. Please read this in combination with the priced tables

Letter	Rarity	Letter	Rarity	Letter	Rarity
A	Very Common	B	Common	C	Scarce
D	Very Scarce	E	Rare	F	Almost Impossible

Country	Office	Comments
Argentine	Buenos Ayres	Rarity B. Nothing is particularly difficult here. Even the 1d plates and 1862 issues can be found. Good strikes abound. About 10% of cancels are in blue.
Bolivia	Cobija	Rarity F. Very rare for all values. Less than a dozen genuine examples have been seen by the author in twenty years. No matter what value you put on these it is not enough! 3 types of canceller known.
Brazil	Rio, Bahia, Pernambuco	Rarity B-C. Nothing that difficult here. Bahia and Pernambuco are slightly scarcer than Rio but still nothing that difficult.
Chile	Valparaiso	Rarity A. Nothing difficult here except the 2½d, 10s, £1 and 1880 issues for the reasons stated above. Even the 2s Brown is quite easy to find used here. The 1862 4d is known on a cover with 3 x 4d and 2 x 1s. 1862 3d known on cover in pair with 1858 1d plate 89
	Caldera, Coquimbo	Rarity C-D. Coquimbo is more difficult than Caldera, and both can be found cancelled in blue. If anything C37 in black is more difficult than blue. The 1862 4d and 1865 1s used in Caldera are known from three covers to Germany in 1866. Loose examples have not been seen by the author. Both these places are 20 times scarcer than Valparaiso. The ½d - 2d values are particularly difficult here especially from Coquimbo.
Columbia	Carthagena	Rarity C. Nothing unusual here. The C65 error is at least 2 - 3 times scarcer than the C56
	Panama	Rarity A-B. Apart from the 2½d and 1880 issues as already mentioned, nothing is particularly difficult.
	Colon, Santa, Martha & Savanilla	Rarity C-D. Colon is surprisingly difficult, the 4d value is by far the commonest for all offices. The 4d Sage green used in Savanilla being far easier than the earlier 4d Vermilion. Nothing particularly unusual, nevertheless all are difficult in any quantity.
Cuba	Havana	Rarity D. Surprisingly difficult for what was such a large office, especially the 6d and 8d.
	St. Jago	Rarity E. Very difficult - at least five times rarer than Havana. The vast majority of stamps offered are smudgy strikes of Rio C83. A very difficult one to price as only a few are known.
DWI	St. Thomas	Rarity A. Very common.
Dominican Republic	Porto Plata, St. Domingo	Rarity D-E. A very difficult area. The 1s used in Porto Plata is by far the commonest value seen. St. Domingo is the more difficult of the two. We think they would fit between Havana and St. Jago in terms of rarity.
Ecuador	Guayaquil	Rarity B. Nothing really that difficult here - slightly scarcer than Valparaiso and Callao and probably on a similar par to Panama. Plenty of forgeries seen particularly on the 1d plates, most of which are relatively easy to detect.
Haiti	Jacmel, Port Au Prince	Rarity B. Jacmel is relatively common, Port Au Prince is slightly more difficult. Each listing is probably unique.
Mexico	Tampico	Rarity D-E. This is really very difficult, the 1d and 4d values being the commonest. Several 2s values with poor C83 strikes offered as C63 have been seen. Do not underestimate Tampico.
Nicaragua	Greytown	Rarity C. An odd one this, the latter issues are ten times easier than the earlier ones with most stamps encountered with CDS's for 1879-82. Beware of suspect circular cancels. Anything earlier is much more difficult and is cancelled by the C57 duplex. The 5s plate 4 and 10s are probably both unique. The 5s has been seen and its authenticity is dubious. Also seen is the 1s green with the C57 horizontal oval numeral which is supposedly the unique example of this.
Peru	Callao	Rarity A. Apart from the early 1862-65 issues nothing difficult. The duplex cancel is very scarce.
	Arica, Iquique and Islay	Rarity C-D. These three are all about equal, Iquique is slightly scarcer than the other two. Arica and Iquique can be found cancelled in blue 40-50% of the time and Islay very rarely. These three should probably be placed on a par with, or fractionally easier than, Caldera and Coquimbo. Iquique cancels on piece are always used with Peruvian stamps. It is difficult to find C42 on one stamp - the mark covers 2 stamps
	Paita	Rarity E. Very rare - at least 4-5 times more difficult than Arica etc.

Peru (continued)	Pisagua	It is not believed that the cover with the 2s blue was cancelled in Peru, more likely by an inspector in transit in London. 1d and 2d plates exist cancelled D65 in red - who knows??
	Pisco	Rarity F. Without doubt the rarest os all the South American Offices. All values are priced at different levels, but they could all be the same as we doubt whether more than 10-15 examples exist with genuine cancels. There are a lot of fakes about usually on stamps that were issued after the office shut!
Porto Rico	San Juan	Rarity A-B Relatively common the 1862 and 1865 9d are the only difficult stamps here.
	Mayaguez	Rarity B-C. Not as easy as San Juan but still not difficult.
	Ponce, Arroyo	Rarity C-D. Getting progressively more difficult. F83 in red is very rare. It is known on the 9d and 1s values both cancelled by an additional C51 in black.
	Naguabo	Rarity F. Very difficult, on a par with Coboja, although 20 years ago a page of 20 10d values used here were found. Due to the high volume of mail with Spain the 10d value is easier in Porto Rico than some other offices.
Uruguay	Montevideo	Rarity D-E. This office is very hard to find, at least 10 times rarer than Argentina or Brazil. The very early 1857 and 1862 issues being particularly difficult. This office is on a par with Havana or Aguadilla.
Venezuela	La Guayra	Rarity C-D. Not too bad but as superb cds's are found from 1877 onwards, huge premiums normally apply. The 4d Vermilion is by far the commonest stamp seen here. The use of the Crowned Circle to cancel stamps is a major rarity.
	Cuidad Bolivar	Rarity E-F. Very difficult, the 4d Sage green with a red cds is by far the commonest. Some of the stamps are really scarce. Among those seen by the author are three 1d Pl.133 (on cover, D22 numeral), three 2s blue (all off centre red cds), two 1s Pl.8 and 13 (Red cds) and one 5s (black cds without PAID at base). The numeral cancellation is far scarcer than the cds, although nowhere near as attractive.

Type	AO1 Kingston Jamaica Single Cancel	Double Cancel	AO2 St. Johns Antigua	AO3 -AO4 Georgetown	AO5 Nassau Bahamas	AO6 Belize	AO7 Dominica	AO8 Montserratt	AO9 Charlestown Nevis	A10 Kingstown St. Vincent
½d Rose (1870 - 79)										
1d Red (1841) Imperf										
1d Red-brown 1855 p16 Die II										
1d Red-brown 1855 p14 Die II										
1d Red-brown 1855 Die II p16 LC										
1d Red 1857 LC p14	£150	£200	£400	From £300	£1750	£750	£200	£1000	£375	£500
1d Red Plate 1864 - 79										
1½d Rose -red, Plate 1 or 3										
2d Blue 1841 Imperf										
2d Blue 1855 LC p14			£750							
2d Blue 1858 LC p16										
2d Blue 1858 Pl 7-15		£500	£500	From £700	From £1000		Plate 7 - £600		Plate 7 & 8 £1500	
2½d Rosy-mauve 1875 Blue paper										
2½d Rosy-mauve 1876 Plates 3 - 17										
2½d Blue 1880 Plates 17 - 20										
2½d Blue 1881 Plates 21 - 23										
3d Carmine 1862										
3d Rose 1865 Plate 4										
3d Rose 1867 Plates 4 - 10										
3d Rose 1873 Plates 11 - 20										
3d Rose 1881 Plate 20/21										
3d on 3d Lilac 1883										
4d Rose 1857	£140	£120	£400	£120	£350	£300	£300	*	£300	£325
4d Rose 1857 Glazed paper										
4d Red Plate 3 or 4 1862										
4d Vermillion 1865 Plate 7 - 14										
4d Vermillion Plate 15 1876										
4d Sage-green (1877) Plate 15 & 16										
4d ... brown 1880 Wmk Garter Pl17										

Type	AO1 Kingston Jamaica Single Cancel	AO1 Double Cancel	AO2 St. Johns Antigua	AO3 - AO4 Georgetown	AO5 Nassau Bahamas	AO6 Belize	AO7 Dominica	AO8 Montserrat	AO9 Charlestown Nevis	A10 Kingstown St. Vincent
4d Grey-brwon 1880 Wmk. Cross Plates 17 & 18										
6d Lilac Embossed 1854					£3250					
6d Lilac 1856	£35	£110	£130	From £100	£275					
6d 1862 Plates 3 & 4										
6d 1865 Plates 5 & 6										
6d 1865 Wmk. error										
6d Lilac 1867 Plate 6										
6d Lilac 1867 Plate 6, 8 or 9										
6d Buff 1872 Plates 11 & 12										
6d Chestnut 1872 Plate 11										
6d Grey 1873 Plate 12										
6d Grey 1873 Plates 13-17										
6d Grey 1881 - 2 Plates 17 & 18										
6d on 6d Lilac										
8d Orange 1876										
9d Straw 1862										
9d Bistre 1862										
9d Straw 1867										
10d Red-brown 1867										
1/- 1847 Embossed										
1/- Green (1856)	£300	*	£1500	£1000	£1800	£1200	£1200	£1200	*	
1/- Green (1856)Thick paper										
1/- Green 1862										
1/- Green 1862 K Variety										
1/- Green 1865 Plate 4										
1/- Green Plates 4, 5, 6, 7 (1867)										
1/- Green 1873 Plates 8 - 13										
1/- Orange-brown Plate 13										

Type	AO1 Kingston Single Cancel	Jamaica Double Cancel	AO2 St. Johns Antigua	AO3 -AO4 Georgetown	AO5 Nassau Bahamas	AO6 Belize	AO7 Dominica	AO8 Montserrat	AO9 Charlestown Nevis	A10 Kingstown St. Vincent
1/- Orange-brown 1881 Plates 13 & 14										
2/- Blue 1867										
2/- Brown 1880										
5/- Rose 1867 Plates 1 and 2										
5/- Rose Plate 4 1882 Blued paper										
5/- Rose Plate 4 1882 White paper										
10/- Grey-green 1878										
10/- Grey-green 1883										
£1 Brown-lilac 1878										
£1 Brown-lilac 1882										
1880 ½d Deep green										
1880 ½d Pale green										
1880 1d Venetian red										
1880 1½d Venetian red										
1880 2d Pale rose										
1880 2d Deep rose										
1880 5d Indigo										
1881 1d Lilac 14 dots										
1881 1d Lilac 16 dots										
1883 - 4 ½d Slate blue										
1883 - 4 1½d Lilac										
1883 - 4 2d Lilac										
1883 - 4 2½d Lilac										
1883 - 4 3d Lilac										
1883 - 4 Dull green										
1883 - 4 5d Dull green										
1883 - 4 6d Dull green										
1883 - 4 9d Dull green										
1883 - 4 1/- Dull green										

Type	A11 Castries St. Lucia	A12 Basseterre St Christopher	A13 Tortola Virgin Islands	A14 Scarborough Tobago	A15 St George Grenada	A18 English Harbour Antigua	A25 Malta	A26 Gibraltar	A27-78 Jamaica
½d Rose (1870 - 79)							From £18	From £20	
1d Red (1841) Imperf							From £2000	From £1100	
1d Red (1854) p16 Die I SC							£250		
1d Red-brown 1855 p16 Die II SC								£130	
1d Red-brown 1855 p14 Die II LC						£4500			
1d Red-brown 1855 Die II p16 LC							£55		
1d Red 1857 LC pl4	£850	£500	£3250	£650	£350		£7	£10	£100
1d Red 1861 Alph IV									
1d Red Plate 1864 - 79							From £10	From £15	
1½d Rose-red Plate 1 or 3							£300	Plate 13 - £375	
2d Blue 1841 Imperf							£3000		
2d Blue 1854 SC Die I pl6	*								
2d Blue 1855 LC pl4							£50	£100	£400
2d Blue 1858 LC p16									
2d Blue 1858 Plates 7 - 15		Plate 7 £850			Plate 7 - £850	Plate 7 - £4500	From £12	From £15	
2½d Rosy-mauve 1875 Blue paper							£50	From £75	
2½d Rosy-mauve 1876 White paper							£25	From £20	
2½d Rosy-mauve 1876 Plates 3 - 17							From £20	From £15	
2½d Blue 1880 Plates 17 - 20							From £10	From £10	
2½d Blue 1881 Plates 21 - 23							from £10	From £12	
3d Carmine 1862							£85	£120	
3d Rose 1865 Plate 4							£40	£45	
3d Rose 1867 Plates 4 - 10							From £20	From £25	
3d Rose 1873 Plates 11 - 20							From £25	From £32	
3d Rose 1881 Plate 20/21							£600	*	
3d on 3d Lilac 1883							£350	£115	
4d Rose 1857	£350	£300	£3500	£275	£225		£28	£40	£95
4d Rose 1857 Glazed paper							£90		
4d Red Plate 3 or 4 1862							£25	£35	

Type	A11 Castries St. Lucia	A12 Basseterre St Christopher	A13 Tortola Virgin Islands	A14 Scarborough Tobago	A15 St' George Grenada	A18 English Harbour Antigua	A25 Malta	A26 Gibraltar	A27-78 Jamaica
4d Vermillion 1865 Palte 7 - 14							From £15	From £20	
4d Vermillion Plate 15 1876							From £120	£200	
4d Sage green (1877) Plates 15 & 16							£65	£85	
4d Grey-brown 1880 Wmk. Garter Pl. 17							£125	£185	
4d Grey-brown 1880 Wmk. Crown Plates 17 & 18							£30	£35	
6d Lilac Embossed 1854							£1850		
6d Lilac 1856	£195	£165	£1100	£220	£150	£140	£35	£35	£225
6d 1862 Plates 3 & 4							£28	£28	
6d 1865 Plates 5 & 6							£27	£25	
6d 1865 Wmk. Error							£1000		
6d Lilac 1867 Plate 6							£30	£35	
6d Violet 1867 Plate 8 or 9							From £20	£25	
6d Buff 1872 Plates 11 & 12							£80	From £110	
6d Chestnut 1872 Plate 11							£25	£25	
6d Grey 1873 Plate 12							£85	£85	
6d Grey 1873 Plates 13 - 17							£25	£25	
6d Grey 1881 - 2 Plates 17 & 18							£50	£150	
6d on 6d Lilac							£90	£80	
8d Orange 1876							£250	£350	
9d Straw 1862							£400	£200	
9d Bistre 1862							£400	£450	
9d Straw 1865							£500	£550	
9d Straw 1867							£100	£130	
10d Red-brown 1867							£100	£110	
1/- 1847 Embossed						*	£2000		
1/- Green (1856)	£1000	£1200	*	£1100	£1000	*	£65	£75	£500
1/- Green (1856) Thick paper							£220		
1/- Green 1862							£50	£60	

Type	A11 Castries St. Lucia	A12 Basseterre St Christopher	A13 Tortola Virgin Islands	A14 Scarborough Tobago	A15 St George Grenada	A18 English Harbour Antigua	A25 Malta	A26 Gibraltar	A27-78 Jamaica
1/- Green 1862 K Variety							£2500	£1600	
1/- Green 1865 Plate 4							£50	£60	
1/- Green Plates 4, 5, 6 & 7 (1867)							From £20	From £22	
1/- Green 1873 Plates 8 - 13							From £35	From £40	
1/- Orange-brown Plate 13							£225	£250	
1/- Orange-brown 1881 Plates 13 & 4							£60	£75	
2/- Blue 1867							£150	£170	
2/- Brown 1880							£2000		
5/- Rose 1867 Plates 1 and 2							£275	Plate 1 - 500	
5/- Rose Plate 41882 Blued paper							£1100		
5/- Rose Plate 4 1882 White paper							£1000		
10/- Grey-green 1878							£2000		
10/- Grey-green 1883									
£1 Brown-lilac 1878									
£1 Brown-lilac 1882									
1880 ½d Deep green							£10	£17	
1880 ½d Pale green							£10	£17	
1880 1d Venetian red							£8	£17	
1880 1½d Venetian red							£275	£190	
1880 2d Pale rose							£30	£40	
1880 2d Deep rose							£30	£40	
5d Indigo							£50	£85	
1881 1d Lilac 14 dots							£25	£20	
1881 1d Lilac 16 dots							£6	£7	
1883-4 ½d Slate blue							£10	£15	
1883-4 1½d Lilac							*		
1883-4 2d Lilac							£60	£60	
1883-4 2½d Lilac							£15	£12	

Type	A11 Castries St. Lucia	A12 Basseterre St Christopher	A13 Tortola Virgin Islands	A14 Scarborough Tobago	A15 St' George Grenada	A18 English Harbour Antigua	A25 Malta	A26 Gibraltar	A27-78 Jamaica
1883-4 3d Lilac							*	*	
1883-4 4d Dull green							£120	£120	
1883-4 5d Dull green						*	£120		
1883-4 6d Dull green							*		
1883-4 9d Dull green							*		
1883-4 1/- Dull green							*		
1883 5/- Blued							£1200		
1883 5/- White							£750		

Type	A80 - A99 Mailboats	B01 Alexandria Egypt	B02 Suez Egypt	B03 B12 B56 B57 Mailboats	B32 Buenos Ayres	C Constantinople	C28 Montivideo Uraguay	C30 Valparaiso Chile
½d Rose (1870 - 79)		£15	£25			From £20		
1d Red (1841) Imperf								
1d Red (1854) p16 Die I SC						*		
1d Red-brown 1855 p16 Die II SC						*		
1d Red-brown 1855 p14 Die II LC						£15		
1d Red-brown 1855 Die II p16 LC								
1d Red 1857 LC p14	From £25	£5	£8	From £40	£40			
1d Red 1861 Aph IV						*		
1d Red Plate 1864-79	From £20	£8	£10	From £40	£30	From £8	£60	£20
1½d Rose-red Plate 1 or 3						£150		£40
2d Blue 1841 Imperf								
2d Blue 1854 SC Die I p16						*		
2d Blue 1855 LC p14								
2d Blue 1858 LC p16								
2d Blue 1858 Plates 7-15	From £40	£8	£12	From £50	£30	From £10	Plate 9 & 13 £60	£30
2½d Rosy-mauve 1875 Blue paper		£50	£45			From £40		
2½d Rosy-mauve 1875 White paper		£30	£30			From £25		Plate 2 £150
2½d Rosy-mauve 1876 Plates 3-17						£15		Plates 4 & 8 £150
2½d Blue 1880 Plates 17-20						£12		
2½d Blue 1881 Plates 21-23						8.50		
3d Carmine 1862	From £200	£85	£100		£350	£95		
3d Rose 1865 Plate 4	From £200	£40	£55	From £75	£80	£50	*	*
3d Rose 1867 Plates 4-10	From £50	£40	£20	From £75	£35	£40	£50	£30
3d Rose 1873 Plates 11-20		£20	£30			£20		£25
3d Rose 1881 Plates 20/21						Plate 21 *		
3d on 3d Lilac 1883						*		
4d Rose 1857	From £150	£30	£40		£80	£30	*	
4d Rose 1857 Glazed paper								
4d Red Plate 3 or 4 1862	From £85	£35	£35	From £90	£65	£25	Plate 4 *	*

Type	A80 - A99 Mailboats	B01 Alexandria Egypt	B02 Suez Egypt	B03 B12 B56 B57 Mailboats	B32 Buenos Ayres	C Constantinople	C28 Montivideo Uraguay	C30 Valparaiso Chile
4d Vermillion 1865 Plates 7-14	From £50	From £20	£20	From £55	£35	From £15	From £35	From £30
4d Vermillion Plate 15 1876		£130	*			£110		£200
4d Sage green (1877) Plates 15 & 16		£100	£100			£65		£125
4d Grey-brown 1880 Wmk. Garter Pl 17						*		
4d Grey-brown 1880 Wmk. Cross Plates 17 & 18						£25		
6d Lilac Embossed 1854	From £120							
6d Lilac 1856	From £85	£38	£40	From £120	£70	£45	*	
6d 1862 Plates 3 & 4	From £80	£30	£30	From £100	*	£25	Plate 4 £120	£40
6d 1865 Plates 5 & 6		Plate 6 £30	£30	From £80	£60	£25	£65	*
6d 1865 Wmk. error						£25		
6d Lilac 1867 Plate 6	From £75	£30	£35	From £75	£60	£20	*	*
6d Lilac 1867 Plate 6, 8 or 9	From 350	£28	£20	From £55	£50	£40	Plates 8 & 9 £65	£40
6d Buff 1872 Plates 11 & 12		£45	£45		Plate 11 £60	£20	*	£50
6d Chestnut 1872 Plate 11		£25	£30		£35	£50	*	£30
6d Grey 1873 Plate 12		£55	£75			£20	£140	£140
6d Grey 1873 Plates 13-17		£20	£20			£30	£30	£30
6d Grey 1881-2 Plates 17 & 18							*	*
6d on 6d Lilac						£55		
8d Orange 1876	*		*			£250	£220	£220
9d Straw 1862		£120	£140		£375		*	*
9d Bistre 1862		*	*		£375			
9d Straw 1865	*	*			£375		*	*
9d Straw 1867	*	*	*		£200		£300	£140
10d Red-brown 1867	From £400	£120	£130	From £400	£200	£100	£300	£200
1/- 1847 Embossed								
1/- Green (1856)	From 3200	£100	£110		£200	£80	£200	
1/- Green (1856) Thick paper								
1/- Green 1862	From £200	£50	£70		£120	£45	£150	

Type	A80 - A99 Mailboats	B01 Alexandria Egypt	B02 Suez Egypt	B03 B12 B56 B57 Mailboats	B32 Buenos Ayres	C Constantinople	C28 Montivideo Uruguay	C30 Valparaiso Chile
1/- Green 1862 K Variety		*	*			*		
1/- Green 1865 Plate 4		£30	£40		£150	£45	£200	*
1/- Green Plates 4, 5, 6, 7 (1867)		£12	£12		From £50	From £10	Plates 4 & 5 £60	£30
1/- Green 1873 Plates 8-13		From 322	From £22		Plate 8 - *	From £25		£40
1/- Orange-brown Plate 13						£130		£250
1/- Orange-brown 1881 Plates 13 & 14						£40		
2/- Blue 1867		£90	£120		£100	£75	£170	£90
2/- Brown 1880								£1500
5/- Rose 1867 Plates 1 & 2		£150	£200		£250	£175	Plate 1 £350	Plate 1 & 2 £220
5/- Rose Plate 4 1882 Blued paper						£750		
5/- Rose Plate 4 White paper						£700		
1/- Grey-green 1878								£2500
10/- Grey-green 1883								
£1 Brown-lilac 1878								£3500
£1 Brown-lilac 1882								
1880 ½d Deep green						£8		
1880 ½d Pale green						£10		
1880 1d Venetian red						£8		
1880 1½d Venetian red						£120		
1880 2d Pale rose						£40		
1880 2d Deep rose						£40		
1880 5d Indigo						*		
1881 1d Lilac 14 dots								
1881 1d Lilac 16 dots								
1883-4 ½d Slate-blue						£5		
1883-4 1½d Lilac						£12		
1883-4 2d Lilac						£60		
1883-4 2½d Lilac						£45		
1883-4 3d Lilac						£7		

Type	A80 - A99 Mailboats	B01 Alexandria Egypt	B02 Suez Egypt	B03 B12 B56 B57 Mailboats	B32 Buenos Ayres	C Constantinople	C28 Montivideo Uraguay	C30 Valparaiso Chile
1883-4 4d Dull green						£125		
1883-4 5d Dull green						£90		
1883-4 6d Dull green						£200		
1883-4 9d Dull green								
1883-4 1/- Dull green								

Type	C35 Panama Columbia	C36 Arica Peru	C37 Caldera	C38 Callao	C39 Cobija Bolivia	C40 Coquimbo Chile	C41 Guayaquil Ecuador	C42 Islay Peru	C43 Paita Peru
½d Rose (1870-79)	£35	£70		£35		*	£40	£40	
1d Red (1841) Imperf									
1d Red (1854) p16 Die I									
1d Red (1854) p16 Die II									
1d red-brown 1855 p16 Die II									
1d Red-brown 1855 p14 Die II									
1d Red-brown 1855 Die II p16 LC									
1d Reed 1857 LC p14						*	*		
1d Reed 1861 Alph IV									
1d Red Plate 1864-79	£20	£55	£35	From £25		*	£30		Pl 127 & 147 £90
1½d Rose-red Plate 1 or 3	£45	*	*	*			Plate 3 £65	*	
2d Blue 1841 Imperf									
2d Blue 1854 SC Die I p16									
2d Blue 1855 LC p14									
2d Blue 1858 LC p16					*				
2d Blue 1858 Plates 7-15	£30	Plate 14 £80	Plate 6 & 9 £40	From £20	Plate 14 *	*	£25	£40	Plates 9 & 14 £90
2½d Rosy-mauve 1875 Blue paper									
2½d Rosy-mauve 1875 White paper	£150								
2½d Rosy-mauve 1876 Plates 3-17	£150								
2½d Blue 1880 Plates 17-20	Plate 19 *								
2½d Blue 1881 Plates 21-23	*								
3d Carmine 1862	£175			*				£80	
3d Rose 1865 Plate 4	*		£55	£50		*	£90		
3d Rose 1867 Plates 4-10	£30	*	Plates 5 & 7 *	From £25	Plate 6 *	Plate 8 *	£30	£40	
3d Rose 1873 Plates 11-20	£30	£50	From £40	From £25	*	£60	£40		£90
3d Rose 1881 Plate 20/21	*								
3d on 3d Lilac 1883									
4d Rose 1857									
4d Rose 1857 Glazed paper									
4d Red Plate 3 or 4 1862	£75	*	*	*		*	£80	£90	

Type	C35 Panama Columbia	C36 Arica Peru	C37 Caldera	C38 Callao	C39 Cobija Bolivia	C40 Coquimbo Chile	C41 Guayaquil Ecuador	C42 Islay Peru	C43 Paita Peru
4d Vermillion 1865 Plate 7-14	£30	£45	From £40	From £20		£60	£30	£40	£90
4d Vermillion Plate 15 1876	£200	*		£200			£225	*	
4d Sage green (1877) Plate 15 & 16	£130	£160	Plate 16 *	£120	Plate 15 £500	£140	£140	£120	*
4d Grey-brown 1880 Wmk. Garter Pl 17									
4d Grey-brown 1880 Wmk. Crown Plates 17 & 18	£35								
6d Lilac Embossed									
6d Lilac 1856									
6d 1862 Plates 3 & 4	£55	*	Plate 4 £70	*		£70	£100	£60	Plate 3 £120
6d 1865 Plates 5 & 6	£50	*	*	*		*	£55	£60	£90
6d 1865 Wmk. error									
6d Lilac 1867 Plate 6	*	£60	£60	£50		£60	*	£150	£90
6d Violet 1867 Plate 8 or 9	£40	£55	£60	£40	Plate 9 £450	£60	£50		£100
6d Buff 1872 Plates 11 & 12	£40	£70	*	From £45	Plate 11 - *	*	£50	*	£100
6d Chestnut 1872 Plate 11	£35	£70	Plate 11 *	£30			*	*	*
6d Grey 1873 Plate 12	£140	£130	*	£130			*		*
6d Grey 1873 Plates 13-17	£30	£50	From £40	From £30	£350		£40	£40	
6d Grey 1881-2 Plates 17 & 18	Plate 17 £50								
6d on 6d Lilac									
8d Orange 1876	£220	*	£350		£400	*	£250		
9d Straw 1862	£200	*			£300	*	£220		*
9d Bistre 1862									
9d Straw 1865		*			£200			£300	
9d Straw 1867	£175	£175	£150	£150			£120	£130	
10d Red-brown 1867	£200	*	£220	£220		£250	£220	£150	£350
1/- 1847 Embossed									
1/- Green (1856)									
1/- Green (1856) Thick paper									
1/- Green 1862		*							

Type	C35 Panama Columbia	C36 Arica Peru	C37 Caldera	C38 Callao	C39 Cobija Bolivia	C40 Coquimbo Chile	C41 Guayaquil Ecuador	C42 Islay Peru	C43 Paita Peru
1/- Green 1862 K Variety									
1/- Green 1865 Plate 4	£130	*	*	*		£120	£120	*	*
1/- Green Plates 4, 5, 6, 7 (1867)	£30	£50	From £40	From £30	Plate 4 & 5 £350	£60	£30	£60	Plate 4 £100
1/- Green 1873 Plates 8-13	£40	£50	From £50	From £40	£350	£70	£50	£70	£80
1/- Orange-brown Plate 13	£260								
1/- Orange-brown 1881 Plates 13 & 14	Plate 3 £85								
2/- Blue 1867	£100	£150	£150	£100	£350	£125	£120	*	£225
2/- Brown 1880	£1500	£1500	£1500			£1500	£1600		
5/- Rose 1867 Plates 1 & 2	Plate 1 & 2 £250	Plate 1 & 2 £275	Plate 2 £350	£250	Plate 2 £500	£275	£290	Plate 1 *	Plate 1 £450
5/- Rose Plate 4 1882 Blued paper									
5/- Rose Plate 4 1882 White paper									
10/- Grey-green 1878									
10/- Grey-green 1883									
£1 Brown lilac 1878									
£1 Brown-lilac 1882									
1880 ½d Deep green									
1880 ½d Pale green									
1880 1d Venetian red	£40								
1880 1½d Venetian red									
1880 2d Pale rose									
1880 2d Deep rose	£70								
1880 5d Indigo									
1881 1d Lilac 14 dots	£130								
1881 1d Lilac 16 dots									
1883-4 4½d Slate-blue									
1883-4 1½d Lilac									
1883-4 2d Lilac									
1883-4 2½d Lilac									
1883-4 3d Lilac									

Type	C35 Panama Columbia	C36 Africa Peru	C37 Caldera	C38 Callao	C39 Cobija Bolivia	C40 Coquimbo Chile	C41 Guayaquil Ecuador	C42 Islay Peru	C43 Paita Peru
1883-4 Dull green									
1883-4 5d Dull green									
1883-4 6d Dull green									
1883-4 9d Dull green									
1883-4 1/- Dull green									

Type	C51 St. Thomas (BWI)	C56/C65 Carthagena Columbia	C57 Greytown Nicaragua	C58 Havana Cuba	C59 Jacmel (Haiti)	C60 La Guayra Venezuela	C61 San Juan Porto Rico	C62 Santa Martha Columbia	C63 Tampico Mexico
½d Rose (1870-79)	£25		£55	£55	£40	*	£35	Plate 6 £70	
1d Red (1841) Imperf									
1d Red (1854) p16 Die I									
1d Red-brown 1855 p16 Die II									
1d Red-brown p14 Die II									
1d Red-brown 1855 Die II p16 LC									
1d Red-brown LC p14	*						*		
1d Red 1861 Alph IV									
1d Red Plate 1864-79	£20	£40	£35	£40	£30	£35	£25	Plate 106 £50	£75
1½d Rose-red Plate 1 or 3	£40	Plate 3 £50			Plate 3 £50	*	£40		
2d Blue 1841 Imperf									
2d Blue 1854 SC Die I p16									
2d Blue 1855 LC p14									
2d Blue 1858 LC p16									
2d Blue 1858 Plates 7-15	£20	£40	*	£50	£30	£40	£25	£65	£120
2½d Rosy-mauve 1875 Blue paper									
2½d Rosy-mauve 1875 White paper					Plate 4 *				
2½d Rosy-mauve 1876 Plates 3-17									
2½d Blue 1880 Plates 17-20									
2½d Blue 1881 Plates 21-23									
3d Carmine 1862									
3d Rose 1865 Plate 4	£50	*		£90			£55		
3d Rose 1867 Plates 4-10	£25	*			£30		£30		
3d Rose 1873 Plates 11-20	£20	£40	£35		£30	£40	£30		
3d on 3d Lilac 1883		*	*	*					
4d Rose 1857									
4d Rose 1857 Glazed paper									
4d Red Plate 3 or 4 1862	£25				Plate 4 £75				

Type	C51 St. Thomas (BWI)	C56/C65 Carthagena Columbia	C57 Greytown Nicaragua	C58 Havana Haiti	C59 Jacmel (Haiti)	C60 La Guayra Venezuela	C61 San Juan Porto Rico	C62 Santa Martha Columbia	C63 Tampico Mexico
4d Vermillion 1865 Plates 7-14	£100	£40	£35	£35	£30	£35	£30	£45	Plate 12 & 13 £60
4d Vermillion Plate 15 1876	£120	£200	£175	£200	£220	£220	£200		
4d Sage green (1877) Plates 15 & 16		£140	£120		£140			£140	£75
4d Grey-brown 1880 Wmk. Garter Pl 17			£225		£250			£250	
4d Grey-brown 1880 Wmk. Crown Plates 17 & 18			Plate 17 £50		Plate 17 £40				
6d Lilac Embossed 1854									
6d Lilac 1856	£100								
6d 1862 Plates 3 & 4	£50								
6d 1865 Plates 5 & 6		*		Plate 15 *	£40	*	£50	£65	
6d 1865 Wmk. error	£50								
6d Lilac 1867 Plate 6	£50						£55		
6d Violet 1867 Plate 8 or 9	£40	£50			Plates 8 & 9 £45	*	£40		
6d Buff 1872 Plates 11 & 12	£50				£45	£75	£50		
6d Chestnut 1872 Plate 11	£25				*		£30		
6d Grey 1873 Plate 12	£120	£140			*	£130	*		
6d Grey 1873 Plates 13-17	£25	£40	£50	Plate 15 *	£30	£40	£35	Plate 14 *	
6d Grey 1881-2 Plates 17 & 18									
6d on 6d Lilac									
8d Orange 1876	£225	£300	£225		£250	£225		£250	
9d Straw 1862	£200				£170	*	£200	*	
9d Bistre 1862	£200								
9d Straw 1865	£300						£300		
9d Straw 1867	£120			£220	£120	*	£130		
10d Red-brown 1867	£150			£240	£220	*	£300		
1/- 1847 Embossed									
1/- Green (1856)									
1/- Green (1856) Thick paper		*							
1/- Green 1862									

Type	C51 St. Thomas (BWI)	C56/C65 Carthagena Columbia	C57 Greytown Nicaragua	C58 Havana Cuba	C59 Jacmel (Haiti)	C60 La Guayra Venezuela	C61 San Juan Porto Rico	C62 Santa Martha Columbia	C63 Tampico Mexico
1/- Green 1862 K Variety									
1/- Green 1865 Plate 4	£80	*	*	£110	£80	£110	£80	£120	
1/- Green Plates 4, 5, 6, 7 (1867)	£20	£40	*	£40	£25	Plate 4 & 7 *	£30	£50	£100
1/- Green 1873 Plates 8-13	£30	£50	£40	£50	£40	£45	£40	Plate 8 *	Plate 8 £150
1/- Orange-brown Plate 13		*	£300		£275				
1/- Orange-brown 1881 Plates 13 & 14			Plate 13 £75						
2/- Blue 1867	£90	£200	£110	£160	£90	£150	£100	£200	£400
2/- Brown 1880			£1600		£1500				
5/- Rose 1867 Plates 1 & 2	£200	Plate 1 £375	£250	£300	£270	£250	£275	Plate 2 £375	
5/- Rose Plate 4 1882 Blued paper			£1500						
5/- Rose Plate 4 1882 White paper									
10/- Grey-green 1878			£2250						
10/- Grey-green 1883									
£1 Brown-lilac 1878									
£1 Brown-lilac 1882									
1880 ½d Deep green					£40				
1880 ½d Pale green									
1880 1d Venetian red			£55		£40				
1880 1½d Venetian red			£55		£60				
1880 2d Pale rose									
1882 2d Deep rose					£80				
1880 5d Indigo									
1881 1d Lilac 14 dots									
1881 1d Lilac 16 dots									
1883-4 1½d Lilac									
1883-4 2d Lilac									
1883-4 2½d Lilac									
1883-4 3d Lilac									
1883-4 Dull green									

Type	C79 Mailboat	C81 Bahia Brazil	C82 Pernambuco Brazil	C83 Rio de Janeiro	C86 Porto Plata Dominican Rep	C87 St Domingo Dominican Rep	C88 St Iago de Cuba	D22 Cuidad Bolivar Venezeula	D26 Mailboat
½d Rose (1870-79)					£80	£90	*		
1d Red (1841) Imperf									
1d Red (1854) p16 Die I									
1d Red-brown 1855 p16 Die II									
1d Red-brown 1855 Die II p16 LC									
1d Red 1857 LC p14				£30					
1d Red 1861 Alph IV									
1d Red Plate 1864-79 Pl.72 recorded 2007		£30	£30	£25	£45	£50	£150	Plate 133 £175	Plate 98 & 125*
1½d Rose-red Plate 1 or 3		Plate 3 £75			£90		Plate 3 - *		
2d Blue 1841 Imperf							£150		
2d Blue 1854 SC Die I p16						£100			
2d Blue 1855 LC p14									
2d Blue 1858 LC p16									
2d Blue 1858 Plates 7-15		£40	£40	£25	Plate 14 & 15 £55	£75		*	
2½d Roay-mauve 1875 Blue paper									
2½d Roay-mauve 1875 White paper									
2½d Rosy-mauve 1876 Plates 3-17					£140				
2½d Blue 1880 Plates 17-20									
2½d Blue 1881 Plates 21-23									
3d Carmine 1862									
3d Rose 1865 Plate 4		*	£80						
3d Rose 1867 Plates 4-10		£35	£35	£25	£70		Plate 5 *	Plate 5 - *	
3d Roase 1873 Plates 11-20		Plate 11 - *	Plate 11 *	Plate 11 *		Plate 18 *		Plate 11 £125	
3d Rose 1881 Plate 20/21									
3d on 3d Lilac 1883									
4d Rose 1857									
4d Rose 1857 Glazed paper									
4d Red Plate 3 or 4 1862									
4d Vermillion 1865 Plate 7-14		£40	£40	£35	£80	£70	£150	£60	£500

Type	C79 Mailboat	C81 Bahia Brazil	C82 Pernambuco Brazil	C83 Rio de Janeiro	C86 Porto Plata Dominican Rep	C87 St Domingo Dominican Rep	C88 St Jago de Cuba	D22 Cuidad Bolivar Venezeula	D26 Mailboat
4d Vermillion Plate 15 1876					£250	£300	£400		
4d Sage green (1877) Plate 15 & 16					£200	£200		£150	
4d Grey-brown 1880 Wmk. Garter pl 17									
4d Grey-brown 1880 Wmk. Crown Plates 17 & 18								Plate 17 *	
6d Lilac Embossed 1854									
6d Lilac 1856									
6d 1862 Plates 3 & 4									
6d 1865 Plates 5 & 6			*	Plate 5 £70					
6d 1865 Wmk. error									
6d Lilac 1867 Plate 6		£60	£60	£55					
6d Violet 1867 Plate 8 & 9	£65	£50	£50	£40	Plate 8 *		£250		Plate 8 *
6d Buff 1872 Plates 11 & 12		£65	£50	Plate 11 £40			Plate 11 *		
6d Chestnut 1872 Plate 11		£65	£40	£35					
6d Grey 1873 Plate 12		*	*	*					
6d Grey 1873 Plates 13-17		Plate 13 *			£90				
6d Grey 1881-2 Plates 17 & 18						*			
6d on 6d Lilac									
8d Orange 1876					£350				
9d Straw 1862									
9d Bistre 1862									
9d Straw 1865		£300	£300	£250		*	*	*	
9d Straw 1867		£180	£180	£120			*	*	
10d Red-brown 1867	£300		£220	£200			£500		
1/- 1847 Embossed									
1/- Green (1856)									
1/- Green (1856) Thick paper									
1/- Green 1862									
1/- Green 1862 K variety									

Type	C79 Mailboat	C81 Bahia Brazil	C82 Pernambuco Brazil	C83 Rio de Janeiro	C86 Porto Plata Dominican Rep	C87 St Domingo Dominican Rep	C88 St Jago de Cuba	D22 Cuidad Bolivar Venezeula	D26 Mailboat
1/- Green 1865 Plate 4		£120	£120	£90		*	£300	£120	*
1/- Green Plates 4, 5, 6, 7 (1867)		£40	£40	£30	Plate 4 & 7 £90			£400	
1/- Green 1873 Plates 8-13		Plate 8 & 9 £55		£45	£90	£90	*		
1/- Orange-brown Plate 13									
1/- Orange-brown 1881 Plates 13 & 14									
2/- Blue 1867		£180	£170	£100	£250	*	*	£600	
2/- Brown 1880									
5/- Rose 1867 Plates 1 & 2		Plate 1 £275	£275	Plate 1 & 2 £275	*		Plate 1 *	£950	
5/- Rose Plate 4 1882 Blued paper									
5/- Rose Plate 4 1882 White paper									
10/- Grey-green 1878									
10/- Grey-green 1883									
£1 Brown-lilac 1878									
£1 Brown-lilac 1882									
1880 ½d Deep green									
1880 ½d Pale green									
1880 1d Venetian red									
1880 1½d Venetian red									
1880 2d Pale rose									
1880 2d Deep rose									
1880 5d Indigo									
1881 1d Lilac 14 dots									
1881 1d Lilac 16 dots									
1883-4 ½d Slate-blue									
1883-4 1½d Lilac									
1883-4 2d Lilac									
1883-4 2½d Lilac									
1883-4 3d Lilac									
1883-4 Dull green									

D74 of forged cancels on this office

Type	D74 Pisco & Chincha Islands - Peru	D87 Iquique Peru	E53 Port au Prince Haiti	E88 Colon Columbia	F69 Savanilla Columbia	F83 Arroyo Porto Rico	F84 Aquadilla Porto Rico	F85 Mayaquez Porto rico
½d Rose (1870-79)		£80	£45		£85	£50	Plate 6 £75	£40
1d Red (1841) Imperf								
1d Red (1854) p16 Die I								
1d Red-brown 1855 p16 Die II								
1d Red-brown 1855 p14 Die II								
1d Red-brown 1855 Die II p16 LC								
1d Red 1857 LC p14								
1d Red 1861 Alph IV								
1d Red Plate 1864-79		£60	£30	£35	£60	£40	£60	£25
1½d Rose-red Plate 1 or 3			£60	£75	£100	*	*	£35
2d Blue 1841 Imperf								
2d Blue 1854 SC Die I p16								
2d Blue 1855 LC p14								
2d Blue 1858 LC p16								
2d Blue 1858 Plates 7-15	*	£90	£40	£40		Plate 14 - *	Plate 14 - *	£30
2½d Rosy-mauve 1875 Blue paper								
2½d Rosy-mauve 1876 Plates 3-17			£250					
2½d Blue 1880 Plates 17-20								
2½d Blue 1881 Plates 21-23								
3d Carmine 1862								
3d Rose 1865 Plate 4								
3d Rose 1867 Plates 4-10		£70	Plate 6 & 7 £35	*	*	£45	*	£35
3d Rose 1873 Plates 11-20		£170	£30	£40	Plate 20 £100	£45	Plate 12 - 13	£35
3d Rose 1881 Plate 20/21					Plate 20 £100			
3d on 3d Lilac 1883								
4d Rose 1857								
4d Rose 1857 Glazed paper								
4d Red Plate 3 or 4 1862								
4d Vermillion 1865 Plates 7-14	£1000	£50	£35	£40	£45	£40	£100	£30

Type	D74 Pisco & Chincha Islands - Peru	D87 Iquique Peru	E53 Port au Prince Haiti	E88 Colon Columbia	F69 Savanilla Columbia	F83 Arroyo Porto Rico	F84 Aquadilla Porto Rico	F85 Mayaguez Porto rico
4d Vermillion Plate 15 1876		£225	£225	*	£225	£225	*	£85
4d Sage green (1877) Plate 15 & 16		£150	£110	£150	£150			Plate 15 - *
4d Grey-brown 1880 Wmk. Garter Pl 17			£200	£275	£300			
4d Grey-bown 1880 Wmk. Cross Plates 17 & 18			£40	£55	Plate 17 £55			
6d Lilac Embossed 1854								
6d Lilac 1856 Thick paper								
6d 1862 Plates 3 & 4								
6d 1865 Plates 5 & 6	£1000							
6d 1865 Wmk error								
6d Lilac 1867 Plate 6								
6d Lilac 1867 Plate 6, 8 or 9		*		*	*			Plate 9 £650
6d Buff 1872 Plates 11 & 12		£80				£50	*	£50
6d Chestnut 1872 Plate 11		*				£45		£40
6d Grey 1873 Plate 12		£150		*				£120
6d Grey 1873 Plates 13-17		£75	*	£40	£60	£40	*	£35
6d Grey 1881-2 Plates 17 & 18								
6d on 6d Lilac								
8d Orange 1876		£300	£275	*	£275			£225
9d Straw 1862								
9d Bistre 1862								
9d Straw 1867		£150		*		£220	£275	£150
10d Red-brown 1867		*		*		£220	£275	£200
1/- 1847 Embossed								
1/- Green (1856)								
1/- Green (1856) Thick paper								
1/- Green 1862								
1/- Green 1862 K Variety						*		
1/- Green 1865 Plate 4	*							

Type	D74 Pisco & Chincha Islands - Peru	D87 Iquique Peru	E53 Port au Prince Haiti	E88 Colon Columbia	F69 Savanilla Columbia	F83 Arroyo Porto Rico	F84 Aquadilla Porto Rico	F85 Mayaquez Porto rico
1/- Green Plates 4, 5, 6, 7 (1867)		£60		£35	£55	£40	£85	£30
1/- Green 1873 Plates 8-13		£55	£50	£50	£60	£50	£85	£35
1/- Orange-brown Plate 13			£300	£275	£300			
1/- Orange-brown 1881 Plates 13 & 14			£90	£120	£170			
2/- Blue 1867	£1000	£150	£120	£120		£170	£220	£120
2/- Brown 1880			£1700	£1500				
5/- Rose 1867 Plates 1 & 2			£300	£350	Plate 2 £375	Plate 2 - *		
5/- Rose Plate 4 1882 Blued paper								
5/- Rose Plate 4 1882 White paper								
10/- Grey-green 1878			£3500					
10/- Grey-green 1883								
£1 Brown-lilac 1878								
£1 Brown-lilac 1882								
1880 ½d Deep green								
1880 ½d Pale green			£50					
1880 1d Venetian red			£60	£100				
1880 1½d Venetian red			£70					
1880 2d Pale rose			£80	*				
1880 2d Deep rose								
1880 5d Indigo								
1881 1d Lilac 14 dots								
1881 1d Lilac 16 dots								
1883-4 ½d Slate-blue								
1883-4 1½d Lilac								
1883-4 2d Lilac								
1883-4 2½d Lilac								
1883-4 3d Lilac								
1883-4 Dull green								
1883-4 5d Dull green								

Type	D74 Pisco & Chincha Islands - Peru	D87 Iquique Peru	E53 Port au Prince Haiti	E88 Colon Columbia	F69 Savanilla Columbia	F83 Arroyo Porto Rico	F84 Aquadilla porto Rico	F85 Mayaquez porto rico
1883-4 6d Dull green								
1883-4 9d Dull green								
1883-4 1/- Dull green								

Type	F87 Smyrna	F88 Ponce Porto Rico	G Gibraltar	G06 Beyrout Lebanon	M Malta	247 Fernando Po	582 Naguabo Porto Rico	942 969 974 975 981 982 Cyprus	0X0 Crimea
½d Rose (1870-79)	£20	£40		£25			*	£200	
1d Red (1841) Imperf					£1200				*
1d Red (1854) p16 Die I			£250		£100				£50
1d Red-brown 1855 p16 Die II			£450		£650				
1d Red-brown 1855 p14 Die II			£250		£150				£5
1d Red-brown 1855 Die II p16 LC					£45				£80
1d Red 1857 LC p14			£20		£15				
1d Red 1861 Alph IV									
1d Red Plate 1864-79	£10	£30		£12			£250	£120	
1½d Rose-red Plate 1 or 3	£165	£80		£175				£1200	
2d Blue 1841 Imperf					£2000				£700
2d Blue 1854 SC Die p16			£300		£500				£600
2d Blue 1855 LC p14			£45		£40				£90
2d Blue 1858 LC p16	*		£275		£175				£175
2d Blue 1858 Plates 7-15	£12	£40	£250	£15	£30			£150	
2½d Rosy-mauve 1875 Blue paper	£45			£50					
2½d Rosy-mauve 1875 White paper	£22			£20					
2½d Rosy-mauve 1876 Plates 3-17	£12			£15				£45	
2½d Blue 1880 Plates 17-20	£9			£10					
2½d Blue 1881 Plates 21-23	£8			£9				£350	
3d Carmine 1862									
3d Rose 1865 Plate 4									
3d Rose 1867 Plates 4-10	£20	*		Plate 10 - *					
3d Rose 1873 Plates 11-20	*	£40		£25			£400		
3d Rose 1881 Plates 20/21									
3d on 3d Lilac 1883									
4d Rose 1857			£40		£25				
4d Rose 1857 Glazed paper			*		£120				£500
4d Red Plate 3 or 4 1862									

Type	F87 Smyrna	F88 Ponce Porto Rico	G Gibraltar	G06 Beyrout Lebanon	M Malta	247 Fernando Po	582 Naguabo Porto Rico	942 969 974 975 981 982 Cyprus	0X0 Crimea
4d Vermillion 1865 Plate 7-14	£20	£40		£25		*	£600		
4d Vermillion Plate 15 1876	£120	£200		£125		*	*		
4d Sage green (1877) Plates 15 & 16	£75	£150		£85				£400	
4d Grey-brown Wmk. Garter Pl 17	*			*					
4d Grey-brown 1880 Wmk. Crown Plates 17 & 18	£25			£35					
6d Lilac Embossed 1854					£2500				£800
6d Lilac 1856			£30		£30				
6d 1862 Plates 3 & 4									
6d 1865 Plates 5 & 6									
6d 1865 Wmk. error									
6d Lilac 1867 Plate 6									
6d Violet 1867 Plate 8 or 9				*					
6d Buff 1872 Plates 11 & 12	£50	£60		£55				£1500	
6d Chestnut 1872 Plate 11	*	£60		£30					
6d Grey 1873 Plate 12	£65	*		*				£300	
6d Grey 1873 Plates 13-17	£20	£50		£20		*	*		
6d Grey 1881-2 Plates 17-18	£35								
6d on 6d Lilac	£75								
8d Orange 1876	*			£275				£4000	
9d Straw 1862									
9d Bistre 1862									
9d Straw 1867	£200			£220			*		
10d Red-brown 1867	£100	£225		£120			£550		
1/- 1847 Embossed									
1/- Green (1856)			£80		£100				
1/- Green (1856) Thick paper			*		£130				£800
1/- Green 1862									
1/- Green 1862 K Variety									

Type	F87 Smyrna	F88 Ponce Porto Rico	G Gibraltar	G06 Beyrout Lebanon	M Malta	247 Fernando Po	582 Naguabo Porto Rico	942 969 974 975 981 982 Cyprus	0X0 Crimea
1/- Green 1865 Plate 4	*								
1/- Green Plates 4, 5, 6, 7 (1867)		£35		£22					
1/- Green 1873 Plates 8-13	£25	£45		£30				£650	
1/- Orange-brown Plate 13	£125			*					
1/- Orange-brown `88' Plates 13 & 14	£35	*		£40					
2/- Blue 1867				£110			£550		
2/- Brown 1880									
5/- Rose 1867 Plates 1 & 2	*	£250		£400			Plate 2 £3500		
5/- Rose Plate 4 1882 Blued paper									
5/- Rose Plate 4 1882 White paper									
10/- Grey-green 1878									
10/- Grey-green 1883									
£1 Brown-lilac 1878									
£1 Brown-lilac 1882									
1880 ½d Deep green	£7			£8					
1880 ½d Pale green	£7			£9					
1880 1d Venetian red	£12			£10					
1880 1½d Venetian red	£80			£120					
1880 2d Pale rose	£35			£40					
1880 2d Deep rose	£35			£40					
1880 5d Indigo	£50			£65					
1881 1d Lilac 14 dots	£4			*					
1881 1d Lilac 16 dots	£12			£5					
1883-4 1½d Slate-blue	£50			£15					
1883-4 1½d Lilac	£50			£50					
1883-4 2d Lilac				£40					
1883-4 2½d Lilac	£10			£8					
1883-4 3d Lilac									
1883-4 4d Dull green	*			£125					

Type	F87 Smyrna	F88 Ponce Porto Rico	G Gibraltar	G06 Beyrout Lebanon	M Malta	247 Fernando Po	582 Naguabo Porto Rico	942 969 974 975 981 982 Cyprus #	0X0 Crimea
1883-4 5d Dull green	£80			£75					
1883-4 6d Dull green									
1883-4 9d Dull green									
1883-4 1/- Dull green	£200			£175					
1887 ½d Orange	£5			£7					
1887 6d Purple	£15			£20					
1887 1/- Green	£90			£100					
1887 ½d Blue-green	£7			£15					
1887 1/- Green & red	*			£150					

It should be noted prices can vary dependant on office location in Cyprus

Control	½d		1d		'Jubilee' Line added to selvedge ½d		1d	
	I	P	I	P	I	P	I	P
None		* £85		* £350				* £750
A		£15		£100				
B		£22		£30		£140		
C		£15		£30		£12		
D		£15		£12	£14	£12		
E		£160	£95	£14		5.00		
F				£14	£50	4.50		
G				£14	£110	4.50		£10
H				8.00	5.00	4.50		£10
I				£30	£10	4.50	£70	3.00
J				£25	£20	4.50	£70	3.00
K					£16	4.50	£70	3.00
L					£16	4.50	7.00	3.00
M					5.00	4.50	7.00	3.00
N					5.00	4.50	5.00	3.00
O					5.00	4.50	2.50	3.00
O over N							£1500	£1500
P					5.00	4.50	£25	3.00
Q					5.00	4.50	5.00	3.00

Control	½d Blue green		1d	
R	5.00	4.00	7.50	3.00
S			3.00	3.00
T			3.00	3.00
U			3.00	3.00
V			3.00	3.00
W			3.00	3.00
X			3.00	4.50

Prices shown are for single stamp with control, mounted mint

* Price for a lower right hand corner pair, with selvedge intact

I = Imperforate through margin

P = Perforated through margin

Control	Continuous 'Jubilee' line						Interrupted 'Jubilee' line					
	½d E1		½d E2		1d E3		½ E1		½d E2		1d E3	
	I	P	I	P	I	P	I	P	I	P	I	P
A	4.00	5.00			5.00	£15						
B	4.00	£20			5.00	£15	£25					
C	5.00	£95			5.00	£12	6.00	£75			£14	£70
C4	4.00	£75			£5	£15	5.00	£95			6.00	£75
5.00		£45					4.00	£95	4.00	£75	6.00	£70
D5									4.00	£35	6.00	£75
E5									4.00	£15	6.00	6.00
E6									4.00	£95	6.00	£75
F6									4.00	£18	6.00	6.00
F7									4.00	£15	6.00	6.00
G7									5.00	4.00	6.00	6.00
G8									5.00	5.00	6.00	6.00
H8									4.00	4.00	6.00	6.00
H9									5.00	5.00	6.00	6.00
I9									5.00	4.00	6.00	6.00
I10									4.00	5.00	5.00	6.00
J10									4.00	4.00	5.00	6.00

Perf. 14		½d E27		1d E28	
A 11(c)				£12	5.00
A 11(w)		6.00	6.00	£60	£15

Perf. 15 x 14		½d E32		1d E33	
A 11 (c)		£85	£125	£35	£45

Prices shown are for a mounted mint single stamp with control

(c) denotes close spacing between the figures - 1.5mm (1d vlues only)

(w) denotes wide spacing between the figures - 2mm (1d values only)

1911 - 1912 Definitives

Watermark Imperial Crown. Die 1A

Prices shown are for single stamp with control, mounted mint

Control	A. 11		A 11 (w)		A 11 (c)	
	I	P	I	P	I	P
½d			£20	£10	*	*
1d	£200	£125	£12	£12	£50	£100

Watermark Imperial Crown. Die 1B

Control	A. 11		A 11 (w)		A 11 (c)	
	I	P	I	P	I	P
½d			£15	£15	£15	£10
1d	£17	£17	£55	£275	£12	£20

Watermark Imperial Crown. Die 2

Control	B.11		B 11		B. 12		B 12 (w)		B 12 (c)		B13	
	I	P	I	P	I	P	I	P	I	P	I	P
½d			£10	£20		£15000	£15	£12	6.00	6.00		
1d	£25	£30	£10	£10	£20	£25	8.00	8.00	£12	£10		

Watermark Royal Cypher. Die 2

Control	B.11		B 11		B. 12		B 12 (w)		B 12 (c)		B13	
	I	P	I	P	I		I	P	I	P	I	P
½d							£10	£10	£12	£10	£10	£10
1d							£10	£12			£17	£17

Watermark Multiple Cypher. Die 2

Control	B.11		B 11		B. 12		B 12 (w)		B 12 (c)		B13	
	I	P	I	P	I		I	P	I	P	I	P
½d					£3000	£3000	£12	£15	£12	£12		
1d					£4000	£4000	£20	£20				

Notes: All controls with dot between letter and number were Somerset House printings

A 11 (w) denotes wide spacing - 2mm   A 11 (c) denotes close spacing - 1½mm
B 12 (w) denotes wide spacing - 6mm   B 12 (c) denotes close spacing - 4½mm

Control B12 Wide (I)   B12 Narrow (I)   B12 Wide (P)

1912 - 1924 Wmk. Royal Cypher

Control	½d		1d		1½d		2d Die 1		2d Die II		2½d		3d		4d	
	I	P	I	P	I	P	I	P	I	P	I	P	I	P	I	P
A. 12 (w)					8.00	£250							£15	£150		
A. 12 (c)					£10						£10	£650	£20	£25		
B.13	2.00	£325											£12	£20	7.00	£65
C 12			1.00	1.00												
C 13	1.00	1.00	1.00	1.00	6.00	6.00					7.00	7.00	5.00	5.00	6.00	6.00
C.13							5.00	5.00					£12	£45		
C 14	8.00	8.00	5.00	5.00			4.00	5.00			£15	9.00				
D 14	1.00	1.00	1.00	1.00	5.00	7.00	3.00	3.00			£35	£35	5.00	5.00	6.00	6.00
E 14	1.00	1.00	1.00	1.00							8.00	7.00	5.00	6.00		
F 15	1.00	1.00	1.00	1.00	£12	£15	3.00	£10					5.00	5.00	6.00	6.00
G 15	2.00	2.00	1.00	1.00	£12	£20	5.00	5.00			7.00	8.00	£17	£17	6.00	6.00
H 16	1.00	5.00	1.00	1.00	6.00	£20	3.00	£250			7.00	7.00	£15	£50	6.00	£55
I 16	1.00	1.00	1.00	1.00			3.00	£35			7.00	£12	5.00	5.00	6.00	9.00
J 17	1.00	1.00	1.00	1.00	8.00	£10	3.00	7.00			8.00	£12	6.00	7.00	6.00	6.00
J. 17											£450					
K 17	9.00	£12	2.00	2.00			8.00	£22			8.00	£250			£10	£1500
K 18	4.00	5.00	1.00	1.00	8.00	£12									6.00	£10
18					£1350	£1350										
L 18	5.00	6.00	2.00	2.00	3.00	3.00	4.00	6.00			£10	9.00	8.00	8.00		
M 18	7.00	7.00	£10	£10	6.00	5.00					£20	£15	7.00	7.00	6.00	6.00
M			£8000													
19					£7500	£7500										
M 19	1.50	1.00	2.00	2.00	4.00	4.00	£15	£20			£15	£15				
N 19	2.00	2.00	1.00	1.00	4.00	4.00	3.00	8.00			8.00	8.00	5.00	5.00	7.00	7.00
O 19	6.00	6.00	5.00	5.00	4.00	4.00	£12	£70			9.00	9.00				
O 20	3.00	3.00	£10	£10	4.00	4.00	4.00	4.00			£10	£10	6.00	6.00	6.00	6.00
P 20	1.00	1.00	1.00	1.00			3.00	3.00			7.00	9.00	6.00	6.00		
Q20	6.00	6.00	1.00	1.00	9.00	9.00	3.00	3.00								
Q 21	1.00	2.00	9.00	8.00	8.00	8.00	3.00	3.00			£25	£25	8.00	8.00	£55	£55
R 21	1.50	1.50	6.00	6.00			3.00	3.00			£12	£12	6.00	6.00	6.00	6.00
S 21	£12	£12	£15	£15			7.00	7.00	£20	£17	£20	£17	£15	£12	£60	£40
S 22	£12	£12	8.00	8.00			6.00	6.00	7.00	7.00	£35	£40	6.00	6.00	£30	£30
T 22	3.00	2.00	2.00	1.00	4.00	4.00	£15	£20	£10	8.00	£12	£12	£10	£10	6.00	6.00
U 22	2.00	2.00	5.00	5.00	5.00	5.00			£12	£12			7.00	7.00	£45	£35
U 23	1.50	1.50	£10	£10	4.00	4.00			7.00	7.00	£10	£10	7.00	6.00	£25	£15
V 23	1.00	1.00	1.00	1.00	4.00	4.00			8.00	7.00	£12	£12	7.00	7.00	8.00	8.00
W 23	9.00	£12	4.00	3.00	5.00	6.00			7.00	7.00			£10	£10		
W 24	£165	£165	£15	£15	£165	£165			£165	£195						
No control *							£40	£40								

* Price is for bottom left hand pair with selvedge   All controls with dot between letter and number were Somerset House printings.

A. 12 (w) denotes wide spacing between 'A' and '1' - 4mm   A. 12 (c) denotes close spacing between 'A' and '1' - 1 ½mm

1912 - 1924 Wmk. Royal Cypher

	5d		6d			7d		8d		9d		10d		1s	
Control	I	P	I		P	I	P	I	P	I	P	I	P	I	P
B.13	£10	£12								£12					
C.13			£12		£12	£25		£22				£30	£850	£20	£30
C 13						£15	£15								
C 14	7.00	7.00													
D 14	7.00	7.00	9.00			£15	£15	£30	£22			£25	£25	£20	£25
E 14			9.00		8.00						9.00			£450	£450
F 15	7.00	7.00	£25		£650	£25	£35	£20	£20	£10	£25	£30	£25	£20	£18
G 15	7.00	7.00	8.00			£15	£15	£20	£20	£10	£15	£30	£25	£15	£15
H 16	7.00	9.00	8.00			£12	£12	£20	£20	£15	£10	£20	£30	£15	£20
I 16	8.00	£10	8.00					£25	£25	£10	£30	£20	£30	£15	£35
J 17	7.00	7.00	8.00			£13	£13	£20	£20	£10	£10	£20	£18	£15	£18
K 17	7.00	£35	9.00							£10	£10			£15	£85
K 18								£275	£20	£35	£12	£35	£20		
L. 18			8.00		£35										
L 18	7.00	8.00	£10			£12	£140			£10	£10			£12	£12
M 18			8.00		£850										
M 19												£20	£30	£18	£15
N 19	7.00	8.00	8.00		£75					£10	£10			£15	£15
O 19	£12	£12	8.00							£10	£12	£20	£20	£15	£18
O 20										£10	£10			£15	£15
P 20			9.00							£10	£10			£20	£20
Q20			£10							£15	£40			£18	£15
Q21	£10	£15										£20	£40		
R 21	£30	£40	£10							£15	£10			£15	£15
S 21	£15	£20	£10		£175					£10	£10	£25	£20	£15	£15
S 22	8.00	£225								£12	£12	£25	£35	£15	£15
T 22	7.00	7.00	£11		£450					£60	£50	£45	£60	£15	£15
U 22			£10											£20	£30
U 23	£10	£10								£50	£60	£25	£25	£15	£15
V 23	8.00	£20	9.00							£50	£50			£20	£20
W.23			8.00												
A.24			£10												
B.24			£85												

			6d	
Control			I	P
Q.20			£50	
R.21			£60	

All 6d values were printed by Somerset House and all controls had a dot between the control letter and the control number, except for L. 18 imperf which exists with or without the dot.

1924 - 1935 Watermark Multiple Block Cypher

Control	½d I	½d P	1d I	1d P	1½d I	1½d P	2d I	2d P	2½d I	2½d P	3d I	3d P	4d I	4d P
A 24	1.50	£10	3.00	£15	1.00	£10	£20							
A 24 EP					£350									
B 24	1.50	£40	2.00	£35	1.00	£85	3.00	£95	6.00		8.00		£11	
B 24 EP			£225		£350									
C 25	1.50	£60	2.00	£15	1.00		3.00		6.00		£25		£11	
D 25	1.50			£45	1.00		3.00		£10		8.00			
D 25 EP					£350									
E 26	1.50	£200	2.50		1.00		3.00		6.00		8.00		£16	
E.26					£850									
F 26	1.50	£75	2.00		1.00	£65	3.00							
G 27	1.50	£45	2.00		1.00		3.00		6.00	£150	8.00	£200	£11	
H 27	1.50	£45	2.00		1.00	£65	8.00		£25					
I 28	1.50		2.00		1.00	£85	6.00	£175	8.00		8.00		£11	
J 28	1.50		2.00		1.00		8.00							
K 29	4.00		5.00		2.50	£125	4.00		7.00		£25		£15	
L 29	75	£175	2.50	£175	1.00		4.00							
M 30	1.50		3.00		1.00		4.00		6.00		£10		£11	
N 30	1.50		2.00		1.00	*	3.00		6.00		£15			
O 31	1.50	*	2.50		1.00		8.00		£1500				£11	
P 31	1.50		2.00		1.00		3.00				£10			
Q 32	1.50		2.00		1.00		3.00		£10				£11	
R 32	1.50		8.00		2.00		4.00	£250	£10		£10		£15	
S 33	1.50		3.00		1.00		£25		£22		£30			
T 33	1.50		2.00		1.00		3.00		£15		£18		£11	
U 34	2.50		5.00		5.00		6.00							
V 34	2.00	£40	5.00	£75	5.00	*	5.00		£12		£15		£15	
W 35									£15	£150			£55	
X 35													£11	£850

EP - Denotes the experimental paper printings.

1924 - 1935 Watermark Multiple Block Cypher

	5		6d (c)		6d (o)		9d		10d		1s	
Control	I	P	I	P	I	P	I	P	I	P	I	P
A 24	£25	£85					£15	£10	£80	£60	£20	£65
B 24			£15								£85	
C 25	£20		£15	*			£10					
D 25			£20		£135				£45		£30	
E 26					7.00	£750						
F 26	£20				9.00		£10		£95		£25	
G 27					7.00				£45			
H 27	£40				7.00						£35	
I 28	£15				£10	£20	£10				£25	
J 28					8.00	£20	£12		£45		£35	
K 29	£20				7.00						£95	
L 29	£20				7.00		£10		£45		£25	
M 30	£50				7.00	£600						
N 30					£10		£12				£25	
O 31	£22				£10				£85			
P 31					7.00		£10				£30	
Q 32	£30				7.00				£80			
R 32					£12		£12				£30	
S 33	£25				£12	*			£75		£75	
T 33	£275				7.00		£50					
U 34	£55								£185		£35	
V 34	£25				£12		£18		£175		£35	£125
W 35					£12	£15	£30		£50		£40	
X 35	£20				£10	£15	£12	£45			£35	
Y 36			£50		7.00							
Z 36			£20		7.00							
A 37					8.00							
B 37					£100	£450						
C 38					£15							
D 38					£15	£75						

All 6d values were Somerset House with dot bewteen letter and figures, except from V 34 and after which were Harrison

1934 - 1937 Photogravure

All prices on this page are for mounted mint Cylinder control blocks of four or six, unmounted mint at 50% more.

Control	U34 (A)		V34 (A)		V34 (B)		V34 (D)		W35 (C)		W35 (D)	
	No dot	Dot	No dot	Dot	No dot	Dot	No dot	Dot	No dot	Dot	No dot	Dot
Large Format												
1d					£15	£15						
1½d	£30	£30	£25	£25	£20	£20						
Intermediate Format												
½d					£15	£15			£35	£35		
1d					£50	£50			£185	£185		
1½d					£40	£40						
1½d											£150	£125
2d											£40	£40

			Fractional Controls							
Control	W35 (D)		X35 (D)		Y36 (D)		Z36 (D)		A37 (D)	
	No dot	Dot	No dot	Dot	No dot	Dot	No dot	Dot	No dot	Dot
Small Format										
½d	£12	£12	£10	£10	£10	£10	£20	£20		
1d	£85	£85	£10	£10	£10	£10				
1½d	£40	£20	£10	£10	£10	£10	£12	£12		
2d			£12	£12	£12	£12	£15	£15	£15	£15
2½d	£25	£25			£40	£40				
3d	£50	£35	£40	£40	£25	£25	£25*	£25*		
4d	£675	£50	£35	£25	£25 *	£25*				
5d			£225	£225	£75	£75	£50 *	£50 *		
9d			£125*	£125*						
10d					£115 *	£125*				
1s					£140	£140	£140 *	£140*		

The letter in brackets after the control shows the layout of the control/cylinder block, as illustrated below.
* Denotes control exists with varying degrees of 'boxing'.

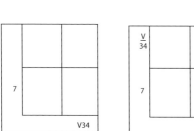
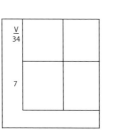
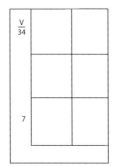
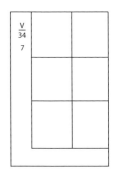

    Position A   Position B   Position C   Position D

1936 - 1937 Watermark Block Cypher KVIII

All prices on this page are for mounted mint Cylinder control blocks of six, unmounted mint at 50% more.

Control	A36		A37	
	No dot	Dot	No dot	Dot
½d	£10	£10	£10	£10
1d	£10	£10	£12	£12
1½d	£10	£10	£10	£10
2½d	£15*	£15*		

1937 - 1947 Watermark Block Cypher GVIR

All prices on this page are for mounted mint Cylinder control blocks of six, unmounted mint at 50% more.

Dark Colours

Control		Marginal Rule			A37	B37	C38	D38	E39	F39	G40	H40	I41
		A37	B37	D38									
½d	No dot	5.00	6.00		2.00	2.00	2.00	2.00	2.00	2.00	2.00		2.00
	Dot	5.00	6.00		3.50								
1d	No dot	5.00	5.00		2.00	2.00	2.00	2.00	2.00	2.00	2.00	2.00	2.00
	Dot	5.00	5.00			4.50							
1½d	No dot	8.00	7.00		2.00	2.00	2.00	2.00	2.00	2.00	2.00		
	Dot	8.00	7.00						3.50	3.50			
2d	No dot					4.00	5.50	4.00	4.00	4.00	4.00	4.00	4.00
	Dot					£12	£200	£12	£12	£15	£12	£15	£15
2½d	No dot	£20	£20	£35					9.00		2.50	2.50	2.50
	Dot	7.00	7.00	£25					£15		£15	£10	£10
3d	No dot						£20	£20	£20		£20	£20	
	Dot						£45	£45	£45		£45	£45	

Control		D38	E39	F39	G40	H40	I41	J41	K42	L42	M43	N43	O44	P44	Q45	R45	S46	T46	U47	None
4d	No dot	900	9.00		9.00		900		9.00*				9.00							9.00
	Dot												9.00							9.00
5d	No dot	£20	£20		£20		£20		£20	£20*										
	Dot								£40	£20*										
6d	No dot	£30	£15	£15	£15	8.00	£20	£15	£15	£15	£17	£15	£15		£15		£15	£15	£15	£15
7d	No dot		£55*														£75			£55
	Dot																£55			£55
8d	No dot		£55*										£55				£55*			£60
	Dot																			£60
9d	No dot		£60		£60	£60	£60		£60	£80		£80	£60	£65		£60				£70
	Dot																			£60
10d	No dot		£55	£90	£55	£90	£65	£55	£55	£65	£55	£55			£55			£55	£65	£55
	Dot														£55			£55	£65	£65
11d	No dot																			£40
	Dot																			£35
1s	No dot		£60		£60	£65		£65	£60		£65		£60		£60		£65		£60	£40
	Dot												£60		£85				£85	£35

* An astrerisk next to a price denotes that the control exists with varying degrees of 'boxing'

All prices on this page are for mounted mint Cylinder control blocks of six, unmounted mint at 50% more.

Pale Colours

Control		J41	K42	L42	M43	N43	O44	P44	Q45	R45	S46	T46	U47	None
½d		8.00	£10	£20	£10	£10	8.00	£10	8.00	8.00	£12	£10	8.00	8.00
1d		7.00	£10	7.00	7.00	7.00	7.00	7.00	7.00	7.00	8.00	7.00	7.00	7.00
1½d				£12		£12	£15	£50	£12	£22	£12		£12	£12
2d		£11	£12	£15	£12	£12	£12	£15	£20	£20	£12	£11	£15	£12
2½d		6.00	7.00	£12	£15	£12	£10	£12	£12	£10	7.00	7.00	7.00	7.00
3d	No dot	£18	£18	£18	£18	£18	£18	£20	£20	£20			£18	

New Colours

	No Dot	Dot
½d	£15	£15
1d	£15	£15
1½d	£13	£13
2d	£15	£15
2½d	£11	£11
4d	£22	£22

1914 - 1925 Watermark Royal Cypher (Sideways)

Prices are for mounted mint singles

Control	½d I	½d P	1d I	1d P	1d chalky I	1d chalky P	1½d I	1½d P	2d I	2d P	3d I	3d P	4d I	4d P	5d I	5d P	1s I	1s P
D.14		£12		£12						£10						£45		
D 14	2.00	2.00	3.00	3.00					3.50	3.50					£38	£120		
E 14			3.00	2.00														
F.15																		£55
G 15			2.00	£27														
H 16									3.00	3.00								
I 16	2.00	2.00	2.00	3.00					3.50	3.50								
K 17			2.00	2.00					6.00	3.00								
L 18											9.00	£15						
N 19	2.00	2.00	2.50	2.00														
O.19																		£40
O 19									3.50	3.50								
O 20											8.00	£12						
P 20			3.00						3.00	4.50								
Q 20			9.00										£45	£38				
Q 21			£10	£23														
R 21	2.00	£18	2.00	4.00					3.00	9.00								
S .21																		£50
S 21			2.00	3.00														
S 22		3.00	3.00	3.00														
T 22			3.00	2.00							9.00	£12						
U 22	2.00	£18					£75											
U 23			2.00	2.00			£75		£12	9.00								
V.23																	£75	
V 23							£75	£75			£10	£12						
W23	8.00	£11									£12	£18						
B 24					£12													
C 25					£12													

1914 - 1925 Watermark Multiple Block (Sideways)

Prices are for mounted mint singles

Control	½d I	½d P	1d I	1d P	1½d I	1½d P	2d I	2d P	3d I	3d P	4d I	4d P	5d I	5d P	1s I	1s P	2s 6d I	2s 6d P
A 24							6.00				£38				£375			
B 24		3.00	£12		£75				9.00		£15				£18		£50	
B 24 EP									£90									
C 25							6.00								£18			
D 25							£12											
E 26							8.00		9.50		£18				*	£22		
F 26							6.00		8.50		£30				£18			
G 27									9.00						£18			
H 27							£38			£20							£50	
I 28	1.50		2.50				8.00		£12			£30			£18		£50	
K 29		£12	2.50	£22			7.00		£12		£18				£18		£50	
L 29	2.00		2.50				5.00		£12		£15						£50	
M 30	2.00						6.00								£18			
N 30			3.50						9.00		£38		£45				£38	
O 31	3.00		2.00				6.00		9.00				£45		£18		£50	
P 31	3.00						£10											
Q 32	2.00		3.00				6.00		£10		£38		£45		£18		£50	
R 32							6.00		£10		£38				£18		£50	
S 33	1.50		3.00	£26									£45		£18		£50	
T 33							£33		£12		£60							
U 34	8.50		£18	£18									£50		£28		£60	
V 34							£22				£38						£60	
W 35	4.00		£11						£12				£50		£28			
X 35							9.00				£38				£22		£60	
Y 36	3.00		4.00	*			9.00		9.00	£12								
Z 36																	£60	

EP - Denotes the experimental paper printing.

1936 - 1937 Watermark Multiple E8R Crown (Sideways)

Prices are for unmounted mint singles, lightly mounted approximately 30% less

Control	½d I	½d P	1d I	1d P	2d I	2d P	3d I	3d P	4d I	4d P	5d I	5d P	1s I	1s P	2s 6d I	2s 6d P
A 36									£45		£45		£24			
A 37	£22	3.00	7.00		£12		9.00				£60				£300	
C 38															£450	

1937 - 1938 Watermark Multiple GVIR Crown (Sideways)

Prices are for unmounted mint singles, lightly mounted approximately 30% less

Control	½d I	½d P	1d I	1d P	2d I	2d P	3d I	3d P	4d I	4d P	5d I	5d P	1s I	1s P	2s 6d I	2s 6d P
B37							£15		£100				£90			
C 38	£12		7.00		7.00		£15		£100		£23		£90		£90	
D38							£18								£90	£150
E 39	£12	£250	7.00		7.00				£100		£18		£100		£120	
F 39							£70									
G40	£35	£65	7.00	*	*	7.00			£140		£23		£23			
H 40									£140							
I 41			7.00	7.00	*	£30		£16		£18		£18			£190	*
J 41													£90			
K 42				7.00	*	7.00	£70	*		£100			£90		£260	£250
L 42													£200			
M 43			7.00		7.00		£16		£100		£30		£90			
O 44			9.00		£45		£18		£150		£30		£90		£100	
P 44									£100		£18		£90		£110	*
Q 44			*		*											
Q 45			£60		7.00										£350	
R 45							£18						£90			
S 46													£100		£330	
T 46									£100		£18					
U 47			7.00		7.00		£16	*								*
'None' (pair)	£22	£22	£11	£11	£11	£11	£24	£24	£150	£150	£24	£24	£130	£130	£150	£200

In 1881 Parliament passed 'The Customs and Inland Revenue Act' which authorised the use of 1d postage stamps to pay fiscal duties and certain 1d revenue stamps to be used for postal purposes. This authorisation came into effect from 1st June 1881 and the latter part of the year saw widespread use of the current 1d Inland Revenue stamp to pay postage. The new combined "Postage and Inland Revenue" 1d lilac was not issued until about 12th July 1881. The authorisation for dual purposes was extended to all values up to 2s6d with effect from 1st January 1883.

The fiscal stamps allowed for postage were those inscribed "Inland Revenue", although the fact that the post office notice announcing the change referred to "Receipt Stamps" vicariously allowed the earlier "Receipt", "Receipt and Draft" and "Draft" stamps to be used for postage. Copies are seen of Customs, Foreign Bill, Law Courts etc. stamps used postally but these were never authorised, although many seem not to have been surcharged.

The pricing basis for Fiscal stamps is as follows:
1. Be guided by notes for surface printed issues.   2. The price for postally used is based on fine used.
Illustrations of stamps and watermarks are reduced in size.

Please note that there is a wide range of shades - most of which are worth much the same.

Surface Printed Issues

Authorised 1 June 1881
Printer: De La Rue & Co.

Simple Cabled
Anchor Watermark

Ornate Cabled Anchor
Watermark

Draft or Receipt Stamps. (a) Wmk. Ornate Cabled Anchor (inverted).
Perf. 15½ x 15

No.		Description	M/M	Used	✉
F5	**1d**	**Reddish lilac** on blued paper	£50	£25	£200
F5a		Watermark upright	£100	£50	-

(b) Wmk. Simple Cabled Anchor. Perf. 15½ x 15

No.		Description	M/M	Used	✉
F6	**1d**	**Lilac**	5.00	7.00	£60
F6a		Watermark inverted	£80	-	-
F6b		'SPECIMEN'	From £60	-	-
F7	**1d**	**Lilac** on blued paper	5.00	7.00	£70

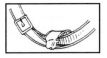

Die I. Square buckle,   Die II. Octagonal buckle,
lighter shading as shown.   heavier or solid shading as shown.

Receipt Stamps. Wmk. Ornate Cabled Anchor (inverted). Perf. 15½ x 15

No.		Description	M/M	Used	✉
F1	**1d**	**Blue** (Die I)	£15	£20	£100
F1a		Watermark reversed (Die I)	£60	£80	-
F1b		Watermark upright (Die I)	£60	£80	-
F2	**1d**	**Blue** (Die II)	£14	£20	£100
F3	**1d**	**Blue** on blued paper (Die II)	£30	£35	£200
F3a		Watermark upright (Die II)	£70	£70	-

Inland Revenue Stamps Provisional. F7 overprinted 'INLAND REVENUE'
in red in two lines.

No.		Description	M/M	Used	✉
F8	**1d**	**Reddish lilac**	£250	£225	£450
F8a		Watermark reversed	£400	£350	-

Draft Stamps. Wmk. Ornate Cabled Anchor (inverted). Perf. 15½ x 15

No.		Description	M/M	Used	✉
F4	**1d**	**Brown**	£40	£40	£200
F4a		Watermark upright	£120	£120	-
F4a		Ochre brown	£40	£40	£200
F4b		Tete-beche pair (Brown)	£5000	-	-

Postal Fiscal Stamps

No.		M/M	Used	⊠

(a) Wmk. Simple Cabled Anchor. Perf. 15½ x 15

F9	**1d** **Reddish lilac**	5.00	6.00	£50
F9a	Watermark inverted	£75	-	-
F9s	'SPECIMEN'	From £50	-	-
F10	**1d** **Reddish lilac** on bluish paper	6.00	6.00	£50
F11	**3d** **Pale reddish lilac**	£200	£100	£200
F11s	'SPECIMEN'	From £60	-	-
F12	**3d** **Pale reddish lilac** on bluish paper	£200	£110	£200
F13	**6d** **Reddish lilac**	£70	£75	£150
F13s	'SPECIMEN'	From £75	-	-
F14	**6d** **Reddish lilac** on bluish paper	£85	£75	£150

Orb Watermark

Anchor Watermark

Height: 16mm   18mm   20mm

Corner Ornaments

Small sometimes broken   Small always broken   Large   Very large

(b) Wmk. Anchor (16mm). Perf. 15½ x 15

F15	**1d** **Reddish lilac**	4.00	6.00	£50
F16	**1d** **Reddish lilac** on bluish paper	5.00	7.00	£50
F17	**3d** **Pale reddish lilac**	£80	£60	£110
F17s	'SPECIMEN'	From £100	-	-
F18	**3d** **Pale reddish lilac** on bluish paper	£100	£60	£120
F19	**6d** **Reddish lilac**	£60	£70	£115
F19a	Watermark inverted	£200	-	-
F20	**6d** **Reddish lilac** on bluish paper	£70	£70	£120

	Chin		Neck	
Shaded	Unshaded	Half outline	Full outline
Die I	Die II	Die III	Die IV

(c) Wmk. Anchor (18mm). Perf. 15½ x 15

F21	**1d** **Reddish lilac** on bluish paper	£10	£10	£90
F21s	'SPECIMEN'	From £80	-	-
F22	**3d** **Pale reddish lilac** on bluish paper	£70	£70	£120
F22s	'SPECIMEN'	From £80	-	-
F23	**6d** **Reddish lilac** on bluish paper	£60	£50	£150

New design. (a) Wmk. Small Anchor. Perf. 14

Die I

F30	**1d** **Purple**	1.50	4.00	£40
F30a	Wmk. inverted	£40	£30	
F30s	'SPECIMEN'	From £20	-	-
F31	**1d** **Purple** on bluish paper	3.00	2.00	£30

Die II

F32	**1d** **Purple**	£12	£15	£150
F32s	'SPECIMEN'	From £20	-	-
F33	**1d** **Purple** on bluish paper	£12	£15	£150

(d) Wmk. Anchor (18mm). Perf. 14

F24	**3d** **Pale reddish lilac** on bluish paper	£300	£175	£300
F25	**6d** **Reddish lilac** on bluish paper	£140	£60	£150

Die III

F34	**1d** **Purple**	3.00	4.00	£50
F34s	'SPECIMEN'	From £20	-	-
F35	**1d** **Purple** on bluish paper	3.00	4.00	£50

(e) Wmk. Anchor (20mm). Perf. 14

F26	**3d** **Reddish purple** on bluish paper	£225	£90	£150
F26s	'SPECIMEN'	From £90	-	-
F27	**6d** **Reddish lilac** on bluish paper	£100	£90	£150

Die IV

F36	**1d** **Purple**	2.00	1.00	£25
F37	**1d** **Purple** on bluish paper	2.00	1.00	£25

(b) Wmk. Orb. Perf. 14

Die IV

F38	**1d** **Purple**	4.00	3.00	£25
F38a	Wmk. inverted	£75		
F39	**1d** **Purple** on bluish paper	4.00	3.00	£25

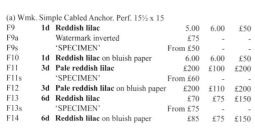

Small Anchor Watermark

(f) Wmk. Small Anchor. Perf. 14

F28	**1d** **Purple**	5.00	£10	£45
F29	**1d** **Purple** on bluish paper	5.00	£10	£45
F29a	Watermark inverted	£40	-	-

Coloured Embossed Issues

Authorised 1 January 1881
Printer: Somerset House

Each stamp has a single capital letter in the design, which shows the die used.

Inland Revenue Stamps
(a) Bluish paper. No watermark. Imperforate

No.			M/M	Used
F40	**2d**	**Pink. Die A**	£250	£500
F41	**3d**	**Pink. Die C**	£100	£250
F41a		Pink. Die D	£275	
F41b		Tete-beche pair, Die C	£1200	
F42	**6d**	**Pink. Die T**	£750	
F42a		Pink. Die U	£150	£400
F42b		Tete-beche pair, Die U	£2000	
F43	**9d**	**Pink. Die C**	£250	
F43a		Tete-beche pair, 'SPECIMEN'	£750	
F44	**1s**	**Pink. Die E**	£400	£500
F44a		Pink. Die F	£150	£300
F45	**2s**	**Pink. Die K**	£400	£600
F46	**2s6d**	**Pink. Die N**	£750	
F46a		Pink. Die O	£200	£450

Thick letters   Thin letters

(b) 'INLAND REVENUE'(thick letters) underprint in green. Bluish paper. No watermark. Perf 12½

No.			M/M	Used
F47	**2d**	**Pink. Die A**	£200	£500
F46a		Tete-beche pair	£2000	
F48	**3d**	**Pink. Die C**	£750	
F48a		Pink. Die D	£750	
F49	**9d**	**Pink. Die C**	£750	£300
F50	**1s**	**Pink. Die E**	£400	£600
F50a		Pink. Die F	£200	£450
F51	**2s 6d**	**Pink. Die O**	£100	£250

(c) 'INLAND REVENUE'(thin letters) underprint in green. White paper. Wmk. Small Anchor. Perf. 12½

No.			M/M	Used
F52	**1s**	**Pink. Die F**	£200	£400

(d) 'INLAND REVENUE'(thin letters) underprint in green. White paper. Wmk. Small Anchor. Perf. 12½

No.			M/M	Used
F53	**2d**	**Vermilion. Die A**	£200	£350
F53a		Vermilion on bluish paper. Die A	£200	£350
F54	**9d**	**Vermilion. Die C**	£250	£450
F54a		Vermilion on bluish paper. Die C	£250	£450
F55	**1s**	**Vermilion. Die E**	£175	£300
F55a		Vermilion on bluish paper. Die E	£175	£300
F55b		Vermilion. Die F	£500	
F55c		Vermilion on bluish paper. Die F	£500	
F56	**2s 6d**	**Vermilion. Die O**	£175	£300
F56a		Vermilion on bluish paper. Die O	£175	£300

(e) 'INLAND REVENUE'(thin letters) underprint in green. White paper. Wmk. Orb. Perf. 12½

No.			M/M	Used
F57	**2d**	**Vermilion. Die A, 'SPECIMEN'**		
F58	**9d**	**Vermilion. Die C, 'SPECIMEN'**		
F59	**1s**	**Vermilion. Die E, 'SPECIMEN'**		
F60	**2s 6d**	**Vermilion. Die O**	£450	£600
F60a		Vermilion on bluish paper. Die O	£450	£600

<u>Please note.</u> All the above Embossed issues are rare on cover and are worth 2-3 times the postally used price.

In 1870 the many private telegraph companies, then in existence, were nationalised and a unified Government service introduced. Ordinary postage stamps were used for accountancy and a large proportion of the stamps of this period bearing circular date stamps were used for this purpose.

This form of accountancy proved inadequate and large losses were being made. To help clarify the exact income, special Telegraph stamps were issued in 1876. These had no other use, although they were sometimes wrongly used as postage stamps and passed through the postal system incorrectly, particularly after 1881 when the stamps were discontinued and of no other use.

Surface printed by De La Rue & Co. with check letters in the two lower corners and plate numbers shown in the two upper corners, where appropriate. All watermarks have been illustrated in the normal position, as seen from the back of the stamp, to ease identification for the collector. Sideways watermarks are shown in the direction they appear as sideways watermark, sideways-inverted therefore face the opposite direction.

Large Garter Watermark
(sideways inverted)

1877 (1 March) Wmk. Large Garter (sideways-inverted). Perf. 14

No.			M/M	F/U
T11	**4d Green.** Plate 1		£20	£20
T11s	'SPECIMEN'		From £20	-

Shamrock Watermark

1876 (1 Feb.) Wmk. Shamrock. Perf. 14

No.			M/M	F/U
T1	**½d Orange.** Plate 5 (1.4.80)		3.00	8.00
T1s	'SPECIMEN'		£14	-
T2	**1d Brown.** Plate 1		4.00	3.00
T2a	Wmk. inverted		£75	-
T2s	'SPECIMEN'		£15	-
T3	**1d Brown.** Plate 2		6.00	3.00
T3a	Wmk. inverted		£100	£50
T3s	'SPECIMEN'		£16	-
T4	**1d Brown.** Plate 3		6.00	4.00
T4s	'SPECIMEN'		£20	-

1877 (1 March) Wmk. Spray (sideways). Perf. 14

No.			M/M	F/U
T12	**6d Grey.** Plate 1		£18	6.00
T12s	'SPECIMEN'		From £18	-
T13	**6d Grey.** Plate 2		£75	£30

1881 (March) Wmk. Imperial Crown (sideways). Perf. 14

No.			M/M	F/U
T14	**6d Grey.** Plate 2		£50	£25

Spray
Watermark
            Imperial Crown
Watermark

1876 (1 Feb.) Wmk. Spray (sideways). Perf. 14

No.			M/M	F/U
T5	**3d Carmine.** Plate 1		£15	£12
T5a	Wmk. sideways inverted		£100	£60
T5s	'SPECIMEN'		£18	-
T6	**3d Carmine.** Plate 2		£15	£10
T6a	Wmk. sideways inverted		-	£150
T6s	'SPECIMEN'		£20	-
T7	**3d Carmine.** Plate 3		£25	£15
T7a	Wmk. sideways inverted		£160	-
T7s	'SPECIMEN'		£25	-

1881 (March) Wmk. Imperial Crown (sideways). Perf. 14

No.			M/M	F/U
T8	**3d Carmine.** Plate 3		£25	£20
T9	**3d Carmine.** Plate 4		£100	£60
T10	**3d Carmine.** Plate 5		£80	£50

1876 (1 Feb.) Wmk. Spray (sideways). Perf. 14

No.			M/M	F/U
T15	**1s Dark green.** Plate 1		£35	£12
T15s	'SPECIMEN'		From £20	-
T16	**1s Dark green.** Plate 2		£20	£12
T16a	Wmk. sideways inverted		£100	£70
T16s	'SPECIMEN'		From £25	-
T17	**1s Dark green.** Plate 3		£25	£10
T17s	'SPECIMEN'		From £25	-
T18	**1s Green.** Plate 4		£40	6.00
T18a	Wmk. sideways inverted		-	-
T18s	'SPECIMEN'		From £75	-
T19	**1s Green.** Plate 5		£18	6.00
T19a	Wmk. sideways inverted		-	-
T19s	'SPECIMEN'		From £20	-
T20	**1s Green.** Plate 6		£25	6.00
T20a	Wmk. sideways inverted		-	-
T20s	'SPECIMEN'		From £25	-
T21	**1s Green.** Plate 7		£80	£10
T22	**1s Green.** Plate 8		£35	£12
T22s	'SPECIMEN'		From £25	-
T23	**1s Green.** Plate 9		£35	£10
T24	**1s Green.** Plate 10		£40	£10

1880 (Oct.) New colour. Wmk. Spray (sideways). Perf. 14

			M/M	F/U
T25	**1s**	**Brown orange.** Plate 10	£70	£40
T25s		'SPECIMEN'	From £20	-
T26	**1s**	**Brown orange.** Plate 12	£70	£40

1881 (Feb.) Wmk. Imperial Crown (sideways). Perf. 14

T27	**1s**	**Brown orange.** Plate 10	£45	£30
T27a		Wmk. sideways inverted	£70	£35
T27s		'SPECIMEN'	From £50	-
T28	**1s**	**Brown orange.** Plate 12	£120	£35

1877 (1 March) Wmk. Spray (sideways). Perf. 14

T29	**3s**	**Blue.** Plate 1	£22	8.00
T29a		Wmk. sideways inverted	-	£125
T29s		'SPECIMEN'	£25	-

1881 (Feb.) Wmk. Imperial Crown (sideways-inverted). Perf. 14

T30	**3s**	**Blue.** Plate 1	£2500	£1200
T30a		Wmk. sideways inverted		

Maltese Cross
Watermark

Large Anchor
Watermark

1876 (1 Feb.) Wmk. Maltese Cross. Perf. 15 x 15½

T31	**5s**	**Rose.** Plate 1	£280	£15
T31a		Pale rose	£200	£10
T31s		'SPECIMEN'	From £35	-
T32	**5s**	**Rose.** Plate 2	£550	£70

1880 (Nov.) Wmk. Maltese Cross. Perf. 14

T33	**5s**	**Rose.** Plate 2	£1800	£90

1881 (May) Wmk. Large Anchor (sideways). Perf. 14

T34	**5s**	**Rose.** Plate 3	£1800	£220
T35	**5s**	**Rose.** Plate 3 on bluish paper	£1800	£220
T35s		'SPECIMEN'	From £300	-

1877 (1 March) Wmk. Maltese Cross. Perf. 15 x 15½

T36	**10s**	**Grey green.** Plate 1	£400	£65
T36s		'SPECIMEN'	£85	-

1877 (1 March) Wmk. Three Shamrocks (sideways). Perf. 14

T37	**£1**	**Brown lilac.** Plate 1	£1500	£180
T37s		'SPECIMEN'	From £200	

1877 (1 March) Wmk. Three or more Shamrocks (sideways-inverted). Perf. 15 x 15½

T38	**£5**	**Orange.** Plate 1	£5500	£850
T38s		'SPECIMEN'	From £800	-

Before the issue of the ½d postage stamp on 1 October 1870, for use on printed matter, there was no cheap way of distributing circulars, etc. through the postal system. There was a great need and in 1865 private enterprise decided to fill the gap in the form of the 'Edinburgh and Leith Circular Delivery Company'. They were quickly followed by many others.

In 1868 the Post Office went to Law to regain their monopoly, winning their case and an Appeal heard in June 1869. As a final attempt to remain in business, before the Appeal hearing, a Limited Circular Delivery Company was registered in February 1868 and incorporated under 'The Companies' Act of 1862. New stamps were produced including two new towns, Birmingham and Manchester, but were not used pending the Appeal Court judgement. These stamps, sometimes thought of as forgeries, are more correctly described as 'prepared to use but not issued'. As they never served a postal use we do not list them here.

Many forgeries exist, some contemporary to the genuine issues. Most are easily recognised by their crude production, the paper used or bogus colours and values. Over a period of twenty years and including the contemporary types, six series of forgeries have been identified. Their continued appearance was almost certainly due to the lack of information at this time about the genuine issues.
Circular Delivery Company Stamps used on cover are very rare and few stamps off cover are found with a handstamp cancellation although two types are known to have been issued. Stamps with coloured pencil lines, usually blue, are virtually all from a dealer's stock defaced at the request of Post Office Officials. They informed him that it was a serious offence to have mint undesirable items in stock.

The Circular Delivery Companies effectively ceased trading from June 1868 having provided a cheap and useful service to the public for just over two years. That this fulfilled a genuine commercial need cannot be doubted since public protests were made at every level when the Post Office took further legal action in 1868. The matter was taken up in the House of Commons in April 1869, when it was demonstrated that many countries had stamps with face values well below one penny. The Postmaster-General promised to look into the matter. On 1 October 1870 the first ½d rate for postcards and printed paper up to 2 ounces was introduced, which could, at least indirectly, be attributed to the initiative of the Brydones local delivery services.

Printed in Lithography. Imperforate, unless otherwise stated.

1867 Aberdeen. Perf. 13

CD1	**¼d**	Orange brown	£60
CD2	**½d**	Blue	5.00

1867 Dundee. Imperf.

CD3	**¼d**	Maroon	£60
CD4	**½d**	Vermilion	£60

1866 Clark & Co., Edinburgh. Imperf.

CD5	**¼d**	Blue	£15
CD5a		Pale blue	£15

CD6

CD15

CD16

1865 Edinburgh & Leith. Type A. Imperf.

CD6	**¼d**	Green. Roulette 7	£15
CD7	**¼d**	Green. Perf. 12	£60
CD8	**¼d**	Slate blue. Roulette 7	8.00
CD9	**¼d**	Grey lilac	£10
CD9a		Greenish grey	5.00
CD10	**¼d**	Pearl grey. Perf. 12	£100
CD11	**¼d**	Greenish grey. Perf. 11¾	£8
CD12		Greenish grey. Pin perf. 10½	£40
CD13		Greenish grey. Roulette 7	£40

1866 Colours changed.

CD14	**¼d**	Rosy mauve	2.50
CD15		Mauve. Perf. 11¾ - 12	£60

Type B

CD16	**¼d**	Grey lilac	3.00
CD17	**½d**	Green	£12
CD18	**¼d**	Pin perf. 10½	7.00
CD18a		Reddish lilac. Pin perf. 10½	7.00
CD19	**¼d**	Green. Pin perf. 10½	£18

1867 12 Elder Street. Type C

CD20	**¼d**	Red brown	2.50
CD21	**¼d**	Black on yellow. Roulette 7	£90
CD22	**¼d**	Black on yellow. Imperf.	£150
CD23	**¼d**	Red brown. Roulette 7	£100

1865 12 St. Andrews' Square. Type D

CD24	¼d	Green. Roulette 7	£100
CD25	¼d	Green. Imperf.	£125
CD26	2d	Yellow. Roulette 7	8.00
CD27	3d	Brown red. Roulette 7	£100
CD27a		Imperf	£125

1866 Parcel Delivery Co. Type E

CD28	2d	Orange	4.00
CD29	3d	Brick red	5.00
CD30	2d	Orange. Roulette 7	£50
CD31	3d	Brick red. Roulette 7	£50
CD32	2d	Orange. Pin perf. 10½	£50
CD33	3d	Brick red. Pin perf. 10½	£50

CD34   CD38

1867 Glasgow. Horizontal laid paper. Imperf.

CD34	¼d	Black	2.50
CD35	½d	Vermilion	2.50
CD36	¼d	Black. Pin perf. 10½	£15
CD37	½d	Vermilion. Pin perf. 10½	£15

1866 Liverpool. Imperf.

CD38	¼d	Dark brown	£10

1867 Perf. 13

CD39	¼d	Red brown	3.00
CD40	½d	Lilac	4.00

CD41   CD42

1866 London. Imperf. Thick soft wove paper

CD41	¼d	Deep blue	4.00
CD42	½d	Blue grey	3.00
CD43	½d	Dull purple	3.00
CD43a		Pale lilac	£15
CD44	¼d	Deep blue. Clean perf. 11½	6.00
CD45	½d	Blue grey. Clean perf. 11½	6.00
CD46	¼d	Deep blue. Rough perf. 11½	£100
CD47	½d	Deep blue (error of colour). Rough perf. 11½	£100
CD48	¼d	Deep blue. Pin perf. 10½ - 11	8.00
CD49	½d	Blue grey. Pin perf. 10½ - 11	£100
CD50	½d	Dull purple. Pin perf. 10½ - 11	8.00

1867 Thinner hard wove paper. Rough perf. 11½

CD51	¼d	Deep blue	£25
CD52	½d	Reddish lilac	6.00
CD52a		Showing papermakers watermark *	£18
CD52b		Watermarked paper *	£18

1867 London and District. Imperf.

CD53	¼d	Green	£10
CD54	½d	Brown rose	£50
CD55	¼d	Brown rose (error of colour)	£150
CD56	¼d	Green. Perf. 13	2.50
CD57	½d	Pink. Perf. 13	3.00
CD58	¼d	Pink (error of colour). Perf. 13	£20
CD59	½d	Brown purple. Perf. 13	£25
CD60	¼d	Brown purple (error of colour). Perf. 13	£130
CD61	½d	Lilac rose. Perf. 13	£14
CD62	¼d	Lilac rose (error of colour). Perf. 13	£80

CD64   CD69

1867 Metropolitan. Rough perf. 11½

CD63	¼d	Rose (thick hard wove paper)	4.00
CD63a		Showing papermakers watermark *	£12
CD64	¼d	Rose (pelure paper)	4.00
CD65	¼d	Rose (pelure paper). Imperf.	£100
CD66	¼d	Orange yellow (error of colour)	£100
CD67	½d	Orange (Thick hard wove paper)	£12
CD67a		Showing papermakers watermark *	£30

1867 National. Perf. 13

CD68	¼d	Green	£60
CD69	½d	Blue	6.00
CD70	¾d	Yellow	£14
CD71	1d	Red	6.00

* The watermark found on the stamps listed is that of the paper maker and reads 'A. COWAN & SON' or 'EXTRA SUPERFINE' in double lined letters with 'A C & S' script monogram.

The Colleges of Oxford and Cambridge Universities were allowed the privilege of running their own local postal service. This practice generally ceased in 1886, although Keble continued until 1890.

Used should be collected on cover (all scarce to rare) as generally the stamps were uncancelled or marked in manuscript. Used prices are for stamps on cover.

Oxford University

Keble Type A   Keble Type B   Keble Type C

Keble Type B1 with round O's in Spiers & Son, etc.
Keble Type B2 with oval O's in Spiers & Son, etc.

1871 - 82 Keble College. Type A

No.	Description	M/M	☒
C1	Vermilion. Perf. 10½	£175	£600
C2	Vermilion. Perf. 11¾ (1872)	£130	£700
C3	Rosy magenta. Perf. 10¾ (1873)	£140	£900
C4	Magenta. Perf. 10¾ x imperf. (1876)	£320	£2500
	Type B		
C5	Ultramarine (1). Perf. 11½ (1876)	£30	£400
C6	Ultramarine (2). Perf. 11½ (1879)	£30	£300
	Type C		
C7	Ultramarine. Perf. 12 (1882)	2.50	£250

Merton Type A   Merton Type B   Merton Type C

1876 - 83 Merton College. Type A

No.	Description	M/M	☒
C8	Royal blue. Perf. 12½ x imperf. (1876)	£200	£1100
C9	Milky blue. Perf. 11¾ x imperf. (1877)	£220	£800
	Type B		
C10	Dull blue. Perf. 12½ x imperf. (1876)	£600	£2000
	Type C		
C11	Mauve. Perf. 12 (1883)	£10	£300

Lincoln   Hertford   Exeter

1877 Lincoln College

No.	Description	M/M	☒
C12	(1d) Indigo. Perf. 14½	£45	£600

1879 Hertford College

| C13 | Mauve. Perf. 11½ | 6.00 | £1200 |
| C13a | Imperforate | 4.00 | |

1882 Exeter College

| C14 | Salmon. Perf. 11¾ | £10 | £400 |

All Souls   St. John's   Balliol

1884 All Souls College

No.	Description	M/M	☒
C15	Ultramarine. Perf. 11½	£22	£800

1884 St. John's College

| C16 | Dull blue. Perf. 12 | 4.00 | £300 |

1885 Balliol College

| C17 | Scarlet. Perf. 11½ x imperf. | £45 | |

Cambridge University

Selwyn   Queen's   St. John's

1882 Selwyn College

No.	Description	M/M	☒
C18	Black. on pink paper Imperf.	£42	£2500

1883 Queen's College

| C19 | Green. Perf. 11½ | £20 | £2500 |

1884 St. John's College

| C20 | Scarlet. Perf. 12 | £10 | £3000 |

SPECIMEN

Type 1

19.75 x 2.5 mm

SPECIMEN

Type 2

20 x 2.75-3 mm

SPECIMEN

Type 3

21 x 2.5 mm

SPECIMEN

Type 4

18 x 2.5 mm

SPECIMEN

Type 5

18.25 x 2.75-3 mm

SPECIMEN

Type 6
18.25 x 3 mm

SPECIMEN

Type 7
16.5 x 2.75 mm

SPECIMEN

Type 8
19.5 x 2.5 mm

SPECIMEN

Type 9
14.75 x 1.75-2 mm

SPECIMEN

Type 10
20 x 2.5 mm

SPECIMEN

Type 11

20.25 x 3 mm

SPECIMEN

Type 12

15.5 x 1.75 mm

SPECIMEN

Type 13

15.25 x 1.5 mm

SPECIMEN

Type 14

14.5 x 2-2.25 mm

SPLCIMEN

Type 15

15.5 x 2.5 mm

SPECIMEN

Type 16

16 x 2.75 mm

SPECIMEN

Type 17

14.75 x 2 mm

SPECIMEN

Type 18

9.75-10 x 1.75 mm

SPECIMEN

Type 19

12.5 x 2 mm

SPECIMEN

Type 20

11.25 x 1.25 mm

SPECIMEN

Type 21
13 x 1.75 mm

SPECIMEN

Type 22
12.25 x 1.75 mm

SPECIMEN

Type 23
10.5 x 2 mm

Where 'SPECIMEN' overprints are known on both imperforate and perforate stamps of the same issue or the issue exists in more than one colour, the price quoted is for the cheapest only.

Queen Victoria

		Type 1	Type 2	Type 3	Type 4	Type 5	Type 6	Type 7	Type 8	Type 9	Type 10	Type 11	Type 12	Type 13	Type 14	Type 15
V22	1d Red brown	£1500														
V23	2d Blue, plate 3	£2500														
V24	2d Blue, plate 4	£2500														
V27	2d Deep blue, plate 4	£1600														
V31	2d Blue, plate 4	£1600														
V41	1d Red brown		£900													
V44	1d Rose red					£300	£300				£180					
V50	½d Rose red, plate 3		£200													
V55	½d Rose red, plate 9		£2000								£250					
V56	½d Rose red, plate 10								£200	£180						
V57	½d Rose red, plate 11								£200	£180						
V59	½d Rose red, plate 13									£180						
V62	½d Rose red, plate 19									£180						
V113	1d Rose red, plate 121		£300			£200										
V139	1d Rose red, plate 146									£180						
V154	1d Rose red, plate 164								£180							
V173	1d Rose red, plate 183									£180						
V188	1d Rose red, plate 198									£180						
V197	1d Rose red, plate 207									£180						
V214	1d Rose red, plate 224									£180						
V216	1½d Rose red, plate 1		£200			£200			£200	£180	£200					
V217	1½d Rose red, plate 3						£300									
V220	2d Blue, plate 9	£250														
V221	2d Blue, plate 12		£400													
V222	2d Blue, plate 13					£250										
V223	2d Blue, plate 14					£250			£200	£180						
V224	2d Blue, plate 15										£250					
V225	6d embossed	£1500	£1500													
V226	10d embossed, die 1	£1500	£2000													
V229	10d embossed, die 4		£2000													
V231	1s embossed, die 1	£1500	£2000													
V232	1s embossed, die 2		£2000													
V234	4d small garter		£500	£500												
V236	4d medium garter		£500													
V237	4d medium garter		£500													
V238	4d medium garter				£500											
V239	4d large garter		£350		£250		£250									
V241	6d emblems		£250				£250		£200							

Specimen Overprints

Where 'SPECIMEN' overprints are known on both imperforate and perforate stamps of the same issue or the issue exists in more than one colour, the price quoted is for the cheapest only.

		Type 1	Type 2	Type 3	Type 4	Type 5	Type 6	Type 7	Type 8	Type 9	Type 10	Type 11	Type 12	Type 13	Type 14	Type 15
V242	1s emblems		£350				£350		£350							
V243	3d plate 2		£350		£200	£350	£350	£200	£350							
V244	4d plate 3		£250			£350		£200	£350							
V245	4d plate 4		£350													
V246	6d plate 3		£250					£200	£350							
V247	6d plate 4		£250													
V248	9d plate 2		£300			£200		£200	£350							
V249	1s plate 2		£250													
V250	3d plate 4		£250													
V252	3d plate 5		£250			£250			£200							
V253	3d plate 6		£250						£200							
V254	3d plate 7		£250			£250										
V255	3d plate 8								£200	£350						
V257	3d plate 10		£250			£250			£250							
V262	4d plate 11		£250													
V263	4d plate 12									£400						
V265	4d plate 14								£225							
V266	6d plate 5															
V268	6d plate 6	£500	£600						£180							
V269	6d plate 8					£200			£180							
V270	6d plate 9		£400						£180	£250						
V271	6d plate 11					£200			£250							
V272	6d plate 12		£350			£220										
V273	9d emblems		£450						£350	£200	£200	£350				
V274	9d spray		£400						£250		£400	£400				
V275	10d red brown		£350			£200		£250		£500						
V276	1s emblems	£350														
V277	1s plate 4		£325			£325			£250	£200						
V278	1s plate 5		£325			£325			£250	£200						
V279	1s plate 6								£250	£200						
V280	1s plate 7									£200						
V281	2s blue		£350					£250	£250	£250	£350					
V282	2s brown									£900						
V284	5s plate 1		£600			£600			£500	£350						
V285	5s plate 2									£1100						
V286	5s plate 4									£1100						
V288	10s maltese cross								£1200	£4000						
V290	10s anchor (blued)									£2500						
V291	£1 maltese cross															
V292	£1 anchor (white)									£4000						
V293	£1 anchor (blued)					£4000				£4000						

Where 'SPECIMEN' overprints are known on both imperforate and perforate stamps of the same issue or the issue exists in more than one colour, the price quoted is for the cheapest only.

Queen Victoria

Cat	Description	Type 1	Type 2	Type 3	Type 4	Type 5	Type 6	Type 7	Type 8	Type 9	Type 10	Type 11	Type 12	Type 13	Type 14	Type 15
V294	£5 white paper									£3000		£3000				£3000
V295	£5 blued paper									£2000		£2000				
V299	2½d blued plate 1								£200		£300					
V302	2½d plate 3									£120						
V304	2½d plate 5								£200	£120						
V305	2½d plate 6									£120						
V306	2½d plate 7									£120						
V307	2½d plate 8									£120						
V309	2½d plate 10									£120						
V315	2½d plate 16									£120						
V317	2½d plate 17									£120						
V323	2½d plate 23		£300													
V326	3d plate 14								£200	£120	£200					
V329	3d plate 17								£200	£120	£200					
V330	3d plate 18									£120						
V331	3d plate 19									£120						
V334	3d plate 21									£120						
V335	3d on 3d									£120						
V336	4d vermilion									£120						
V337	4d green plate 15									£120						
V338	4d green plate 16									£120						
V339	4d garter									£300						
V340	4d crown plate 17									£120						
V341	4d crown plate 18									£120						
V343	6d plate 14								£200	£120	£200					
V344	6d plate 15								£200	£120						
V345	6d plate 16									£120						
V347	6d plate 17									£120						
V348	6d plate 18									£170						
V349	6d on 6d									£200						
V350	8d orange								£350	£1500						
V350B	8d purple-brown								£1800							
V354	1s plate 11								£120	£120	£150					
V355	1s plate 12								£120	£200						
V356	1s plate 13									£200						
V357	1s orange-brown									£100						
V358	1s crown plate 13									£120						
V359	1s crown plate 14									£120						
V360	1/2d green									£50						
V361	1d venetian red									£50						
V362	1½d venetian red									£50						

Specimen Overprints

Where 'SPECIMEN' overprints are known on both imperforate and perforate stamps of the same issue or the issue exists in more than one colour, the price quoted is for the cheapest only.

		Type 1	Type 2	Type 3	Type 4	Type 5	Type 6	Type 7	Type 8	Type 9	Type 10	Type 11	Type 12	Type 13	Type 14	Type 15
V363	2d rose									£75						
V364	5d indigo									£100			£400	£500		
V365	1d 14 dots									£50						
V366	1d 16 dots									£50			£300			
V367	2s6d blued									£250						
V368	5s blued									£600		£800				
V369	10s blued									£1100						
V369a	10s cobalt blued									£1500						
V370	2s6d white paper									£300		£300	£350	£350		
V371	5s white paper									£300		£400	£350			
V372	10s white paper									£350		£400		£500		
V372b	10s cobalt									£1500						
V373	£1 crowns									£1100		£1100	£1100			
V374	£1 orbs											£2500				
V375	£1 green									£400		£600		£600	£600	£600
V376	½d slate blue									£40						
V377	1½d lilac									£60						
V378	2d lilac									£60						
V379	2½d lilac									£60						
V380	3d lilac									£60						
V381	4d dull green									£120						
V382	5d dull green									£120						
V382A	5d line under 'd'									£3000						
V383	6d dull green									£120						
V384	9d dull green									£120						
V385	1s dull green									£120						
V386	½d vermilion									£30	£200		£60			
V387	½d blue-green												£400			
V388	1½d jubilee						£400						£75			£500
V389	2d jubilee									£50	£250		£100			
V390	2½d jubilee						£400			£50			£100	£200		
V391	3d jubilee						£400			£60			£100			
V392	4d jubilee						£400			£60			£100			
V393	4½d jubilee									£200						
V394	5d die I jubilee									£75			£100	£400		
V395	5d die II jubilee									£200			£250			
V396	6d jubilee									£60	£250		£120			
V397	9d jubilee						£400			£60			£125			
V398	10d jubilee									£100			£250			
V399	1s dull green									£80	£250		£160			£250
V400	1s green and carmine															£350

King Edward VII

		Type 14	Type 15	Type 16	Type 17			Type 14	Type 15	Type 16	Type 17	Type 19
E1	½d blue green	£200				E25	10d dull purple (chalky)			£500		
E2	½d yellow green			£300	£125	E26	1s dull green (chalky)			£500		
E3	1d scarlet	£150	£250	£300	£125	E27	½d dull yellow green		,		£200	
E4	1½d dull purple	£250				E28	1d rose red				£200	
E5	2d yellowish		£350			E30	3d purple				£200	
E6	2½d blue	£100				E31	4d bright orange				£200	
E7	3d dull purple	£200				E38	2d deep dull green				£200	
E8	4d green and brown			£200		E40	6d dull purple				£250	
E9	4d orange				£500	E41	7d slate grey				£250	
E10	5d dull purple			£200		E42	9d dull reddish purple				£300	
E11	6d slate purple	£200				E43	10d dull reddish purple				£300	
E12	7d grey black				£500	E44	1s green				£300	
E13	9d dull purple			£225		E45b	6d bright magenta				£3000	
E14	10d dull purple			£225		E46	6d 'dickinson'					£1000
E15	1s dull green			£200		E47	2s6d lilac	£250	£250			
E16	2d tyrian plum			£25000		E48	5s bright carmine		£250	£1500		
E18	1½d dull purple (chalky)			£500		E49	10s ultramarine		£300	£1500		
E19	2d grey green (chalky)			£500		E50	2s6d dull purple (chalky)			£1500		
E20	3d purple (chalky)			£500		E51	£1 dull blue green		£800	£2500		
E22	5d dull purple (chalky)			£500		E52	2s6d dark purple				£850	
E23	6d dull purple (chalky)			£500		E53	£1 deep green				£1250	
E24	9d dull purple (chalky)			£500								

King George V

		Type 18	Type 19	Type 20	Type 21			Type 18	Type 19	Type 20	Type 21	Type 22
G14	½d royal cypher	£120	£150			G35	1½d block cypher	£60			£200	
G15	1d royal cypher	£120	£150			G36	2d block cypher	£70				
G16	1½d royal cypher	£200	£180			G40	5d block cypher	£125				
G17	2d royal cypher (die I)		£180			G43	9d block cypher	£125				
G19	2½d royal cypher	£80	£180			G44	10d block cypher	£125				
G20	3d royal cypher	£100	£180			G45	1s block cypher	£125				
G21	4d royal cypher	£100	£180			G63	2s6d waterlow			£400	£1250	
G22	5d royal cypher		£180			G64	5s waterlow		£600			
G23	6d royal cypher	£160	£200			G65	10s waterlow		£800	£1500		
G25	7d royal cypher		£180			G66	£1 waterlow	£2500	£2000			
G26	8d royal cypher		£180			G67	2s6d de la rue	£1000				
G27	9d royal cypher (agate)		£250			G68	5s de la rue	£1100				
G29	10d royal cypher		£250			G69	10s de la rue		£2000			
G30	1s royal cypher		£250			G70	2s6d bradbury	£500	£800			£900
G33	½d block cypher	£60			£150	G71	5s bradbury		£900			£950
G34	1d block cypher	£60			£150	G72	10s bradbury	£1000				£1200

Forgeries

The Lowden Forgery (1913)

The forgeries of the 1911 £1 value were made early in 1913 by John Stewart Lowden, a London stamp dealer, who was prosecuted shortly after their discovery the same year. They were made by photo-lithography from a block of 8 genuine stamps. They are normally found affixed to brown paper resembling that used for tobacco consignments from the Channel Islands and the forged cancellation resembles that which was officially used. Occasionally the stamps are found 'used' in combination with genuine definitives.

£1 green 'used' - £675 (in combination with genuine stamp(s) £1150)

The Stock Exchange Forgery (1872)

Fraudulantly produced and sold examples of the 1s plate 5 and plate 6. The stamps were produced and sold by a Post Office clerk at the London Stock Exchange and not detected until nearly 30 years after the deception. Both plates exist with both 'possible' and 'impossible' check letterings.

1s green, plate 5 - £375 (impossible lettering £475)   1s green, plate 6 - £950 (impossible lettering £1,350)

German Propoganda Forgeries (1944)

Definitive stamps similar in colour and design to that of the 1937 series were placed on sale in Stockholm in November 1944 together with similar 'forgeries' of the 1935 silver jubilee and 1937 coronation stamps. The stamps were mounted on sheets with the caption 'special stamp in memory of the first day of invasion'. The designs were altered to include an 'encircled cross', 'star of david' and 'hammer and sickle'. The normal inscriptions were replaced in Russian. The stamps are not known to be used postally, the 'used' examples being 'cancelled' at source. However, they are popular and have been acknowledged as being collectable philatelic items for many years.

Definitives ½d to 3d values - £30 each ('used' £35 each)   Commemoratives - £85 each ('used' £95 each)